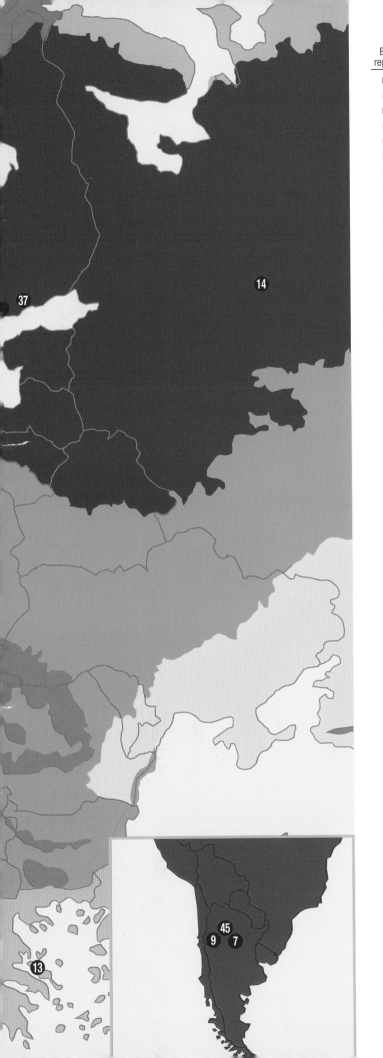

To the young generation of European landowners,
who will be the trustees and who will have
the responsibility of finding new solutions
for the new challenges of the 21st century,
and of guaranteeing a viable future
for private rural property in Europe.

To Ramón García-Morales, who stands a true example
for every rural landowner in Europe.

CREATING THE FUTURE OF THE COUNTRYSIDE

THE EUROPEAN ESTATE

Edited by C. Otero

FRIENDS OF THE COUNTRYSIDE

©Carlos Otero Muerza
©IIMA. Instituto Ibérico para el Medio Ambiente

Edited by: Instituto Ibérico para el Medio Ambiente
Production: Exlibris Ediciones, S.L.
Design: Dinarte, S.L.
Printed by: Gráficas Monterreina, S.A.
ISBN: 978-84-613-6861-7
Legal deposition: M-51115-2009
Cover photo: ifphotos.com (Symondsbury, Dorset/UK)

Printed on UPM Finesse 300, 115 gsm paper.

Sponsored by

ELO is supported by the European Commission Dirtectorate General Environment under the LIFE+ programme Operating Grant Agreement nº 07.0307/2009/SI2535265SUB/A1.

INDEX

FOREWORDS

Comm. Stavros Dimas
D.G. Environment EU

Our European heritage depends as much on the well being of our countryside as on our great towns and cities. The countryside is not just home to our landscape but the palette from which landowners and farmers shape, paint and frame it. How they have done so over the centuries detennines its diversity and beauty.

The basic tools of land, soil, water and biodiversity differ throughout Europe and it is the interest and skills of those working with them that ensure our food production and the extent to which we enhance the landscape. Europe's NATURA complex, the largest in the world, is testimony to the care for our heritage. Our concerns however are not limited to the NATURA confines, broad as they may be, but encompass our entire continent.

Today, climate change has to be added to the long list of pressures on our countryside.

Fanning and forestry as well as soil, water and biodiversity will be tested severely and we must act to ensure their successful adaptation to climate change and to other adverse conditions for the good, not just of the countryside but of us all. It is a task worth undertaking because the prize of a continued diverse and beautiful countryside for future generations is invaluable.

I welcome this publication "Creating the Future of the Countryside – The European Estate". It draws attention to the efforts and achievements of landowners and farmers in ecosystem and landscape restoration, conservation and promotion of biodiversity. It proves that work in these areas is necessary and can be achieved alongside nonnal agricultural production. We need a living countryside providing both our food and our diverse landscape. This, of course, requires efforts from policy makers but mainly from those living and working on the land. Moreover this book goes further than past and current achievements and addresses newer and sometimes controversial themes, such as alternative energy sources including biofuels, water economy and new management models ofnatural resources as alternatives to traditional approaches. It treats the essential issues facing the countryside and should stimulate greater effort to retain our rich European rural heritage.

Brussels, November 2009

Giuseppe Visconti
President Friends of the Countryside-META

When we look at the European countryside our memory immediately goes back to all those that over the centuries have contributed towards creating it as it is now. On one hand the positive achievements of a highly developed agriculture, extensive land reclamation, increased forestry and better social conditions and on the other hand the negatives of land waste, damage to the environment and landscape, deserted rural areas, incorrect use of pesticides and fertilizers and the harm caused to biodiversity. A complex picture, becoming more worrying with every passing day, especially when we consider the new emergencies connected to climate change and food scarcity. The real issue is that humanity needs a strong production capacity (to feed a dramatically increasing population) and a better environment (to mitigate climate change and particularly global warming), both at the same time. Landowners and their land management are deeply involved in the problem which triggers their responsibility and the economic efficiency of their estates.

This book testifies how appropriate management can reconcile production with the environment and foster the revitalization of the rural world by exploiting the various opportunities linked to land.

As a practical response to the countless theories and warnings, we offer examples of the immediate application of sound and reasonable measures contributing to improvements in agriculture, environment and our countryside in general. Much more can and must be done under the schemes debated at the highest global level but, while waiting for them, this is a first step. Friends of the Countryside-Meta, representing a large group of European landowners committed to preserve and promote our countryside for the benefit of the entire community, strongly believes that "creating the future of the European countryside" needs the ceaseless engagement of all human resources linked to land.

Milan, December 2009

Mark T Thomasin-Foster *CBE*
President European Landowners Organization

At this time of great concern about our environment and the future sufficiency of world food supplies it is highly opportune that Carlos Otero and his co-authors have been asked to bring together this celebration of estates across Europe, demonstrating a zenith of excellence in countryside stewardship and ownership. European leadership in the search for sustainable management of our countryside is surely a must as development pressures increase across the globe, and this book provides sixty-two fascinating examples of this achievement.

For over thirty-five years the European Landowners Organisation (ELO), in partnership with its European Union wide membership of national landowning associations, has been representing the interests of rural landowners. Not only does ELO pursue the essential task of representation at European Union level but it also acts as a conduit between the Commission and the Member Associations so that land management policies are practical, fair and proportionate.

The estates depicted in this book display the common theme of the dedication and devotion of the estate owner and manager. Whereas their geographical spread brings differing estate objectives and opportunities, this in turn provides the added wealth of diversity and richness to our rural lands. Security of ownership provides the needed certainty for long term investment and management decision and this certainty is a definite pre-

cursor to the goal of a sustainable countryside. The estates portrayed here are perhaps just a cameo of the vast wealth of stewardship resource being devoted to farms and estates across Europe. It is the heritage of the natural resources of water, soil and air when coupled with the richness of our biodiversity, culture, landscape and the human element, which provides the building blocks for successful estate stewardship. However, this success would not be possible without a viable and profitable underlying business and it is here that we witness the real skill of those involved in their estate management, thereby providing the fabric for the future of the countryside.

May I add my thanks to those of ELO in recognising the splendid contribution these estate owners have made in allowing their achievements to be recorded in this book. It is through the excellent writings of Carlos Otero and his co-authors that we can enjoy this example of the immense benefit brought to society by the dedication of sound landownership.

Finally I acknowledge our deep gratitude for the generous sponsorship given by the UPM Kymmene Group, Case New Holland and the Instituto Ibérico para el Medio Ambiente y los Recursos Naturales, which has made this prestigious publication possible.

London, December 2009

François Debiesse
CEO BNP Paribas Wealth Management

For years, ELO and Friends of the Countryside have been fighting to defend and promote the interests of the European Countryside, the diversity of its agriculture and its defence against environmental damage. This fight has evidently already been an efficient and successful one, but it will never end for one major reason: it is not a fight to defend the past, it is a fight for the future, for our future which will depend on our capacity to preserve our world, to promote biodiversity, to defend our lands, our forests, our landscapes, our environment, to implement a much more sustainable approach towards our capacities and resources, to improve social conditions in a rural world.

That's why BNPP Wealth Management is happy and proud to have become a close partner of ELO and Friends of the Countryside, because we share the same values and objectives, because we are committed, as a bank, to the same approach and fight for real sustainable development. BNPP has chosen, as its signature, to be "the bank for a changing world". Your struggles will obviously enable this changing world to become a better one...This book is a perfect illustration of what you are doing, and so efficiently !

Paris, December 2009

Jussi Pesonen
President UPM-Kymmene Group

Wood is used traditionally in the production of paper and wood products. However, the future of wood looks more versatile than that. Bioenergy, biofuels and biochemicals as well as wood in combination with other materials will open up totally new business and work opportunities in rural areas. UPM is active in finding new ways to use wood – a natural, renewable and recyclable raw material.

Biorefineries just round the corner

Biofuels refined from forest biomass will boost the image and use of wood. The goal of the European Union is that by 2020 one fifth of the energy used in the member states would come from renewable resources. The share of biofuels used in transport is to rise to ten percent by 2020 in all member states. To reach this target, new innovative solutions are needed.

UPM plans to become a significant player in the field of high-quality, second-generation biofuels. The main raw material in the production of liquid transportation fuels such as biodiesel would be energy wood: bark, harvesting residues, wood chips and stumps. Technical solutions and commercial concepts are currently under development.

Second-generation biofuels offer greater environmental benefits than the first generation. For example, the CO_2 emissions of UPM's biodiesel would be 85% lower than for fossil fuel.

UPM - a pioneer in using bioenergy

Bioenergy is an ecological and sustainable source of energy. It reduces the need for fossil fuels and thus the emissions of greenhouse gases into the atmosphere.

By the early 1990s UPM had already started building a new mill site combining heat and power plants that use forest energy wood as fuel. Simultaneously, UPM began innovative work to develop its harvesting techniques and solutions for handling large amounts of biomass in its mill power plants.

These investments, in addition to measures to increase energy efficiency, have lowered CO_2 emissions by 40% per produced paper tonne since 1990. Globally, 62% of fuels used at UPM's mills are biomass-based and CO_2 neutral and thus do not accelerate climate change.

Sustainable forest management secures future forests

Forests produce a valuable raw material – wood. Sustainable forest management secures the vitality of the forests now and for future generations. One of the key principles in UPM's sustainable forest management is safeguarding biodiversity.

Biodiversity means the variety of life around us; it includes diversity within species, between species and among species. People as well as businesses are dependent on natural resources. Safeguarding biodiversity gives us future options involving resources that are so far unknown and unutilised.

UPM has developed a global biodiversity programme for the company's forests. The programme aims to maintain and increase biodiversity in managed forests as well as promote best practices in sustainable forestry.

Based on the experience gathered from managing its own forests, UPM is able to offer a high level of forest management services to private forest owners. In Finland UPM Metsä and in the UK UPM Tilhill are reliable and sought-after partners for several thousands of forest owners.

UPM's vision is to be the front-runner of the new forest industry. Our competitiveness is based on cost leadership, change readiness and leading innovation. Our products are made of renewable raw materials and are recyclable. UPM consists of three Business Groups: Energy and pulp, Paper, and Engineered materials. The Group employs around 24,000 people, and it has production facilities in 14 countries. In 2008, UPM's sales amounted to EUR 9.5 billion. UPM's shares are listed on the Helsinki Stock Exchange. www.upm-kymmene.com

Helsinki, December 2009

Gabriel de l'Escaille
President Young Friends of the Countryside

The next generation of landowners is about to face multiple new challenges: while they will actively participate in actions to reverse climate change, environmental degradation, biodiversity loss and threats to the cultural landscape, they will also have to respond to the need to feed a growing world population in an environmentally sustainable way and to respond to the increased demand for renewable sources of energy.

In such a context, land managers of tomorrow will more than ever play an essential role in the promotion, conservation and preservation of natural resources through the sustainable use of their land and its components.

The future European countryside will demand much of the next generation, but is also full of opportunities.

It is up to this generation to decide on the path to take and to think about the sort of Europe they will be living in.

Preparing the next generation of landowners.

Being aware of these challenges and convinced that the most efficient way to tackle them was by leveraging our knowledge and experience, we[1] created "Young Friends of the Countryside", a European membership organization for rural business people, rural entrepreneurs, future and young private landowners aged between 20 and 35 years old.

The objectives pursued by YFCS are:

1) To raise awareness amongst its members about:
- European environmental policies.
- European rural business opportunities.

- Inheritance of Estates & Historic Houses, and management processes.

2) To leverage members' innovative countryside management related experiences.

3) To represent and channel the YFCS voice at EU level through the European Landowners Organization.

Achievements of the next generation of landowners

In four years YFCS has grown to become a recognized not-for-profit international organization numbering 170 active members representing 16 European countries. So far, no less than 38 seminars and activities have been organized in different European countries bringing together over 1200 members and multiple key players from European Institutions, think tanks and leading businesses. Knowledge is efficiently captured and shared through our online private platform which also facilitates interaction between our members. These achievements have been made possible due to the commitment of the YFCS Board and the logistical support provided by the European Landowners Organization and BNP Paribas.

YFCS has developed its activities based on three principles

European presence: working together with ambassadors representing YFCS in different European countries allows YFCS to effectively promote the crucial message of private initiative and property for a prosperous countryside all over Europe. The YFCS members also play a crucial role in promoting this vision: they represent multiple member states and different perspectives, being mostly future landowners, but also young environmental lawyers, consultants, EU representatives and students who are or will be directly and actively involved with the countryside.

---

[1] Gabriel de l'Escaille (BE), Christoph zu Stolberg-Stolberg (DE), Frans von Chrismar (NL), Sebastian Hillgarth (UK), Patrick Reventlow-Grinling (DK), Gregory Keane (IR), Alastair Kerr (UK), Robin du Parc Locmaria (BE), Luigi Galimberti Faussone (IT).

Environmental vision: Without land management, society and nature are in trouble. This works in both directions: land management and society need nature; and in crowded areas such as ours, nature needs the care of land management, farming and society. The future of Europe's countryside is thus dependent on the individual management decisions of its millions of entrepreneurs and landowners. The next generation needs to be prepared to take over this challenge when the time comes, but it also needs to communicate this message.

Entrepreneurial spirit: Being a Countryside family business network, YFCS aims to foster the spirit of enterprise, to facilitate exchange of business know-how and to encourage and support young entrepreneurs with its annual entrepreneurial award. The objectives of this prize are to promote the entrepreneurial spirit within the YFCS network, to promote family enterprises and to give motivated people the opportunity and support needed to launch their own project. Moreover, it seeks to engage YFCS members to develop projects that address the imminent needs for developing a healthy and sustainable countryside while also serving as good practice to the wider community.

Brussels, December 2009

INTRODUCTION

Carlos Otero
Editor, President IIMA

Following the encouraging reception given to "Patrimonio Natural y Propiedad Rural en España, 1999" *(Natural Heritage and Rural Ownership in Spain)*, published by Spanish Association of Rural Landowners (APROCA) and IIMA, which assessed 43 examples of private land, flora and fauna management, two years later, we were given the opportunity to prepare a second book, this time focussed not just on Spain but on the entire European Union, with some of the most remarkable examples of natural resource management and conservation carried out by rural landowners in Europe.

Under the auspices of the ELO (European Landowners Organisation) and Friends of the Countryside, and once again with the support of the IIMA, 61 private estates were selected to feature in the long and arduous task that finally brought about the publication of *Europe's Natural and Cultural Heritage* (2003).

This new book, published entirely in English, has been widely distributed throughout Europe. Indeed, it has turned out to be a powerful letter of reference about the work of the ELO or Friends of the Countryside. Furthermore, it has been extensively used by all national organisations of private landowners. When the 10,000 copies of the first edition had almost sold out, in 2007, the decision was taken to continue along the same lines with the publication of another book that would tackle certain aspects not previously touched upon and which would also provide true, well-documented

information about the work of private landowners in Europe.

After the decision had been taken, the work then took a further two years to depict these new 61 examples of private land management ...but from a different viewpoint. Up to now, in the two previous books, the main objective had been to highlight the role of private initiative and private rural landowners in the conservation of soil, landscapes, forests, flora and fauna; and it is true that they provided magnificent model examples of such land management.

However, during the preparation work for those two books, we realized how many other aspects, initiatives, projects and innovations apart from the work to preserve the Natural Heritage were also carried out on those estates.

Issues such as the preservation and use of our Historical Heritage, third generation agriculture, new renewable sources of energy, landscape protection, conservation and, more importantly, restoration, the preservation of the most emblematic species of endangered wildlife, new techniques and philosophy in forest husbandry, the change and modification in local climate constants which, unfortunately, have never been constant but highly variable and which forced us to adapt to changes and modifications in the climate conditions on the sites, the passing-down of complex estates that require complicated management, the transfer of knowledge itself, the role of private Foundations within this heritage of landscapes and historical values, even the reasons that lead some of us to explore new natural environments in distant lands. All these topics were fascinating and attracted our attention, so that finally, under the valuable sponsorship once again of ELO and Friends of the Countryside, with the support of IIMA and the generosity of all those that have backed this initiative – BNP-Paribas, Case-New Holland and UPM-Kymmene Group – as well as the invaluable, generous and unwavering aid of the 61 landowners included in our final selection of European Estates, we have been able to publish this third book – which feels more like the third volume of a future collection of examples of the magnificent work performed by European rural landowners.

This third book is entitled *Creating the Future of the Countryside, The European Estate*. The book contains 61 sites – all of which once again represent magnificent examples of the challenges currently faced by European rural landowners. Having reviewed the issues mentioned above, we finally chose to structure the book into 8 themes as follows:

- **Theme I:** Agriculture: continuity and innovation.
- **Theme II:** Landscape and Nature.
- **Theme III:** Fauna, Flora and Wildlife Estates.
- **Theme IV:** Forestry.
- **Theme V:** Climate change and new energies.
- **Theme VI:** Agrotourism and Historical Heritage.
- **Theme VII:** Transmission & Private Foundation in the rural world.

The 61 estates selected are presented within these 8 themes and stand as model representatives of solutions and techniques, proven results, and wise, expert decision-making and management. This does not mean that those estates covered in one theme are not related to those in another section. Most of the estates have a very complex, integrated management scheme that combines a series of innovative techniques to address a wide range of challenges and goals. This scheme preserves the landscape while also encompassing the enlightened exploitation of forest resources, the creation of natural treatment and purification systems for surface waters, the conservation of endangered wildlife, but also hunting and fishing; it develops a system to exploit bio-fuels to produce energy, while at the same time it takes short-term profitability into account by introducing innovations that guarantee investment and improvement without disregarding the transmission of this inheritance or the conservation of historical values. Nonetheless, there is always a prevailing trait, a more vanguard and innovative characteristic, a more significant contribution, and by identifying that dominant trait or characteristic, we have been able to class the estates and topics under one theme or another, with the hope that, in this sorting task, we have not made serious errors.

This book was not written to the same method as its two predecessors. On this occasion, special emphasis has been given to the participation of the actual landowners. In fact, they - the rural landowners represented herein, their managers and technicians – were the ones that drafted the majority of the texts included in this book, and for that reason, I believe this edition is of a more remarkable and significant value. It provides at least 61 different opinions based on direct personal experience, the events and decisions taken in their own individual lives, the successes, failures, projects and initiatives taken under their sole and exclusive responsibility, the savouring of their success and achievements, the suffering and determination to correct their mistakes, and their never-ending search for the ideal management and conservation model.

Such personal experiences render this book of special value. It represents a more or less homogenous collection woven together by a central thread but nevertheless, the reader will undoubtedly be surprised by many of the opinions and experiences shared on these pages.

Madrid, December 2009

Theme 1

Agriculture: Continuity and Innovation

THE ESTATES OF EUROPE SAFEGUARDING THE FUTURE IN AN UNCERTAIN WORLD

Caroline Cranbrook
Policy Committee Member, CLA (Country Land & Business Association)

Europe and its countryside face a future of great challenges – climate change, loss of natural resources, loss of biodiversity, population increase, encroaching urbanisation, landscape degradation, disappearance of traditional knowledge and uncertain food supply.

Weather patterns are forecast to become more extreme and varied, with higher temperatures and rising sea levels. Climate change will also be accompanied by the spread of novel pests and diseases, affecting crops, animals, forests, biodiversity and man.

Natural resources will become scarcer. In just a few centuries mankind has used up world resources which took millions of years to develop minerals (especially oil), water, soil, land and wildlife. These resources are finite and, with existing knowledge, many of them cannot be regenerated or substituted. Simultaneously, the world's population grows relentlessly, while climate change will force migration on a massive scale. In 2008, for the first time in history, more people lived in towns than in the country. This figure is expected to increase to 70% by 2050. Pressures on the land and on food production will be very great indeed.

The trend to urbanisation is accompanied by the loss of understanding of countryside dynamics and a loss of rural knowledge and skills. It is happening at every level, throughout society. For instance, shoppers no longer comprehend the connection between the food they eat and the land that produced it. Even European legislation and European governments are tending to move away from knowledge and science based decision-making when dealing with food production or the environment. As the result, sentiment often replaces common-sense when decisions are made about wildlife and the countryside. Complex regulatory regimes are also introduced that can be inappropriate for the agricultural and environ-

mental problems they are intended to address and then are difficult to alter when circumstances change.

Most serious of all is the world-wide problem of food. Demand is expected to double by 2050 but the global food supply is not keeping pace with this growth rate. During the past three years the world has consumed more food than was produced in the same period. Many of the most productive areas will be severely affected by climate change. More food will have to be produced with fewer greenhouse gas emissions, less water, less essential minerals, less energy and more pests and diseases. The temptation will be to bring new, less suitable land into cultivation, causing even greater loss of biodiversity. The ELO believes that it would be better for mankind to increase output by improving the management of land already in cultivation and by reducing waste throughout the food chain. In the developed world, the supermarkets' requirements for cosmetic perfection and the associated packaging result in significant wastage. In addition, in many under-developed areas, agriculture is very poorly managed, resulting in low yields and much wasted food because storage facilities are lacking or inadequate.

Although the staggering price rises and food shortages in 2008 were short-lived, it is forecast that the cost of food will continue to increase. As Professor Paul Krugman said in 2009 at the ELO/Syngenta Brussels conference, 2008 was a dress rehearsal for future food crises. There is also the shaming situation where millions in the under-developed nations are poorly nourished or starving, while people in the developed world suffer increasingly from obesity and diseases which are often related to eating too much unsuitable food.

In this difficult situation, Europe and European landowners have a critically important part to play. In times of great uncertainty, the fundamental need and the greatest challenge is to maintain food and environmental security, as has been powerfully argued in *The 21st Century Land Use Challenge* (ELO. 2008. Brussels).

In Europe, we start with a perceived advantage that our part of the world, the mid-latitudes of the northern hemisphere, will be less seriously affected by climate change and may even benefit. These latitudes are destined to become mankind's bread basket. Three quarters of Europe's land is rural and the majority of this is privately owned. For centuries, even millennia, land managers have been the guardians of Europe's agriculture, its forests, its animals, its biodiversity, its wild places and the knowledge, skills and traditions to maintain them. It is true that land managers have also been responsible for the industrialisation of agriculture and its consequences but this has happened largely because of the increasing demand for food from an industrialised, urbanised society. Without land managers, Europe would starve and without them the future of our environment would indeed be bleak.

Land ownership is the fundamental condition which underpins continuity. Farming, forestry and the environment all need long-term, inter-generational planning and knowledge, often handed down over hundreds of years. Understanding the lie of the land, knowing which crops do well on which fields, planning agricultural rotations, keeping rare livestock breeds, planting and managing forests, maintaining knowledge and skills, caring for the landscape, preserving wildlife and the habitats that support them – all these need a long view. It is the landowners who inherit these responsibilities and hand them on to future generations. Private property ownership does not necessarily guarantee this precious continuity of responsibility and knowledge – but it is the basic requirement.

European land owners, land managers, have a prime duty to maintain the environment and to deliver environmental policies. However, we have an equally important responsibility which is to feed our European populations – and even beyond. We need to produce more food with fewer resources and with less environmental impact. It will not be easy and we will be relying on governments to provide greater support for scientific re-

search into new technologies and into new ways of coping with the constantly changing threats of plant and animal diseases and pests. But land managers, are good at responding to new challenges. They are traditionalists and are in a position to draw on the experience of the past but they are also great innovators and quick to adapt to new situations.

We cannot achieve the great task ahead without help, not only from government-supported research but also from the public. Numerous opinion surveys show that the majority of consumers support farmers, support locally produced food, support the countryside – but these views are largely aspirational. The public has become increasingly disconnected from the land, from agriculture and from the realities of food production. Although there is much sympathy for farmers there is little knowledge and much concern as to how food is produced. We urgently need to close this knowledge gap – to help educate and reconnect the public with food production and to show that, far from working in opposition to the environment and nature conservation, land managers are its mainstay. We need the public on our side in order to give governments the confidence to provide the support that we will need to maintain Europe's food and environmental security.

Private land ownership creates public goods. Without the long history of land ownership we would have lost the infinite variety and beauty of the European farmed and managed landscape, the intricate patterns of terraced fields, the mosaics of lowland grassland and mountain meadows, the great Mediterranean sierras, the managed forests, the small woodlands, the Iberian cork forests and *dehesas*, the bare, rolling uplands, the wildlife they support, the well-kept villages, the traditional local foods that are produced from traditional breeds of animals and varieties of plants – and much else besides. Their continued existence largely depends on the continuity and foresight of private ownership.

Private land ownership is likewise critically important to maintaining both our connections with the past and our survival in the future. Much of our European heritage is based on the history, the knowledge, the skills and the experience which is maintained by our estates and farms. All over Europe this is a vital part of our varied cultural identity: continuity with the past provides the understanding and the confidence on which to build the future.

The detailed descriptions of the estates featured in *Europe's Natural and Cultural Heritage* and in this volume, *The Estates of Europe*, provide abundant evidence of the imagination and work involved over many, many years in maintaining the heritage in the care of landowners. The accounts are fascinating, impressive and show in detail the many and varied public goods they provide. What comes across very strongly is that there is a sense of responsibility among landowners which goes beyond economics. This was well described by Giuseppe Paterno dei Marchese di San Giuliano during an interview for the BBC in 2008 when he said that "For our survival we have to live with rather than on this earth. I believe that farming and land ownership must give back to the earth what has been created by three millennia of farming".

The people of Europe depend on land owners for their food and they depend on them for the landscapes, the wildlife and the heritage that they care about. It is up to us to publicise the connection and to create a greater understanding of the vital role played by the estates of Europe. The future of all of us will depend on it.

PRICE FOR NATURE – MORE VALUE TO LAND PROPERTY

Thamás Marghescu

Whereas some of us have just begun to understand and accept the conventional system of sustainable development – with the 3 pillars of economy, society and environment allegedly holding up its roof – others have started to question the functioning of that system. The environmental pillar is in constant competition with the economic pillar. It is always the environmental pillar which has to give way to support the economy and society to the detriment of nature and natural resources. Economic growth is therefore based on the often irreversible exploitation of nature. Although many parts of our societies claim to be more and more "sustainable", nature and related biological diversity is often irreversibly disappearing.

A new approach to sustainable development is based on the fact that nature provides so called "ecosystem services", including water, food, climate change adaptation and mitigation and other functions which in the past were titled as "non-monetary" functions or "by-products" of nature.

Ecosystem services are in fact our life support systems that form the pre-condition for human life on earth. Hence, they are increasingly seen as the base for a new construct of sustainability – where the pillars of economy and society are built firmly on the foundation of natural resources and the environment. The big change is that the former vertical pillar of environment is turned horizontal and thus forms the foundation for economy and society. The environment – and thus nature –

> "…we cannot go on with this economic model based on the destruction of biodiversity and the abuse of most of human kind".
>
> *Pavan Sukhdev, Deutsche Bank*
> Study Leader of "The Economics of Ecosystems and Biodiversity"
> From Global crisis a "window of opportunity"
> Julio Godoy, 2008
> http://www.ipsterraviva.net/tv/IUCN2008/currentNew.aspx?new=1156

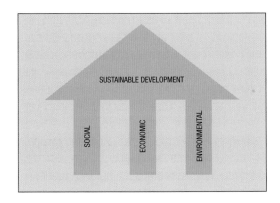

are upgraded from being "just a pillar" and are thus no longer in competition with the economy. In this scenario, the economy needs to strictly respect the support provided by nature and not endanger its own existence.

"In the past, nature did not really have an economic market value and in the interest of the economy and economic growth, nature was disappearing along with its ecosystem services. GDP growth created jobs, avoided recessions, and has thus become a preferred yardstick for progress. However, GDP growth does not capture many vital aspects of national wealth and wellbeing, such as changes in the quality of health, the extent of education, and changes in the quality and quantity of our natural resources" (Pavan Sukhdev, 2008). If you cut a hectare of forest, the GDP increases. However, taking into account the interruption, reduction or even complete destruction of ecosystem services from that one hectare of forest, the GDP actually shrinks.

In the developing world nature is valued very highly and in traditional systems environmental resources are used sustainably. Yet, development is always paired with the destruction of nature and the diminishing of ecosystem services. Especially in times of crisis – when luxury items become less and less important and often sheer survival is in the foreground – natural resources become central to people's interests.

The G8 Presidency of Germany in 2007 commissioned a study by the European Commission

and the Federal Government of Germany – which is presently focusing on the valuation of ecosystem services (The Economics of Ecosystems and Biodiversity, TEEB). The first results are expected in late 2009. The outcomes of the study will help design and conduct regional, national and local assessments of the value of ecosystem services. This will form the basis of experimenting with a green economy, where nature becomes a true and valued asset for development. It is important to run experiments in defined, pilot economies at different levels (local, national, regional) and in different parts of the world, for nature provides ecosystem services in different ways depending for example on the variety of ecosystems. The level of importance of ecosystem services in an economy varies tremendously depending also on prevailing conditions related to different degrees of supply and demand.

The need for a revolutionary paradigm of sustainability is especially apparent now that world economies are tumbling. Rather than rebuilding economies as they were before, now there is an opportunity to build a new economic order, a chance to change for the better: an economy where nature has a price, where ecosystem services are no longer regarded as by-products of land provided free of charge to societies. Financial resources have to flow for the provision of ecosystem services.

Nature has by and large been kept outside of the market-driven economy. By giving it a price through valuating ecosystem services, nature becomes part of a new economic order, as a priced asset or capital.

When money is flowing it is important to determine who is paying and who is benefiting from

> Nature is the world's largest development agency providing daily life support to 6 billion people.
> *Tamás Marghescu, 2006*

In Munich (Germany), farmers in the water protection zone –where the city's water is collected– receive an annual sum of 240 Euros per hectare from the city administration for reducing the number of animals they graze on their pastures and to limit the use of pesticides and fertilizers. As a result, the nitrate concentration in the drinking water of Munich is reduced by 50 percent. The payments to farmers are equivalent to one cent per cubic metre drinking water. The technical filtering of water would otherwise cost the City of Munich 30 cents per cubic metre.

payments. If the resource or the land is state-owned, the state budget needs to provide for the payments to the entrusted manager of the land – provided that the management of the land is geared at the provision of ecosystem services in defined good quality and quantity. By paying taxes, citizens are ultimately responsible for the payment to the landowner. Tax payers may be asked to not only pay taxes, but also specifically to pay for the services provided to him or her, as expressed within the price of a production unit (e.g. per litre of used water).

If the resource, the land, is privately owned, the private landowner has to receive a monetary payment for the services provided by his or her property. It is of the utmost importance that the landowner should receive a "payment" and not a "compensation" for providing ecosystem services with a given value.

Of all services delivered by natural land, the provision of clean water is probably the most important. Examples show that the investment in natural systems for water storage and filtering is far cheaper than investing in technical infrastructure. It is hence an economically-wise decision to invest in green infrastructure (a new term for natural ecosystems and their ecological networks), rather than in conventional, physical infrastructure.

Just now, when leaders are investing billions in the construction of infrastructure (roads, airports etc.) to create jobs and fight the economic meltdown (similar to the Great Depression of the 1930s), it should be remembered that this infrastructure could be very harmful to nature and the environment. However, one could think about labour intensive ways and means to improve na-

tural infrastructure so as to provide more and better ecosystem services. Connecting isolated sections of forests in a water protection area by means of afforestation could be a meaningful way of spending parts of the billions provided as "stimuli packages" for a new economy. Not in vain have governments started to secure land areas important for water production so as to remain or be transformed into state property. They are trying to ensure that these areas are not transformed in the course of "development" into other land use forms.

In the whole discussion about ecosystem services, the issues related to climate change must also be taken into account. Forests are a pool for carbon sequestration and a means for climate change adaptation. Whereas decision-makers are designing schemes to compensate forest resource owners and users in the south to avoid the destruction or degradation of their forest resource (REDD = Reducing Emissions from Deforestation and Forest Degradation), owners and guardians of forests in the north provide the service of carbon mitigation and climate change adaptation free of charge, along with other non-monetary services of their ecosystems.

Landowners need to stand up and demand payment for the services provided by their properties. These payments could result in a revolution in income generation from land property. It is a great chance to properly reward the ecological management of land while nurturing a true and shared interest between landowners and nature conservationists. Nature conservation is ready to go this path in partnership with landowners.

HISTORY OF THE OLIVE - AN ANCIENT CROP

Marquis of Valdueza

The Olive *(Olea europea)* belongs to the Oleaceae family and is the only species within the family to bear an edible fruit. It originates from the wild *Olea chrysophylla* via the Wild Olive Tree *(Olea oleaster* or *Olea europaea oleaster)*. It is a typical Mediterranean plant, and in the year 2006 was grown on 10,371,000 hectares throughout the world, of which 97% were in the Mediterranean basin.

The origin of the species is lost in time, its expansion coinciding with, and also being confused with, the various civilizations which developed around the Mediterranean Sea. It is thought that it is an ancient tree, its origins dating somewhere around 12,000BC. Cultivation of the olive began in Asia Minor, between the Rivers Tigris and Euphrates, about 6,000 years ago, although other theories assert that it originated in Africa, namely in Ethiopia and Egypt.

At the time of Ancient Egypt references were made to the olive groves of the Nile, which probably came from Syria. The Phoenicians introduced it to Greece in about 1600 BC. The remains of an oil press constructed out of lava stone have been found on the island of Thera.

The first half of the 1st century BC saw the expansion of the olive into Assyria. From 600 BC it was grown throughout the Mediterranean basin, extending to Libya, Algeria, Tunis and the island of Sicily, spreading from there to southern Italy. *Plinius* referred to an oil which, held in the mouth, helped to whiten teeth and heal damaged gums and, used alone or mixed with wine, was used to heal wounds or help infant hygiene. The Romans continued to expand the olive into countries along the Mediterranean coast, where it was used as a sign of goodwill to those whom they conquered.

It seems that the olive arrived on the Iberian Peninsula as a result of the Phoenicians (1050 BC) but that society hardly took notice of it until the arrival of the Romans. Colmuela, living in the 1st century BC and considered the first great agronomist in history, distinguished three types of olive oil: summer oil *(Oleum aestivum)*, green oil *(Oleum viride)*, which was the best appreciated, and mature oil *(Oleum maturum)*. This is the first reference to the differentiation of oil by quality.

During their occupation of the Iberian Peninsula, the Arabs brought their own varieties and saw cultivation thrive. Abu Zacarias, in his book on Agriculture, devotes much attention to the cultivation of the olive. Andalusia, once known as Baetica, was full of ring-shaped mills and presses *(ma'sara*, from which derives the modern Spanish word for an oil-press: *almazara)*. Further legacies of the Arab occupation can be seen in the Spanish words for the olive fruit – *aceituna* from al *zaitona* – and olive oil – *aceite*, from *al zait.*

The olive tree was taken to the Americas following the Discoveries. King Charles I offered a reward of 10,000 *maravedís* every year to the first person in the New World who could obtain a *quintal* (in those days 46 kilograms) of olive oil, but then increased the offer to 15,000 *maravedís* because it was so difficult to get the plant to adapt to the tropical climate of Central America. In 1560 there were plantations in Mexico, Peru, California, Chile and Argentine.

Nowadays olives are grown on all five continents and in many different latitudes, and new plantations are found in countries such as Australia, China, Japan and South Africa.

There are a multitude of references to the plant in literature. The oldest are some tablets dated to about 2500 BC in Ebla in the north of Syria. The Old Testament contains numerous references to olive oil and to olive cultivation. The story of the Great Flood in the Book of Genesis even tells of Noah sending a dove with an olive branch as a sign that the waters had receded from the face of the earth. The Arabs considered the olive to be a holy tree, and olive oil to be a symbol of light, as is read in the Koran.

As well as the Old Testament and the Koran, the olive appears in many other books such as the Iliad and Odyssey by Homer, Dante's Divine Comedy and the Songs of Petrarch. Homer compared the fall of an olive in a hurricane to the fall of Euphorbus, defeated by Menelaus king of Sparta, and points out that the stake used by Ulysses to blind Polyphemus was of olive wood.

In ancient Greece, those who had devoted great service to their country and the winners of the Olympic Games were crowned with olive leaves. Even today a dove with an olive branch in its beak is universally recognised as the symbol of peace.

The olive has been mentioned in the literary works of many different authors writing in Spanish, such as García Lorca, Neruda and Antonio Machado. The latter's poetry was strongly influenced by the beauty of this age-old tree which made such an impression on him during his years teaching French near the Andalusian town of Baeza.

The fruit of the olive has two uses. Its flesh can either be eaten whole, once it has been processed, or in the form of olive oil which is extracted by entirely mechanical means.

By far the greatest proportion of olives produced in the world today (around 90%) is used to produce olive oil. The Mediterranean countries of the European Union – Spain, Italy, Greece, France, Portugal, Malte and Cyprus – between them produce over 75% of world production. The remainder is basically split between Tunisia, Turkey, Syria and Morocco.

As soon as one enters the estate at Perales there are immediate indications that good olive oil is produced here. The building that houses the oil mill, which is classical but equipped with the most up-to-date technology, is both modern and striking. An agronomist manages the land and the fifty thousand olive trees planted on the estate, with the assistance of specialist technicians. Then one notices the irrigation system which, we are told, supplies the appropriate amount of water that accords with the measured rainfall.

The principal aim is to produce olive oil of high quality – extra virgin – making certain that every stage of the process guarantees that the integral attributes and properties of the oil remain intact.

Depending on the different varieties grown on the estate, the fruits start to ripen in the middle of November. This is a period of the year when the olives start to turn from green to yellow and then to purple, and when the process of lipogenesis comes to an end – the chemical process responsible for the formation of the basic components of olive oil, namely the triglycerides.

The oil mill separates the oil from the other fruit contents.

The olive growing on the tree reaches its maximum quality when it is at its optimum state of ripeness. It should be harvested before it falls to the ground, since fallen fruit indicates that it is overripe and that imperfections have started to appear that are irrecoverable.

Harvesting the crop has to be carefully synchronised with the work of the oil mill, so that they are processed on the same day as they are picked.

The olives are transported in washable plastic crates, designed so that they pack together without causing any damage to the fruits themselves. Transporting the olives loose in trailers or other means should be avoided as much as possible, because pressure and weight can damage them, causing them to split and ferment, which in turn leads to unpleasant smell and taste.

Fundamental to this operation is the work of the Yard Manager (*jefe de patio* in Spanish) who separates the best fruit in order to mill it on the very same day as it is harvested.

The Yard Manager is often the same person as the Mill Master (*maestro de almazara*), and it is he who decides and checks the working parameters of the mill, the length of milling and the optimum temperatures, in order to obtain oils of the highest quality.

On the Perales estate the reception pit, into which the olives are first tipped, is very wide and consists of a cement floor so that no soil or stones are inadvertently added to the fruit. Hygiene is exhaustive at all times, not just during processing but at the end of the working day as well. The whole mill must be left clean for the next day's work.

The aim is to try and ensure that the olives arrive in a clean state and do not require washing.

The conveyor belt has a small water spray and air flow facility to eliminate dust and leaves. Olives destined for Extra Virgin oil should not be washed at all. This prevents the loss of antioxidants, which are highly soluble. The oil mill also comprises all the facilities necessary for the staff, as well as tasting and sampling rooms, meeting rooms, visitors' reception, etc.

Åminne Gods

Boreal

Location: Salo, South-west Finland, Finland.
Surface: 2,186 ha.

CLIMATIC DATA

Average rainfall
mm/cm²/year

Snow days: 85

630 mm

Temperature (ºC)

30 — max
5 — average
-25 — min

SUMMARY

Åminne Gods is located by the Halikko river, approximately 1.5 km from an inlet of the Baltic Sea.

The fields around the estate are flat, apart from the river bank which has created a very unusual landscape for this part of Finland. In 2001, the family took over the estate and started an ambitious renovation and expansion programme. A large area of land adjacent to the water has been converted into natural habitats for wildlife, and responsible long-term cutting plans for the forestry have been put in place.

Today, Åminne Estate, well-known for its Finnish historical heritage, together with the farm buildings and landscape, is now being maintained and the typical building characteristics of the region are being preserved. All this contributes to a rural living environment where the family, the employees and tenants can live in a sustainable and environmentally friendly way.

Åminne Gods Estate

Åminne Manor was originally built by Magnus Wilhelm Armfelt in 1793, since when it was significantly expanded.

HISTORY

Founded in the late middle ages, the estate of Åminne was owned for four centuries by the Horn af Åminne family. Many Horns were prominent in Swedish history, with Arvid Horn rising to President of the King's Council and Prime Minister in the early 18th century. The family had been knighted in 1407 and created Counts in 1772 in the service of their king as judges, military commanders and members of the Council.

Situated as Finland is between present-day Sweden and Russia, political conflict and wars affected both the life of Åminne's owners and the size of the estate throughout much of its history. By the 17th century the Horns had established themselves at Court in Stockholm and only occasionally visited their Finnish estates. During the Great Nordic War and the following occupation (1713-1721) they were joined by many other members of the Finnish nobility as much of south western Finland was *de facto* evacuated.

Upon the death of her parents in 1748, Baroness Catharina Ebba Horn bought Åminne from her relatives who had shared in the inheritance. Like them, she also lived in Sweden where she later married Count Ulrick Barck, and consequently had to hire an able administrator for her Finnish estates. Thus director Adolph Bush was introduced to Åminne and given a free hand to improve the estate. It was he who first suggested that vast gardens and a park should be laid out. There had been some fruit tree plantations and vegetable gardens before his time, but now the aesthetic aspects of gardening were becoming *en vogue*. In a letter to his employer in the early 1770s he wrote:

"The Englishmen have, when planning and laying out a park, in later times come closer to nature. They have changed uniformity into a kind of disorder, which pleases the eye. In great Parks this idea deserves properly to be followed. But everything that can be seen at a glance must have symmetry".

Bush was of the opinion that great masses of trees adjacent to the main buildings created disharmony. On flat ground, trees "obscure the view and cut off the architecture". But across the river was a totally different matter. The west bank of the river was well suited for a park of natural style, only a bridge had to be built to connect it to the buildings on the eastern bank and what was to be the new manor house.

"The nature has at Åminne created the most beautiful Material to form into an English Park. The headland on the other Side of the River, grown with several kinds of broadleaf-trees, could with small costs be a Pleasure Garden of the newer Taste."

Bush received a favourable reaction to his ideas from Countess Horn and started work on the park in the English or "natural" style in the mid-1770s. The fulfilment of his plans had to wait for the next owner however. Catharina Ebba Horn, by then a Countess of the Holy Roman Empire, passed away in 1781 and the estate was sold to Baron Magnus Wilhelm Armfelt in 1786 in order that he create a *fidei-commissariat* for the benefit of his son, the chamberlain and colonel Gustaf Mauritz Armfelt and his male heirs in eternity. The purchase was in part financed with the 10,000 riksdaler that Gustaf Mauritz had received as a wedding gift from the monarch, Gustaf III, whom he had befriended in Spa in 1780 and then accompanied on the Grand Tour to Italy in 1783-1784.

Gustav Mauriz Armfelt became a great courtier and favourite of the King's, initially responsible for the upbringing and education of the Crown Prince and Head of the King's entertainment and theatre. In the war of 1788-1790 he was promoted General and negotiated the peace with Russia at Värälä. Early in 1792 Armfelt was appointed Warden of Stockholm and a member of the King's Council. Soon after, disaster struck as on March 15, 1792 Gustaf III was murdered at the Opera, and power was taken over by Duke Carl as regent for the young Crown Prince. Personal animosities between the new regent and friends of the murdered king led to Armfelt falling into disgrace and having to flee the country. Rehabilitated in 1799, Gustaf Mauritz visited Åminne in 1801, but diplomatic and military duties on the continent prevented him, now Ambassador to Vienna, from settling down on the estate.

In 1807 he made a long visit to Åminne together with his wife Hedvig, born Countess de la Gardie, and declared his intentions to settle there. The incompetence of the military leadership in the war with Russia in 1808-1809, however, led to Sweden's loss of Finland in the peace of Fredrikshamn. Under the decrees of Tsar Alexander I of Russia, who now ruled Finland as Grand Duke, Armfelt had to take possession of his Finnish estates within a period of two years or forfeit them.

Having failed to establish a close relationship with the new Swedish ruler, Jean Baptiste Bernadotte, who eventually succeeded as Carl XIV Johan, Armfelt decided in 1811 to switch his allegiance to Alexander I. He travelled to Åminne with the intention of personally completing the great reconstruction work that he had started in 1807, but was soon called to St. Petersburg where the Tsar appointed him chairman of the Finland Committee – effectively viceroy – and raised him to Count. Armfelt retained his great vision and enthusiasm for Åminne and managed much of the work by correspondence. The expansion work on the manor building was completed in 1810 after which the interiors were decorated in the new imperial style. A hectic life had started to take its toll, however, and Gustaf Mauritz Armfelt passed way in Tsarskoje Selo in 1814, only 57 years old.

Since Armfelt's time changes have been made in the gardens surrounding the manor on the eastern bank of the river. The fruit tree garden has been removed to the western side, where now only little of the originally vast orchards is left. The ornamental design of the formal garden has also been reduced. The English park on the west bank has basically remained unaltered, although the northern part of it has been used as a pasture for horses, and additional plantations of hardwoods and exotic

conifers were made in the early 1900s and again in the 1930s.

Lack of a male workforce during the war with Russia in 1939-1944 and the reconstruction effort thereafter, combined with falling profitability of agriculture, left the park neglected. Only recently has it been extensively restored with the original late 18th century paths laid out anew and extensive planting of both trees and flowers. Prior to restoration, some 5000 cubic metres of softwood had to be taken out to allow planting of a new generation of oaks and linden.

Despite its eventful life, the Åminne park has grown some beautiful and big broad-leaved trees, particularly the Oaks *(Quercus robur),* which in height and quality are the very best the country has to offer. Oaks with a bigger diameter can be found elsewhere, but these are usually of the rather low, broad "Saving Bank Oak" type. Although their genetic origin is uncertain, the Åminne oaks have been selected for further tree breeding and seed production. Peter the Great's westernization and the Russian occupation in 1713-1721, which followed the Great Northern War, had a devastating impact on the oak forests in southern Finland. Most of the old trees were then cut to satisfy demand from Russian shipyards and from the city of St. Petersburg, which was mostly built on a swamp and therefore needed foundation poles.

Both during Catharina Ebba Horn's and Gustaf Mauritz Armfelt's time tree plants and acorns were

Founded in the late middle ages, the Estate of Åminne was owned for four centuries by the Horn af Åminne family. Saara and Bjorn Wahlroos took over the estate in 2001 and started an ambitious renovation and expansion programme.

Åminne Gods Estate

imported from Germany, Sweden, the Baltic Provinces and later Russia. It is likely that some of the best oaks in the park, identifiable by the fact that they keep their leaves very late in the autumn, are of foreign origin. Most of the great oaks in the park are now between 150 and 190 years of age and were consequently planted by Gustaf Mauritz Armfelt. There is also a younger generation, apparently planted by the last Armfelt at Åminne, Carl Alexander, some 90 years ago. In addition to oaks, the park contains more than 40 species of trees including very good Lime Trees *(Tilia cordata)* and some well-formed Mountain Ashes *(Sorbus aucuparia)*.

Succession

In 1925, upon the death of the last Armfelt, Åminne passed along the female line and for two generations its owners were von Knorrings. In 1999, when Holger von Knorring passed away, his three daughters, all of whom lived abroad, and led by the eldest, Baroness Catharina Palmstierna, began the work to find a successor to the estate. They wanted someone with the interest, knowledge and means to restore the estate and its main buildings to a condition reflecting its unique position in Finnish history. This is, after all, where Tsar Alexander I met with his trusted advisor to agree both on the borders of the Grand Duchy and on the terms to be discussed with Crown Prince Carl Johan, the former Jean Baptiste

Bernadotte, whom he was to meet in Åbo in 1812; decisions which a hundred years later would define the new Republic of Finland.

Saara and Bjorn Wahlroos took over the estate in 2001 and started an ambitious renovation and expansion programme. They did not have a background in estate management or farming, Bjorn Wahlroos having made a career first in academia as a Professor of Economics and later as a banker. He is now chairman of several large corporations in Finland. During the past ten years, not only have most of the buildings been renovated, some 600 hectares of old estate land has been bought back, the main crop, which used to be sugar beet, has been discontinued for more environmentally sound cereals, large tracts of land adjacent to waterways have been converted to cover for birds and other wildlife, and sustainable cutting plans for the forests have been put in place.

DESCRIPTION

The Manor and other buildings

Åminne Manor was originally built by Magnus Wilhelm Armfelt in 1793. It was significantly expanded and reconstructed by his son Gustaf Mauritz in 1807-12. The expansion plans were drawn up by Carl Christoffer Gjörwell, who went on to become City Architect of Stockholm, and building work

The Estate of Åminne Gods present manages more than 50 buildings.

was supervised by the Italian Carlo Bassi. Gjörwell added the wings, a new entrance, the pilasters and the front on to the facade of the building and had it plastered to give it more of a Neo-classical look. Armfelt also attached six medallions of his friends and colleagues in art and culture by the Swedish sculptor Johan Tobias Sergel to the exterior wall between the grand pilasters.

During 2001-2007 the Manor underwent extensive conservation work to return it to its former glory and to install modern bathrooms and kitchens. It is decorated in the late Gustavian and Empire style of the late 18th and early 19th century and today displays the largest collection of period furniture and art in Finland. Åminne Manor also houses two separate libraries, the Armfelt library with some 4400 volumes of French and English literature in an exquisite original setting of empire mahogany and giltwood bookcases, and the modern Wahlroos library, comprising some 5800 volumes of mostly contemporary writings in history, politics, economics and art.

The Åminne Estate presently manages more than 50 other buildings of which the greater part are leased to tenants. During the last ten years most of these houses have been renovated to modern standards. Half a dozen new houses have also been built in traditional style to house the 23 employees on the estate. The main workhorse stables, which in 2001 were a ruin, have been restored and converted into a meeting and dining hall where private events can be organized. The circular *manege* will in the near future be converted to house the Estate Museum.

As a result, valuable settlements, farm buildings and landscapes are now being maintained and building traditions characteristic of the region have been preserved. All this contributes to a rural living environment where employees and tenants can live in a sustainable and environmentally friendly way.

Development of the land and landscape setting

The Åminne Estate covers the valley and lands around the Halikko river in southwest Finland. The Manor is situated some 1.5 km upriver from the inlet of the Baltic Sea. The lands of the estate are typical for this part of Finland: mostly flat, with a river that has cut through the soft soil to form a deep valley in their middle. Most of the agricultural soils are soft sand clay while the forest soil is a mix of clay, sand and gravel with some peat.

The estate owns approximately 60 ha of watercourses in the area including lakes, the river and part of the inlet of the sea.

A total of 2,186 ha of land is devoted to:
- 370 ha agricultural land;
- 12 ha grassland;
- 1,610 ha forest;
- 60 ha water;
- 13 ha infrastructure and housing;
- 26 ha gardens and park.

The Haliko river banks compose an interesting landscape.

Åminne Gods **(Finland)**

Åminne Gods Estate

Mallard, woodpigeon, pheasant and grey partridge are the most abundant game species on Åminne Estate.

More than 10,000 Spruce trees have been planted to provide year-round cover, and a further 15 hectares of agricultural land has been planted with annual cover crops such as maize, sorghum and other game crops, mostly in small and medium sized lots. For Mallard, Goldeneye *(Bucephala clangula)* and other ducks wetlands and ponds have been built, with a positive effect on wildlife in general as different kinds of waders and plovers thrive in the shallow waters. Old grazing grounds on the Halikko Bay shore have also been restored for the Highland Cattle brought in from Starfors in Sweden. The main object of cattle grazing has been to recreate the meadowlands by the bay, overgrown by excessive use of fertilizer in the

Wildlife Conservation

With the Halikko river flowing through the estate and the Salo river adjacent, Åminne provides a wonderful natural habitat for waterfowl. Since 2001, much work has been done on wildlife conservation by further developing an environment suitable for Mallard *(Anas platyrhynchos),* Woodpigeon *(Columba palumbus),* Pheasant *(Phasianus colchicus)* and Grey Partridge *(Perdix perdix).* The estate presently employs two full-time gamekeepers who mostly tend to the birdlife by planting cover crops, developing wetlands, raising partridge and pheasant, and engaging in pest control. The 1,600 hectares of forest, moreover, contain an ample supply of Moose (Elk) *(Alces alces),* White-tailed Deer *(Odocoileus virginianus)* and Roe Deer *(Capreolus capreolus).*

Old grazing grounds on the Halikko Bay shore have also been restored for the Highland Cattle brought in from Starfors in Sweden.

The 1,600 hectares of forest contain an ample supply of Elk *(Alces alces).*

Åminne Gods Estate

1970s and 1980s, and to reduce the flow of nutrients from agricultural fields into the Baltic Sea, but it also produces micro-sites which provide birds with better nesting sites.

Bio-mass plant

Since the 1980s, woodchip has constituted the main source of heating energy at Åminne with oil used only as backup. Today both the Manor, the main farm buildings and the village houses are heated by a central woodchip boiler. In the cold Finnish climate, the boiler consumes around 4000 cubic metres of woodchips per year, mostly from the estate's own forests and chipped, dried and stored on the grounds.

Farmland

With 370 ha of agricultural land and forests in a growth phase, crop production accounts for 72% of estate income. Crops that are produced are as follows:

- 123 ha spring wheat;
- 23 ha winter wheat;
- 28 ha barley;
- 92 ha malting barley;
- 17 ha spring rape;
- 18 ha oats for seeds;
- 5 ha silage;
- 4 ha red canary grass.

When necessary, about 100 hectares of the Åminne fields can be irrigated.

Today the estate is heated by a central woodchip boiler. The picture of the left show stumps for bio-energy.

Landscape in winter.

Åminne Gods **(Finland)**

KARI EHNROOTH, MANAGER OF THE ÅMINNE ESTATE, STATES THAT:

"The biggest threat to production is the general decrease in the profitability of farming. Due to the high latitude, the yields are far from those in Central Europe, and production costs have risen more rapidly than consumer prices. Climate change has recently somewhat extended the growing season, but also increases the risk of plant diseases and pests spreading from Central Europe to Finland".

Planting of spruce seedlings.

Åminne Gods Estate

Forestry

Forestry presently accounts for only 14% of estate income since excessive cutting in the 1980s and 1990s must now be corrected for. Cutting will gradually be increased and forestry is expected to account for close to a third of income 10-15 years from now. The woodlands are mostly covered with conifers:

- 63% of Pine,
- 22% of Spruce,
- 14% of Birch.

The forestlands of Åminne are less flat than the agricultural fields. The hills offer a natural mosaic of different types of forest, watercourses, lakes and ponds.

The estate´s forests are managed in a sustainable way based on a ten-year plan. Much of the practical work is made up of pruning pulpwood to allow room for timber growth together with improvement work in young stands. This takes place annually together with some harvesting of mature stands of 60 to 90 years of age. After final felling replanting is based on the same local species that have been harvested, usually by planting new seedlings or with natural regeneration.

As members of the Finnish Forest Certification System (FFCS), which is part of the Programme for Endorsement of Certification Schemes (PEFC), we are obliged to closely follow the principles required for sustainability. Replanting has to take place immediately after final felling and wildlife has to be taken into consideration in the management of the forests. The Finnish Forest Act and Nature Conservation Act also require the Estate to leave some habitats of special importance untouched.

Kristoffer Ranken, forestry manager at Åminne Estate, states that:

"The challenge of the future will be to maintain efficiency in the management of the forests and simultaneously ensure that the highest environmental standards are applied".

Åminne Gods Estate

A large area of land, adjacent to the water has been converted into natural habitats for wildlife.

"Assuming the responsibility for an estate that is also a historic monument is a daunting task", says Björn Wahlroos. "You may not be under immediate pressure to produce financial results, but you are every bit as much responsible for the outcome. At Åminne we have been faced with the task of undoing some of the evil implications of history: of wars, expropriation and reduced circumstances. We have been offered the opportunity to contribute, in a small way, to the preservation of history and of national heritage. It has been a privilege and a pleasure".

But Åminne is not, nor is it intended to be, a museum. "It is our home, and the estate is home to a great many of our employees as well", says Björn Wahlroos. "It is a thriving part of the Finnish countryside and as such, over the longer run, must also be able to carry its weight in economic terms. The great challenge of the EU and its member states is to reconcile the interests of taxpayers with those of us who live on the countryside. Only by offering city-dwellers a clean and attractive countryside, sprinkled with history and tradition and full of activity can we ever convince them that they should contribute to its preservation. The CAP and other support systems will just have to change, to provide more incentives to protect the environment and our heritage".

Björn Wahlroos

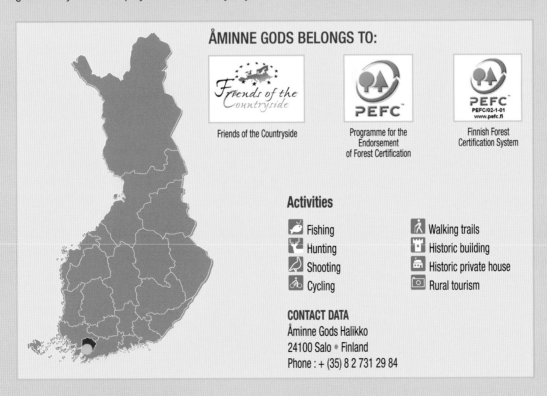

ÅMINNE GODS BELONGS TO:

Friends of the Countryside

PEFC — Programme for the Endorsement of Forest Certification

PEFC/02-1-01 www.pefc.fi — Finnish Forest Certification System

Activities

- Fishing
- Hunting
- Shooting
- Cycling
- Walking trails
- Historic building
- Historic private house
- Rural tourism

CONTACT DATA
Åminne Gods Halikko
24100 Salo • Finland
Phone : + (35) 8 2 731 29 84

Castiglion del Bosco Estate

Castiglion del Bosco

Mediterranean

Location: Castiglion del Bosco, Montalcino, Tuscany, Italy.
Surface: 1,751 ha.

CLIMATIC DATA

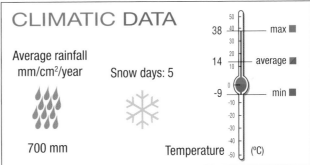

Average rainfall
mm/cm²/year

Snow days: 5

700 mm

Temperature (°C)

38 — max
14 — average
-9 — min

SUMMARY

Situated in the heart of Tuscany's Brunello winemaking region, Castiglion del Bosco is one of Tuscany's largest contiguous estates. It is located in the Val d'Orcia, 12 kilometres northwest of Montalcino in the Province of Siena, just 95 kilometres south of Florence and 200 kilometres north of Rome. Its vast property spans ten kilometres, comprising nearly 1800 spectacular hectares of protected nature reserve. Castiglion del Bosco is a magnificent piece of Tuscany and is enjoyed exclusively by private members and a select group of guests.

The majestic estate has seen many changes in its 800-year history, yet it has changed very little. Scattered across the property are remnants of a rich past: a circular Etruscan stronghold dating back to 600 BC, a 12th century castle fortress, ruins of an early Gothic chapel (c. 900 BC) and the Chiesa di San Michele Arcangelo, with its spectacular Lorenzetti fresco.

Today, Castiglion del Bosco is a completely restored Private Membership Estate with a focus on the land, the wine, the history as well as building a unique multi-generational legacy for its members and their families. The debut of Il Borgo offers a fortunate few a limited opportunity to taste the exquisite lifestyle that can only be experienced at Castiglion del Bosco.

Castiglion del Bosco is situated in the heart of Tuscany's Brunello winemaking region.

HISTORY

One of the oldest contiguous estates in Tuscany and located on the Via Francigena, Castiglion del Bosco has an incredibly rich history. Members become stewards for this historic treasure, preserving and continuing its legacy.

Five million years ago, sea levels dropped, leaving sand and clay deposits across the Val d'Orcia. The Radicofani and Amiata volcanoes erupted spreading a dark substance known as trachyte, resulting in a soil mixture perfect for growing Sangiovese grapes.

Archeological digs confirm that the Etruscans occupied Castiglion del Bosco as far back as 600 BC — prizing its elevated position as a military outlook.

Castiglion del Bosco Castello, built in the 12th century.

Castiglion del Bosco Estate

The Via Francigena, leading from Canterbury to Rome, was established and used for centuries by thousands of pilgrims. The road passed through Castiglion del Bosco where pilgrims found shelter in the Pieve San Michelle.

In the 12th century, Castiglion del Bosco's Castello was built in classic medieval style; its form is similar to that of Rocca of Tentennano, located not far from the estate. In the early 13th century, the family of Cacciaconti of Trequanda surrounded the hilltop bastion with stone walls. Still standing today are remnants of the walled enclosure, a gate and the partially destroyed Castello.

By 1208, Castiglion del Bosco held a prominent position in the Sienese Republic, paying the highest property tax of all estates.

Badia Ardenga, a beautiful old abbey located near the Fiume Ombrone, was frequented by emperors and popes travelling along the ancient Via Francigena route. Built before 1000 AD, the original formation is still intact today. According to legend, the German Emperor Henry VII of Luxembourg and his army went to the abbey to take communion during their stop in Buonconvento in 1313. Allegedly, the monks poisoned the Eucharist and the Emperor was found dead in the church.

In 1318 Castiglion del Bosco was taken over by the Gallerani family, prosperous merchants who held public offices in Siena. It has been said that Cecilia Gallerani was the subject of Leonardo da Vinci's painting "The Lady with an Ermine" and a muse for the "Mona Lisa".

Upon Ciampolo Gallerani's death in 1339, ownership of Castiglion del Bosco passed to the Piccolomini family, who conquered the castle after a long and bloody siege. During this period, the fortification was restored.

In 1349, Pietro Lorenzetti painted the fresco "Annunciazione dei Santi" in the Church of San Michele in Castiglion del Bosco's Il Borgo. It was rediscovered in 1876 and fully restored to its original glory. Pietro and his brother, Ambrogio Lorenzetti, who painted the fresco *"Allegory of Good Government and Bad Government"* in the Palazzo Pubblico in Siena, belonged to the famous Sienese School which flourished during the late Middle Ages and foreshadowed the art of the Renaissance.

Ferruccio Biondi Santi, who is said to have resided on the Castiglion del Bosco estate from

1888, abandoned the Canaiolo, Ciliegiolo and Colorino grape varieties and concentrated on an isolated Sangiovese clone producing the now famous Brunello di Montalcino wine. At that time, there were only a handful of Brunello di Montalcino wine producers.

In 1967 Castiglion del Bosco became one of the founding members of the Consorzio del Vino Brunello di Montalcino. The organisation was created as a voluntary association of producers who regulate and control the quality of Brunello production. Brunello was among the first Italian wines to be granted the titles DOC (Controlled Denomination of Origin) and DOCG (Controlled and Guaranteed Denomination of Origin).

The Val d'Orcia was considered a site of 'outstanding universal value' by the World Heritage Committee according to Article 1 of the 1972 World Heritage Convention, making Castiglion del Bosco a World Heritage Site.

In 1975, the number of Brunello di Montalcino producers increased to 25 vintners producing approximately 70,000 cases and, according to the Consorzio del Vino Brunello di Montalcino, in 1995 there were 120 producers making 300,000 cases. Today, there are well over 200 producers in the Consorzio, producing over 500,000 cases of Brunello.

The Val d'Orcia Artistic, Natural and Cultural Park was founded in 1996. The Park, which encompasses the Castiglion del Bosco property, is an Area Naturale Protetta di Interesse Locale (Protected Natural Area of Local Interest) focused on increasing awareness of the cultural and environmental heritage, as well as manufacturing and marketing of local products.

When the present owner, Massimo Ferragamo purchased the estate in 2003, along with Corky Severson, they decided to restore and develop Castiglion del Bosco into one of the finest Private Membership Clubs in the world.

In 2004, UNESCO added Val d'Orcia to its list of World Heritage Sites and from Spring 2008, Il Borgo was unveiled after painstaking restorations, offering 16 elegantly appointed guest suites (the complete collection of 26 suites and guestrooms will be available by Spring 2009) as well as a cooking school, two restaurants, a fitness centre (October 2008), a tasting room, an infinity pool, and other distinctive amenities within its historic buildings.

DESCRIPTION

The Vision

The restoration of Castiglion del Bosco is the vision of Massimo Ferragamo and Corky Severson. Their passion for the property is reflected in a commitment to quality and authenticity in creating

In 1888 Ferruccio Biondi Santi abandoned the Canaiolo, Ciliegiolo and Colorino grape varieties and concentrated on an isolated Sangiovese clone, producing the now famous Brunello di Montalcino wine.

G. Janssens

an extraordinary legacy that can be passed from generation to generation. To a hand-selected team of experts, seasoned at the world's top hotels, they have awarded the responsibility of delivering on their promise of impeccable service, exceptional amenities and a warm, welcoming atmosphere.

Their collective wish is for Castiglion del Bosco to be a place for members and a select group of guests to return again and again, building lasting family traditions and friendships, while experiencing the Tuscan way of life – spectacular food and wine, fantastic sport, luxurious relaxation, a tradition of craftsmanship and a generosity of spirit – all set against a breathtaking landscape.

Brief description

In addition to a deeply rooted appreciation for history and viniculture, Tuscans are sports enthusiasts. The opportunities for outdoor sports at Castiglion del Bosco estate are diverse: fly fishing, hunting, horseback riding, hiking, cycling, hot-air ballooning and, of course, witnessing Il Palio, the infamous equestrian event that takes place each summer in Siena.

The estate lies within the slopes of the Val d'Orcia, an undulating landscape known for its enchanting beauty and juxtaposition of colours and textures. This land, deep green in spring and golden in fall, is also rich in art and culture. Ancient sites are carefully preserved, dating back to the Etruscan era, blending with art from the Medieval and early Renaissance periods. The area is also famous for its agriculture. The vineyards of the Val d'Orcia, including Castiglion del Bosco's own, produce the most coveted Italian wines, Brunello di Montalcino and its younger sibling, Rosso di Montalcino.

Infrastructure

Located in the most picturesque areas on the estate are twenty 17th- and 18th-century Tuscan farmhouses that once supported the Estate's traditional agricultural activities.

Just as it has been for hundreds of years, Il Borgo is the heart of the estate. Perched on one of the highest hilltops, its ten buildings include the original landowner's villa, the Cantina Vecchia, Scuderie, Chiesa di San Michele Arcangelo and Canonica (priest's house). These buildings have

The restoration of the estate from 2003 was the vision of Massimo Ferragamo and Corky Severson.

Castiglion del Bosco Estate

The cellar, known as the Barriccaia, – a wine sanctuary.

Castiglion del Bosco Estate

been respectfully renovated to accommodate many of the estate's exceptional amenities, including 24 suites

These homes, ranging in size from 3,000 to 6,000 square feet, have been transformed into luxurious villas for the exclusive use of Castiglion del Bosco members. Some are secluded in the forest, others overlook vineyards and olive groves, a few are nestled in the Borgo and one sits proudly next to the castle ruins, but all enchant with stunning views of the Tuscan countryside.

While each villa is unique, the décor for all follows a common style, paying respect to the heritage and rich colours of the surrounding Sienese landscape. Through the careful selection of materials and furniture, from antiques and special pieces created by local craftsmen and fabrics made of the softest natural fibres, each villa reflects a combination of local history and a warm, inviting atmosphere.

Network of roads

The commercial airports in Pisa, Firenze and Grosseto, along with Siena's private airstrip, are all within easy driving distance of Castiglion del Bosco. The estate's helipad also allows for direct airport-to-estate transfer.

Economic activities

An estimated 70% of the estate's total income derives from *Tourism*:

The six-star amenities at Castiglion del Bosco reflect the true essence of 'La Vera Toscana' – luxurious relaxation, exceptional cuisine and great sport, all set against the picturesque backdrop of the Val d'Orcia and cultivated for the exclusive enjoyment of Castiglion del Bosco members and guests:

- **The Spa:** A serene oasis specializing in unique therapies based on organic ingredients from the estate, this sanctuary of 12,000 square feet was conceptualized by spa visionary Anne Bramham.
- **The Canonica:** The "priest's house" is located at the center of Il Borgo and houses a cooking school where members and guests can watch or participate in the preparation of the region's spectacular cuisine. La Canonica also features an enoteca wine bar, bottega and the Orto, an organic kitchen garden.
- **Dining:** Two restaurants and a cosy bar showcase seasonal menus using the finest local ingredients complemented by an extensive list of Castiglion del Bosco and regional

The Estate is the 5th largest producer of Brunello di Montalcino wine.

- **The Gardens:** A magnificent amenity within itself, the extensive gardens of the estate encompass a radiant Tuscan palette for all seasons, including a terrace of cutting flowers, rustic olive trees, manicured fruit orchards and sprawling Sangiovese vineyards. The splendid Orto, designed by the Vatican's garden landscaper, is home to more than 180 varieties of robust vegetables and aromatic herbs grown for the Canonica.

- **Golf:** Golf at Castiglion del Bosco blends the magnificent Tuscan landscape and the playing challenges of a Tom Weiskopf-designed, 18-hole championship course (opening Spring 2010). After an exhilarating round, members and guests can enjoy the hospitality of the Club House, which features a pro shop, bar and Tuscan Griglia. Troon Golf, a world leader in luxury golf management, oversees the golf programme.

Another 26% of the estate's total income is estimated to come from the *Winery*.

The estate's 70 hectares of vineyards, all of which are licensed to produce Brunello, extend over two areas of the property, providing different exposures and climatic characteristics.

While winemaking at Castiglion del Bosco has been a craft for centuries, until fairly recently the vineyards were cultivated solely for personal consumption by each family living on the estate. Today, Castiglion del Bosco wines are consistently recognised for their excellence.

As one of the founding members of the Consorzio del Vino Brunello di Montalcino, the organisation that regulates and controls the quality of Brunello production, Castiglion del Bosco introduced the world to its exemplary vintages through the emergence of a commercial operation in the late 1950s. In 2004, acclaimed international Wine Master Nicolo D'Afflitto took command of winemaking at Castiglion del Bosco, along with locally trained enologist Cecilia Leoneschi. Under their careful direction, the estate is yielding more modern Brunellos that are attracting critical acclaim.

The first two weeks of October signal the beginning of the harvest, when the ripened grapes are picked by hand and make their way to the estate's new 39,000 square-foot winery, a complete gravity-fed facility. Following a double

wines. The traditional Osteria offers a casual ambiance to gather for food and wine.

- **Wine Tasting:** Set within *Castiglion del Bosco's* critically acclaimed Winery – the 5th largest producer of the cherished Brunello di Montalcino – the tasting room offers a portfolio of Castiglion del Bosco's exemplary vintages. The Winery also houses the Barriccaia, a wine sanctuary filled with rows of traditional French barrique barrels.

- **Sport:** Extensive sporting facilities span the property, from a state-of-the-art fitness centre (October 2008) and soccer fields to courts for tennis and bocce (Italian *boules*). Castiglion del Bosco also features miles of picturesque hiking and biking trails that hug spectacular ridges and meander past streams, waterfalls and hidden historic sites. The beautiful Maremma horses, used by traditional Tuscan herdsmen, guide guests through a network of riding trails extending to the far-reaching corners of the property. An outfitters station for fishing is currently under development.

Uses of lands	Surface (ha)
Arable Land	180
Vines	60
Forest (UNESCO)	1300
Water (Lakes/Rivers)	3
Infrastructure-Housing	50
Gardens	7
Golf Course	150
Total:	1,750

grape selection done entirely by hand, ensuring that only the best grapes go into fermentation, the grapes are poured into stainless-steel tanks. Since no pumps are used in this phase, the grapes do not suffer any damage before they are fermented. Here the Sangiovese grapes spend 15 to 18 days in fully automated fermentation tanks, where the temperature and mixing is programmed electronically to ensure optimum quality, flavour and richness. After fermentation, Castiglion del Bosco Brunello ages in French oak barriques. Current production includes the acclaimed "Campo del Drago" Brunello di Montalcino, Brunello di Montalcino, and Rosso di Montalcino, along with a limited quantity of CdBianco. In addition, the estate produces its own grappa, olive oil and honey.

The fundamental goal of winemaking at Castiglion del Bosco is to remain faithful to the land and the characteristics of the grapes. The estate's members have the unique opportunity to help contribute to this goal and participate in all aspects of the vinification process, from picking and sorting to bottling and tasting. Other membership privileges include a spectacular members-only dining and tasting room, personal wine storage lockers within the Cantina, an annual allotment of Castiglion del Bosco wines and grappa, and invitations to exclusive wine events. Guests of Il Borgo also enjoy special opportunities to engage in the winery experience.

Il Borgo is the heart of the estate. This is the original Villa of the landowner.

Castiglion del Bosco Estate

Castiglion del Bosco **(Italy)**

NATURAL HERITAGE

As a protected nature reserve within the Val d'Orcia Parco Naturale, Castiglion del Bosco boasts spectacular natural beauty. Nearly three-quarters of the estate is blanketed in forest – home to Wild Boar *(Sus scrofa)*, deer, Foxes *(Vulpes vulpes)*, Porcupines *(Hystrix cristata)*, Badgers *(Meles meles)*, hawks and pheasants. Each season a diverse selection of flora add visual drama and fragrance – Italian Stone Pine *(Pinus pinea)*, chestnuts, ancient oaks, olive trees, stately Italian Cypress *(Cupressus sempervirens)* and smaller species such as Bay Laurel *(Laurus nobilis)*, Thyme *(Thymus vulgaris)*, Rosemary *(Rosmarinus officinalis)*, brilliant Red Poppies *(Papaver rhoeas)* and acres of terraced grapevines.

In 2004 the Val d'Orcia was added to the UNESCO list of World Heritage Sites under these criteria:

- **Criterion(iv)**: The Val d'Orcia is an exceptional reflection of the way the landscape was rewritten in Renaissance times to reflect the ideals of good governance and to create an aesthetically pleasing picture.
- **Criterion(vi)**: The landscape of the Val d'Orcia was celebrated by painters from the Sienese

School, which flourished during the Renaissance. Images of the Val d'Orcia, and particularly depictions of landscapes where people are depicted as living in harmony with nature, have come to be seen as icons of the Renaissance and have profoundly influenced the development of landscape thinking.

The landscape of Val d'Orcia is part of the agricultural hinterland of Siena, redrawn and developed when it was integrated in the territory of the city-state in the 14th and 15th centuries to reflect an idealised model of good management and to create an aesthetically pleasing picture. The landscape's distinctive aesthetics, with fortified settlements on the hilltops, inspired many artists. Their images have come to exemplify the beauty of well-managed Renaissance agricultural landscapes. The inscription covers an agrarian and pastoral landscape reflecting innovative land-management systems; towns and villages; farmhouses; and the Roman Via Francigena and its associated abbeys, inns, shrines, bridges, etc.

The territory of the Val d'Orcia is characterised by hilly landscape with gently rolling hills and valleys typical of "the Sienese Crete", and a rich variety of vegetation. The river Orcia springs from a gorge and winds its way across the valley. The geographical history of the area began 5 million years ago when the sea receded, leaving behind sand and clay deposits which gave origin to the surface of the valley. Later, two volcanoes, Radicofani and Monte Amiata, covered the surface with lava, which when it cooled, became a rock now known as trachyte.

The estate is one of the founding members of the Consorzio del Vino Brunello di Montalcino.

G. Janssens

(iv) To be an outstanding example of a type of building, architectural or technological ensemble or landscape which illustrates (a) significant stage (s) in human history.
(vi) To be directly or tangibly associated with events or living traditions, with ideas, or with beliefs, with artistic and literary works of outstanding universal significance. (The Committee considers that this criterion should preferably be used in conjunction with other criteria).

Erosion of the soil has played a major role in the formation of the landscape with the clay soil laid bare, forming craggy badlands known as 'calanchi' and clay knolls otherwise called 'biancane' or 'mammelloni', which can be seen in the areas of Casa a Tuoma (Pienza), Ripalta (San Quirico), Lucci- olabella, Beccatello, and Torre Tarugi (Pienza), Con- tignano, Pietre Bianche and the Poggio Leano (Radicofani).

North west of Bagno Vignoni a magnificent rocky gorge covered with woodlands and Mediter- ranean maquis opens out onto the vineyards of Montalcino and then continues to the sea. On the slopes of Monte Amiata are forests of beech and chestnut trees and of particular interest and rare beauty is the Holm Oak woods *(Quercus ilex)* of Scarceta. The Abetina del Vivo with its ancient Sil- ver Fir trees *(Abies alba)* is situated near the old vil- lage of Vivo d'Orcia, famous for its springs which provide water for much of the area.

Apart from the holm oak, the other tree species found throughout the area are the Turkey Oak *(Quercus cerris)* and Downy Oak *(Q.pubescens)* which cover the territory in woodlands which be- come thicker towards the Maremma. However the tree which has become a symbol of the Val d'Orcia is the Cypress *(Cupressus sempervirens).*

The Val d'Orcia Natural Park is a paradise for the ornithologist. The turtle dove is a migratory bird which nests here and spends the winter in North Africa.

It is an ornithologist's paradise with the Barn Owl *(Tyto alba)*, Long-eared Owl *(Asio otus)*, Eagle Owl *(Bubo bubo)* and Little Owl *(Athene noctua)*, as well as birds of prey such as the Buzzard *(Buteo buteo)*, Short-toed Eagle *(Circaetus gallicus)*, Hen-Harrier *(Circus cyaneus)* and Kestrel *(Falco tinnunculus)*. You can also spot the Black and Green Woodpeck- ers *(Dryocopus martius* and *Picus viridis)*, the Raven *(Corvus corax)* and Hooded Crow *(C. cornix)*, the Wryneck *(Jynx torquilla)*, Spotted Flycatcher *(Musci- capa striata)* and Bee-eater *(Merops apiaster)*, to name but a few.

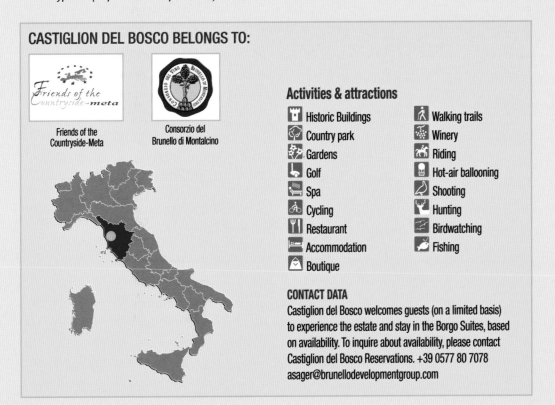

CASTIGLION DEL BOSCO BELONGS TO:

Friends of the Countryside-Meta

Consorzio del Brunello di Montalcino

Activities & attractions

- 🏰 Historic Buildings
- 🌳 Country park
- 🌿 Gardens
- ⛳ Golf
- 🛏 Spa
- 🚴 Cycling
- 🍽 Restaurant
- 🛏 Accommodation
- 👜 Boutique

- 🚶 Walking trails
- 🍇 Winery
- 🏇 Riding
- 🎈 Hot-air ballooning
- 🦅 Shooting
- 🦌 Hunting
- 🦅 Birdwatching
- 🐟 Fishing

CONTACT DATA

Castiglion del Bosco welcomes guests (on a limited basis) to experience the estate and stay in the Borgo Suites, based on availability. To inquire about availability, please contact Castiglion del Bosco Reservations. +39 0577 80 7078 asager@brunellodevelopmentgroup.com

N

Table of References

1. Avenue
2. House Court
3. House
4. Terrace
5. Lawn Terraces
6. Kitchen Court
7. Car Port
8. Grove
9. Guest House
10. Fireplace
11. Covered Terrace
12. Swimming Pool
13. Office Pavilion
14. Parking
15. Tower
16. Stable Court
17. Covered Arena
18. Bridge
19. Village Entrance
20. Sculpture

Danilovka

Boreal

Location: Benitsy locality, region of Kaluga, Russia.
Surface: 650 ha.

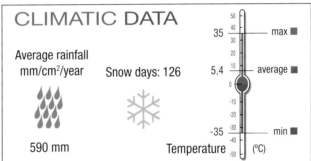

CLIMATIC DATA

Average rainfall
mm/cm²/year

Snow days: 126

590 mm

Temperature (°C)

35 — max

5,4 — average

-35 — min

Throughout much of the territory there are only two distinct seasons: winter and summer. Spring and autumn are usually brief periods of change between low temperatures and high temperatures. In recent years a change in climatic patterns has been occurring, as winters become milder with less snow (thus often putting winter crops more at risk) and significantly wetter springs and summers.

SUMMARY

Danilovka is situated 95 km southwest of Moscow city centre near the Protva River.
The project started four years ago and primarily concerns the development of a modern farm and the design of gardens and landscapes including architectural elements. Despite the fact that 80 years of bolshevism will take a lot of time to eradicate and despite the risk of re-nationalisation of land, the present landowner is facing a great challenge:
"We really have to start everything from zero; actually the whole point, in addition to our personal interest in this beautiful and fascinating challenge, is to raise our son (and hopefully more children to come) in the spirit of a property with its lifestyle, its responsibilities, the necessity to have quite a vast spectrum of knowledge to deal with all its aspects. It is a little part of our planet, which we want to take good care of". M.Orloff.

Danilovka Estate is situated next to the town of Borousk,
95 Km soth-west of Moscow.

J. Hill

Alexei Orloff,
Mikhail's Grandfather.

HISTORY

Before the 1917 revolution the area seemed to have been in the hands of small land owners. After the revolution and the confiscation by the communists of all land from the peasants and land owners, several kolkhozes and sovkhozes were created. In the 1960s, after a disastrous reform carried out by Nikita Khrushchev, the village of Benitsy was abandoned with a very few houses still inhabited.

From this time, having lost its rural community, the village turned into a "dacha", a Russian word for seasonal or year-round second homes located in the countryside of Russian cities.

Benitsy is located on a hill overlooking a small plain joining Benitsy to Satino situated approximately 4 km to the east. During the Napoleonic wars of 1812, a lot of actions and battles took place in this area. The Russian canons were placed on Benitsy hill, while the French canons were on the hill of Satino.

In the nearby town of Borovsk, Napoleon spent his last days in Russia before returning to France. In Borovsk he is said to have signed the decree of evacuation of the "Grande Armee", while his armies were fighting the last battles against the Russian Army in Maloyaroslavets approximately 25 km from Danilovka.

In 1812, when the French started evacuating the area (and Russia in general), a small church dedicated to the Saints Cosimus and Damianus was erected the same year in the middle of the village. The communists transformed the church into a horse stable and the last priest was assassinated in front of his church. Recently the villagers started restoring the church. A new cross has been placed on a new roof, and some liturgies have already taken place.

The Protva river was navigable until the 12th century, and on the corner of the river downstream from the village was the last port. It seems that quite a lot of trade went on, as some coins, including Byzantine ones, were found when people started building new houses in the village, which shows the extent of international trade at the time.

In the 15th century, Tsar Ivan III prepared his armies in the area of Borovsk for a big battle against the Tatar Invaders. Later the area was again the arena for big battle when the Poles invaded the area and destroyed the last centre of Russian resistance by killing Prince Wolkonsky right in the main cathedral of the Pafnutiev monastery.

Konstantin E. Tsiolkovsky, the famous father of Russian astronautics, lived in Borovsk, where he was a teacher in the local school. His theories were the launching pad for extraordinary developments in the conquest of the cosmos during the 20th century.

Family History

The present owner Mikhail Orloff[1] was born on 2nd September 1966 in Lausanne, Switzerland. Mikhail's grandfather, Alexei Orloff, a Russian aristocrat born in 1897, took part in the civil war from 1918 to 1920 under General Denikin and then General Wrangel. He was part of the heroic army, which, without any resources, spent almost two years in the military camp at Gallipoli in the Dardanelles hoping to get an opportunity to oust the red terror from Russia.

Alexei Orloff ended up in exile in Switzerland, where Mikhail's father Piotr Orloff was born in 1938. In 1965, Piotr Orloff married Princes Fadia of Egypt, the third daughter of Egypt's last ruler King Farouk I. Princess Fadia ended up in Switzerland after the 1952 revolution in Egypt. She died in 2002 and is buried in the royal Mosque of El Rifai in Cairo, where almost all the rulers of Egypt and members of royal family from the last royal dynasty as well as the last Shah of Iran are buried. King Farouk I's full name was "His Majesty Farouk I, by the Grace of God, King of Egypt and Soudan, Sovereign of Nubia, of Kordofan, and of Darfur".

After a military coup in July 1952, directed by Gamal Abdel Nasser, Farouk abdicated and went to Rome where the former king lived the rest of his life and died in 1965. Immediately following Farouk's abdication, the monarch's baby son was proclaimed king as King Ahmed Fuad II, but for all

---

[1] In Russian, the name is spelled Orlov. According to an old tradition, Russian family names ending in − ov were translated into an ending in − off when passing from Cyrillic to the Roman alphabet. This custom was abandoned after the revolution in 1917, but is still maintained by the White Russians and their descendents.

intents and purposes the monarchy had been de facto abolished. In June 1953, the revolutionary government formally abolished the monarchy and Egypt was declared a Republic.

The Orloff Russian noble family, who produced several distinguished statesmen, diplomats and soldiers, managed vast properties before the revolution. Mikhail's great-great-uncle had been closely involved with the Russian Prime Minister Piotr Arkadievitch Stolypin in agrarian reforms at the beginning of the 20th century.

Mikhail's great-grandfather Sergei Stepanovitch Orloff was heavily involved in the legal reforms undertaken by the imperial government in the late 19th century. He was a magistrate in the Government of Kharkov (now in the Ukraine).

The neighbouring estate belonged to the Maximovitch family. Young Mikhail Maximovitch grew up with Alexei Orloff, Mikhail's grandfather, and became his best friend. Many years later, in exile, Mikhail Maximovitch became Archbishop John of Shanghai, one of the leading spiritual mentors of the Russian Orthodox in Russia abroad, who then became a Saint very venerated by Russian Orthodox in Russia and all around the world. Alexei

Piotr Orloff married Princes Fadia of Egypt, the third daughter of Egypt's last ruler King Farouk I. In the picture is King Farouk on duty.

Danilovka Estate

Orloff and the future Archbishop John of Shanghai both had their hearts and spirituality deeply rooted in their beloved Russian land, in values shared by all people who were living in the depth of this immense empire.

The estate is situated on slightly hilly ground, surrounded by woods.

Hill

The wood used for the construction comes from the regions of Arkhangelsk on the shores of the White Sea.

DESCRIPTION

Mikhail's first cousin, Bishop Ambrosii (Prince Piotr Cantacuzene), directly descended from the Byzantine Emperors, played an important role in the reunification of the Russian church and the Russian church abroad (created in exile after the Russian revolution to preserve Russian orthodoxy from total domination by the Communist regime), which took place in 2005.

Alexandra, Mikhail's wife, was born in Fergana in the Pamir mountains. Her father, Vladimir Feodorovitch Norenko was a professional officer in the Russian (then Soviet) Air Force. The family has therefore lived in different strategic areas of the country. Originally, Alexandra's family comes from

There are three log-houses, built in very traditional Russian style.

Omsk in Siberia. Vladimir Feodorovitch is now the "intendant" of the property.

Mikhail and Alexandra had a son Feodor born in Moscow in 2005. He is the first member of the family to be born in Russia since the 1917 revolution.

Property Overview

"Danilovka" is located next to the ancient town of Borovsk, in the "rayon" (like "commune" in French) of Borovsk, in the "oblast" (like "county" in English, or "department" in France or "canton" in Switzerland) of Kaluga.

The name "Danilovka" was given to the estate as a reminder of the former family property of the owners' grand-parents in Russia before the 1917 revolution. The former family estate was located in another region of the Russian Empire (presently Ukraine). The present owner decided to use the same name, not to be hung up on the nostalgia of a lost past, but to re-establish an element of continuity, which in his view is the essence of the spirit of any property.

The Surrounding Area

There are no other similar private properties around (in a European or Anglo-Saxon sense) as all Russian properties were completely destroyed by the communist regime. The estate was purchased piece by piece between 2004 and 2006 and is the only one of its kind in this area.

The estate is positioned on slightly hilly ground, surrounded by woods, and is limited on one side by the Protva River. This river flows into the Oka River further downstream, and the Oka in turn flows into the Volga, the Mother of all Russian rivers.

The estate surrounds a small village called Benitsy. There are references to this village as far back as the 10th century, but today it is mainly made up of "dachas" for Muscovites coming there on the weekends. The nearby town of Borovsk was founded in the 14th century and has conserved its historical aspect. There is an old monastery-fortress dating back to the 11th century. It resisted numerous attacks by the Polish army on the Moscow principality and has become one of the main seats of Russian orthodoxy.

The soil is sandy clay loam with a low degree of acidity. The land had been traditionally exploited for almost two decades with farmers using land for personal subsistence with a few cows. Between

1917 and 1990, the entirety of agricultural land in Russia was exclusively in state ownership and the transition to a market-oriented economy had to start with privatisation of land and farm assets.

The property is crossed by a small stream, which goes into the Protva. The woods are mainly made softwoods and Birch (*Betula* spp.) trees, with Willow (*Salix* spp.) along the rivers and wet areas.

Alongside the stream, there is an interesting ecosystem, which will be the subject of a wetland conservation project. .

General Infrastructure

Following the Russian rural architectural style, three houses are currently under construction. They are log-houses, built in very traditional Russian style. The wood used for the construction comes from the regions of Arkhangelsk on the shores of the White Sea and of Nizhny Novgorod on the shores of the Volga.

It is proving to be quite a challenge to build simple houses in a traditional style, because, as one of the consequences of the communist regime, traditional craftsmen and therefore their associated cultural knowledge have all but disappeared.

These houses are constructed on the northern part of the estate overlooking the River Protva.

Apart from this, an old farm building formerly used for housing cows is falling down but shows a spirit of Russian entity.

Currently there are no roads at all. They will be developed little by little alongside the master plan prepared by Francois Goffinet, outlined below.

Table of References

1. Entrance
2. Main Gate
3. Driveway
4. Meadow
5. Danilovka Court
6. Chapel
7. Avenue
8. House Court
9. House
10. Guest House
11. Office
12. Stable Yard
13. Central Arena
14. Village Entrance
15. Village Church
16. Farm Entrance
17. Farm
18. Barn
19. Paddocks
20. Fields
21. Pole Fields
22. River
23. Lakes
24. Woodlands
25. Ponds
26. Village Cemetery

Master plan of Danilovka Estate.

MASTERPLAN OR MASTERPIECE

Mikhail and Alexandra have asked François Goffinet to help them set the base of a rational and organised management of the space. François Goffinet insisted on the need to start at the very beginning with a master plan, which will then serve as central backbone for everything that is planned and happening on the territory of the estate, in order to avoid disorders and future problems.

In addition to being an instrument of work, François Goffinet immediately became a vector of inspiration and dreams reflecting the natural beauty of the site, with his superb landscapes into which he inserts stunning buildings. It is clear that all these admirable buildings and tree lines do not exist yet. It represents considerable work. But even if this does not all come to life now, or only very slowly, the very fact that it all exists in our hearts is already an important source of inspiration for all of us each time we look at the estate or do something on it. The most precious thing that we can pass to the next generation is not necessarily something fully achieved, but a family dream, a source of inspiration, which is significantly larger than one's life. And thanks to François Goffinet, these dreams are coordi-

nated in space and time. Of course, these plans and drawings increase the feeling of responsibility towards this extraordinary place.

A recent visit has been made to the estate to discuss the needs of the family and to assess the potential of the site. The master plan shows a general representation of the property respecting its past, its current and prospective uses. A site survey has been undertaken to analyse the existing conditions and potential of the estate.

If gardens usually reflect the metaphysics of their time, here they celebrate the respect of traditions, land and the family.

Discovering this site was not without emotion; indeed, the interplays of commercial, military and religious history have left many unusual traces, preys of several archaeological investigations in the region.

But the beauty of this land translates with generosity the importance of this area, bathed in brilliant brightness and luminosity.

The symbolic and applied mathematic is somehow a step in this universe which nature gives us and that we try to understand and humbly translate. All is "connection and harmony".

Danilovka (Russia)

Masterplan by François Goffinet. Illustrations by Peter Lorenzoni.

Danilovka Estate

South Elevation.

Danilovka Estate

Chapel.

Danilovka Estate

Avenue to Stable Court.

May the ordinance of the plan guide future generations in the deepest respect of the generous and fragile elements which nature gives us and that we try here to gather harmoniously.

On the road leading to the village of Benitsy, some stone bollards discreetly mark the entrance to the property.

Further along the drive and away from the sight of the road, the gates are discovered in the shadow of a 'rond-point' or circle of trees forming a colonnade.

The gateway consists of wrought-iron gates and rustic stone pillars, which celebrate the entrance and set the tone for the discovery of the property.

The driveway, framed by an avenue of trees planted in groups of three, provides the start, and then follows through the hilly landscape for more than a kilometre, unfolding in an uninterrupted walk and crescendo of anticipation, a new site to discover at every turn.

The main courtyard is discovered when arriving on the hill facing the principal house and overlooking the view to the woods and the Protva valley. Oval in shape and outlined by a palisade of trees, this majestic courtyard is aligned to the axis of the ridge, planted with an avenue of highly pruned trees, allowing views of the valley to the side and linking the chapel to the west with the stable tower to the east.

The main façade overlooking the main courtyard is adorned by a columned portico with a pediment marked with the family crown above the letter "O"; interlaced by the letters "M" and "A" honouring the founders of the estate.

The opposite facade overlooking the woods and the valley is enlivened by grassy terraces supported by stone walls raising the elevation of the house above the slope of the land.

The chapel, in neo-classical style, recalls the influence of classical architecture in Russia in the 18th and 19th centuries.

The four facades of the chapel, adorned by a columned portico and pediment, enhance a dome crowned with the Orthodox cross.

Dramatic, perched on its promontory, facing the great avenue, it overlooks the park and the beautiful evening light.

To the east, the Great Avenue or the "Constantin Avenue" finally reaches the tower, overlooking the quadrilateral stable courtyard.

From the south, the village access to the property can be found by crossing a bridge above a small pond or moat.

Most important are the functional aspects in the layout and relationship of the buildings and the way they are synthesized with their landscape.

Each curve or each straight line is linked with the flow of the land, accompanying and strengthening the landscape as a whole.

Beware of the interruptions, which unfortunately break the journey of the eye, as well as that of the mind or the heart.

The road will be long but each step is an important link in this pilgrimage, which already unites us.

François Goffinet

Distribution of land-use

Forestry

Russia has the world's largest forest reserves and is known as "the lungs of Europe". Of all the countries possessing vast woodlands, Russia will remain the only one in which forest areas will stay in the ownership of the state. In other words, Russia has declined the idea of private woodland property.

All Russian woods are divided into three categories. The first is reserved land, the second is timberland, and the third is commercial forest.

Although the Danilovka Estate has approximately 30 hectares of forest, there are no forestry operations. The forest area is used as part of the estate's efforts to preserve its natural ecosystems.

Agriculture

Historically, between 1917 and 1990, all agricultural land in Russia was exclusively in state ownership and the transition to a market-oriented economy had to start with privatisation of land and farm assets. Agricultural land was de-nationalized and its ownership (together with the ownership of other farm assets) was legally transferred from the state to the ownership of kolkhozes (collective farming).

As it turned out, however, few peasants were interested in establishing individual farms, and management and operating practices inside large agricultural enterprises remained largely unchanged despite formal reorganization. The lack of enthusiasm for the creation of private farms was attributed to inadequate rural infrastructure, which did not provide processing and marketing services for small producers, and also to the fear that families striking out on their own might lose eligibility for the social services that were traditionally provided by the local corporate farm instead of the municipality.

Furthermore, there was no access to financing, which prevented small farmers from buying adequate machinery, getting access to proper seed quality and being able to sell their products at decent prices in order to be able to finance their working capital needs.

In diametric opposition to corporate farms is the individual farm sector, which consists of the traditional household plots and the newly formed peasant farms.

After traditional farming for subsistence, the estate is harvesting its first crop in 2009. 400 hectares of wheat were produced and looked very promising. Mikhail and Alexandra planted an elite crop with a Russian variety called "Moskovskaya 39". For 2010, they plan to sow winter wheat and winter rape seed.

The soil had been fallow for many years. They first ploughed it once, followed by two cultivations with a TopDown. For this first winter wheat crop, they expect an average yield approaching 5 tonnes. They don't expect to use the plough any more.

Wildlife

Elk *(Alces alces)*, Wild Boar *(Sus scrofa)* and Fox *(Vulpes vulpes)* can be found every day within the estate but sadly Russia is unable to control widespread poaching, which has a devastating impact on wildlife.

A project to restoration and conserve wetlands near the stream crossing the property is being planned. Every year, migratory birds such as Storks *(Ciconia* sp.) nest just behind the main house.

A Sustainable and long-term family Project:

One does not own a property, but is responsible for a property which one receives from one's parents and must past it forward in better condition to the next generation. We hope that through this property (amongst other things) our children will work at their own future with a spirit of continuing our roots and our national history, after having been so awfully damaged by the communist regime. Hopefully this property will inspire others to do the same. If many people with passion, drive and hard work each look after a little bit of our national territory, then there is hope for it to become again the glorious landscape it once was, the extraordinary sanctuary for wildlife which we need so desperately, the bread-basket to feed our population as well as other countries, and the source for so much inspiration for poets, painters, writers and other members of our extraordinary national culture and identity.

The estate is bordered by the Protva River.

Danilovka Estate

Danilovka **(Russia)**

PRIVATE OPINION

The most precious thing, which God gave to humanity, is our planet. An estate is a tiny part of this wonderful planet of ours. It needs to be managed, facing so many challenges, putting together so many skills and sciences. Of course, there is immense satisfaction in seeing it grow, improve and become more and more beautiful. Also extraordinary is the feeling of setting things up which will only come to maturity in one or two generations in the future, with no chance of us ourselves seeing it completed. But it requires an immense set of skills and dedication. It is hard work to preserve the bio-systems, to improve the quality of the soil, to stimulate the health of the trees and to increase the beauty of our landscapes, which indeed are also a reflection of our level of culture. Moreover, both the climate and the economy are in constant change, which requires the additional capacity to adapt and think laterally. Living on land naturally causes a certain level of conservatism to develop, but it mainly requires being constantly on the leading edge of progress.

In Russia, by taking land from its owners and giving the illusion that it belongs to everybody, the communists actually damaged our beautiful landscapes and our beautiful nature. They also destroyed our leadership in agriculture at an international level. There is not a single forest or field in our country which would not be filled with garbage. A lot of fields are suffering from acidity created by excessive use of fertilizers. By killing tens of millions of responsible farmers and replacing them with kolkhoz workers, centuries-old traditions have disappeared from Russia. In the past, each region had very specific traditions closely linked to our land. Our old culture is mainly attached to the countryside. Both Tchaikovsky and Rachmaninov (among many others) wrote their masterpieces on their estates, drawing their inspiration from the Russian countryside; Tolstoy wrote in Yasnaya Poliana, alternating his writing with long hours spent on his fields. The estate of Abramtsevo was one of the nests of Russian culture in the late 19th century. Russia really grew out of its countryside.

With 127 million hectares of arable land, and approximately 20% of the entire land surface on the planet, Russia should be the country of estates "par excellence", able to maintain a rich rural tradition and culture in addition to feeding its population and creating strong export flows. There should be a full diapason, ranging from huge to small estates; there is truly enough space for everybody. The reality is very much the opposite. The countryside is poor, and people who could afford it don't have the desire or the "savoir-faire" to buy land not only to do business but to put it together with a certain life-style. And Russia is a net importer of food… But in addition, people are afraid of space. Rich people live in expensive ghettos instead of developing an estate, benefitting from a beautiful landscape, creating jobs in rural areas and supporting the development of rural populations, taking some responsibilities for the management of a small part of our national territory, becoming a vector for ecological sustainability and adding a small stone to re-develop our enormous and potentially superb countryside.

The reason is simply that nobody knows what to start with; the number of tasks and responsibilities is associated with a set of endless problems rather than an easy life-style. Land rights are still a serious question to be addressed, and even if property rights are duly registered, there is always the risk of becoming the target of so-called "raiders". By eradicating the land-owner class (all of them, from large to small), the communists transformed the countryside into an enormous workshop, taking away from it all cultural and spiritual considerations. And today, this workshop is almost bankrupt, operating in survival mode. If in Europe many people tend to move out to the countryside, in Russia we see very much the reverse trend.

When we decided to create an estate, we really wanted to show a modest example of what could be done. We ourselves are indeed going through a tremendous learning curve. At times the number

Several events have determined the life of Mikhail Orloff. Born in Lausanne, Switzerland in 1966. Alexandra, Mikhail's wife, was born in Fergana, in the Pamir mountains. His son, Feodor was born in Moscow in 2005. He is the first member of the family to be born in Russia since the 1917 revolution.

J. Hill

of challenges and difficulties is a bit frightening. We are really starting from zero. Apart from a beautiful piece of land, there was absolutely no infrastructure available, no qualified workers available, and no market mechanisms.

We also wanted to make sure that our children grow with a practical understanding of all the challenges in managing an estate (and our planet in general), with a certain distance and discernment from certain fallacies carried out by too many media and supported by too many politicians to collect votes. Feeding the world, maintaining wildlife and protecting our environment and eco-systems are dramatic and urgent problems, which cannot and must not be taken separately (or even worse, ignored). But there are no easy solutions, and those who propose easy solutions are pushing us further into the trap, losing time instead of attacking an urgent problem at the root with its full complexity. We believe it is also our contribution to be a modest part of an urgent need to take good care of our planet. We believe it is fundamentally important to prepare the next generation to be aware of what takes place outside cities, and the best way to do this is direct exposure to managing an estate.

But this doesn't go without serious challenges. The market is highly non-transparent and non-efficient. It is therefore difficult to obtain decent prices for the goods produced, and even more so to achieve a premium for higher quality goods. The small size of the estate does not allow economies of scale to be achieved. We will therefore need to focus on efficiency and finding a certain edge.

Another current challenge is the deep disrespect of villagers and tourists, who drive their cars, motorbikes and quad-bikes through cultivated or cropped fields, thus causing significant damage to the crops. Everybody had got used to the idea that this land was abandoned, and therefore belonged to everybody. There are therefore difficulties in imposing the fact that this is private property which requires a different level of culture and behavior.

But all in all, it is a blessing to have the privilege to have a small corner of Mother Russia to take good care of, where after so many decades in exile our family can re-establish its roots. Although everything is different, we hope to be able to reconstitute a bit of continuity with a lost past, to be part of building a better future. If only policymakers would promote this kind of project, if only the countryside would become again a vector of cultural and economic development, our country would again return to its very essence and develop its enormous potential: feed itself, feed other countries, and be a source of ecological and environmental safety.

Mikhail Orlov

DANILOVKA BELONGS TO:

Friends of the Countryside

Friends of the Countryside

Activities

🦌 Hunting
🦆 Shooting
🐎 Equestrian
🐟 Fishing

CONTACT DATA
Mr. Mikhail Orlov
m.orlov@bailington.com

Dehesa de Luna

Mediterranean

Location: La Roda, Albacete, Castilla-La Mancha, Spain.
Surface: 2,900 ha.

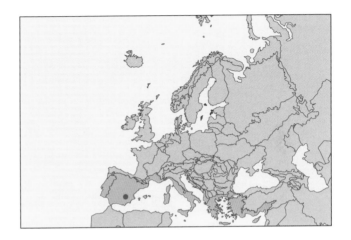

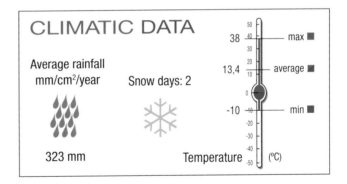

CLIMATIC DATA

Average rainfall
mm/cm²/year

Snow days: 2

323 mm

Temperature (°C)

38 — max
13,4 — average
-10 — min

SUMMARY

Dehesa de Luna is located in the south-west corner of the municipality of La Roda in the province of Albacete (Castilla-La Mancha, Spain). The estate belongs to the bioregion known as the Campos de Montiel.
It extends to 2,900 hectares and its average height above sea level is 800 m. The estate contains extensive vineyards and its landscape alternates between Mediterranean forest lands, dehesa (the typical dry agricultural landscape of the central Spanish plains), olive-trees and areas replanted with native species.
The plains offer habitat for numerous animals, such as the Great Bustard (Otis tarda), a species in danger of extinction.
This mosaic of different vegetation helps to promote one of the main values of the estate, the Red-legged Partridge (Alectoris rufa).

Dehesa de Luna Estate

In the landscape of Dehesa de Luna, vineyards alternate with mediterranean forest, *dehesas* and olive-trees.

The main house is located in San José, wich is also where the wine cellar, farm buildings and shooting lodge are situated.

DESCRIPTION

Dehesa de Luna is located in the south-west corner of the municipality of La Roda in the province of Albacete (Castilla-La Mancha, Spain). The property has a surface area of 2,900 ha. It is set in rolling countryside and there are no important variations in height. The landscape is formed by natural forests, newly replanted forests, cropping land, vineyards, olive-groves and almond-groves. Its average elevation is 800 m above sea level.

STAFF

Name	Qualification	Years of service	Full-time Part-time	Tasks
J.L. Asenjo	Agricultural Eng.	4	Full-time	Winery management
L.E. Moraleda	Agricultural Eng.	1	Full-time	Wine production
M.A. Cortijo (maintenance)	Foreman	8	Full-time	Crop production
Farmhands 8		Variable	Full-time	Crop production
Farmhands 10		Variable	Part-time	Crop production
Gamekeepers 4		12	Full-time	Game reserve maintenance

In general the agricultural soils are shallow and calcareous. The pH is high (between 7.8 and 8.1). Its surface is stony, and of little depth. These soils have low fertility and low water retention. The woodland soils are very similar, but even shallower and poorer.

There are no natural lakes and watercourses. The estate's water requirements are served by wells. Dehesa de Luna has a 20,000 m^3 dam available in case of forest fire.

The main activities of the estate are: small game, cereal production and winery:
- Cereals: 1,100 ha (dry land).
- Vineyards: 82 ha (irrigated).
- Olive trees: 36 ha (dry land).
- Olive trees: 18 ha (irrigated).
- Almond trees: 40 ha (dry land).

The majority of the arable surface is devoted to wheat. Depending on the year and location, other cereals are cultivated, such as barley, oats and rye.

Dehesa de Luna **(Spain)**

The vineyard is the basis for the production of high quality wine called Pago de Luna. Nowadays the varieties grown are Tempranillo, Graciano, Cabernet Sauvignon, Syrah, Petit Verdot and Merlot. During 2009, the construction of a winery will be an important estate project.

The olive groves produce high quality Picual olives. The construction of an olive oil press on the estate is a possible future development.

In 2008, we started to plant almond trees. Nowadays, we have 40 ha, but we are planning to increase this to 100 ha.

There is no regular production from the woodlands. However, we replanted 1000 ha using native Mediterranean species.

The most important activity is shooting the wild red-legged partridge. Other small game species are rabbit and iberian hare.

There are five inhabited areas: Casas de Luna, San José, San Antonio, Santa Isabel and Pozomorcillo. The main house is located in San José, where we can also find the farm buildings and the shooting lodge.

Maldonado

P. Maldonado

The two main activities in Dehesa de Luna are red-legged patridge management and quality wine production.

The management of wild rabbit on the estate is focussed on maintaining a stable population over time.

Dehesa de Luna (Spain)

RED-LEGGED PARTRIDGE MANAGEMENT IN DEHESA DE LUNA

Dehesa de Luna is the border: here the plains stop and the Campos de Montiel begin. Two different weather conditions and two different soils. How many times has the rain stopped as it reaches the estate's border? How many times has the estate been left white by the frost or burned by the sun, whilst its neighbours are unaffected? What is the similarity between the deep fertile soils of the plains and the thin rocky soils of Dehesa de Luna? The ungenerous nature of the showers, the arbitrary temperatures and the poor soils mean that agriculture, cattle farming and game-shooting are somewhat uncertain and always reluctant to give.

With its 2,900 hectares and its special environmental conditions, Dehesa de Luna has been traditionally used for dry cereal cropping, sheep farming and breeding of the red-legged partridge. However, when the current owners bought the estate in 1996, partridge breeding became the main objective. Since 2005 a further project to produce high quality wine *Vino de pago* has been developed. Nowadays, therefore, it is partridge management and commercial wine production which are the major points of focus of the estate, other enterprises such as cattle farming or intensive cereal cropping having been abandoned.

The partridge management starts with plans for field use and the selection of the crops and the cultivation techniques to be applied. The estate has three extensive landscape units: crops, replanted areas, and natural Mediterranean woodland. These units form a highly diverse mosaic, and provide ideal conditions for breeding and shooting the red partridge.

Wheat accounts for 90% of the dry cereal area. Currently, the total cereals area is approximately 1,100 ha and the majority of the land taken back from cropping has been replanted with native species, mainly Kermes Oak *(Quercus coccifera)*, Evergreen Oak *(Quercus ilex)* and Broom *(Genista lydia)*. The high proportion of wheat compared to the rest of the cereals can be explained by the fact that the end of the wheat cycle fits well with the highly important hatching of the last partridge nests. In any event, and independent from the optimal dates, the start of harvest is subject to whether the breeding is far enough advanced. Bearing this in mind, and as a normal rule, harvesting is not done at night and the height of the cutter-bar is set to more than 30 cm. In addition, the low cereal yields (1000-1500 kg/ha) reflect the very restricted use of artificial fertilizer, herbicides and other plant protection measures. This is firstly due to agronomic reasons, and secondly in order to protect the partridge population.

By contrast, other crops, such as barley, rye, triticale and oats, are cultivated in smaller amounts. The estate also has 54 ha of olive trees grown on dry land, 40 ha of almond trees and 82 ha of vineyards. All these crops are scattered throughout the estate, a fact which enhances landscape diversity as well as the food and shelter resources available for the partridge. Furthermore, maintaining the soil in which these trees and vines grow is an important measure, and is achieved by retaining a permanent cover of vegetation with the purpose of preventing erosion and improving the poor soils of the estate. This cropping technique has great benefits for the partridge population not only because of the soil protection but also as a result of the food and shelter that this vegetative cover provides. In order to get it established, winter cereals are mainly used and, in smaller measure, other small grasses such as Brome Grass *(Bromus sp.)* and Fescue *(Festuca sp.)*.

The harsh environmental conditions of Dehesa de Luna make it necessary to guarantee the provision of water for the partridges. The work required to achieve this is impressive due to the high number of drinkers spread across the estate (1 every 10 ha

The estate contains 60 artificial stone warrens, located in places where the rabbit population needs to be reinforced.

C. Otero

approximately). Similarly, the provision of food (mainly wheat) in those areas, or in those seasons or years when the estate cannot maintain the partridge population, is another important task in managing the red-legged partridge. Lastly, all of this is complemented by adequate predator control, in which the application of approved techniques and the expert wisdom of the game-keepers allow the populations of opportunist predators to be kept at levels that are compatible with partridge breeding.

There is no alternative to this, and, as is the case in all well managed reserves, the continuous availability of water and food, and the scarcity of opportunist predators, are exploited by other game species such as Rabbits *(Oryctolagus cuniculus)*, Iberian Hares *(Lepus granatensis)*, Turtle Doves *(Streptopelia turtur)* and Wood Pigeons *(Columba palumbus)*, as well as non-game species such as Great Bustards *(Otis tarda)*, Little Bustards *(Tetrax tetrax)* and Black-bellied Sandgrouse *(Pterocles orientalis)*.

At Dehesa de Luna the wild rabbit is the crucial secondary player. Without it, it would not be pos-sible to maintain an abundant population of partridge, because it allows a lower predatory pressure on the partridge. However, this old ally can become the enemy if, by excessive density of population, it takes shelter and food away from the partridge. The management of the wild rabbit is focused on maintaining a stable population through time, avoiding the excesses that serve to decrease food supplies or the shortages that make the partridge the only target of the predators. The estate contains 60 artificial warrens, located in places where the population needs to be reinforced. The estimated average density is 5 or 6 individuals per ha, which allows an average game pressure of between 1.8 and 2 rabbits per ha per year, through hunting with shotguns and dogs and the capture of live rabbits with ferrets, at the appropriate times.

If the wild rabbit is a secondary player, the hare is even more so. The estate contains an estimated hare population of one animal per 5 ha. Shooting hares in Dehesa de Luna, as well as turtle doves and wood pigeons, is anecdotal.

Hunting lodge.

Alfredo Gómez Torres had two passions in Dehesa de Luna: The natural production of red-legged partridge and the growing and production of wine of magnificent quality. The continuity of his project is guaranteed.

The final results of all the planning, work and efforts put in by the owners and workers take us to an average density of approximately 3 partridges per ha before the game season opens. Partridge shooting in Dehesa de Luna is done exclusively in driven beats. Thanks to the topography and the landscape of Dehesa de Luna we have still drives and stands of great beauty and difficult shooting. Driven shoots like those of La Mata de la Culebra, Palomar de Santa Isabel and Cerro de los Guardas are already a thing of the past and live in the memory of those lucky sportsmen that were able to enjoy them. Depending on the breeding success of each year, the annual bag varies between 0.7 and 1 partridge per ha.

Francisco Ruiz de la Torre
and José Luis Asenjo

LA CAÑADA DEL NAVAJO

Even its name sounds good. It is beautiful and original: the vineyard of "La Cañada del Navajo", the vineyard of Dehesa de Luna. The vineyard of "La Cañada del Navajo" was born, as was almost everything in Dehesa de Luna, because of Alfredo's wishes. It brings together his personal desire to develop

a great vineyard in order to produce a great wine, with his professional desire to ensure great viticulture.

The location and all the characteristics of this vineyard are not random, but have a cause. From a professional point of view, a vineyard has been created in which the knowledge of viticulture has been applied to every corner and detail. And it is done without economic, social or traditional constraints and without fanciful personal convictions. All this gives "La Cañada del Navajo" a universal character.

The whole vineyard has a sense, an order or a purpose designed to contribute to the final aim, the wine. This is not random either. The management of Ignacio, the opinions and wishes of Alfredo, the advice from José Luis and even from us, have planned and shaped this wine, which is not singular like its vineyard, but plural.

The vineyard, our vineyard, represents the plurality that has to come together in the singularity, the wine, our wine. The weather is hostile, with mediterranean rainfall and continental temperatures. It rains when it is cold, very cold. And when it is hot, very hot, there is drought. Along with this highly changeable weather, the topography is diverse, passing smoothly from the bottom of the creek *(cañada)* to hillsides of different exposures. The passage of time has given Dehesa de Luna different kinds of soils. Within the vineyard, the calcareous and superficial soils of the hillsides finally become the significantly deeper and more fertile soils of the creek, as a result of the slow accumulation from their surroundings.

The varieties, rootstocks, irrigation, pruning and management of the vineyard management are as diverse as the microclimate and soil conditions. One of the constant guiding objectives is to optimise the use of resources in such a way that human actions, together with the cultivation techniques, allow the genetic conditions of the different varieties to express in this climate, and in each soil, the desired characteristics that they can bring.

The traditional peninsular varieties, Tempranillo and Graciano, combine with the more northerly Cabernet-Sauvignon, Shiraz and Petit Verdot. And in each site, different training system such as vertical shoot positioned, with short pruning of guyot pruning, vertical cordons and sprawl systems, seek to ensure the best of the best, and the best of the worst.

The disintegration and integration of the landscape and the surroundings, the respect and tolerance in the environment, with the environment and for the environment that take place in this vineyard, are present in the meticulous use of irrigation and the careful management of the grassy soils, in order to achieve the balance, harmony and expressivity of the grapes, the fruit of the vine and the work of man.

**José Ramón Lissarrague
and Bárbara Sebastián**

The main varieties of grape grown on Dehesa de Luna are Tempranillo, Graciano and Cabernet Sauvignon.

Dehesa de Luna **(Spain)**

PAGO DE LUNA

Spain is a wine country. Possibly by culture and tradition and certainly by area, it is the principal wine country in the world. And within Spain, Castilla-La Mancha represents half of all Spanish vineyards, which means the largest area of vineyards in a single district of the whole world, above and beyond all the producer countries with the exception of France and Italy.

For centuries the importance of the region as a wine producer, both within and beyond our borders, has been decisive, not only as a producer of high quality wines for direct consumption, but as an improver of other wines of lesser grade and colour, or as a producer of alcohol to fortify others.

The start of the drastic drop in consumption in the last quarter of the twentieth century, in addition to changes in taste and consumer habits, have meant that the wines of Castilla-La Mancha have fallen into a crisis, making its huge grape production unviable.

This situation has led a lot of businessmen to pursue excellence and the recognition of their wines through the value of their own estate or property, independently from the great overarching umbrella that the region provides.

Within Castilla-La Mancha, small new *Denominaciones de Origen* (Guarantees of Origin) have therefore sprung up, such as Manchuela, Ribera del Jucar or Ucles. Moreover, a new concept has arisen in Spain, known as *Vinos de Pago*, referring to the wines produced exclusively from grapes from a specific estate, with recognized quality and their own personality. In France this is called *Cru*.

Fortunately, the geography of Castilla-La Mancha allows many ecosystems to exist. This gives the opportunity to create very individual wines in many of the local areas, although it also requires special courage, due to the fact that, sadly, the region's prestige is not at its height at this moment. One of these ecosystems is, without doubt, the estate of Dehesa de Luna.

However, the creation of a *Vino de Pago*, a true high quality and unique personality wine, does not only depend on good land. There are a lot of personal criteria that create the difference, and which demand the effort, the dedication and the devotion of somebody very special.

The first exercise is to reflect on what kind of wine one wishes to make. The personality of a wine is not something that arises by chance, and there are many factors that man can use to create it. At Dehesa de Luna a plan was made to produce two levels of wine. The highest in the range will be a complex wine based on the large number of variables within the vineyard – a wine that can be cellared and which has enough structure to handle it, but at the same time elegant and without edge, based on the fruit but very well supported by the notes given by long aging in barrels of french oak, and searching for the aromas and flavours of the land where it is born. The second wine will appeal above all to those whose pleasure lies in drinking it immediately – intense fruity aromas minimally influenced by a brief aging in the barrel, full of taste in the mouth but discrete, rich and friendly.

Having successfully defined the final product, Luna has now been provided with all the tools to ensure that this does not fail, and we will certainly succeed in making great wine. Indeed, Pago de Luna will be also known for making one of the best wines of the world.

Ignacio de Miguel Poch (Enologist)

Dehesa de Luna Estate

Pago de Luna vineyards.

DEHESA DE LUNA BELONGS TO:

APROCA
Castilla-La Mancha

Friends of the Countryside

Rise Foundation

Activities & attractions

- Winery
- Shooting
- Birdwatching

CONTACT DATA

José Luis Asenjo
Agropecuaria Vallefrío Nueva, S.L.
C/ Tomás Navarro Torres, 4 • E-02630 La Roda, Albacete, Spain
www.pagodeluna.com • contacto@pagodeluna.com
Tel.: +34 967 54 85 08 • Fax: +34 967 54 80 22

Het Loo

Atlantic

The property is divided between two Member States of the EU:
State 1: Region: Limburg-Hamont; Bocholt / Kaulille, Belgium.
State 2: Zuid Limburg-Weert; Noord Brabant-Budel, The Netherlands.
Adjacent estates:
– Hork (private estate) owned by Jo Spaas, member of FCS;
– Lozenheide (publicly owned property, ANB, Belgium);
– Ringsselven owned by the families Powis de Tenbossche, Dor en Nystar SA, The Netherlands.
– Hoort owned by Jean de l'Escaille de Lier.
Total surface: 655 ha.

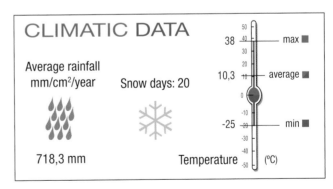

CLIMATIC DATA

Average rainfall mm/cm²/year

Snow days: 20

718,3 mm

Temperature (ºC)

38 — max
10,3 — average
-25 — min

SUMMARY

Consecutive generations of the l'Escaille family, owners of Het Loo, have always made great efforts to combine the conservation of biodiversity with the development of economic activities. As a result, the estate is today a mosaic of ecosystems, which includes agricultural land, forestry, grassland, wetland, hedges and water systems. This diversity of lands provides excellent habitats for many species of flora and fauna, the result of close and wise interaction between man and nature, and it would no longer be possible if agriculture were prohibited.

Het Loo Estate

The property of 655 hectares is divided between Belgium and the Netherlands.

HISTORY & FAMILY

The de l'Escaille family originates from Burgundy but in the 15th century developed close links with the Netherlands; they settled in different parts of the Duchy, notably Jodoigne, in the 16th century. Within this branch, two brothers are of particular note in the 18th century: Louis, an important landowner and public figure who was established in the house that is today the Belgian Parliament, and Pierre, a a veteran of the Napoleon's Grande Armée and who was only demobilised at the surrender at Fontainebleau after the Russian Campaign.

The history of the estate begins with Pierre, who married Marie d'Erp de Holt und Baerlo. After his death his widow, who already owned land in her own right at Budel and Weert (Netherlands) which she had inherited from her mother (née van Voorst tot Voorst), had the opportunity of buying the neighbouring estate in Belgium in 1874 for her two bachelor sons Joseph and Rasse, to put them to work.

Joseph de l'Escaille built the present house, and used his knowledge of agronomy – he was an engineer – to create an estate which at the time comprised almost 700 hectares. He also founded the Salvatorian Convent built on one part of the property. Since Marie de l'Escaille d'Erp, every owner of the estate has been one of the family.

During the First World War Belgium and The Netherlands were separated by an electrified border fence. This made the management of the estate very complicated. At the time of the Treaty of Versailles, Bernard de l'Escaille, grandson of Pierre and a minister plenipotentiary, attempted to get the border between the two countries slightly adjusted so as to unify Het Loo into just one country. Alas this did not happen and Het Loo still requires double management, under Belgian and Dutch law.

In this chapter we will concentrate on the Belgian part of the estate, contrary to what was described in the previous book in which we presented a wider view of the whole estate.

The present landowner, Thierry de l'Escaille, inherited Het Loo as a child in 1960 from his great-aunt Marie, a niece of Joseph. Being still a child he was not able to devote himself to the management of the estate until he had completed his University degree.

HISTORY & FACTS

In 1945, after the deportation and death of the presumed heir to Het Loo, Henri de l'Escaille, the farm business was rented to small farmers, whilst the surviving owners retained some thirty hectares for their own needs and to keep one man employed.

This situation lasted until 1960. When Thierry de l'Escaille, a child, inherited the estate from his great-aunt, his guardian leased the last of the freehold land to the former farm workers and brought the personal involvement in farming to a de facto end. The property, no longer lived in, became a holiday residence.

However in 1977, when Thierry was at university studying the historical evolution of relations between landlord and tenant, he grew concerned by what he had learned and understood that he had to regain possession of this land which was constrained by tenant law. Having taken a further degree in agronomy he embarked on long negotiations with the forty or so tenants.

Thierry wanted to avoid the social tensions that would arise. He favoured the return of the land on the retirement of the tenant farmers, whilst allowing the next generation no possibility of succeeding their parents. The land in Belgium was recovered at intervals over the period from 1978 and 1992, and in The Netherlands it took until 2009 – and is still not complete.

With this experience behind him, he and two partners founded the Agriland company in 1985. Today the company manages more than 8000 hectares of farmland in France and Belgium, and is involved in direct production and the implementation of agri-environmental measures.

OVERALL DESCRIPTION

Conserving the historical heritage

The castle is Neoclassical in style and was built in three periods. Construction began in 1852, continued in 1875 and was finally completed in 1905. It is attributed to the architect Mathieu Christiaens.

The collection of buildings listed as Historic Monuments in 2008 comprises the central element of the castle, the farm and the caretaker's lodge. These are surrounded by a landscaped park with lakes, avenues and pathways, clumps of trees and rhododendrons. The park was originally inspired in a plan by the architect Creten (1875) and was completely restored by Thierry de l'Escaille's wife after 1983.

Water resources

The Meuse River, the most important river in the province, passes 20km from the estate. Two small rivers emanating from the Canal de Campine cross the estate, resulting in hard limestone water characterized by low nitrate levels, thanks to the purifying effects of *Phragmites*. Originally used for irrigating the poplar plantations – a technique that fell into disuse in the 1970s – the water from the canal has since been used to feed the eight ponds which cover a surface area of 6 hectares.

Several wells have been created in order to ensure the irrigation of marketable crops which were introduced in 1983 and which have a higher water demand. At times of drought, the vegetables need to be irrigated between 10th June and 20th July, at night, in order to avoid loss by evaporation or thermic shock. This supplementary infrastructure provides a means of insurance against unforeseen climatic uncertainties, as the next decade is forecast to show an accentuated climate with very dry springs and summers combined with more intensive rainfall and therefore flooding.

Soils, climate, flora and vegetation

The soils existing in Het Loo were formed during the tertiary period, and are heavy sand and lime, ranging from very dry to very wet, and even to marshy in some areas.

The relief is light, and ranges from +42 to +37 metres.

The climate is typical of the Campine area, with cold winters and warm summers, cold nights and warm days. Spring frosts can last until early June.

Because of the irrigation system coming from the Canal de Campine, Het Loo has developed a particular flora with some species specific to the Meuse basin (see list). The eutrophic vegetation of the Campine region is found on areas which have never been irrigated.

120 hectares of land is wooded, of which 12 hectares are planted with softwoods – Scots Pine *(Pinus sylvestris)*, Corsican Pine *(Pinus nigra)*, Larch *(Larix* spp.*)*, Spruce *(Picea* spp.*)* and some recently introduced Douglas Fir *(Pseudotsuga menziesii)* – and 78 hectares are broadleaf trees – Poplars *(Populus* spp.*)*, native and American Oaks *(Quercus* spp.*)*, Ash *(Fraxinus* spp.*)*, Beech *(Fagus* spp.*)*, Birch *(Betula* spp.*)* and Alder *(Alnus* spp.*)*.

The collection of listed buildings is situated in diversified countryside, of which the central element is the site of the castle.

Het Loo Estate

Het Loo has several ponds, filled from rivers and springs, and boreholes that were created during the war.

INTEGRATED MANAGEMENT AT HET LOO ESTATE

1. Agriculture & Land Management

Since 1981, the year in which Thierry de l'Escaille personally took over the management of the estate, the agricultural sector has undergone significant change. On the land let to a multitude of small farmers for their livestock – an average area of 3 hectares – there is now an agro-industrial enterprise which nevertheless builds in sustainable development and respect for the environment.

Despite the relatively small area of land cultivated (130 hectares in Belgium), it benefits paradoxically from light soils which are inadequate for sugar beet cultivation but profitable for marketable crops, which are used by an industrial canning firm (Noliko) located nearby. One third is maize, one third vegetables (beans, potatoes and peas), and the remainder is cereals. Miscanthus was introduced in 2007 on 0.5 hectares to provide biofuel – the so-called 'second generation', in other words manufactured from bio-mass rather than foodstuffs.

About ten hectares are either left as grassland – the owner has had no livestock since 1994 – or left fallow as habitat and shelter for game species – planted with oilseed rape or mustard. Winter cover is assured on 85% of the land each year, offering good uptake of nitrates, protection from erosion and excellent forage for wildlife.

The use of plant protection products, which is ever more strictly controlled, is reducing considerably. The banning of certain products moreover could put the cultivation of beans in peril.

The manure used is essentially organic, either pig slurry injected into the soil or chicken manure which is spread onto the land. In both cases this has diminished by 40% over 5 years. Only triticale now requires the use of chemical fertilisers.

Management of the business on a day-to-day basis is done by one full-time man, while a local contractor undertakes the major ground and tillage work – which avoids investment in expensive material and therefore the problem of achieving good returns.

Since 2006 many of the fields have been surrounded by hedges, which provide exceptional shelter for wildlife and a great medium for biodiversity. The density of wild game, the enormous concentration of birds, and their variety, attest to this. These hedges have a beneficial effect on the crops which are protected from sharp spring frosts.

2. Forestry

- The production of broadleaved woodland, essentially native and American oaks, ash, alder, silver birch and some beech. The native oak is generally of mediocre quality, and its value is more environmental and scenic than economic. The American oak,

Farming activity at Het Loo is based on sustainability and aims to integrate farming and the environment in the best possible way.

an "exotic" species, is alas tending to be replaced, under pressure from forestry agencies, by other more "native" species.

Small diameter wood, or wood of poor quality, is stockpiled in winter to be sold locally as firewood. This does not generate much income but allows the estate to maintain a cared-for aspect. A certain number of dead trees – well away from roads and tracks – are now retained standing as an essential reservoir of biodiversity.

- The production of softwoods which were originally destined for wood for the mines – in particular the Scots pine – and were planted at small intervals in order to produce small diameter trunks, a technique which fell into disuse after 1970.

Large plantations of pines were cut in the 1960s to pay inheritance taxes and have been replanted with smaller and more varied parcels including the introduction of larch, Weymouth Pine *(Pinus strobus)* – subsequently abandoned – and recently Douglas fir. These parcels sometimes also contain hardwoods.

- Poplars were, until the last century, traditionally grown on the flood meadows and irrigated by the hard water of the River Meuse.

They were destined for matches and later the paper industry. In addition, the leaf forage gathered from the ground was sold to the military camp at Leopoldsburg, transported there on the Canal de Campine which borders the estate.

These poplar groves are no longer submerged in water each spring and have been progressively (since the 1990s) replanted with new Euro-American clones whose spectacular growth represents the estate's most important forestry resource. Nevertheless, since 1994 the appearance of the disease known as rust on certain specimens may compromise a part of their future, and the estate may be obliged to fell them early as fungicidal treatments have been banned for environmental concerns. In choosing the clones, the law of prudence remains valid: alternate varieties in order to spread the risks.

These poplar groves are nowadays an area of remarkable biodioversity, where, between the lines of trees and the hedges, maize, rape and other treats for wildlife are grown.

All these choices reflect the desires of the estate's owner. Thierry de l'Escaille, in his role as vice-president of the Royal Belgian

Inès de l'Escaille.

Het Loo Estate

Night Heron *(Nyctocorax nycticorax)* nesting in Het Loo.

Forestry Society is following in his mother's footsteps. She was passionate about forestry and, with her husband, (re)created no fewer than 12 woodland avenues in 25 years while supervising the training of staff to trim and prune.

Forestry decisions are made in agreement with, and after advice from, a Forest Engineer, in order to meet the terms of the management plan established for 20 years and approved by the Nature and Forests agency. It has not yet been considered desirable to establish a "Detailed Management Plan", which is felt by the owner to be too constraining.

3. Wildlife Conservation

Ever since the estate was purchased, **wildlife management** has claimed the attention of each successive owner. It is a long term task which began with Rasse de l'Escaille, who was passionate about entomology and whose collection of insects is today housed in the Bolland foundation.

In 1961 an agreement was reached with a group of ornithologists from the Belgian Nature Reserves (today known as Natuurpunt), under the leadership of Hubert Lehaen, which put in place a survey of birds on the estate. 132 species of bird have been recorded on this land, as well as a particularly interesting group of bats. Several nesting and roosting boxes have been installed to encourage nesting. In 2009, a total of 200 nest boxes housed several varieties of Tit *(Parus sp)* as well as

Up to 13 species of duck can visit Het Loo each season. In the picture Mallard (*Anas platyrhynchos*).

Pied Flycatcher *(Ficedula hypoleuca)* and Short-Toed Treecreeper *(Certhia brachydactyla).*

Since 1983 the owner has not permitted any forestry work to be done between April and the end of June, in order to respect the nesting period. In the same spirit the water levels in the ponds and wetlands are kept stable thanks to the construction of sluices. Mowing and trimming the sides of roads and tracks, fields and meadows is now done later in the season in order to protect the young Hares, Roe Deer and ground-nesting birds.

Roe Deer *(Capreolus capreolus)* first appeared in the mid 1970s. The habitat and biotope that has been developed and maintained – crops grown in rotation, hedges, wet areas, ponds, woodland and scrub – has allowed this species to multiply hugely; there is now one Roe Deer every two hectares. Pheasants and several species of Ducks are found in large numbers for the same reasons. This habitat was deliberately planned at a time when the farming world was only thinking of tearing up, flattening and clearing land for cultivation. The results of the efforts undertaken are still evident today.

Furthermore, new species have made their entrance into the landscape, but not all of them have always been welcome: Wild Boar *(Sus scrofa)* have come up from the Meuse, Red Deer *(Cervus elaphus)* have been introduced at great expense under a European programme called LIFE in the Netherlands, and there are Egyptian Geese *(Alopochen aegyptiacus)*, Canada Geese *(Branta canadensis)*, Cormorants *(Corvus marinus)* and Coypu *(Myocastor coypus)*. Controlling these pests and invasive species is a new challenge that must be met.

Hunting and shooting

Het Loo is a member of the European network of *Wildlife Estates*. The network promotes the principles of sustainable management and conservation of wildlife and flora by integrating the management of hunting and shooting into it.

Furthermore the estate is also part of the Hunting Association of Hamont-Achel (WBE) which brings together the different estates and lands across 5,500 hectares to manage and coordinate shooting plans and neighbourly matters.

Hunting and shooting are conducted sustainably, which is made possible by the varied management of the land and by maintaining population levels that allow breeding when winter is over.

SPECIES

Forest species
- European Beech *(Fagus sylvatica)*
- Pedunculate Oak *(Quercus pedunculata)*
- Sessile Oak *(Quercus petraea)*
- American Red Oak *(Quercus rubra)*
- Pin Oak *(Quercus palustris)*
- Ash *(Fraxinus sp.)*
- Hybrid Larch *(Larix eurolepsis)*
- Black Pine *(Pinus nigra)*
- Scots Pine *(Pinus sylvestris)*
- Corsican Pine *(Pinus laricio corsicana)*
- Douglas Fir *(Pseudotsuga menziesii)*

Herbaceous species
- Heather *(Calluna vulgaris)*
- Spotted Orchid *(Dactylorhiza fuchsii)*
- Wild Strawberry *(Fragaria virginiana)*
- Raspberry *(Rubus idaeus)*
- Bilberry *(Vaccinium myrtillus)*
- Blueberry *(Vaccinium uliginosum)*

- Bog Myrtle *(Myrica gale)*

Mammals
- Roe Deer *(Capreolus capreolus)*
- Hare *(Lepus europaeus)*
- Rabbit *(Oryctolagus cuniculus)*
- Polecat *(Mustela putorius)*
- Weasel *(Mustela nivalis)*
- Pond Bat *(Myotis dasycneme)*
- Greater Mouse-eared Bat *(Myotis myotis)*

Birds
- Marsh Warbler *(Acrocephalus palustris)*
- Kingfisher *(Alcedo atthis)*
- Tree Pipit *(Anthus trivialis)*
- Bittern *(Botaurus stellaris)*
- Nightjar *(Caprimulgus europaeus)*
- Common Redpoll *(Carduelis flammea)*
- Black Tern *(Chlidonias niger)*
- Quail *(Coturnix coturnix)*

- Lesser Spotted Woodpecker *(Dendrocopus minor)*
- Black Woodpecker *(Dryocopus martius)*
- Hobby *(Falco subbuteo)*
- Pied Flycatcher *(Ficedula hypoleuca)*
- Icterine Warbler *(Hypolais icterina)*
- Red-backed Shrike *(Lanius collurio)*
- Great Grey Shrike *(Lanius excubitor)*
- Black-tailed Godwit *(Limosa limosa)*
- Bluethroat *(Luscinia svecica cyanecula)*
- Common Crossbill *(Loxia curvirostra)*
- Woodlark *(Lullula arborea)*
- Grey Wagtail *(Motacilla cinerea)*
- Golden Oriole *(Oriolus oriolus)*
- Tree Sparrow *(Passer montanus)*
- Black Redstart *(Phoenicurus ochruros)*
- Common Redstart *(Phoenicurus phoenicurus)*
- Great Crested Grebe *(Podiceps cristatus)*
- Whinchat *(Saxicola rubetra)*
- Stonechat *(Saxicola torquata)*

- Serin *(Serinus serinus)*
- Common Sandpiper *(Tringa hypoleucos)*
- Barn Owl *(Tyto alba)*
- Eurasian Hoopoe *(Upupa epops)*

Fish
- Eel *(Anguilla anguilla)*
- Carp *(Cyprinus carpio)*
- Pike *(Esox lucius)*
- Burbot *(Lota lota)*
- Perch *(Perca fluviatilis)*
- Roach *(Rutilus rutilus)*
- European Catfish *(Silurus glanis)*
- Pike-perch/Zander *(Stizostedion lucioperca)*

Amphibians and Reptiles
- Toad *(Bufo bufo)*
- Frog *(Rana temporaria)*
- Salamander *(Salamandra salamandra)*

Quarry species are the Roe Deer, which is stalked on foot only, and Duck, Pheasant, Wood Pigeon and Rabbit. On the other hand, out of concern to preserve certain fragile populations, the Hare *(Lepus europaeus)* and the Grey Partridge *(Perdix perdix)* are never shot, even though they are present on the estate.

Fishing on the estate has always been a traditional leisure activity. The various streams and ponds support Eel *(Anguilla anguilla)*, Pike *(Esox lucius)*, Zander *(Stizostedion lucioperca)* and Perch *(Perca fluviatilis)* and even a few Trout *(Salmo trutta)*. In 2006 a first census of fish stocks and species, undertaken by the LIKONA Institute, identified some rare species such as the Spined Loach *(Cobitis taenia)*.

4. Biodiversity enrichment

Biodiversity is constantly being enhanced. Currently a project to plant 2,300 metres of broad-leaved hedge is in progress under a European rural development programme (CAP Pillar II).

Managing the water and water quality is regularly assessed. Since 2001 strips of land ten metres wide, taken from the cultivable area, have been sown with grass along the main ditches in order to prevent the seepage of fertilisers and pesticides. The presence of freshwater mussels and crayfish is testament to the water quality.

Starting this year, some measures which encourage microfauna have been put into place. 1.5 hectares of land have been sown with pollen-

Het Loo Estate

Het Loo Estate

The efforts undertaken to enrich the landscape at Het Loo are still evident today.

Robert de l'Escaille bringing trees to be planted.

Het Loo Estate

Restoring elements of the landscape has been a concern for almost the last 15 years.

5. Landscape Enrichment

Since 1980 the owner has undertaken the restoration of buildings that are nowadays listed as Historic Monuments, followed by the restoration of the park, the paths and the visual perspectives. The current owner will probably never see the final result of what has been designed and undertaken, but these works are very promising. The refurbishment of several ponds has contributed enormously to improving the landscape.

6. Environmental Constraints

Once the sector plans finalised in 1974 had been put into practice, 80% of the estate was classed as a "Nature Zone" which at the time meant nothing more than a constraint on the right to build.

In 1982, the Flemish regional authorities designated the estate as a *Natura 2000 – Birds zone (vogelrichtlijn)* by a simple piece of cartography at first, to which would be added a whole series of

bearing plants under an action plan launched by "Syngenta called pollinators". This should increase the number of insects to the benefit of a multitude of birds.

We should recall the programme of winter cover on 85% of the arable land which offers shelter for wild animals as well as enriching the soil.

To encourage the spontaneous growth of a rare plant, Bog Myrtle *(Myrica gale)*, all competing vegetation is removed every second year. This is a voluntary conservation effort which is a nett cost.

The older flood meadows planted with poplar are mown later in the season in order to safeguard the flowering of certain rare species such as the Paper-white Narcissus *(Narcissus papyraceus)*, Bluebell *(Hyacinthoides non-scripta)*, Lesser Celandine *(Ranunculus ficaria)* and Common Spotted Orchid *(Dactylorhiza fuchsia)*.

Such a management policy is only feasible when there is an underlying economic activity, which in this case is agriculture. Banning agriculture would mean returning to a system in which the taxpayer is obliged to meet the costs of the action carried out.

In other words, should nature itself depend solely upon the public, who would immediately have to pay professional environmentalists and devote subsidies to it?

In managing natural areas, if long-term and large-scale environmental policies can or should be made by public, regional, national or European agencies, then implementing them may perfectly well be left to the private sector on the condition that the latter enjoys a certain freedom of action and sufficient financial resources.

Het Loo Estate

management restrictions in the 2000s. The owner however considered this designation to be a validation of his management decisions and appreciates it as a protection against urban pressure. He believes that Natura 2000 is an opportunity insofar as the management constraints remain viable. With this in mind, the European Landowners Organisation has begun a constructive dialogue between private owners, administrative authorities and environmental protection agencies.

Classifying the estate in the Natura 2000 network could have had some serious consequences on the park and the buildings – notably the prohibition of re-building in the case of a fire. However, the estate's listing as a Historic Monument in 2008 goes beyond Natura 2000 in protecting the existence of the buildings.

On the other hand, the 1996 'Nitrates Action Plan' posed a very serious threat to the survival of the estate, as a result of inadequate transposing of the Nitrate Directive in the Flemish region and the prohibition of fertilisers and pesticides in the zones which had been classified as 'Nature' in 1974.

All farming activity should have ceased in 1998, with no compensation whatsoever, if Thierry de l'Escaille and Michel de Broqueville had not founded the Association of Rural Property Owners of Flanders (VLE) in order to face up to this digression. The Association will shortly be working on the coherent application of European directives in Flanders. It has so far obtained a guarantee that farms in the 'Nature Zones' may continue to operate for another two generations. As far as fertiliser is concerned, the use 170 kilos of Nitrogen (N) per hectare is assured, which is compatible with the practical farming requirements.

Finally, there is a very small corner of the estate which is classed as "Flemish Ecological Zone" (VEN) where no farming activity can be carried out. However, as it is at one extreme of the property, in a wet valley, it does not harm the estate's development.

In areas of flat ground, it is the views, openings, colours, variety and different levels of plants that make the landscape work.

Thierry de l'Escaille de Lier.

Het Loo Estate

CHALLENGES & ROLES FOR FUTURE GENERATIONS

Agriculture

Scientific developments offer access to new agricultural technologies, such as **GMOs** which may one day be authorised. Whether it be to fight against climate change or to adapt to the constraints of the Nitrates Plan, the challenge will be to choose the appropriate utilisation without endangering biodiversity.

In the next few years, the growing of second-generation **bio-fuels**, manufactured from vegetable residues (wood, straw, miscanthus, etc.) will very probably be adopted and accepted by the agricultural world. However it is important for the next generation to maintain two outlets – food and energy – within its production.

Care must be taken not to overturn the balance of nature where this new technology is employed on a large scale, as we must not forget that the earth's primary purpose is to provide food for mankind. It is only once this objective has been achieved that one can begin to exploit it for energy purposes.

Sylviculture

As well as what has just been mentioned in connection with the production of bio-fuels from ligno-cellulose material such as spruce or poplar, the most urgent challenge in the short term is the choice of new Poplar clones that are rust-resistant.

In addition the owner hopes that the next generation is able to keep the current wide choice of forestry tree species that is available to plant. He is convinced that maintaining plantations of varieties which are classed by the forestry authorities as exogenous or non-native represents not just a contribution to biodiversity but also an economic opportunity. The principal non-native and non-invasive species envisaged are Douglas Fir *(Pseudotsuga menziesii)*, Corsican Pine *(Pinus corsicana)* and American Oak *(Quercus rubra)*.

Environmental constraints

If the majority of the new constraints have been successfully integrated by the current generation, the guarantee of being able to farm – and de *facto* the survival of the estate – is not assured beyond the children of the present owner whilst a reasonable solution remains to be found by the Flemish public authorities.

Climate change

The future generation will perhaps put into practice choices for improving the carbon sequestration balance and extracting some financial reward from it. This cannot be envisaged at present as long as a carbon credits exchange mechanism which includes forestry and farming activities remains to be implemented.

Oak alley in Winter.

Het Loo Estate

Succession

Ensuring that one's children inherit one's assets has always been the legitimate concern of each owner. Each successful succession is above all a planned one, in order to avoid a situation in which paying taxes ruins the efforts of a whole life-time. Owners must have a deep and personal knowledge of their fiscal environment and succession issues.

It is also essential that the future generation is prepared for this by receiving training and guidance from an early age. The fact of being born on an estate, of having spent one's childhood there, creates in adults – which they will grow into – a very strong sense of belonging. We have to emphasise here the role of the wife and mother of the family who, living full-time on the estate at Het Loo, has encouraged her children to develop deep roots on the property. By encouraging their schooling in the regional language they will be able to integrate into the social, cultural and political environment of their region. As their children have grown up, their parents have equally been careful to involve them, according to their interests, in the many decisions that have to be taken in connection with the estate.

It is also necessary for parents to be prepared to respect the decisions – perhaps unexpected – which their children will take in order to assure, in turn, the profitability and continuity of the estate.

Conclusion

The philosophy which guides the management of the estate leads us to one question: are we ca-

Het Loo Estate

Gabriel de l'Escaille.

pable of contributing to world food security whilst at the same time protecting the environment? Is it a realistic aim? We believe that it has to be.

For decades, those who have managed Het Loo have tried to resolve this difficult equation: quality agricultural and forestry production and ensuring environmental services (scenery, biodiversity and quality of natural resources).

If quality of life has no price, it nonetheless has a cost to the owners.

We believe that this subtle balance may be maintained by innovations for which the coming generations will be responsible, but also by political recognition of the owner's actions. These will of course need to be supported at both European and regional level.

Whilst political programmes by their very nature are sometimes limited to relatively short-term horizons, private family management of land presents the immense advantage of long-term vision. 'It is only by knowing where one has come from that one can decide where one is going".

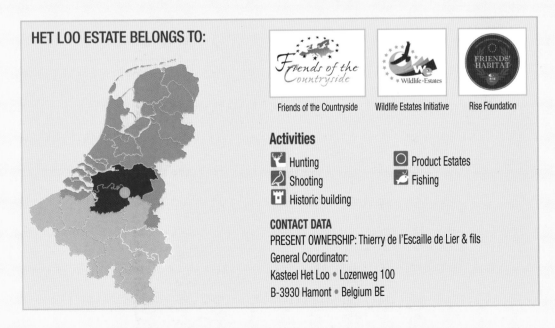

HET LOO ESTATE BELONGS TO:

Friends of the Countryside   Wildlife Estates Initiative   Rise Foundation

Activities

- Hunting
- Shooting
- Historic building
- Product Estates
- Fishing

CONTACT DATA

PRESENT OWNERSHIP: Thierry de l'Escaille de Lier & fils
General Coordinator:
Kasteel Het Loo • Lozenweg 100
B-3930 Hamont • Belgium BE

Jarras-Listel

Mediterranean

Location: Aigues-Mortes, Gard, Camargue region, France.
Surface: 800 ha.

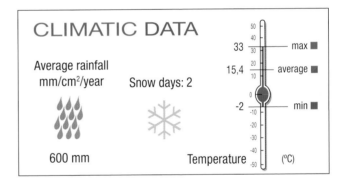

CLIMATIC DATA

Average rainfall
mm/cm²/year

Snow days: 2

Temperature (°C)

600 mm

33 — max ■
15,4 — average ■
-2 — min ■

SUMMARY

The Camargue... a magical word which has always conjured up images of sun, of animals, and men and women with their warm friendly accents. Located very close to the city of Aigues-Mortes, the Domaine de Jarras is just waiting to be discovered. Jarras, the Vineyard in the Sands, planted on an island known since time began as the Isle de Stel, is full of history and the sound of the knights who followed King Louis IX, Saint Louis, in the Crusades to the Holy Lands.
At the end of the 19th century, the only vines to have escaped the *Phylloxera* epidemic which had devastated vineyards all across France were those planted on sand. The insect which destroyed them could, luckily, not establish itself in sand. These original vines remained unaffected. The estate of Jarras is unique for several reasons: for its vines growing in the sand, its protected and diverse flora and fauna, its name and its history that are thousands of years old. But the truly original feature of the Jarras Estate is its environmental policy which plays a highly important role and which makes it a model of sustainable management.

J. Roche

Aerial view of the Île de Stel.

The bulls are part of the spirit of Jarras. The work of the Camarguais horsemen, their precise movements and the courage of their horses can all be admired on the estate. They drive the bulls to areas of grazing or to enclosures especially reserved for them.

Old cellar dating from 1883.

HISTORY

As early as the 11th century, the monks of the abbey of Psalmody were already producing wine on land that now belongs to the estate of Jarras. During the 13th century, wine production continued but was part of Saintes-Maries-de-la-Mer, in Provence, rather than the Languedoc. In 1550 flood defences on the River Rhone were introduced, and the area was divided into different administrative sectors. Jarras was once again placed back in the Languedoc, under the yoke of the town of Aigues-Mortes.

During the course of the 19th century, *Phylloxera*, a parasitic insect of the Hemiptera order which feeds on the roots of the vine, decimated the majority of European vineyards. To resist the parasite, vines throughout the entire world have been cultivated, from that time onwards, on grafted American stock which is naturally resistant to the insect. Only vines in Chile and those grown on sand have been able to resist the parasite and are not grafted. Jarras is thus one of those rare vineyards where the original stock (known as "Franc de pied") is still present.

During the Second World War, the vines were virtually destroyed and 35,000 mines were laid on the estate. A significant restoration plan was started in 1950 in order to defuse the network of mines and reinstate the vines on their plots. The plots were consolidated, and a quantity of sand was taken from the natural surroundings. Some of the present-day lagoons were created during the course of this work.

The establishment of the cellar in the manor house ("mas") at Jarras in 1883 marks the start of the history of the Domaines Listel, which became a registred trademark in 1955. The estates belonged to the Compagnie du Salins du Midi until 1994, and from 1994 until 2005 Listel was owned by Val d'Orbieux, the wine-producers group in the Aude. Since 2005 the company has been part of the Vranken-Pommery Monopole group, whose aim is to practise a policy of sustainable land use on the Listel estates, and principally on the Estate of Jarras.

DESCRIPTION

The Estate of Jarras is part of the Domaines Listel company, which extends over 2,750 hectares in the "petite Camargue". There are seven estates in this area: Jarras (800 ha), Bosquet (755 ha), Daladel (320 ha), Petite Sylve (430 ha), Saint Jean la Pinède (300 ha), La Félicité (60 ha), Montcalm (55 ha) and Pin du Fer (30 ha). Jarras is narrow, and runs north-west/south-east over a length of about 8 km. The company is the second largest landowner in the Gard. Its principal activity is the production of wine, of which it produces about 46 million bottles each year. Four million of these come from the estate of Jarras. Its originality lies in the nature of the soil "terroir" which is uniquely sandy across all the estates. The Jarras Estate comprises 419 ha of vines and 381 ha of natural sites – in the widest sense – each blending with the other and forming a true mosaic. The geo-morphology of the area comprises an ancient coastal belt which originally stretched from the Jarras Estate as far as the Grand Radeau in the commune of Saintes-Maries-de-la-Mer in the Bouches-du-Rhône. Listel is a contraction of "Isle de Stel", the name of the old island on the estate.

The Jarras estate is located between the communes of Aigues-Mortes and Grau du Roi, in the *département* of the Gard within the Languedoc-Rousillon region. It is part of the deltaic complex of the river Rhone, which includes the delta of the Camargue (80,000 ha), the Plan du Bourg of the eastern Camargue (30,000 ha) and the Camargue Gar-

The flamingo is a mythical creature and the symbol of the Camargue's richness.

Jarras Listel Estate

doise (the western Camargue) (40,000 ha), which extends across the two *départements* of the Gard and the Bouches-du-Rhône. Its geographical coordinates are 43° 31' 49.29" N; 4° 10' 41.89 " E.

The Camargue Gardoise was recognised by the Ramsar Convention in 1966. The convention's aim is the conservation and rational use of wetlands by local, regional and national means as well as by international cooperation, at the same time as contributing towards achieving sustainable development throughout the entire world. The Camargue Gardoise was also included in the Camargue Biosphere Reserve in 2007. The Man And Biosphere network (UNESCO) seeks to provide scientific data which allow appropriate responses to be formulated for problems of sustainable development of populations and management of natural resources. The Camargue is bounded by the Rhône-Sète canal and the Petit Rhône, and is divided into two principal sectors: fluvial lakes and marine lagoons, the latter being that which characterises the Jarras Estate.

Old vertical-axis windmill used to pump water.

Jarras Listel Estate

The estate is also included in the Natura 2000 network.

As regards geomorphology, the principal geographical characteristics are as follows. The Jarras Estate is an old coastal belt formed by a channel of the Rhone. Historically speaking, the estate depended upon the river floods for its supply of fresh water. Today, this is achieved by an artificial system of canals, and the principal source of fresh water comes from the navigation canal between Aigues-Mortes and the sea. The ground water table, which takes the form of a freshwater lens approximately 60 cm deep, is thus uniquely replenished by rainfall. The peninsula is surrounded by the Mediterranean Sea and by saltmarshes. Salt water is therefore present in the entire subsoil of the estate, and forms a saline corner which penetrates inside the soils. The fresh water lies above it, closer to the surface. In recent years, rainfall levels have not been sufficient to replenish the ground water table and, as sea levels rise, salt water is invading. Add to this the increasing salinity of the water channels passing through the estate, also due to the rise in sea levels, and the increase in strength of the maritime winds.

The sand belt at Jarras was formed between 1008 and 1521 by sediment transported by the Rhone through a channel known as "La Ville". The countryside was characterised by a mosaic of lagoons, dune vegetation – pines, juniper, pistachio, etc. – and open habitats with brackish (i.e. both saline and fresh) water which make up the typical Mediterranean scenery.

Today the soil on the estate is composed of 2% clay and 70% sands, which gives it a water retention capacity of between 6 and 7% in sandy areas and 20% in the clay-rich areas. The soil is very prone to wind erosion in view of its very low cohesive property. Soil organic matter is very scarce at Jarras, and the soil has a relatively weak nutrient retention index.

Fresh water is circulated through the vineyards by means of a network of 49 kilometres of canals, made up of 20 individual areas of water measuring between 18 ares and 19 hectares. The bulk of these follow a natural cycle and dry out in the summer, whilst two of the 20 are controlled by man and remain full of water during the summer period.

TOWARDS A SUSTAINABLE USE OF THE ESTATE

The Listel company is looking to develop the sustainable use of the estate of which it is in charge. Even if the production of wine remains the principle activity, accountability for the environment becomes essential in order to guarantee a viable planet for future generations. Listel has a management plan, which is a reference document and which describes the state of knowledge of the estate. It determines the way forward for management and plans the actions required to ensure that the heritage of the estate is conserved. It also defines the pillars of scientific study that must be conducted in order to grow the knowledge of the estate. It allows assured continuity and coherence of management, both spatially and chronologically.

An old grape conveyor belt.

Wine production which respects the environment

Listel wishes to link its agriculture with conservation of its biodiversity, and, at the same time, to a collective awareness of man's responsibility to preserve the environment. The company has therefore committed itself to maintain or improve the agricultural practices involved in wine-growing. This involves reducing the environmental footprint of the practice and also arranging agricultural work according to the demands of species which use the vines as breeding sites or source of food. Natural sites are, of course, a priority in terms of conservation, but Listel also aims to integrate the vine into its conservation schemes, with a wish to move towards a "synergy" between agricultural activity and conservation of its biodiversity.

Every winter, barley or rye is sown between the rows of vines in order to protect the dunes from natural erosion caused by the Mistral. The vineyards are used by flocks of 1,000 sheep, watched by shepherds, an example of the spirit of conservation of the ecological heritage which prevails at Jarras.

87

Let us look at four traditional agricultural practices on the Listel estates, which are known to be favourable to the environment:

Rush bedding: This involves covering the soil between the rows of vines in order to avoid erosion by the wind, particularly in winter. It is a method that was used throughout the vineyards until the mid-1960s, and thereafter solely in the young vine shoots. It is a traditional activity still practised today. Historically, rushes were used, although nowadays it is dried reed stems, gathered locally, that allow us to fight the erosion.

Winter greening of vine plots: Since the mid 1960s, the estate has practised winter greening of the plots. Seed is sown after the grapes are harvested (late September – early October) and the ground is managed until the vines come back into leaf (late April – early May). Barley was used for the first fifteen years, and then, because the soil had become poorer, several mixes were tested. In 1970 a rotation of barley, rye, triticale, oats, brassicas and legumes was trialled for the first time. Between 1970 and 1975 this gave way to a mix of vetches and rye. Since 1976 an annual rotation of rye, barley and oats has been adopted. Winter greening suits game species as well as the biology of the soil.

Winter grazing by sheep amongst the vines: Some years after the first winter greening of the plots (early 1970s), sheep grazing was introduced. Dependent on the foraging potential of the plots, between 800 and 1000 sheep graze on the estate, in one or two flocks. They graze amongst the vines from December until April, and the faeces left behind constitute a significant portion of the nitrogenous material which the vines receive.

Biological pest control: At present, 200 of the 419 hectares of the estate's vines are managed biologically. This is done by the sexual confusion method. Certain moths and butterflies attack fruit trees, and the vine is regulated attacked by a specific moth (*Eudermis* sp.). Biological control aims to break the chemical communication between the male and female. Synthetic pheromones are released into the atmosphere from small capsules, to mimic the sexual pheromones. Males and females cannot then detect each other, and as a result all breeding is prevented, and therefore development of the predatory population is prevented. This technique is only used in 0.5% of vineyards and orchards in Europe.

Common gladiola.

Preserving the diversity of the Camargue scenery and the species associated with it, and improving the knowledge base.

Biological diversity, or "biodiversity" for short, is defined as the diversity of forms of life on the Earth: genes, species, populations and ecosystems. Certain human activities such as agriculture, which have degraded the earth's soils, fresh water and the oceans, are the origin of the rapid decline in biodiversity, a process which is both current and irreversible. France is ranked fifth amongst countries sheltering the most species threatened (231 out of 983). Regions such as the Camargue, therefore, a humid area well known for its biodiversity, agriculture and cultural heritage, have been recognised by international organisations as being of world heritage whose preservation is crucial. In terms of agriculture, biodiversity is not just the origin of cultivated plants; it has other essential functions such as control of disease (genetic diversity of crops), pest control in crops (auxiliary plants, natural predators, etc.), pollenisation (80% of cereals grown in Europe depend on pollenisation), etc. Thus, safeguarding the biodiversity present at Jarras contributes to action at world level in favour of the plant and of mankind. Knowledge of this diversity and its functions (both ecological as well as sociological) is a prerequisite for its conservation.

In this context, several objectives have been set in response to the mission of sustainable use of the estate and therefore to the conservation of its biodiversity: limiting the spread of invasive species; encouraging species to breed; monitoring the evolution of natural sites; adding to knowledge of the land, etc. They refer to concrete action such as monitoring and eradicating invasive plant species (*Baccharis* sp. and *Cortaderia* sp.), managing nest-sites for waders and gulls, supplying fresh water in the canals, etc. At the same time, acquisition of knowledge is assured either internally or in partnership with public bodies. For example, in 2009, a study on the functional role of biodiversity was undertaken in partnership with INRA (French National Institute for Agricultural Research). It involved understanding whether natural sites adjoining plots of vines could be considered as supporters of the vines in combating certain insect pests.

The Jarras estate is opening its doors this year to the Francophone Colloquium on Conservation Biology, organised by the CNRS (National Centre of Scientific Research) at Montpellier. The visit to the estate was chosen in order to illustrate a concrete example of an enterprise that has taken positive steps towards conserving biodiversity.

Developing a model for sustainable hunting

According to the European Charter on Hunting and Biodiversity, the development of hunting envisages "the use of wild game species and their habitats in a way and at a rate that does

Nest of Avocet
(Recurvirostra avosetta).

Jarras Listel Estate

List of species and habitats of significant heritage value at European and/or national level and their representation on the Jarras Estate. Criteria used: Bern Convention, Habitat Fauna & Flora Directive, Birds Directive, Red List (National and World), protective legislation by ministries

English name	Latin name	Representation
Habitats		
Mediterranean lagoons		Good
Mediterranean salt steppes	*Limonietalia*	Average
Dune forests of Umbrella Pine		Good
Coastal dunes with Juniper		Good
Fixed coastal dunes of the Mediterranean	*Crucianellion maritimae*	Good
Flora		
Sea Lavender	*Limomium girardianum*	Average
Cancerwort	*Kickxia cirrhosa*	Good
Fauna		
Twaite Shad (fish)	*Alosa fallax*	Poor
Natterjack Toad (amphibian)	*Bufo calamita*	Poor
European Pond Turtle (reptile)	*Emys orbicularis*	Rare
Stone Curlew (nesting bird)	*Burhinus œdicnemus*	Good
Great Spotted Cuckoo (nesting bird)	*Clamator glandarius*	Good
Black-winged Stilt (nesting bird)	*Himantopus himantopus*	Good
Avocet (nesting bird)	*Recurvirostra avosetta*	Good
Little Bustard (non-nesting bird)	*Tetrax tetrax*	Rare
Great Egret (non-nesting bird)	*Egretta alba*	Average
Some mammals		
Southwestern Water Vole	*Arvicola sapidus*	Indeterminate
Common Pipistrelle, Soprano Pipistrelle, Kuhl's Pipistrelle, Nathusius's Pipistrelle	*Pipistrellus pipistrellus, P. pygmaeus P. khulii, P. nathusii*	Good
Greater Horseshoe Bat	*Rhinolophus ferrumequinum*	Rare

not lead to the long-term decline of biodiversity or hinder its restoration. Such use maintains the potential of biodiversity to meet the needs and aspirations of present and future generations, as well as maintaining hunting itself as an accepted social […] and cultural activity… When hunting is conducted in such a sustainable manner, it can positively contribute to the conservation of wild populations and their habitats and also benefit society".

Hunting as it is organised on the Jarras estate by the Works Council is focused in precisely this way. The rules for hunting hares is a good example: the creation of plots for hunting, the prohibition of hunting in the rows of vines, no unleashing, and a restriction on quarry numbers. There is therefore a proper understanding of how rare the game resource is. However, no means of evaluating the sustainability of hunting exists at Jarras. Developing it consists, amongst other things, of gathering data on game species (hares, Red-legged Partridge *(Alectoris rufa)* and Woodpigeon *(Columba palumbus)*. Estimating the breeding density and breeding success will allow any drop in numbers to be anticipated or compensated, whether by man or not.

Developing tourist activity oriented towards a discovery of the natural heritage

Green tourism is a branch of tourism whereby the principal objective is to enjoy nature, scenery and countryside, and/or individual species, whilst at the same time respecting the ecosystems visited. It is an activity which comprises both education and interpretation, and helps to make people aware of the need to preserve their natural and cultural assets. It is in this spirit that Listel took the decision to allow its heritage to be discovered and to make the public aware of the question of biodiversity conservation and of how agriculture must respect the environment. Measures were taken to restrict the impact of visitors to natural sites, and their impact on the species that live there (guided tours only, limited to a certain number each day), to manage the waste that tourists leave behind, and to undertake restoration work on old buildings by managing space for species that depend on them (bats and nocturnal birds of prey).

Shelduck *(Tadorna tadorna)* next in holes in the ground.

WILDLIFE

The wish to create a synergy between the farming activity and biodiversity conservation, as explained above, is translated into action by measures which aim to encourage breeding on certain species whose populations are in decline in Europe. Laro-limicolous birds and the Stone Curlew *(Burhinus oedicnemus)* are two examples. The former are all the water birds comprising seagulls and terns, as well as shorebirds of the Charadriiformes order (birds which feed in mud flats), which, for their breeding sites, select small islands with greater or lesser degrees of vegetation separated from the embankment by a stretch of water. On the Jarras Estate, the water residue from cleaning the wine tanks is channelled into two settling ponds to evaporate and to precipitate the organic matter which it contains. These are areas of water that are isolated and far-removed from the noise and bustle of agricultural activity. A floating raft has been constructed in one of the ponds to provide an additional breeding site for the Common Tern *(Sterna hirundo)* and the Little Term *(Sterna albifrons)*. This is incorporated into the Natura 2000 agreement, and is monitored by biologists covering this group of birds in the Ca-

margue. The Stone Curlew *(Burhinus œdicnemus)* nests in certain vine plots on the estate where it finds suitable ground and a habitat influenced by the winter-feeding sheep. At the time when the first springtime work is being started in the vineyards, the young chicks are only a few days old. In order to encourage their survival, work on the rows of vines where a stone curlew is nesting is delayed by a fortnight so that the chicks are more mobile and can leave the nest when machinery passes.

The estate wishes to be an example of good practice, and its hunting activity is carried out with the aim of improving knowledge of the game species present. Two long-term surveys have been organised in order to estimate variations in population of the European Hare *(Lepus europaeus)* and Red-legged Partridge *(Alectoris rufa)*. The populations of both are reduced between February and March (in the case of the hare) and between March and April (for the partridge). The methods used are recorded in the regional and national management plans for small game of the ONCFS (National Office of Hunting and Wildlife). These counts are supplemented by bags and tallies which inform how the quota is fixed and what pressures exist during the hunting season.

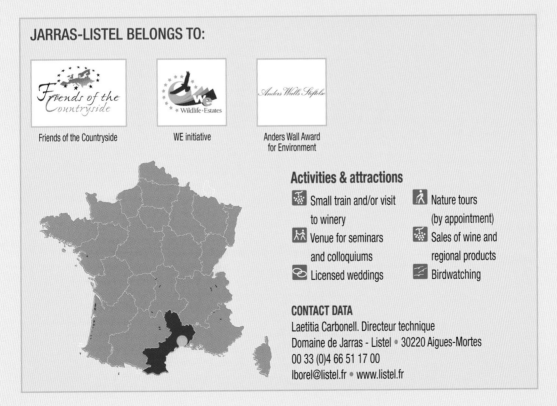

JARRAS-LISTEL BELONGS TO:

Friends of the Countryside

WE initiative

Anders Wall Award
for Environment

Activities & attractions

- Small train and/or visit to winery
- Venue for seminars and colloquiums
- Licensed weddings
- Nature tours (by appointment)
- Sales of wine and regional products
- Birdwatching

CONTACT DATA

Laetitia Carbonell. Directeur technique
Domaine de Jarras - Listel • 30220 Aigues-Mortes
00 33 (0)4 66 51 17 00
lborel@listel.fr • www.listel.fr

Rías Baixas

Atlantic

Location: West coast of A Coruña province and coast of Pontevedra province, Galicia, Spain.
Surface: Coastline of 500 km.

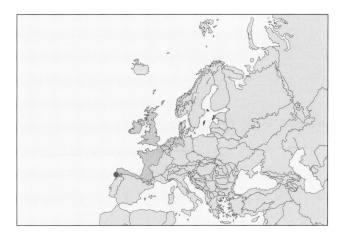

CLIMATIC DATA

Average rainfall
mm/cm²/year

Snow days: 1

1700 mm

Temperature (°C)

39.6 — max ■
14 — average ▨
-5.7 — min ■

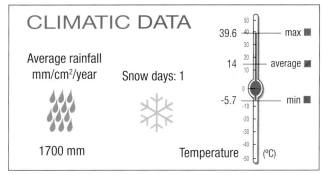

SUMMARY

Since 1963 there has been a steady evolution in the way in which the extraction of bivalves and gastropods from the beaches of the estuaries and inlets of Galicia (known as *Rías*) is both perceived and implemented. During this time, and particularly since 1995 when the zones were marked out, the fishermen and women have become professional, have rationalised extraction and have moved from being simple extractors of a marine resource to being farmers and growers. All shellfish zones are protected and approved by the Fishermans Guilds, and members carry a shellfisher's carnet which binds them to management tasks such as cleaning, selecting, seeding larvae, patrolling against poachers, checking and, finally, fishing.
Shellfishing is the method of fishing consisting of any extractive activity designed to catch shellfish. A distinction should be made between that which is done afloat in boats and that done on foot. The former is more suited to men, whilst collecting shellfish on foot is usually done by women. Of the 8096 permits issued in respect of collection on foot (known as the *permex*), 95% are issued to women.
Collecting shellfish on foot is carried out in the Rias of Galicia, in the intertidal zones during low tide, although some activity is carried out from boats.

The coastline of Galicia stretches over 1,200 km and includes 400 km of beaches and 100 km of abrupt cliffs. These 500 km have a large tidal flux and contain one of the best underwater *fields* in the world, highly productive, particularly of shellfish.This large shellfish field is now being cultivated, after a surprising evolution in local customs that has taken place over the last 15 years.

TURGALICIA

Acuarium Galicia

DESCRIPTION

The Rías Baixas (Galician for "Lower Rias") are a part of *Costa del Marisco* facing the Atlantic Ocean in the southern part of the Galicia region of Spain. They consist of the southern part of the Province of A Coruña and the entire Province of Pontevedra. To the South the Rias Baixas border the Portuguese coast, and ends at Cape Finisterre to the North.

The area takes its name from the five large *rías*, or flooded river valleys, which form estuaries along the coast, with its biggest city port in Vigo. These five *Rías* are:

1. Ría de Corcubión.
2. Ría de Muros e Noia.
3. Ría de Arousa.
4. Ría de Pontevedra.
5. Ría de Vigo.

TECHNIQUES

Collecting shellfish on foot and afloat

Collecting shellfish on foot is done in the zones of the intertidal fringes of the beaches whenever low tide occurs during the morning. Bivalves and gastropods are gathered, such as clams, cockles and razor-shells. The women who work the beaches scratch about in the sand with various tools to uncover the molluscs which they collect in buckets or sacks. This activity has its own strict calendar and the women who gather have to have a carnet, issued by the Autonomous Government. In other words, gathering shellfish is not a free-for-all activity but is regulated and divided into territorial areas by the Guilds or Producer Organisations.

Bivalves can also be harvested from boats but, given that between the fisherman and the sandy bottom in which the molluscs hide there is a layer of sea water that may be deep or shallow, the tools used to sift the sand are on a long stick. Fishing for shellfish afloat in boats also means that crustaceans such as spider crabs, crabs and lobsters are caught in nets and creels. Barnacles are gathered on foot, among the rocks, after jumping from small boats onto the base of cliffs and rocks. The former activity is most frequent along the Costa da Morte in the province of A Coruña, the latter in the area of Cedeira (A Coruña).

Types of shellfish

Grooved Carpet-shell Clam / Almeja fina (Ruditapes decussatus)

Its shell is formed from two equal valves, joined by a ligament which allows it to open and close. It buries itself in the sand using its muscular axe-shaped foot.

It is the most highly prized in the market because of its excellent quality and ability to live longer out of the water than any other variety. Its valves are uniform in colour, varying between brown and white depending on the area in which it breeds. Its habitat is the intertidal zone and it can bury itself 15 to 30 cm deep.

Method of gathering: Either on foot or in boats. In the latter case the fishermen look for this bivalve by sifting through the sand on the bottom of the sea with a rake on a long stick.

Cockle / Berberecho (Cerastoderma edule)

It has two heart-shaped valves and large nerves, and moves by using its leg. The white shell is swollen and convex, with a series of radial ridges.

Cockles usually live in the intertidal area, buried just under the sand. They can live in depths of 10 metres of water. They are also found at the river mouths.

They feed on small animals and phytoplankton which they filter from the water through their gills. They grow very fast, reaching market size in the first year. The largest specimens reach a diameter of 4 cm. They lay their eggs in the spring.

Although not as highly appreciated as clams, their flesh retains the characteristic taste of the sea.

Method of gathering: This bivalve, like the clam, can be gathered either on foot using little rakes or hoes, or using special long-handled rakes worked from boats near the coast.

Carpet-shell Clam / Almeja babosa (Venerupis pullastra)

The colour of the Carpet-shell Clam varies between grey, cream and brown. The characteristics which distinguish it from the others are that it is a little longer and the syphons are joined along its whole length. The shells show concentric rings. Although the culinary qualities of this clam are about the same as the grooved carpet-shell clam, they are not quite as prized as they are weaker and cannot last as long out of the water. This makes it difficult to export them, and there is a high consumption rate in Galicia. They are collected by long-handled rake from small boats along the coast, or on foot by using appropriate devices.

Method of gathering: Either on foot on from boats. In the latter case the fishermen look for this bivalve by sifting through the sand on the bottom of the sea with a rake on a long stick.

Manila Clam / Almeja japónica (Ruditapes philippinarum)

The colour of the shell varies between brown, grey and black, and shows some more marked lines which form small squares. Manila Clam cultivation was introduced into Galicia because of its rapid growth, but production levels are low on account of the high quality of the indigenous varieties.

Method of gathering: Either on foot on from boats. In the latter case the fishermen look for this bivalve by sifting through the sand on the bottom of the sea with a rake on a long stick.

Wedge Clam / Cadelucha (Donax trunculus)

The shell is subquadrangular in shape; the two valves are similar and have a straight hinge, and numerous small and even teeth.

Externally it has radial ridges and is sometimes covered by a hairy periostracum. It is dark grey-brown in colour with lighter markings. The periostracum is grey-brown.

It is abundant in Galicia on open sandy beaches which are washed by sea water.

Method of gathering: It is gathered by the traditional method – on foot with a hoe or small rake – and is much prized. Nowadays it is collected at many different sites: Pindo, Lira, Corcubión, Aguiño, Bayona, Vilarrube (Valdoviño), O Barqueiro, etc., but consignments are now arriving from Huelva (Andalusia), especially from large commercial beds. It is more commonly found in the marketplace today thanks to development programmes.

Rayed Artemis / Reló (Dosinia exoleta)

Almost circular, and white on the inside with thick valves that are also circular. The shell is usually light in colour with small but bright and colourful zigzag bands. It has thick concentric striations.

Method of collecting: Almost always collected by rakes worked from small fishing boats. Also by hoe on the shoreline, as it is relatively abundant in certain zones that are accessible at low tide.

Portuguese Oyster / Ostión (Crassostrea angulata)

The two valves are unequal and rather long; the lower one is larger and convex. It frequently looks 'twisted' in appearance, from lying close to the surface with other oysters. The surface of the shell is very rough, with heavily flaked growth rings. The valve lips are usually very fragile so that it can be opened by breaking these with a knife which is then inserted into the crack to cut the adductor muscle. The species found in the Iberian Peninsula is *Gryphea* or *Crassostrea angulata.*

The cultivation of the Portuguese and the Pacific oyster is practically the same. At a certain stage the larvae fix themselves onto a hard smooth substrate to begin their sessile life. The grower takes advantage of this fact by placing appropriate objects to which the larvae attach themselves. Examples of the many types of device used are: clay tiles, plastic tiles, strings and bouquets of buckets or shells.

FROM NEW EXTRACTION TO SPECIALIST GROWING

During the 1990s, following the creation of a specific department dealing with fishing, aquaculture and shellfish, there was a huge leap forward in both quality and quantity and the start of a series of important debates.

Excessive exploitation of resources led those who represented the sector to address seriously the recovery of shellfish stocks.

It became necessary to turn to marine cultivation and professionalization. At that time the majority of skippers and owners resolved that harvesting shellfish should be a professional activity. This was extremely important, because the fact that they themselves had decided that this was so, obliged them to submit to the same working standards that existed in other activities. The result was that the Fisheries Law as well as Decree 127/93, which began to regulate the shellfish sector from that moment on, also obliged the workers to be registered.

The groups of shellfish gatherers in Galicia who gathered on foot (mostly women) had at their disposal a huge area of over 6500 hectares, but were only obtaining economic returns that were plainly insufficient – 0.14 €/m² – which equates to one clam or ten cockles per square metre.

However, using new methods of cultivation it became possible to achieve greater profitability.

The steps taken towards professionalization since that time have been to limit the number of shellfish gatherers, train them and ensure that they registered in a special maritime regime. However their returns had to be higher. A more flexible system of closed seasons was introduced for the reason that the previous model was far from responding to the biological criteria that were being revealed.

Although the origin of this transformation in the shellfish sector was the result of the spatial and temporal coincidence of several factors, if one had to identify a defining moment at the start of this change, it would be the 1st Reunion of the Women Shellfish Gatherers of Galicia in 1995.

The Galician plan, as well as courses introduced by the New Opportunities for Women programme (NOW) and the new focus provided by the Galician Fisheries Extension Service have driven the engines for the changes that have taken place in the shellfish sector since 1995.

In the mid 1990s the gathering of shellfish on foot had started to be recognised by official bodies as an activity of prime economic and social importance, which produced 4000 tonnes of molluscs and bivalves, with a market value of 15,025,300 Euros, and which generated a significant number of jobs.

Knowledge was needed about the growth and other factors which influence the viability of seeding clams from hatcheries in order to achieve greater profitability, and for this purpose biologists and shellfish gatherers started work on seeding.

The result of these experiments was that on Wednesday 26th July 1994 the shellfish gatherers of the Association of Vilaxoán came together to clean and prepare the estuary of O Rial in order to seed one and a half million grooved carpet-shell Clams *(almeja fina)* and four hundred kilograms of Carpet-shell Clam *(almeja babosa)*.

The problem in the previous year had been the high mortality on the beaches of seed from the hatchery. Therefore the 10,000 square metres (in round figures) were seeded in three different cultivation systems: the first was the traditional method, i.e. on the sand with no protection; the second was also seeded on the sand but protected by a mesh net to deter predators; the third consisted of watching the tiny clams grow in plastic trays before seeding them on to the sand somewhat later. Experiments were also conducted on the cultivation of oysters on tables and in bags, methods that are commonly used in France.

From extractors to growers – another method of working

The cultivation programme was highly successful and in practice it served to bring about a change of mentality, "from people who move from being mere collectors to understanding that they are part of a production chain". The experiments in cultivating clams and oysters in bags had to be organised in shift patterns. There was no longer any point in everyone going "just to look at the bags and clean them" all at the same time. They were jobs that required a lot of people working in a relatively small area, which would not work. So it had to be done in turns, or shifts, and coordinators were appointed to control the shifts.

Shellfish gathering had been done for centuries in the same way, and now scientific organisation was being imposed on the beaches. Organising shift work was a first step in the transformation of shellfish gathering from the traditional to the modern. Furthermore, "once they had managed to organise the working shifts they really managed to discipline themselves to the business plan". The change however brought about other consequences such as a reduction in the number of working days, setting timetables, limiting the number of hours they went out, etc.

It was a far cry from the days when shellfish gathering was free and when the gatherers went down to the beaches "on Saturdays, Sundays and feast days". The business plans had succeeded in spreading the workload throughout the entire year, but still the number of days was excessive. At that moment of transition the workers still thought that profitability was closely related to the number of days on which they could work. The idea of quantity had still not

R. Fernández

been replaced by that of quality, so that the business plans, which they themselves had prepared, show a very high number of days that in turn bore little relation to the opportunities provided by the rhythms of the tides. However, thanks to the technical support from technicians, biologists from the Fishermen's Guilds, the Extension Agency and trainers, this change was also achieved. Thus the business plans went from showing figures of 220 days to figures of 120 or 130 days. Not only did they succeed in reducing the number of theoretical days that featured in the plans, but these became their working guides. Even by 1997 and 1998 they had a degree of control over their business plans that was very high. At the same time they had learned the times when extraction is best done, and as a result of the biologi-

Shellfishing by boat was typically done using a *dorna*, a skiff with symmetrical ends and an almost flat bottom. The prow and stern were sharply pointed. The shellfish were extracted from the sand with rakes.

PROBLEMS AND SOLUTIONS

LOCALITY	PROBLEMS	SOLUTIONS
PONTEVEDRA		
A Guarda	a) Poaching	a) Vigilance and raising awareness
	b) Trade interrupted by poachers	b) Preventing fraudulent sales, checking exports and certificates of origin.
Pontevedra	a) Trade	a) Sell everything in Lourizán. Demand sale invoices
	b) Variable number of gatherers	b) Survey and census of gatherers (Business plan)
Vilanova	a) Poaching	a) Vigilance by the authorities and sorting out concessions and free-for-all gathering
de Arousa	b) Lack of economic resources	b) Economic support from the authorities and a business plan
	c) Organisational problems in participating	c) Try to encourage and promote participation
	d) Cleaning up algae which kills the shellfish	d) Investigate techniques that do not harm the shellfish
Vilagarcía	a) Lack of economic resources	a) Economic support from the authorities and a business plan
de Arousa	b) Organisational problems in participating	b) Try to encourage and promote participation
	c) Lack of techniques and planning	c) Support to engage biologists and secure seed supplies
	d) Trade and low prices	d) Contact more buyers
LUGO		
Barreiros	Poaching	Rigorous vigilance and economic sanctions

C. Otero

The product has managed to establish itself in business channels through local markets. The photograph shows the former manager of the Galician Shellfish Plan, Francisco García de Bobadilla.

which they initially rejected but have now ended up demanding.

Improvements in production are intimately related to the change in the jobs and content of this traditional activity, nowadays transformed into a profession. In the year 2000 extraction accounted for only 23% of the time spent by a shellfish gatherer, the remainder being spent in vigilance, seeding, checking, training, attending meetings and other activities related to the Galicia Programme. The profession has been transformed from within, and nowadays the jobs which need to be done are many and varied.

When they began to form themselves into groups and to seed and cultivate, the shellfish gatherers were very clear in their minds that poaching was stealing and that it was something which as an organisation they could stop. It was a question of protecting a product which had been growing over time thanks to their hard work. The seed was expensive, and they needed to achieve good harvests if they wanted to have work and employment in the future. They then had to explain all this to their neighbours and relations, who were so accustomed to gathering shellfish on a "free-for-all" basis.

cal and economic criteria they could design a business plan for each species.

On the other hand, as in any other business activity, a timetable was set. The time spent working was to be arranged according to the means by which the activity is performed. Shellfish gathering on foot is done from two hours before until two hours after the daylight low tide but with a final cut-off point of five o'-clock in the afternoon.

Previously the women went to the beaches only to extract and gather shellfish. Now they have had to convert themselves into 'workers'. They had to organise the cultivations for "the clam harvest", which meant cleaning, thinning and seeding, as well as watching that nobody stole their production, all of these being issues

External vigilance

Vigilance became an integral part of the tasks surrounding this activity, which the gatherers organised in shifts or in groups. In doing so, they now collaborate with the professional security services. Furthermore their mere presence walking up and down the beaches serves to dissuade poachers.

They patrol day and night, in winter and in summer. It is one of the hardest tasks because they exposed not only to the rigours of the weather but to the possibility that they will have to confront the poachers face to face.

The shellfish sector has moved from a situation in which it was becoming exhausted to one in which it is the gatherers themselves who do the patrolling. Whereas in 1995 there were only five Guilds which undertook any form of vigilance, by the year 2000 there were 17.

B. Marugán

TIME DEDICATED TO THE DIFFERENT TASKS IN SHELLFISH GATHERING

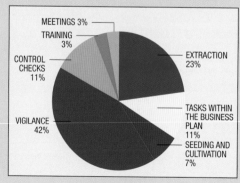

MEETINGS 3%
TRAINING 3%
CONTROL CHECKS 11%
VIGILANCE 42%
EXTRACTION 23%
TASKS WITHIN THE BUSINESS PLAN 11%
SEEDING AND CULTIVATION 7%

SHELLFISHING IN GALICIA - PRESENT REALITY AND A BRIGHT FUTURE

1. The region.
2. The dangers.
3. The challenges and opportunities in the sector:
   - Certificate of origin.
   - Water quality.
   - No to invasive tourism and industry.
4. Acknowledgements.

1. The Region

Galicia and the sea are inseparable. You cannot understand one without understanding the other. The huge food larder of the Rías has supplied the Galician population throughout its entire history and even today fishing activity is one of the most defining characteristics of the region.

Our region – our country – is Galicia, whose geographical situation at the north-west of the Iberian Peninsula and the south-west corner of Europe presents really specific and special climatic and geographical conditions for the world of shallow-water fishing, marine cultivation and especially shellfish.

The region is configured into *Rías*, small fjord-like inlets commonly referred to as being "low", "medium" and "high", which are a consequence of submerged valleys fed by large inland rivers, such as the Umia and Ulla, and smaller ones: the Xallas, Arnego and Verdugo. The nutrients brought down by these rivers, and the temperature of the ocean waters, which in turn are influenced by branches of the Gulf Stream, together form a microclimate of between 12ºC and 18ºC and provide the perfect site for species which we will mention later.

If we take the physical and chemical basis of this sea water, and add to it a coastline of over 1200km of indented shoreline, which contains about 400km of sandy beaches or 100km of steep cliffs, together with a tidal pattern that is one of the largest in Europe – differences of 3.5m between high and low tides – it means that the incoming and outgoing tidal flows stimulate the exchange of water, which with the action of the sun and constant renewal and oxygenation creates a genuine 'cultivated field' of over 500 linear kilometres and is amongst the best submerged crop-growing areas of the world.

Let us imagine a field of wheat in America, or the Pampa, or Wisconsin, or a cultivated Amazon, or rice-paddies in China and Vietnam, of the same dimension. With the prices that our crops fetch – Grooved Carpet-shell Clams *(Ruditapes decussatus)* at 25 €/kg, Cockles *(Cerastoderma edule)* at 4-5 €/kg or Carpet-shell Clams at 12-15 €/kg – we would be looking at the cultivated field with the highest potential in the world. We are entitled to believe that this is the largest ecological industry in Spain, and with the highest production levels, on which the economy of many families in Galicia depends.

If our region really is what we have just described – without being chauvinist – then anyone who knows about this subject would say that we can be proud of our marine heritage but not presumptuous of it.

2. The dangers

The reality of the high and low Rías of Galicia is that they are one sea, one ecosystem, surrounded by human beings, civilization, urbanism and invasive tourism. If there is no sense of ratio in all of this, as our much loved and respected Uxío Labarta taught us many years ago, we will be destroying the Galician coast, something which every person in authority or position of power should always remember to defend and support because it is inheritance of all Galician people.

Fishing and shellfishing in Galicia should always be understood to be not just one single economic activity but also a way of life. This will allow us to speak in the future not only of an activity that is viable and economically stable but also of the whole marine environment, in an attempt to overcome the preconceived idea that fishing in Galicia is exclusively a primary sector and in a state of permanent crisis.

It is in uncontrolled progress and over-fishing that we would identify the immediate dangers to shellfishing and shallow-water fishing.

Unfortunately progress is often associated with invasion and destruction, or in other words excessive colonization. Nobody in his right mind can oppose the growth of our towns and cities and our fishing communities, an increased standard of living, the consolidation and future of our sense of well-being. But somewhere between rational advance, compatible use of resources, complementarity and respect for the natural environment is where we believe we can find some future ground.

F. Hernár

Archipelago of the Cíes's Islands at the mouth of the Ría de Vigo.

We need to emphasise the fact that sustainable tourism is compatible with the conservation of natural resources, but that the practices of invasive tourism do no good for anything. We have to bring together aspects of conservation that allow a sustainable use of the coastline – in other words ensure the richness of marine life and fishing – and maximise production by means of rational and intelligent use of resources.

Let us bear in mind that the real owners of the environment are its inhabitants, both on land and in the sea, and we must resist the belief that one can be destroyed by another. The comments made in connection with over-fishing are the hardest for us, because they do not land on the roofs of the politicians or of town-dwellers or of heartless speculators, but on us and our neighbours, our companions, the people with whom we have the good fortune to live day by day – and for that reason any comment is harder to bear. But in moderation lies

virtue, both in thoughtful and intelligent judgements which offer solutions and in understanding.

A dorna, a traditional Galician fishing boat with a mast and either oars or a sail, is not the same as a speedboat made of plastic reinforced with glass fibre and an engine of 100HP.

Fishing with spun hemp is not the same as fishing with modern nylon or teflon fibres.

A traditional Galician racú boat with an engine of 16-32HP is not the same as one with an Iveco, MAN or Caterpillar engine of 300/600/900HP

The high quality Galician, Spanish or European market is not the same as the absurdities of a deceptively globalised product, for one cannot compare French champagne with its Chinese derivative; and the whole world knows it.

3. Challenges and opportunities in the sector
In general, the prospects for the shellfish sector within the Galician economy are based on a gradual

advance towards semi-cultivation, which would allow the amount of the product cultivated each year to be controlled. In addition it is becoming more professionalised and modernised, generating sufficient added value and stable levels of income for the professionals who devote themselves to this activity.

Improving the quality of the waters in the rías, and therefore the productivity of the shellfish-producing zones, is another future necessity, and for this to happen the local authorities have to develop policies which allow the environment in the *rías* to recover. Shellfishing is a sustainable and ecological activity, now that a sense of respect has been imposed not only for the beaches but for the resources that develop around them.

The future for this business, and the key to its success, lies in giving added value to the product – in other words differentiating ourselves through a seal of quality which allows us to stand out in the market, which is becoming more competitive every day. The quality and security of our fishery products offers us many more advantages when it comes to differentiating ourselves in such a competitive market. Consumers are increasingly becoming concerned about the environmental and health conditions of the products they consume, and we must therefore fight for higher quality and maintain it throughout the whole chain of traceability.

We should also encourage awareness in society and, for the future, through "Lessons about the Sea" for schoolchildren and other pedagogical tools, we can transfer the experience and the importance of the shellfish sector to younger members of society, so that they take part in work for the conservation and the sustainability of resources, coming to appreciate all the work connected with the sea, which is so often undervalued because of a lack of knowledge and incentives.

We believe that it would be useful for the Fishermen's Guilds to have at their disposal a technical corps of specialists which would be in charge of creating and maintaining a mini-hatchery for seeding native species so that they could be self-sufficient in supplies.

4. Acknowledgements

The above should be taken as the opinions of students who knew the great masters of oceanography and marine biology. Amongst these great masters we must highlight Professor Pillay y Tenore, the respected Dr. Andreu and the dearly loved and remembered Dr. Figueras. A particular expert is Professor Robles Pariente, and amongst recent colleagues we should mention Pereira A. and González Vidal, both of whom are sadly no longer alive, as well as a splendid generation of technical experts: Cortés, Bobadilla, Gabeiras, Landín, Guerra, Guerrero, Román, Catoira, Lema, Arnáiz, de Coo, Linares, Iglesias, Rodríguez, Ucha, Gallego, Aboi and Lobeira, all of them young and enthusiastic people who made great efforts towards the survival of our great productive sector: shellfish, shallow-water fishing and marine cultivation.

Raquel Padín Sampedro
(Biologist, Dept. of Environmental Extension, Acquariumgalicia)
Alfredo Fernández Prieto
(General Coordinator, Acquariumgalicia)

RÍAS BAIXAS BELONGS TO:

XACOBEO 2010 Galicia

XACOBEO 2010 Galicia

Activities & attractions

Fishing
Museum
Sailing
Walking trails

Restaurant
Hotel
Estate products

CONTACT DATA
Acquariumgalicia
www. acquariumgalicia.com

Sansaw

Atlantic

Location: Spanning the communities of Hadnall, Clive and Grinshill on the outskirts of Shrewsbury in Shropshire, United Kingdom.
Surface: 1,618 ha.

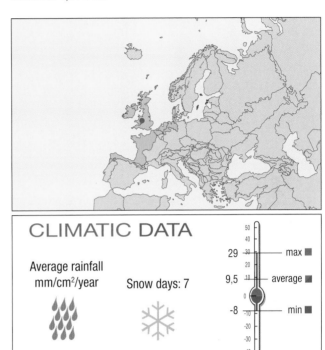

CLIMATIC DATA

Average rainfall
mm/cm²/year

Snow days: 7

655 mm

Temperature (°C)

29 — max
9,5 — average
-8 — min

SUMMARY

The Sansaw Estate combines land management, farming, food production, woodland stewardship and a sizeable property portfolio under its own banner of "modern rural living".

Its policy – which continues to evolve – is to retain a balance between the different aspects of the estate's property portfolio while maintaining a strong commercial edge. This provides a diverse investment which hopefully cushions Sansaw against turbulent economic times, as well as taking advantage of more stable periods.

There has, over the years, been a concentrated effort to transform redundant buildings into hi-tech offices, providing accommodation for forward-thinking businesses. This has created more jobs on the estate now than there were at the end of the 19th century.

Sansaw continues to have a huge stake in the local community and takes the social and environmental implications of its policy very seriously, both in regards to any commercial developments but also, as importantly, in forging relationships and partnerships with statutory and non-statutory bodies active in the community.

The management of 1,600 hectares of lands requires a deep understanding of the environment and of the impact which the estate has upon it, and forms a fundamental aspect of the estate's stewardship.

Owners Robin and James Thompson understand the need for continual momentum, not only to carry Sansaw forward for the next 20 years but for the generations that follow.

J. Todd

Aerial view of Sansaw.

Three generations of Thompsons: William, Robin and James.

J. Stephens

HISTORY

The Thompson family have lived on the Sansaw Estate for the last 146 years, despite trials and tragedies which, at times, could have threatened its very survival.

James Jenkinson Bibby, son of a ship owner who founded the Bibby Line in 1807, bought the Hardwicke Grange Estate from the Hill family in 1862 and acquired the adjacent Sansaw Estate 20 years later.

At the forefront of innovation, both in shipping and as a landowner, James Jenkinson was determined to breed the best livestock for agricultural production and was a pioneer of steam-driven agricultural machinery. He soon established a world-beating herd of Hereford Cattle and flock of Shropshire Sheep —breeds still in evidence on the estate today and which were exported worldwide.

After his death in 1897, he was succeeded by his son, Frank Bibby, who, although Chairman of the flourishing Bibby Line, found life on the estates more appealing. He invested, overseeing the construction of an extraordinary number of imaginatively-designed houses and cottages between the turn of the 20th century and the First World War. Horse-racing was also a huge passion, leading to two Grand National winners in 1905 and 1911.

Following the halcyon Edwardian era, the Estates were hit hard in the 1920s after the deaths of Frank in 1923 and of his son, Captain Brian (Robin) Bibby, in 1929. With two amounts of tax to pay after these deaths, the house was pulled down in 1933 after the High Court in London ruled that a widow and infant child did not require two manor houses to live in!

Brian's wife Ethel, who re-married Ronald (Ruff) Campbell, took over the running of the estate before his death in action during the British Army's retreat to Dunkirk. Brian's daughter, Cynthia, ran the estate with her husband, Denis Thompson, from the end of the Second World War until her death in 1971.

Their son, Robin, returned from Australia and resigned his Army commission to run the estate. He soon started a long-term renovation and modernisation programme. Cottages which were previously difficult to rent soon had waiting lists, while redundant buildings were given makeovers and let to rural businesses. The turnaround under Robin's stewardship was so great that today there are as many people working on the Sansaw Estate as there were 146 years ago, although that employment has changed dramatically.

While 2009 has seen Robin move to the position of Chairman, the introduction of his son, James, as managing director of the estate has seen no let-up in the commercial, social and environmental progression of Sansaw. After serving in Afghanistan and Iraq with the Royal Marines, and having completed a degree in Rural Land Management, James returned to Sansaw in 2006. His succession shows every sign of continuing Sansaw's proud heritage.

DESCRIPTION

Sansaw Estate is spread over 1,600 hectares of let and in-hand agricultural land and woodland in north Shropshire. Out of the 1,400 hectares of agricultural land, 650 hectares are currently farmed to the organic standards set by the UK Soil Association.

Regardless of operation, Sansaw has a commitment to the environment; be it a determination to farm the land 100 per cent organically or to include eco-friendly features throughout its commercial property portfolio. Further environmental initiatives are planned for its residential properties too.

The estate has its own water supply with 52 m³ being pumped per annum, supplying cottages, houses and some farms. The water is pumped from the aquifer 70 metres below the surface by way of a redundant copper mine shaft. The eight kilometres of main water pipe, laid in the 1880s, are in the process of being replaced by the great-grandson of the original contractor.

Sansaw Hall

Sansaw is a distinctive house of the English "Queen Anne revival" style, it was built as a farmhouse in 1775 and was doubled in size during the 1880s, having been bought from the Gardiner family. It was Frank Bibby's home until his father's death, when he moved to Hardwicke Grange. Sansaw became the main family home when Hardwicke Grange was pulled down following Frank's death in 1923. Although half the house was converted into flats after the Second World War it was returned to its former glory between 1971 and 1974 by taking down many of the additions of the late 19th and early 20th centuries.

Agriculture

There is a total of 1,400 hectares of agricultural land on the Sansaw Estate, of which the family farm 320 hectares. The remainder is farmed by tenants involved in a range of disciplines, from dairy farming and egg production to organic beef and breeding ewes.

More than 50 per cent of the estate is either organic or in the process of conversion to organic production. While it is impossible to force tenant farmers into organic farming practices, the management team has implemented an active policy of wherever possible, working with tenants on farmland that is manage by the family.

Sansaw's vision is to have a mixed organic enterprise operating at Sansaw which fits in with the strong environmental message as well as its economic one - maximising the return from the land.

Sansaw Hall in the Autumn.

tephens

Hope Farm Organic Dairy Unit.

There is an inherent responsibility, too, to the land. Without resorting to the use of artificial fertiliser and pesticides, healthy soil encourages healthier animals and healthier crops.

The aim of this long-term view is to protect Sansaw from the inevitable rise in oil price by returning to tried and trusted traditional techniques.

The organic system provides environmental benefits to both flora and fauna. Within the context of the current English agri-environmental schemes, Sansaw is hoping to move from its Organic Entry Level Stewardship (OELS) to the Higher Level Stewardship (HLS) over the next two years. Taking a proportion of the land out of production has led to a rise in the number of nesting birds as well a significant increase in insect life. Sansaw has created an old hay meadow and sown traditional flower mixtures to encourage wildlife diversity, while it also keeps four colonies of bees.

Overview

There are several different farming enterprises on the estate managed in a variety of ways, whether through joint ventures, contract farming or management service agreements.

The Brettell family, who have been farming at Sansaw for four generations, now oversee the management of Sansaw Farms. They also have

Haston Farm Organic Tricicale.

two laying sheds housing 2,000 birds each and a rearing shed housing 2,000 chicks. The colombian black tail chickens produce organic free-range eggs wich are supplied to one of Britain's biggest luxury retailers.

Pigs are reared and finished on 60 hectares of land, some of which is used for the growing of organic potatoes and carrots.

Around 140 hectares of organic cereals are managed under a contract farming agreement, while organic grassland takes up a further 120 hectares.

The farm produces 2,000 tonnes of potatoes, 3,000 tonnes of wheat and other cereals, three million litres of milk, 15 tonnes of beef and lamb, 250 tonnes of pork and one million eggs.

Woodland

While the woodland makes little money for the estate, it is still an important and vibrant part of Sansaw. With 160 hectares to manage, a final crop of Oak *(Quercus robur)* is an essential aim but an arduous, long-term operation. There are small pockets of coppiced Hazel *(Corylus avellana)*, yet with no-one employed directly to look after the woodland it takes something of a back seat. In years gone by there was a saw-mill on the estate but with little value in timber it is currently cheaper to import from abroad. The management team hope to use the wood to produce the estate's own fencing, but it makes no financial sense in the short term. However, with 140 tonnes of thinning taken from the woodland each year, the aspiration is to employ new technology in the form of woodchip - energy from which could be used to heat houses, cottages and commercial properties on the estate.

A Local Nature Reserve covering 36 hectares of woodland has also been established in partnership with Shropshire Council and a local conservation group. Managing an area known locally as Grinshill Hill, partners help re-establish heathland, remove birch scrub and provide valuable access to local communities.

Educational activities

A Forest School has been set up in partnership between Sansaw and Shropshire Council, enabling children to enjoy and learn about working in the countryside. Run throughout Britain and the rest of Europe, Forest Schools have demonstrated success with children of all ages who visit the same local woodlands on a regular basis, giving them the opportunity to learn about the natural environment, how to handle risks and most importantly to use their own initiative to solve problems and co-operate with others.

Sansaw Business Park

Converting redundant buildings into hi-tech offices has proved to be a significant financial investment. The transformation provides businesses with high-quality office space in a stunning location, whilst remaining in line with the estate's assidous environmental agenda.

The Pavilions is a £3 million (€4m) new complex set within a Victorian walled garden: a landmark to 21st century design with its striking glass structure and architectural prestige. Installing a ground-source heating system, using sustainable materials and implementing rainwater harvesting methods has resulted in an 'A' rating for the Pavilions' energy performance.

Even as this book goes to print, in May 2009 the Pavilions won the prestigious Royal Institute of British Architects award for outstanding design, given annually to the best new buildings in each region.

The Pavilions complement the existing Stable block, a collection of historic coach houses set around a central courtyard which have been restored into modern, high-spec, self-contained offices. They are let to a variety of businesses, from independent consultants to web developers.

Sansaw's ability to provide the very latest technology in a rural location is seen as one of its biggest advantages. Having installed a fibre-optic connection onto Sansaw Business Park, the inte-

Educational activities in the Forest School.

J. Stephens

grated voice and data facilities mean the Pavilions and Stables can compete with the best city-centre locations for both technology and back-drop.

Part of Sansaw's commitment to tenants and the local community is its investment in like-minded businesses which operate from the estate. It has invested both physically and financially in a growing stud farm as well as an organic food operation.

Housing

Shropshire suffers the same fate as many rural counties across England, where affordable housing is out of reach for many people, both young and

J. Stephens

The Pavilions - Internal.

J. Stephens

The Pavilions, Sansaw Business Park.

Åsa Thompson
with Raymond Blanc.

J. Stephens

old. With low wages forcing many young professionals and families out of the county, Sansaw has built a number of houses in partnership with local housing associations over the last 25 years.

Selling a 99-year lease and charging a nominal annual ground rent, Sansaw has been able to provide more appropriate accommodation for local people as well as enabling the next generation of Salopians (as the inhabitants of Shropshire are known) to live in the community where they were born.

The estate is investigating other opportunities for future development too, with sites dotted around the surrounding villages which will again deliver both affordable and open-market housing in partnership with local housing associations and developers.

Having successfully implemented new ventures and robust management systems to increase the profitability of Sansaw, the management team is looking to develop a template which can be used on other estates by compiling a handbook on modern estate management.

Social

The estate has a responsibility not only to the family but also to the community at large. It strives to take a 40-year strategic view, while retaining the ability to adapt to changing circumstances. At the heart of the estate's business plan is the continuing success of its farming and commercial operations.

Sansaw Pigs

A joint venture with north Shropshire organic farmers Nick and Chris Taylor, Sansaw Pigs is a limited company with 50 per cent owned by Sansaw Estate and 50 per cent owned by the Taylors. The team has established a solid reputation in less than two years' trading, with 165 sows producing 3,200 fat pigs a year.

In line with both the commercial and social criteria of the estate, Sansaw provided the land and security for the borrowing while the Taylors provided the skills and marketing knowledge for the products. Despite a debilitating outbreak of Foot-and-Mouth (Aphthous Fever) and a huge drop in the market, the venture has still made a reasonable profit. The vision is to deliver exceptional levels of animal welfare and husbandry in an extensive organic farming system in order to consistently produce the best organic pork possible. It has led to contracts with some of the best retailers and gastronomes in the country. World-leading restaurateur Raymond Blanc visited the Estate's pig operation in April 2009, while one of London's finest chefs, Tom Aikens, lent his support in 2008.

The business has diversified as a result of using the Taylors' skills and now produces 1,000 tonnes of potatoes and 300 tonnes of carrots for the supermarkets.

Sansaw Cattle

When James Jenkinson Bibby first arrived in 1862 he established a pedigree herd of traditional horned Hereford cattle. However, during the Great Depression of the 1930s and the lean years that followed, numbers were phased out. While the emotion behind Sansaw's decision to bring back the famous Herefords is obvious, the aim is to slowly build up the herd to 100 breeding cows and turn nostalgia into profit.

Sansaw Sheep

Another reminder of the days of James Jenkinson Bibby's custodianship, the distinctive Shropshire Sheep have also returned to Sansaw's landscape, bringing with them their trademark black legs and wool-covered faces. Producing both great meat and a high-quality fleece, the Shropshires are in great demand both here and abroad.

Employment

There are more people employed on the Sansaw Estate, both directly and indirectly, than there were during James Jenkinson Bibby's era in the late 19th century. The Stables house a variety of individual businesses while the Pavilions is already home to a firm of leading property agents.

The Estate Office houses the core management team which includes a lettings and marketing manager, estate secretary and property manager.

A foreman, two skilled carpenters and a ground-worker form Sansaw's maintenance team, while four members of the Brettell family manage the Sansaw farming operation.

Two gardeners, two housekeepers and a retired head groom help look after the estate's main properties, Sansaw Hall and Alderton House.

A non-salaried board of trustees oversee the best operations of Sansaw. It is comprised of a businessman, a lawyer and an investment banker who bring different layers of expertise to the operation.

Economic stability

The huge volatility in commodity prices can have serious knock-on effects, both on day-to-day operations and long-term investment. Often it is not the strength of fluctuation which causes the greatest problems, but more the degree making farm business planning extremely difficult. Sansaw's diverse base, plus its strong relationships with partners, neighbours, local authorities and banks, helps insulate it to some extent from economic uncertainty.

J. Stephens

The distinctive Shropshire sheep have returned to the Sansaw landscape.

Policy

A estable economic policy is crucial. While the effect of the global recession has been significant, those planning for the long-term have found it even more difficult. Britain's current short term policy based on politics rather than long term stewardship make planning beyond the short term extremely difficult as, unlike governments, estates will be around for generations not years. Sansaw calls for governments to engage in longer term strategic planning for the benefit of the countryside and those responsible for managing it.

J. Stephens

Ed Brettell - Tenant and Farm Manager for Sansaw Farms.

Sansaw (United Kingdom)

MODERN RURAL LIVING

Arable fields with oak trees.

The phrase "modern rural living" underpins the wide range of operations, activities and business that interact on the Sansaw Estate, which offer an alternative way of life that allows people to enjoy the traditional values of Britain's leading country estates without compromising on the latest technology, infrastructure and design. The vision sets out to offer a modern rural lifestyle; encouraging people to live, work, eat, play and relax amidst the simplicity and natural beauty of the countryside.

Although some of the activities at Sansaw generate minimal income, nurturing communities and businesses is seen as beneficial for the long term health of the estate and its surrounding villages. The estate's aspiration is to be the best possible custodians of the countryside, acting as fair and reasonable landlords and enabling future generations to profit socially, environmentally and economically from Sansaw's built and natural environment.

Sansaw has redefined rural living for the 21st century in the same way its ancestors did for the 19th century. Breaking with convention, its owners

J. Steph

brought in a branding company to help come up with a catch-all identity for the estate. The idea was to bring a consistency to the entire operation – a bond and an image that cemented the residential, commercial and agricultural objectives.

The Brand Experience Consultancy was recruited in 2007 with SEA Design subsequently employed to complete all the creative graphics. Branding the estate took some convincing. Robin admits to being less than happy with the concept at the beginning but it has quickly gained a solid reputation and will continue to do so as Sansaw sets out a model for like-minded operations throughout the globe.

Future

Sansaw's future lies in its own hands. Its renovation and modernisation programme, coupled with its respect of the environment and contrasting farming operations, mean the risk has been spread but the rewards remain fruitful. The recent transition from father to son has been instrumental in the estate's continued resurgence and underlines the sense of custodianship and stewardship.

Each generation at Sansaw has known both hardship and crisis. However, the ability to adapt coupled with the determination to improve means there is a bright future ahead for both the estate and its incumbents.

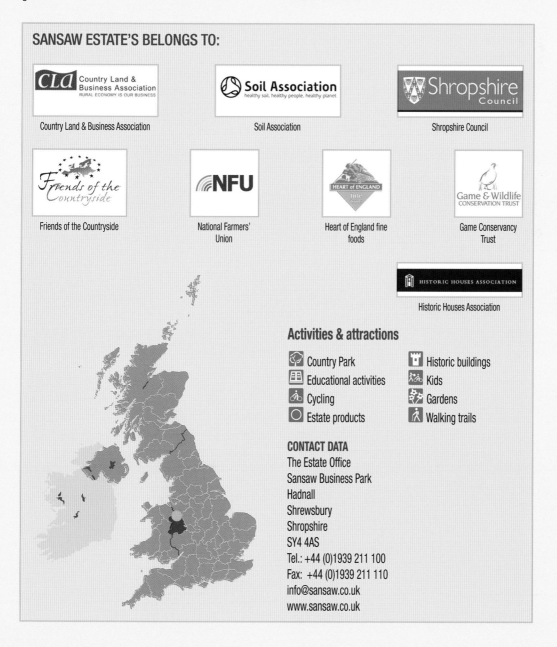

SANSAW ESTATE'S BELONGS TO:

Country Land & Business Association

Soil Association

Shropshire Council

Friends of the Countryside

National Farmers' Union

Heart of England fine foods

Game Conservancy Trust

Historic Houses Association

Activities & attractions

- Country Park
- Educational activities
- Cycling
- Estate products
- Historic buildings
- Kids
- Gardens
- Walking trails

CONTACT DATA
The Estate Office
Sansaw Business Park
Hadnall
Shrewsbury
Shropshire
SY4 4AS
Tel.: +44 (0)1939 211 100
Fax: +44 (0)1939 211 110
info@sansaw.co.uk
www.sansaw.co.uk

Seafield & Strathspey

Atlantic

Location: Scotland, United Kingdom.
Surface: Seafield Estate: 12,250 ha.
Strathspey Estate: 21,790 ha.

Seafield Estate

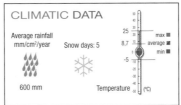

CLIMATIC DATA

Average rainfall
mm/cm²/year   Snow days: 5

600 mm   Temperature

25
8,7   max ■
average ■
min ■
-5
(°C)

Strathspey Estate

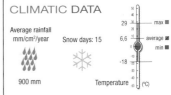

CLIMATIC DATA

Average rainfall
mm/cm²/year   Snow days: 15

900 mm   Temperature

29   max ■
6,6   average ■
min ■
-18
(°C)

SUMMARY

Seafield Estate has the Moray Firth to the north and, apart from Edingight Estate on the south, is surrounded mainly by villages and privately owned farms.

Strathspey Estate is surrounded by moorland, upland farmland and forests. The estate adjoins other traditional private estates: Cawdor, Muckrach, Glen Beg, Lochindorb, Braemoray, Dunphail, Tulchan, Abernethy, Pityoulish, Rothiemurchus, Kinrara, Clune, Corrybrough and Balnespick. The estate is within the Cairngorms National Park which is the largest National Park in the United Kingdom. The Park was established in 2000 because of the unique wildlife, plants, moorlands, forests, rivers, lochs and arctic mountain landscape of the area.

Both Seafield Estate and Strathspey Estate have been in the ownership of the Seafield family for generations. The Late Countess of Seafield gifted most of the Seafield Estate to her son, now the 13th Earl of Seafield, in 1953, and the Strathspey Estate was placed in trust on her death. Strathspey Estate is now managed by a trust as arranged by her grandson Viscount Reidhaven, in 2002.

The lands of Castle Grant, Kinveachy and parts of Abernethy, which now form the Strathspey Estate, have been Clan Grant territory since the thirteenth century. In 1735 Sir Ludovick Grant of Grant married Lady Margaret Ogilvie, the eldest daughter of the second Earl of Seafield. Their son Sir James Grant of Grant, "the good Sir James", was responsible in 1766 for founding the town of Grantown-on-Spey.

The Seafield family has always taken an active interest in the management of the estate and this personal involvement continues to the present day.

Seafield & Strathspey Estate

Both Seafield Estate and Strathspey Estate have been
in the ownership of the Seafield family since the 13th century.

The Earl of Seafield
Seafield Coat of Arms

HISTORY

When the 5th Earl of Seafield assumed the name of Ogilvie in addition to his paternal name of Grant in 1811, the family name then reflected a connection with two areas of Scotland: the area around Cullen on the Moray Firth and Strathspey with its clan background.

The Ogilvies in Banffshire

Banffshire has been the home of the Ogilvies since 1440, when they moved from the parish of Glamis in Angus. Until about 1511, when the family moved to The Castle of Cullen House, Findlater Castle had been the family residence, and the ruins can be seen on the rugged coast between Cullen and Sandend.

Cullen House is a fine example of many Scottish castles in which the influence of French architecture is evident. After the Reformation, landowners became more conscious of their surroundings and in 1820 the 5th Earl of Findlater demolished

the old town of Cullen, which was built around Cullen House and the Old Church and planned beautiful new policies and grounds. The townspeople were moved to a newly designed town, built in a location nearer the coast. It is evident today that Cullen is a planned town. The Seafield family had previously been responsible for founding New Keith in 1751 as the first Georgian planned settlement in the North of Scotland, bringing a key advance in the economy.

A few hundred metres from Cullen House on the site of the old village stands Old Cullen, a Dower House, Georgian in design. Formerly the Factor's house, it is now the residence of the Earl and Countess of Seafield. Having moved to this comfortable home, the Earl secured the future of Cullen House by selling it for conversion to a number of prestige tower houses and flats.

The Grants of Strathspey

The first Grant to establish himself in Strathspey was John le Grant, who acquired Inverallan in

Sir James with Jean Duff, Lady Grant. (Portrait painter, David Allan 1766).

Johnstone Photographers

1316. Strathspey is the middle third of the valley of the River Spey. It extends from southwest of Aviemore some 40 km down the valley to Advie, above it is Badenoch and below is the area known as Speyside.

Castle Grant has probably always belonged to the Grants and was originally built in the early 16th century. Formerly known as Freuchie, Ballachastell or Balloch Castle, it was given the name of Castle Grant in a Crown Charter in 1694 and subsequent alterations were added to the south front.

Grantown was founded in 1765 by James (from 1773, Sir James Grant of Grant), the village being marked out in lots on a barren moor. He was affectionately known as "the good Sir James" after he responded to a severe crop failure and famine in the late 1700's by selling his fine Edinburgh townhouse to buy and distribute grain among the starving people of Strathspey. More than any other person, he brought Strathspey into the modern world during the half century or so in which he administered and guided it from Castle Grant (1763-1811). He promoted the greatest improvement in living conditions there has ever been in this part of the Highlands. At that time, much of the old natural Scots pine forests, which had covered Strathspey from time immemorial, were in decline. Sir James cleared, drained, and planted much of the derelict land adjacent to the town and it is recorded that the plants used in these early plantations were raised from seed gathered in the natural Scots pine forests of Abernethy, and are therefore lineal descendants of the old Strathspey strain. The family today, over 230 years later, continues to be a large woodland owner.

Notable family members

With such a long history and so many influential family members, it is difficult to single out those who should be mentioned specifically. For the most part, the proprietors have devoted themselves quietly to running their estates for the good of the local people and employees, very conscious that they were the largest employers in the area. Some have however had a high profile in the public eye by reason of legend or historical event.

"The good Sir James", referred to above, was the epitome of a Highland Chief, who vastly improved his clanspeople's lives, fed them in time of

James 4th Earl of Findlater and 1st of Seafield. (Portrait painter, Sir Godfrey Kneller, 18th century).

Johnstone Photographers

famine, and provided employment to enable them to avoid the waves of emigration which so hurt the Highlands from time to time.

The 1st Earl of Seafield was Chancellor of Scotland at the time of the Union of the Scottish and English Parliaments in 1707. His signature is on the Act of Union in Westminster. He had a spectacular political career beginning as Commissioner for the Royal Burgh of Cullen in 1689. In 1693 he became Sheriff Principal of Banffshire and Solicitor General, and in 1700 he was made Lord High Commissioner to the General Assembly, becoming Lord High Chancellor of Scotland in 1702.

James, 6th Earl of Findlater and 3rd Earl of Seafield, is noted for his hugely important improving career as Lord Deskford and was the most influential "Improver" of his Age in the North-East of Scotland. He very sadly committed suicide in 1770 and there is no evidence to support the legend that he murdered his Factor.

The family influence extends beyond the shores of Britain to the United States of America where a family descendent, General Ulysses Simpson Grant, became the 18th President. Earlier, General James Grant, a grandson of the "Highland King" (Ludovick Grant, last of Freuchie and first of Grant, c. 1650 - 1716), was the first royal governor of British colonial Florida (1763-73). He is reputed to have practically created the colony once it was secured from Spain at the end of the Seven Years' War.

DESCRIPTION

Land and landscape

On Seafield Estate

The underlying geology is Dalradian and Moinian. From Buckie to Banff, the coast shows a rich diversity of rock types. Quartz, mica and calcareous schists are common. Raised beaches are an interesting feature of this landscape which inland is generally low and undulating with the quartzite Bin, Durn and Knock hills forming important landmarks.

The forest soils are mainly gleys with areas of podzol, particularly in the vicinity of the Bin Hill and Fordyce Hill. More recent planting has taken place on ex-agricultural soils.

On Strathspey Estate

The geology is of metamorphic origin, mainly schist. Granite forms the higher ground as large masses and outcrops. This is friable and forms poor quality, light, sandy soils.

The Spey Valley is of old red sandstone origin and shows extensive deposits in the form of mounds and ridges of coarse gravel and boulders.

The forest soils are predominantly peaty podzols.

The river Spey runs through the Strathspey Estate and is reputedly the fastest flowing river in Scotland.

Strathspey Estate,
Inverness-shire.

Description of the most important economic activities:

The coastal Seafield Estate area benefits from the influence of the Gulf Stream and enjoys relatively moderate temperatures for its latitude. Land use is mainly divided between reasonable sized arable holdings and commercial forestry. On the Strathspey Estate there are upland farms, mature forestry plantations and, for the field sport enthusiast, fishing, hunting and shooting. Strathspey is renowned for its wonderfully diverse range of wildlife, from the riverside flats with Otter *(Lutra lutra)*, Green Plover *(Vanellus vanellus)*, Oystercatcher *(Haematopus ostralegus)* and Osprey *(Pandion haliaetus)* through woodlands with Sparrowhawk *(Accipiter nisus)*, Kestrel *(Falco tinnunculus)*, Buzzard *(Buteo buteo)*, Great Spotted Woodpecker *(Dendrocopos major)*, Capercaillie *(Tetrao urogallus)* and Black Grouse *(Tetrao tetrix)*. The open moorlands continue with their abundance of Golden Plover *(Pluvialis apricaria)*, Merlin *(Falco columbarius)* and Golden Eagle *(Aquila chrysaetos)*, Pine Marten *(Martes martes)*, Fox *(Vulpes vulpes)*, Wildcat *(Felis sylvestris grampia)*, Red Grouse *(Lagopus lagopus scoticus)*, Roe Deer *(Capreolus capreolus)*, Red Deer *(Cervus elaphus scoticus)*, to mention but a few, making this a perfect destination for all wildlife enthusiasts.

Farming

Around 11,300 ha of agricultural land are let to tenant farmers by the family estates with the

Red deer stag in Caledonian pine forest.

D. Dugan

main in – hand farming operation managing around 2,500 ha of arable land along the Moray Firth coastal region. This is a specialist spring barley cereal growing operation supporting the Scottish whisky industry with rotation including winter wheat, barley and oil seed rape to spread sowing and harvest activity. 10,900 tonnes of grain are handled each year and there is a capability to store 9,700 tonnes in purpose-built facilities.

Forestry Management

Commercial woodland on Seafield Estate is predominately Sitka spruce which grows on a 50 year rotation and is intended, mainly, for the UK construction market. In the course of a growing cycle, a number of thinnings may be made to allow the better development of the crop. Much of the timber at Strathspey is native Scots pine which has a much longer growing cycle. All of the family woodlands are certified under the UK Woodland Assurance Standard (UK-

WAS). Compliance with UKWAS involves adhering to agreed principles and practices of sustainable forest management, from initial planning to harvesting. UKWAS is recognised by the Forest Stewardship Council (FSC), which is an international organisation that brings people together to find solutions to promote responsible stewardship of the world's forests.

The Scottish Grouse is the quintessential shooting quarry.

Sporting Tourism

The Strathspey Estate presents some of the finest and highest quality of Scottish sport available amid breathtaking scenery and in the company of professional gamekeepers, deerstalkers and fishing ghillies, who are only too willing to share the knowledge of their sport with guests.

The wide variety of sport available makes a visit to Strathspey Estate a unique experience. Sport includes river fishing for salmon and sea trout, or loch fishing for brown and rainbow trout. For the hunter there is grouse, pheasant, pigeon, partridge, geese, duck, snipe, woodcock, hare and rabbit shooting. For the deer stalker there are roe deer on the low ground and Scotland's magnificent red deer on the open hill.

Traditional Highland lodge accommodation of the highest standard is available with all sport or simply as a relaxing holiday destination where guests can enjoy some of the other leisure activities. This may include visits to nearby Loch Ness, Culloden battlefield or a host of highland castles and distilleries. Other facilities available locally include golf, tennis, horse riding, water sports and hill walking.

Much of the Strathspey Estate is designated as being important under the European Natura 2000 Directive. The Estate management policy has always acknowledged the conservation value of the area and seeks to manage the commercial sporting activities in balance with conservation designations.

Renewable Energy

A windfarm near Banff on Seafield Estate involving seven turbines was officially opened in October 2006. The official duties were carried out by 92 year old Paddy Lyttle, who was a member of the RAF maintenance ground crew at the wartime airfield in 1945. He performed the opening by smashing a bottle of whisky against one of the turbine masts, with a Tornado from 15 Squadron RAF Lossiemouth also performing a flypast. Work began on the windfarm project in 2001 which is estimated to have a life of 25 years, and produce enough energy for 8500 homes - the equivalent of all the properties at Banff, Whitehills and Portsoy and the surrounding area.

It is owned and operated by Boyndie Wind Energy Limited, a subsidiary of Milan-based Falck Renewables. Boyndie is the first windfarm community scheme to exist in Scotland. Falck made a £750,000 stake in the project available through a share offer in 2006, with investors able to invest a minimum of £250 and a maximum of £20,000 in £1 shares in the venture. The offer, which closed last August, was fully subscribed.

Aimed primarily at local people, this means that they are benefiting directly from the siting of the windfarm in their locality. Falck Renewables' Business Development Director, Charles Williams, praised the local community's support for the scheme, and expressed his enthusiasm for Boyndie as the first co-operative of this type in Scotland.

Windfarm at Boyndie, Banff.

THE ESTATE'S SUSTAINABLE DEVELOPMENT POLICY

For generations the family estates have been involved in integrated land use. Well before "sustainable development" became a fashionable management objective, the Seafield family embraced the concept of balancing local conservation, social and economic drivers. However, without doubt, in the twenty first century the interaction of these elements is more challenging and complex. Today the land manager must recognise that the public have a legitimate interest in how private land is managed and, when thought through, there is often a synergy between economic, environmental recreational and cultural issues. The estate considers that land is a multi use asset. Wherever possible, in conjunction with our business operations, we strive to enrich the natural habitat and biodiversity within the footprint of the estate operations. The challenge is to show that our businesses can integrate comfortably with nature and we believe we are achieving this objective in a number of areas. Long term private family ownership of land brings a special committed stewardship by each generation and is financially the most efficient way of securing the maintenance and enrichment of conservation and heritage assets.

Farming in a Nitrate Vulnerable Zone

The application of lime and trace elements used to be calculated on the average requirements of any particular field. For over ten years, arable soils have been analysed using GPS references allowing lime and trace element applications to be accurately applied according to the specific requirements of every sector of each field. This process allows an even growth and yields across the fields, speeds up harvesting, gives cost efficiency and protects the environment from excessive applications. With most of the in-hand farming area on Seafield Estate being situated within a Nitrate Vulnerable Zone, farming is now complex but modern technology allows farm income to be maximised while practising sustainable management systems. More than ever, the estate appreciates that it is a producer of eco-system services. We are involved in the supply of renewable energy and quality food products while seeking to protect water courses

Aviemore Photographic

and improve the natural environment for future generations. The estate is privileged to have such a challenging responsibility.

Fishing for salmon on the Spey river.

River Spey European Natura 2000 Site

The estate manages over 34 km of salmon fishing on the river Spey. The catchment area has been designated a Special Area of Conservation (SAC) and the protected species includes Atlantic Salmon *(Salmo salar)*, Sea Lamprey *(Petromyzon marinus)*, Fresh Water Pearl Mussel *(Margaritifera margaritifera)* and Otter *(Lutra lutra)*. In many fishing beats of the Spey river, good salmon fishing is dependent on pools where the fish gather as they push up the river to the spawning grounds in the upper reaches. Now that the European Natura 2000 designation is in place, it is no longer possible to obtain permission to clear silt from these pools for fear of damaging the protected species. With Spey salmon fishing making such a huge contribution to the economy of the valley, riparian owners have to appreciate that preservation of the conservation asset for the public good is as important as their own economic interest and the employment that the river sustains.

Kinveachy European Natura 2000 Site

This area, just north-west of Aviemore in the Strathspey Estate, demonstrates admirably the complex issues faced by the modern land manager. An area of 2,849 ha has been designated a

Scottish Crossbill
(Loxia curvirostra scotica).

Kinveachy, in the Strathspey Estate, is also a Special Protection Area because of its significant populations of birds including capercaillie and Scottish crossbill.

Special Area of Conservation (SAC) in respect of the Caledonian pinewood forest and moorland. The structure of the woodland is variable, with dense stands of mature woodland separated by open moorland with scattered trees, extensive juniper and bog woodland habitats. It is one of the major tracts of Caledonian forest in Strathspey and considered third largest in the area. It is also a Natura 2000 Special Protection Area (SPA) because of its significant bird assemblages including Capercaillie *(Tetrao urogallus)* and the Scottish Crossbill *(Loxia curvirostra scotica)*. The Scottish Crossbill is Britain's only endemic bird species and around 13% of the total population is on Kinveachy. The open heather moorland, itself an internationally important habitat, is commercially managed for red

grouse shooting and, being at the eastern edge of the Monadhliath Mountains, is a natural wintering area for deer as they seek protection from the prevailing wind on the high ground. This leads to grazing pressure and, ultimately, prevents natural regeneration of the pinewoods.

Traditionally, regeneration would be achieved through fencing deer out of the woodland areas. However, that is not an option on this rich and diverse site, as bird strikes on fencing can cause unacceptable levels of mortality to red grouse, black grouse and capercaillie. A further difficulty is that fencing deer out of the SAC/SPA would cause even greater grazing pressure on the surrounding area, which is itself part of a designated Site of Special Scientific Interest (SSSI) covering 5,335 ha in total.

The owner of these exceptional lands has great responsibilities as steward of assets of such national and international importance. At Kinveachy, the family has had to make serious decisions. Red deer stalking generates a very good income annually, especially when linked with lodge accommodation and other game shooting. The owner of these assets of European significance must manage them responsibly and there are often additional costs involved in doing this. The estate has been fortunate in obtaining financial support for the costs involved in reducing winter densities of deer from 27 per sq km to 4 per sq km, which will allow the regeneration project to develop.

Owning and managing these special European assets within Biodiversity Action Plans is a special privilege demanding that every commercial activity is carefully planned and executed. Many estate woodland operations are designed to improve habitat for capercaillie. Existing deer fencing beyond the Natura 2000 area has been marked with high visibility barrier netting to limit collisions by capercaillie, and dead wood has been created to enrich the biodiversity. Some activities are directed at increasing the colonies of Wood Ants *(Formica rufa)*. Predator control also features highly to protect capercaillie and other ground nesting birds.

The philosophy of future estate management

As a reaction to past failures in land management generally, today, more than ever, there are many single issue pressure groups. Their views are important in identifying where past emphasis may not have been as balanced as it could have

been, but they themselves can skew future decisions and replicate lack of balance in decision making. Helpfully, even in Scotland with a history of political debate on land ownership issues, it is becoming recognised that land ownership is of far less importance than land use and good management. While politicians and pressure groups are often short term thinkers, estate owners make decisions for the long term and intend to pass on their assets in better or at least as good condition as when they received them.

The Seafield family appreciates how important it is to have an economic return from land use. Financial sustainability is the platform from which public benefits are provided and local conservation and social improvements underpinned. The great challenge is to balance these outputs and to be dynamic in delivery, whilst moving with changing public expectations whether generated locally or by European Directives.

Land use constantly changes against the background of many drivers. Today we have renewable energy opportunities in windfarms, like Boyndie on the Seafield Estate, and rental from mobile telephone masts that we could not have anticipated a few years ago. This ability to respond as enablers of government policy often results in land being

managed for many uses at the same time. The sporting grouse moor will often have sheep grazing and perhaps windfarm energy production as well as satisfying the recreational pursuits of walkers and other access takers. Strathspey Estate recently opened a natural burial ground overlooking the River Spey. This beautiful location provides an eco-friendly burial opportunity with no disturbance to the idyllic natural surroundings.

There is considerable satisfaction in developing a management philosophy that allows land use to balance public and family objectives. This requires land-based businesses to operate in harmony with nature over the long term. The great challenge, as landowners become increasingly more understanding of their business impact on nature, is that they reposition themselves to ensure that their economic return is maintained while any environmental collateral damage is eliminated.

It is estate policy to increasingly embrace the local public by distributing newsletters, holding open days and estate visits with a view to integrating the business into the communities of which we are part. A general estate website allows a degree of transparency of operations and provides information that can be utilised by school projects and other interested parties.

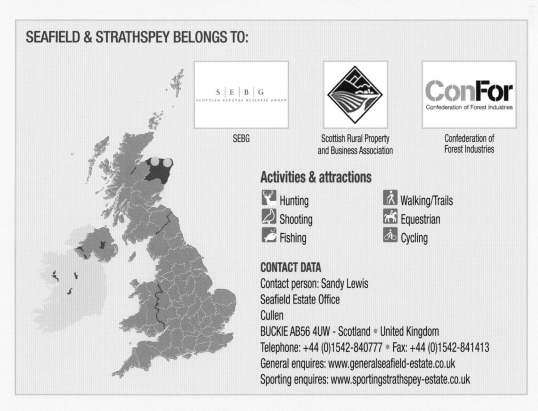

SEAFIELD & STRATHSPEY BELONGS TO:

SEBG

Scottish Rural Property and Business Association

Confederation of Forest Industries

Activities & attractions

- Hunting
- Shooting
- Fishing
- Walking/Trails
- Equestrian
- Cycling

CONTACT DATA
Contact person: Sandy Lewis
Seafield Estate Office
Cullen
BUCKIE AB56 4UW - Scotland • United Kingdom
Telephone: +44 (0)1542-840777 • Fax: +44 (0)1542-841413
General enquires: www.generalseafield-estate.co.uk
Sporting enquires: www.sportingstrathspey-estate.co.uk

Theme 2

Landscape and nature

LANDSCAPE AND NATURE

His Grace the Duke of Westminster

This chapter entitled "Landscape and Nature" encapsulates the remarkable contribution that private owners have made to our managed environment over the centuries. These environments have not been crated by "conservationists", planning authorities, Brussels directives or any of the other multitudes of people and organisations who think they know better. They have been created and managed by individuals and families who have a deep love and instinctive attachment to the countryside. Often with considerable personal and financial hardship, they have battled not only to preserve the environment but also to preserve jobs and the way of life that goes hand in hand with good estate management.

As Europe becomes more urbanised there is a temptation for politicians to legislate to turn our countryside into a playground, a place for recreation or a museum with no prospects for our young people who wish to live and work in the same way as their forebears. We are often told that with good science comes good management. It is surprising therefore that there were no scientists when these landscapes were created. Why is it that scientists have become the new land managers? Sitting in their laboratories, their word is now gospel and governments are legislating accordingly. I can find no evidence during the 30 years that I have managed my estates where science has made a lasting contribution to the debate. On the contrary in many cases it has cost the taxpayer large sums of money on inadvisable projects that withered and died on the vine of incompetence.

The natural environment has been created over centuries and as man has increasingly added to the pressures so nature has adapted. However we must not take nature's patience for granted and in order for many of our species to survive and prosper we must learn that they should be allowed to do so without our interference. "The peace of nature and of the innocent creatures of God seems to be secure and deep, only so long as the presence of man and his restless and unquiet spirit are not there to trouble its sanctity. *Tomas De Quincey, "Preliminary Confessions" (1821- 56)"*.

Many of our "conservationists" and legislators have become myopic over "single species" issues. They approach conservation on the basis of preserving this or that animal or bird, without understanding the balance of nature. It is crucial to understand the food chain from top to bottom and the importance of managing that food chain well. Sadly they continue to plough on with the construction of roads, wind farms, housing estates and other "facilities" that our 21st century urban society demands on sensitive and green field sites.

The following pages amply demonstrate an understanding and sensitivity towards the way these estates are managed. They also demonstrate that nature is a complicated jigsaw; lose one piece and you lose the entire picture; what is more you have lost the fragile foundations, maintained with love, care and sensitivity, upon which nature is built.

I have to confess that in my country, and I suspect in many others, government has rewarded the remarkable contribution that landowners have made over so many years with indifference and often an outright rejection of our views. It saddens me that all too often one has to go to court to prove one's case, when dialogue would have sufficed. Too often political imperatives, rather than common sense, are the driving force.

I am not a "green" or a "conservationist"; I regard such a label as something of an insult. I am a Countryman by birth and inclination and I have endeavoured to manage the balance of nature, using the land as a means of production, as a means of providing high quality food at a profit, whilst at the same time ensuring the countryside is managed in a way that allows wildlife to flourish.

These two aims are not always comfortable bedfellows and the balance is often difficult to maintain, but it is something that must be achieved. If we do not have profitability there will be no jobs, we will not be able to sustain our communities and we will see the indigenous country people leaving for the towns and being replaced by wealthy incomers wishing to own holiday cottages, tearing the living heart out of our rural communities with the inevitable result of school and shop closures and a way of life gone forever.

In my country in the 19th century we saw a massive shift of population to the urban areas during the industrial revolution. However, landowners in those days stabilised the population by building villages, bringing in new methods of farming and investing heavily in infrastructure. This proud legacy we carry forward today. Landowners are re-silient, determined and proud. I am confident that we will carry the torch of our forefathers into the next generations. It will, however, require flexibility of mind, determination and a powerful belief that what we do is right.

The land is a giver and sustainer of life and must be nurtured. As Milton said in Paradise Lost: "Accuse not nature! She hath done her part, Do thou but thine". I feel a strong sense of obligation and responsibility towards what I have been given and, as the "caretaker" for this generation, I have tried to ensure that I have positioned my estates in such a fashion that they will endure and prosper in the years ahead.

In 1963 John F Kennedy made a speech on the responsibilities of citizenship. His words are apt here...

"Our privileges can be no greater than our obligations. The protection of our rights can endure no longer than the performance of our responsibilities".

CHALLENGES AND POLICY FOR LAND USE IN THE EUROPEAN UNION IN THE 21st CENTURY[1]

Allan Buckwell

SUMMARY

The world must double food production during the next four decades but with lower environmental impact than in the last four decades, a challenge which is heightened by climate change. The Common Agricultural Policy (CAP) must evolve to a policy for Food and Environmental Security with a budget adequate to the scale of the task faced.

INTRODUCTION

For the first half century of its existence the CAP has proved to be a robust, and highly adaptable, policy for European agriculture through a period of unprecedented change and it must continue to adapt. Given that farming, forestry and environmental land management are long-term, and the private businesses conducting them have to think in intergenerational terms, the CAP also has to try and maintain some stability. This will be a tough balance to strike.

TWO CHALLENGES FOR AGRICULTURE AND RURAL AREAS: FOOD AND ENVIRONMENT

The Food Challenge
The global food challenge is simple to state: it is to feed the growing human population, and preferably better than we are currently achieving. Total world grain production is still growing but grain production per person peaked in 1985 and has been slowly declining since. Al-

so, as countries get richer they consume more eggs, dairy produce and meat, so the demand for grain tends to grow even faster. Future growth of food output depends on the cropland available. The global area of agricultural land is 4.9 billion hectares. Estimates of how much more land could be brought into cultivation vary from 0.5 billion hectares to 1.8 billion hectares. However, much of this land will have lower productivity and converting much of it will involve significant negative climatic and biodiversity effects. This implies that the intensity of farming will have to rise. It also suggests that the EU should expect to be a growing net exporter of grain.

Two critical factors that affect productivity are soil loss (for which the data are not adequate) and water availability. In the case of water we are now at a stage where, globally, 70% of water pumped from underground or diverted from rivers is used for agriculture. Crop production is highly demanding of water; e.g. 1000 to 3000 litres of water is 'used' to produce 1 kg rice, and livestock production can take even more. The FAO's Director General has estimated that by 2025, 1.8 billion people will be living in regions with absolute water scarcity, and two-thirds of the world population could be living under water stressed conditions. Increasing efficiency of water use in agriculture is therefore critically important.

The Environmental Challenge
The success of economic development in the last two centuries in raising living standards,

---

[1] This article is an abridged version of the paper by this author published in June 2008 by the European Landowners Organisation, the 21st Century Land Use Challenge.

health and longevity for a rapidly growing population has come at considerable environmental cost. The expansion of urban areas and the transport infrastructure which connects them; the exploitation of forests, then coal, oil, gas and minerals; together with the increase of cultivated and grazed areas and changes in agricultural technology substituting mechanisation, fertilisers and crop protection products for labour, have all dug into natural habitats and brought about a fall in biodiversity.

There is international action in the form of the Convention on Biodiversity which seeks to reduce this loss. The EU takes the problem seriously with its Habitats and Birds Directives and a range of other policy actions are in place.

Soil organic matter in most of our farmed areas is poor. This exacerbates soil losses from erosion, and there are indications of loss of vital trace elements. Water quality is also suffering from the impacts of human activity and Europe now has in place the highly ambitious objective of bringing all its water bodies into good ecological status.

Our cultural heritage is also threatened by economic development and changes in technology and scale of farming. The landscapes and features which societies treasure are of immense importance for the general health and wellbeing of society.

Now add Climate Change to the twin challenges

Depending on the collective global response, climate change will increase average temperatures between 2 and 5 degrees Celsius this century. Climate change is expected to further reduce access to safe drinking water and to increase the risk of famine. The increased incidence of extreme weather events will also increase the volatility of crop production. However, not all the effects are negative. The combined effects of higher temperatures and greater CO_2 concentrations can increase crop yields. These impacts will vary enormously by crop and by region. They will also depend greatly on the adaptive skills of scientists, farmers and foresters.

In the tropics where crops are already near their maximum temperature tolerance and in the large areas where non-irrigated dry-land agriculture predominates, yields will decrease markedly. The mid-latitude developed countries – the USA, Europe and Japan – seem relatively less affected than most other parts of the world. In addition, they have the governance and industrial structures, the technology and the research capacity to cope. It could be concluded that they therefore have both the capacity and the moral responsibility to increase their net exports of food as this century progresses.

A particular focus on Bio-energy

Land management is an important contributor of greenhouse gas (GHG) emissions. However, farming and forestry can also contribute significantly to the mitigation of climate change. First, they can capture carbon in soils and trees. Second, they can help other sectors reduce their emissions by enabling energy and material substitution by providing biogas, biomass and biofuels to replace fossil fuels and enabling timber and fibres such as hemp to replace materials such as concrete, brick and steel.

It is certain that during the next couple of decades, the world will divert more crop output into production of biofuels. It is already happening in Brazil and the USA, and the EU has decided on ambitious renewable energy targets. This is bound to raise some agricultural prices. To some extent these price rises will limit the growth of some renewable energy streams. There is no sense in producing biofuels from crops if it is not a cost effective way of reducing transport emissions. There are also exciting prospects for other bio-energy sources. Woody biomass crops, for instance, can utilise soils and plants unsuitable for food production, and can be part of energy systems for renewable heat. And biogas can help us deal with waste, reduce pollution and recycle nutrients, as well as deliver renewable energy. Second generation biomass processes, and use of transgenics, will enable us to develop plants and processes to utilise the energy of the whole crop, leaving the grain for food use, as well as transform woody materials in bio-refineries, delivering both renewable energy and a wide range of high value outputs like biodegradable plastics.

Why must EU policy rise to these challenges?

It makes sense that EU policy should play a key role in rising to the food and environment challenges. First, it seems sensible to build on the last half century of carefully constructed supra-national agreements. Second, nearly all aspects of Europe's natural and cultural environment cross national boundaries, and because of the existence of the single market a large part of environmental policy is designed and agreed at an EU level.

The changing nature and purpose of Europe's key land management policy, the CAP, might be better explained to the public by referring to food and environmental security. This would allow us to move on from the negative associations which the CAP arouses amongst many interest groups. Linking food and environment can also bring together groups in civil society who have been more often in the past at each others' throats; farmers and other land managers and environmental NGOs. The challenge is to turn the whole mindset of the public, politicians, and land managers to create a new rural policy fit for the 21st century – with food security and the preservation of our natural environment at its core.

Lessons for Policy – the elements of Food and Environmental Policy

The core of the food security policy must be to protect the long term food production capacity of the EU. This refers of course to its agricultural land but also to the knowledge, skills and commitment of its farmers and other land managers, the complex infrastructure which characterises the modern food chain, and also to research, development and extension capacity. The long term aim of such policy is to feed the European population and contribute to feeding parts of the rest of the world.

Farmers will say: "this is no problem at all, give us remunerative prices, free us from unnecessary bureaucratic shackles, and we'll do the job!" The problem is how? We are still struggling to find the mix of instruments which create the best guarantee of food security, namely profitable farming. This requires the right balance of domestic agricultural support measures, border measures, competition policy and regulation.

Some of the elements of the policy are well understood. They are measures to:

- Improve food productivity and competitiveness;
- Stimulate research, development & extension;
- Confront and answer citizens' concerns about new biotechnologies, enabling them to be deployed to help improve yields, and combat disease and drought;
- Help farmers integrate farming and the environment, to reduce pollution;
- Encourage them to share resources and work together to try and offset imbalanced market power in the food chain;
- Help raise product quality, differentiating products by locality, traditional breeds, and farming systems; that is, improve marketing;
- Ensure food safety, and
- Provide risk management tools to enable farmers to deal with environmental, market and policy volatility;

The aims of *environmental security policy* are to achieve the food security goals but to do so while enhancing the environment. This will involve sometimes uncomfortable trade-offs between ensuring acceptable living standards and the preservation of environmental capital.

For centuries private land managers have found ways of simultaneously delivering society's food needs as well as stewarding the environment. However, as the pressures to produce more food and energy increase, and yet with smaller negative impact on the environment, we will have to deploy our full ingenuity to deliver what society wants. With imagination, some environmental services can be incorporated into food products. Other services, such as flood protection and carbon sequestration can in principle be traded between businesses or local authorities and the land managers. However, other services will have to be paid for out of public expenditures. Indeed the second Pillar of the Common Agricultural Policy is being developed to do just this.

A great deal more work remains to be done to develop the policies for Food and Environmental Security which will incentivise the right balance between these competing land uses: food, energy and environmental and cultural landscape services. It is also essential that the appropriate scale of public resources are made available to deliver what society wants.

The estates in this book beautifully illustrate how land managers can deliver when the signals are right.

Azienda Agricola Monte Arcosu

Mediterranean

Location: Uta, Cagliari province, Sardinia, Italy.
Surface: 1,064 ha.

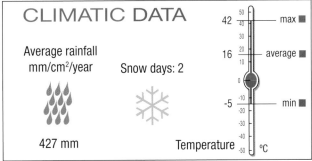

CLIMATIC DATA

Average rainfall
mm/cm²/year

Snow days: 2

427 mm

Temperature

42 — max ■
16 — average ■
-5 — min ■
°C

SUMMARY

Situated in the south-east of the island of Sardinia, the Azienda Agricola Monte Arcosu is a small piece of land of Mediterranean type, 1,064 hectares in size, but which represents an excellent site for the endemic Corsican Red Deer *(Cervus elaphus corsicanus)*, known locally as the cervo sardo, originally from Corsica but, oddly, preserved in Sardinia.

As its full name suggests, the principal activity undertaken on the estate of Monte Arcosu is agricultural in nature, with both irrigated and dry-land crops, although in recent years there has been some diversification into cattle-rearing, timber production, hunting and rural tourism.

The result is an attractive site for lovers of nature, especially birdwatchers, where spectacular species such as the Golden Eagle *(Aquila chrysaetos)* and Bonelli's Eagle *(Hieraetus fasciatus)* can be seen.

The estate slopes gently south-eastwards from the tip of Monte Arcosu at 950 m above sea level, near the plains of Campidano, in Sardinia.

C. Otero

HISTORY

The estate came into the possession of the present owners in the first half of the 20th century. It was used mainly as a shooting estate, the farming being neglected, and with no active management from the owner or family. The mountain slopes were the perfect ground for roaming poachers, goat-herders, wood-gatherers, and so on.

Around 1960-1970 a new impulse was given and, with the aid of loans from the "Cassa del Mezzogiorno", a conversion programme was carried out, comprising 20 km of new dirt roads, two dams and lakes for irrigation and an extensive mains water system that reaches all the fields suitable for grazing by cattle.

Three big new general purpose buildings were built as forage and machinery sheds, as well as fattening yards and two silage pits. Extensive de-stoning of fields was carried out, four new houses for the farm staff were built, and miles of internal electric cable lay, with one diesel production unit next to the workshop.

The property was completely ring-fenced to try to prevent trespassing and poaching. Expertise was brought in to assist the young management and to develop a complete agricultural and livestock rearing programme. A herd of 400 head of suckler cows was gradually built up. From the original core of indigenous "Vacca Sarda", the herd was crossed with Charolais and Limousin blood, to give calves which were fattened on maize silage and sold to the growing beef market in Cagliari, especially during the summer season.

DESCRIPTION

The Azienda, of just over 1,064 hectares, is located in the southern tip of Sardinia, 5 km to the west of Cagliari, the region's capital.

The estate slopes gently south-eastwards from the tip of Monte Arcosu at 950 metres above sea level, down to 100 metres on the plains of Campidamo (the irrigated farming area north-west of Cagliari), thus encompassing many different habitats and biozones.

The soils were formed mainly from granite gravels and sands coming from the erosion of the mountain by water. In fact most of the fields and pastures on the low part of the farm lie in ancient river beds and are composed of alluvial deposits of gravel and stones, sometimes as big as a football.

Vegetation
The different areas, from the top to the bottom are:

- **Mountain top:** Here the scrub and bushy vegetation of *Mediterranean maquis* (a scrubland vegetation of the Mediterranean region, composed primarily of leathery, broad-leaved evergreen shrubs or small trees) clings on to the rocky cliffs, where Wild Boar (*Sus scrofa*), the Barbary Partridge (*Alectoris barbara*), Bonelli´s Eagle (*Hieraetus fasciatus*) and the Corsican Red Deer (*Cervus elaphus corsicanus*) roam freely while the other side of the mountain is a nature reserve of approximately 3,000 ha, owned and poorly managed by the World Wildlife Fund (WWF). The remnants of an iron ore mine tell us of a busy area in the past.

The *maquis* clings on to the rocky cliffs, where golden and Bonelli's eagles and the Corsican red deer find their habitat.

C. Otero

- **Natural forest:** Many springs and creeks abound in this lower part and the trees enjoy a perfect habitat. Mediterranean classics like the Strawberry Tree (*Arbutus unedo*), Holm Oak (*Quercus ilex*), Cork Oak (*Quercus suber*), Olive (*Olea europaeus oleaster*) and Ash (*Fraxinus sp.*), interspersed with Rockroses (*Genus Cistus*), Heathers (*Genus Calluna and Erica*) and Brooms (*Genista* spp.), can reach sizeable proportions. In the 18th and 19th centuries, charcoal was made and carted by mules to Cagliari. In this area, the wild boar is the king.
- **Highland pastures:** Very poor in summer time, these have been mostly converted to an artificial cork oak plantation during the last 10 to 15 years. The different management areas vary in size, up to 200 ha, and each one has two artificial lakes, which in good years can hold up to 50,000-60,000 m³ of water that would otherwise be run-off. The lakes are connected to a 16 km ring main that feeds all the watering troughs for the cattle, and to the irrigation system that reaches the cropping area through gravity.
- **Low plains:** Mainly pastures and arable fields, the soils here are somewhat loamier. In the past, the best fields have frequently been stoned, with hundreds of lorries filled and carted away from the farm, but... after a few years they seem to crop up again, even

when no heavy cultivations are made! Here big fenced fields are grazed by cattle.

Fauna

In terms of the fauna of the Azienda Agrícola Monte Arcosu, the species par excellence is the Corsican Red Deer (*Cervus elaphus corsicanus*), with other big game species such as Wild Boar (*Sus scrofa*) and Fallow Deer (*Dama dama*). In the gully of the Monte Arcosu mountain, a pair of Golden Eagles (*Aquila chrysaetos*) make their nest. Other species include Goshawk (*Accipiter gentilis*), Buzzard (*Buteo buteo*), Woodchat Shrike (*Lanius senator*), Raven (*Corvus corax*), Bee-eater (*Merops apiaster*), Scops Owl (*Otus scops*), Nightjar (*Caprimulgus europaeus*), Cirl Bunting (*Emberiza cirlus*), and Dartford Warbler (*Sylvia undata*).

The reptiles present are the two species of Ringed Snake (*Natrix maura and N. natrix*) and the Green Whip Snake (*Coluber viridiflavus*). Amongst the amphibians one can admire the Tyrrhenian Painted Frog (*Discoglossus sardus*) and the European Tree Fog (*Hyla arborea*), whose skill in mimicry allows it to retreat under the leaves of any plant.

Amongst the butterflies it is worth mentioning the Swallowtail butterfly (*Papilio machaon*), the Two-tailed Pasha (*Charaxes jasius*), *Hyles tithymali* (a moth of the family *Sphingidae*) and the Gypsy Moth (*Lymantria dispar*), insatiable devourer of the leaves of holm oaks and cork oaks.

Zones of open grasslands in the low plains with evergreen oaks and *Asphodelus* sp.

CATALOGUE OF VERTEBRATE ANIMALS. MONTE ARCOSU ESTATE

AMPHIBIANS
- Sardinian Brook Newt *(Euproctus platycephalus)*
- Sardinian Cave Salamander *(Speleomantes genei)*
- Imperial Cave Salamander *(Speleomantes imperialis)*
- Supramonte Cave Salamander *(Speleomantes supramontis)*
- Monte Albo Cave Salamander *(Speleomantes flavus)*
- Tyrrhenian Painted Frog *(Discoglossus sardus)*
- Green Toad *(Bufo viridis)*
- Sardinian Tree Frog *(Hyla sarda)*

REPTILES
- Fitzinger's Algyroides *(Algyroides fitzingeri)*
- Bedriaga's Rock Lizard *(Archeolacerta bedriagae)*
- Tyrrhenian Wall Lizard *(Podarcis tiliguerta)*
- Italian Three-toed Skink *(Chalcides chalcides)*
- Ocellated Skink *(Chalcides ocellatus)*
- Horseshoe Whip Snake *(Coluber hippocrepis)*
- Western Whip Snake *(Coluber viridiflavus)*
- Viperine Snake *(Natrix maura)*
- Grass Snake *(Natrix natrix)*

BIRDS
- Griffon Vulture *(Gyps fulvus)*
- Montagu's Harrier *(Circus pygargus)*
- Goshawk *(Accipiter gentilis)*
- Sparrowhawk *(Accipiter nisus)*
- Buzzard *(Buteo buteo)*
- Golden Eagle *(Aquila chrysaetos)*
- Bonelli's Eagle *(Hieraetus fasciatus)*
- Kestrel *(Falco tinnunculus)*
- Peregrine Falcon *(Falco peregrinus)*
- Sardinian Partridge *(Alectoris barbara)*
- Quail *(Coturnix coturnix)*
- Rock Pigeon *(Columba livia)*
- Wood Pigeon *(Columba palumbus)*
- Turtle Dove *(Streptopelia turtur)*
- Cuckoo *(Cuculus canorus)*
- Barn Owl *(Tyto alba)*
- Scops Owl *(Otus scops)*

- Little Owl *(Athene noctua)*
- Nightjar *(Caprimulgus europaeus)*
- Swift *(Apus apus)*
- Alpine Swift *(Apus melba)*
- Bee-eater *(Merops apiaster)*
- Hoopoe *(Upupa epops)*
- Great Spotted Woodpecker *(Dendrocopos major)*
- Lesser Spotted Woodpecker *(Dendrocopos minor)*
- Calandra Lark *(Melanocorypha calandra)*
- Woodlark *(Lullula arborea)*
- Skylark *(Alauda arvensis)*
- Crag Martin *(Ptyonoprogne rupestris)*
- House Martin *(Delichon urbica)*
- Tawny Pipit *(Anthus campestris)*
- Water Pipit *(Anthus spinoletta)*
- Grey Wagtail *(Motacilla cinerea)*
- Dipper *(Cinclus cinclus)*
- Wren *(Troglodytes troglodytes)*
- Robin *(Erithacus rubecula)*
- Nightingale *(Luscinia megarhynchos)*
- Stonechat *(Saxicola torquata)*
- Wheatear *(Oenanthe oenanthe)*
- Rock Thrush *(Monticola saxatilis)*
- Blue Rock Thrush *(Monticola solitarius)*
- Blackbird *(Turdus merula)*
- Mistle Thrush *(Turdus viscivorus)*
- Marmora's Warbler *(Sylvia sarda)*
- Dartford Warbler *(Sylvia undata)*
- Subalpine Warbler *(Sylvia cantillans)*
- Spectacled Warbler *(Sylvia conspicillata)*
- Blackcap *(Sylvia atricapilla)*
- Firecrest *(Regulus ignicapillus)*
- Spotted Flycatcher *(Muscicapa striata)*
- Coal Tit *(Parus ater)*
- Blue Tit *(Parus caeruleus)*
- Great Tit *(Parus major)*
- Red-backed Shrike *(Lanius collurio)*
- Woodchat Shrike *(Lanius senator)*
- Jay *(Garrulus glandarius)*

- Chough *(Pyrrhocorax pyrrhocorax)*
- Jackdaw *(Corvus monedula)*
- Carrion Crow *(Corvus corone)*
- Raven *(Corvus corax)*
- Spotless Starling *(Sturnus unicolor)*
- Spanish Sparrow *(Passer hispaniolensis)*
- Tree Sparrow *(Passer montanus)*
- Rock Sparrow *(Petronia petronia)*
- Chaffinch *(Fringilla coelebs)*
- Serin *(Serinus serinus)*
- Citril Finch *(Serinus citrinella)*
- Greenfinch *(Carduelis chloris)*
- Goldfinch *(Carduelis carduelis)*
- Linnet *(Carduelis cannabina)*
- Hawfinch *(Coccothraustes coccothraustes)*
- Cirl Bunting *(Emberiza cirlus)*
- Corn Bunting *(Miliaria calandra)*

MAMMALS
- Hedgehog *(Erinaceus europaeus)*
- Greater White-toothed Shrew
  (Crocidura russula)
- Etruscan Shrew *(Suncus etruscus)*
- Common Hare *(Lepus capensis)*
- Rabbit *(Oryctolagus cuniculus)*
- Garden Dormouse *(Eliomys quercinus)*
- Edible Dormouse *(Glis glis)*
- Wood Mouse *(Apodemus sylvaticus)*
- Black Rat *(Rattus rattus)*
- House Mouse *(Mus musculus)*
- Fox *(Vulpes vulpes)*
- Pine Marten *(Martes martes)*
- Weasel *(Mustela nivalis)*
- Wild Cat *(Felis silvestris)*
- Wild Boar *(Sus scrofa)*
- Fallow Deer *(Dama dama)*
- Corsican Red Deer *(Cervus elaphus corsicanus)*
- Mouflon *(Ovis musimon)*

Agriculture

On most of the lower part of the farm, the fields are sown to pasture. Normally, after poor (=dry) years, they are reseeded with a mix of clovers, vetch and oats, known locally as the "Gallura mix", which at later stages tends to be overgrown by the native weed population, especially by plants such as Asphodelum (*Asphodelus* spp.) or Thistles (*Carduus* spp.) which are not eaten by cattle.

The cropping schedule comprises also Durum Wheat (*Triticum durum*), barley and oats. In good years (mild fresh springs) the cereals are harvested in June, with a production of 10-20 dt of grain per hectare due to the very low pH of the soils (5-5.5). Otherwise they are left on the field and happily grazed by the cattle when the grass season is over.

The 30 ha of irrigated fields are very important; alfalfa and maize are grown and sold at a very high price to the local pig growers, or fed to weaning pigs and cattle.

Main activities

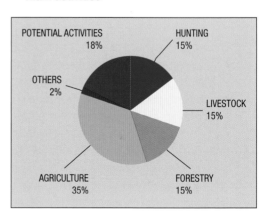

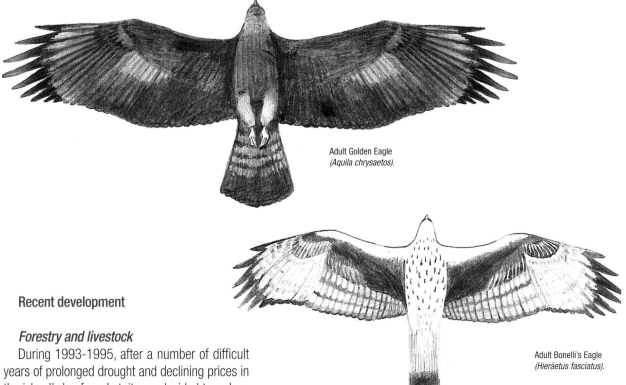

Adult Golden Eagle
(Aquila chrysaetos).

Adult Bonelli's Eagle
(Hieräetus fasciatus).

Recent development

Forestry and livestock

During 1993-1995, after a number of difficult years of prolonged drought and declining prices in the island's beef market, it was decided to reduce the herd of suckler cows to a more manageable size, namely 100-120 head, and to transfer over 200 ha of land to set-aside. Land was taken out of production both on the hillside and on the plains, and after two years a plan to convert the fields into forestry was introduced.

Main house garden.

With the aid of the Cork Institute of Nuoro, a major plantation was established, in staked plantings of 6x3, with alternative lines of Aleppo Pine (*Pinus halepensis*) to shield and protect the young cork oak plants. The Regional Agriculture Authority imposed the choice of the Aleppo pine.

The Forestry Commission was very helpful in advising on practical aspects of the scheme, such as spacing, weeding and soil cultivation, prior to the transplantation of the 110,000 oaks, probably the largest man-made forest in Sardinia. A good proportion of the planting was devoted to local species, mostly the Holm Oak (*Quercus ilex*) to enhance biodiversity.

All the management areas were fenced, since the young oaks had to be protected from grazing animals and intruders. This gave rise to a number of actions from angry poachers. In 2001 they set fire to the wood, destroying the eastern part of the estate. After a few years of renewed rainfall, the Aleppo pine rapidly outgrew the oaks, overshading and competing with them for nutrients. A decision was taken to cut the pines and leave the stands of oaks only. Over four winters (still ongoing) the pines,

which had reached diameters of 40 cm at girth, were cut, chipped and delivered to a national grid biomass power station.

Hunting

Throughout the 1980s and '90s the hunting rights were leased to a local party in exchange for surveillance against the permanent plague of poaching.

After the disastrous fire, the hunting was taken back in hand with a view to re-establishing the right attitude to wildlife. Local wild boar were re-introduced, as well as the Sardinian Partridge *(Alectoris barbara)*. Great efforts have been made to stem the roaming of the once almost extinct "Cervo Sardo" *(Cervus elaphus corsicanus)*. Driven by poachers from the lawless WWF reserve adjacent, the ani-

mals have found a safe haven in Azienda Agrícola Monte Arcosu where there are currently almost 100 specimens present. If proper culling is not allowed soon, problems of overcrowding, disease, etc. will quickly develop.

In order to exploit the possibilities, a rearing unit for wild boar was built, and four previously abandoned buildings have been carefully restored to afford hospitality in the future to parties of 6 or 8 guests.

The Azienda is presently attempting to obtain grants from EU/Regione Sardegna in order to develop paths and trails to link the different sites on the estate: on the mountain top for bird-watching at the coal huts, natural springs and man-made lakes for aquatic life, forest and pastures to see the Corsican red deer, wild boar, etc.

Spurge (*Euphorbia characias*) on the slopes of Monte Arcosu.

C. Otero

Dr Saverio Amann, general manager and Salvatore Loru, Head Game Keeper, at Monte Arcosu.

Alternatives for the management and sustainable use for Monte Arcosu

Big Game

Wild Boar: It would be possible to develop and exploit intensive agro-tourism, by increasing the natural population of wild boar in two fenced areas, each of 300 ha. Inside this 600 ha block, a population of 600 wild boar could be supported, with the aim of hunting annually (2-3 days/year) a quantity of 300 animals.

Delicious artichoke, one of the local vegetable crops.

Birdwatching & Wildlife

Exclusiveness of Monte Arcosu: Monte Arcosu has two exclusive values. On the one hand, its Mediterranean landscape with a climax forest and great floristic variety with a great importance which is a shelter for species of high wildlife value such as golden eagle, Bonnelli's eagle, red kite, griffon vulture, peregrine falcon, barbary partridge, purple gallinule, little bustard, scops owl, little owl, bee eater, roller, hoopoe, stonechat, wheatear, Marmora's warbler, etc...

But in particular Monte Arcosu is home to a highly valuable sub-species, unique in the world and endemic to this island: the Corsican red deer. This deer should really be the only attraction for this place.

Waterfowl shooting

The wetlands present in Monte Arcosu, and especially the two lakes, could hold an important population of released mallard. Capacity – which can be varied depending on demand – could be between 1,500-3,000 mallard shot per year.

The Italian *Sarda*, is the native breed of cattle. It has recently been crossed with Charolais and Limousine bloodlines.

CORSICAN RED DEER
(*CERVUS ELAPHUS CORSICANUS*)

The Corsican red deer is a subspecies of red deer. It gets its name from the island of Corsica, but ironically it became extinct in Corsica in about 1970, and is now endemic to the island of Sardinia.

The origins of the Corsican red deer

Its origins seem to date back to late Neolithic times, as no remains have been uncovered that predate the Holocene period. It was probably introduced to Corsica by the Romans whose habit was to establish populations of deer in lands which they had colonised. In the mid 19th century the species occupied a large part of the eastern plains and its foothills. Two other herds also existed, in Niolu and Falosorma in the north and at Alta Rocca, Sartenais and the mountain of Cagna in the south. From that period onwards, the population started to dwindle, and by around 1900 only a few small pockets of these deer remained. From the 1930s to the 1950s several dozen individuals still survived in the

The origins of this sub-species date back to late Neolitic times. The Romans probably introduced it to Corsica and Sardinia, but ironically it became extinct in Corsica in about 1970, and is now endemic to the island of Sardinia, where just 250 individuals exist, about 100 of them in Monte Arcosu Estate.

G. Paulis

138

thick *maquis* of the flat ground around Aleria and Ghisonaccia on the eastern side of Corsica.

At the same time, a similar reduction in numbers was recorded on Sardinia, where just 250 individuals existed, in three distinct herds.

Description

Of the twenty or so sub-species of the Red Deer, *Cervus elaphus corsicanus,* is an island species of Corsica and Sardinia. It is typically an animal of modest size and generally slower than its opposite number on the continent: adult males are only around 110 cm high at the shoulder and weigh 100-110 kgs, while females stand at about 90 cm and weigh 70-80 kg. The size of its antlers, their shape and number of tines are also less developed, morphological features doubtless imposed by the constraints of the environment in which it evolved.

Biology and habitat

Current monitoring of the reintroduced animals shows certain hardiness in the species in regard to extreme climatic factors of summer drought and winter cold. As far as feed is concerned, although their search for suitable grazing influences the places which the animals frequent, the semi-lignous food resources provided by the maquis seems to hold them in forested zones where they find shelter and are not disturbed.

The future

The species nowadays enjoys strong legal protection; it is classified under Annexe II of the Bern Convention of 1979, as well as under Annexes II and IV of the Habitats Directive of 1992; furthermore it is classified under the list of game species submitted under the compulsory game hunting plan, and currently no shooting is permitted.

A legal debate is under way between supporters of its listing as a «protected species» and its sustainability as a quarry species. The way in which the two different mental attitudes evolve will affect its management.

Bearing in mind the as a resounding success, namely the return of a species that had disappeared from its original habitat as well as the triumph of man's intelligence today over the inconsciousness of his predecessors, we hope and wish that victory by the living will serve as the true example.

P. Benedetti

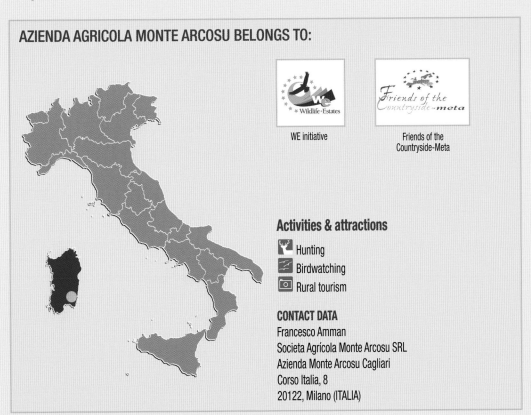

AZIENDA AGRICOLA MONTE ARCOSU BELONGS TO:

WE initiative

Friends of the Countryside-Meta

Activities & attractions

- Hunting
- Birdwatching
- Rural tourism

CONTACT DATA
Francesco Amman
Societa Agrícola Monte Arcosu SRL
Azienda Monte Arcosu Cagliari
Corso Italia, 8
20122, Milano (ITALIA)

Cappoquin

Atlantic

Location: Cappoquin, Co Waterford, Ireland.
Surface: 1,500 ha.

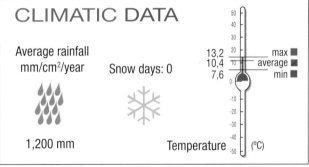

CLIMATIC DATA

Average rainfall
mm/cm²/year

Snow days: 0

13,2   20   max ■
10,4   10   average ■
7,6   0   min ■

1,200 mm

Temperature   (°C)

SUMMARY

Cappoquin Estate is an interesting place. The main house is unique because it is one of the only houses rebuilt same standars as the original after having been burnt in the Civil War of 1920/22. The farm is about 500 hectares and is divided into 3 enterprises managed separately with their own accounting, machinery and objectives. Two of these are the dairy and the arable enterprises, and the third is the orchard, started in 1960. The remainder of the old estate comprises a thousand hectares of unregistered mountain land. The estate is not managed for biodiversity but nonetheless has a naturally high biodiversity value. The future challenges of the estate will be to keep a sufficient degree of profitability and self reliance. Another challenge will be to prevent it from being broken up between generations.

Cappoquin Estate

Main House of Cappoquin Estate.

Cappoquin E

The Keanes are an old Irish family descended from the O'Cahans from Ulster.

HISTORY

The Keanes are an old Irish family descended from the O'Cahans of Ulster whose territory was north of Londonderry close to the River Bann. They were dispossessed in the early seventeenth century after getting on the wrong side of the English settlers and, as far as we know, they relocated west of the Shannon. They disappeared from historical records for some 60 years from 1640 but resurfaced in County Waterford as a legal family. There were also branches serving in the Continental armies. The Cappoquin Estate came into their hands at the beginning of the eighteenth century, first as lease-holders and then as outright owners. In those days landed estates in Ireland consisted of the home farm, a lot of outside tenanted farms, a mountain or two and, in our case, extensive town property.

Cappoquin is at the head of the estuary on the river Blackwater, a well known salmon river. It is as far up the estuary as sea-going boats could reach and became at one stage quite an important place for transhipment and even for iron working; there were local iron ore mines, a good supply of timber and accessible waters. Cannon are even reputed to have been made there.

The house dates from the mid eighteenth century, replacing an older castle. It faces due south and is set high above the valley. Its garden rises up behind and is especially renowned for the views and vistas that open up as one progresses up the hill. Sir John Keane was of sufficiently high profile at the time of independence in 1922 to have had his house burnt by the rebels and even more self confident to have had it rebuilt afterwards. It is an interesting reconstruction because it is one of the only houses rebuilt to the same standards as the original and because modern (reinforced concrete) materials were used. It has an upstairs layout that reflects best practice of the 1930's and a flat asphalted concrete roof. The policy is to try and conserve it without spoiling it by over-modernisation.

The land and town property has been split between Charles and David Keane. It is managed in partnership with the land, licensed to the farming business. A separate company manages the residential property.

DESCRIPTION

The farm is about 500 hectares and is divided into 3 enterprises managed separately with their own accounting, machinery and objectives. The dairy enterprise has 200 cows with a staff of three, though reducing soon to two, a quota of 1.5 million litres, modernised housing facilities and a fairly intensive dietary regime. Both grass and maize silage are made. The cows are turned out in the early spring and brought inside in mid October, earlier or later depending on the weather. There are problems associated with fertility and somatic cell counts. Considerable investment in the facility has recently been made. The arable enterprise covers some 250 hectares and is spread over 5 farms, the furthest being seven kilometres away. About one fifth is rented. It is staffed by a single highly qualified manager, assisted part time by the estate mechanic. It produces oilseed rape

The old trees at the top of the farm are still standing.

Cappoquin Estate

Cappoquin (Ireland)

for bio-fuels, wheat for animal feed and oats for oat flakes. It is well equipped with its own second-hand combine and decent tractors, on the basis that working windows are so short in the uncertain Irish climate that you cannot afford to have a breakdown when the going is good. Yields are high and profits are normally considerably higher than the Single Farm Payment. The orchard, started by Sir Richard Keane in the late 1960's, now extends to over 100 acres and is planted with eating, cooking and cider apples. It has its own cold stores, its own conditioning and packing facility, and makes and markets its own brand of apple juice. Apple production is sold through a chain of supermarkets. The enterprise suffers from the inherent vulnerability of a restricted client base.

Remaining as part of the old estate are a thousand hectares of unregistered mountain land, of which 240 ha were planted with Lodgepole Pine *(Pinus contorta)* and Sitka Spruce *(Picea sitchensis)* in the early 1990's at the start of the EU funded afforestation schemes. With slow rates of growth on marginal land this plantation is variable in quality and is only now approaching its first

thinning. There are a further 24 hectares of lowland forest on land not otherwise suitable for farming because it is either too wet or too steep. About half has been planted in recent years and is managed for diversity as well as for profitability. There are hardwoods – oak, beech, sweet chestnut and ash – as well as Douglas Fir *(Pseudotsuga menziesii)*, Norway Spruce *(Picea abies)* and Larch *(Larix* sp.). There are no employees in the forestry but it is managed together with a professional adviser and specialist contractors.

Up the river 20 minutes drive away to the west is 1.5 miles of salmon fishing let annually. Now that drift-net fishing for salmon at sea has been stopped, this has the potential to be developed as high quality water for fly-fishing. There are annual problems associated with flood damage and efforts are being made to persuade the Authorities at national level to take seriously the proliferation of Cormorants *(Phalacrocorax carbo)* which are capable of devastating young salmon smolts on their way down to the sea.

The Estate used to own the entire town of Cappoquin. What remains today are small one or two

Cappoquin Estate

– bedroom houses which are rented, mostly ready furnished – a trend that has developed in the last five years with the influx from the new Member States. As they become vacant they are modernised to the needs of the market, which has become consistently more demanding in the last 20 years. Rented residential property does not enjoy favourable fiscal status in Ireland and an effective rate of tax of 46% is levied with no allowance made for amortisation of improvements.

Biodiversity

The estate is not managed for diversity. However the old hedges have been largely retained on the home farm and the fields have not been allowed to become gigantic. The old trees are still there and it is a pleasure to climb the hill in the afternoon after a morning in the office, and to study the changes to the topography of the valley where views range from 15 km to the east and 8 km to the west. Once you climb to the top of the farm, the range of mountains 15 km away to the north can be seen. Birds have been surveyed over the years by Bird Watch Ireland (the Irish partner of Bird Life International). Forty four species have been observed, of which 27 are seen every year. There is no regular shooting on the Estate but the new manager of the dairy is keen, and a small unofficial shoot may emerge which will at least give enjoyment to the next generation. There are problems with damage to forestry from the proliferation of Fallow Deer *(Dama dama)*, the inherent dangers of disease contamination from Badgers *(Meles meles)* and the regular need to control Foxes *(Vulpes vulpes)* so that they do not prevent at least some of the Wild Pheasant *(Phasianus colchicus)* surviving.

There are birds of prey on the mountain and maybe the odd Scottish Grouse *(Lagopus lagopus scoticus)*. Being on a hill there are no flighting ponds but there is duck and snipe shooting in the valley, generally managed by local gun clubs. The nearest pheasant shoot is 15 km away.

Invasive species are significant in the area; *Rhododendron ponticum*, Mink *(Mustela lutreola)*, Grey Squirrels *(Sciurus carolinensis)*, Japanese Knotweed *(Fallopia japonica,* syn. *Polygonum cuspidatum)* and Giant Hogweed *(Heracleum mantegazzianum)*.

Cappoquin is at the head of the estuary of the Blackwater River, noted for its salmon.

Cappoquin Estate

THE FUTURE

Looking ahead, profitability is seen as the priority. Unless the estate makes money it has no future and since there is no industrial base to the family there is no outside source of funds. A living has to be made, and the fabric of the house and garden preserved out of the resources of the estate. Nevertheless it is nice to think that one is managing for the benefit of future generations and will perhaps be able to hand over a place in better condition than when it was received, to be proud of and not a burden. It will be important not to have it broken up between the generations and thus great tact will be necessary to prevent "turf wars". If it can be developed as a place of beauty as well as a money-making business then perhaps future generations will accept a lower share in return for greater access.

Lady Keane planted and extended the garden in face of some opposition but now with a young and dynamic gardener it is hoped that more visitors will come to share the pleasure of walking round to admire the plants, the trees and their setting. Most large Irish houses have a hectare or two of walled garden. Cappoquin is no exception. The walls are of stone, lined with brick inside to retain the heat. They are reasonably intact but much work needs to be done on restoration.

Another feature of Irish estates is the farm yard, usually built of stone surrounding a central courtyard, which in the past was often cobbled. The estate no longer has attractive yards, which were sacrificed for commercial considerations.

Support for old heritage property in Ireland is limited to the ability to deduct maintenance costs against pre-tax income. There is some direct help for roofs and for the structure, but it is very limited. There are no VAT concessions. Whatever serious public money is available is directed to properties owned by the State. A Historic House Association has recently been formed with the aim of widening the scope of the concessions and improving the facilities to attract more visitors.

J.C. Keane

It is nice to think that one is managing for the benefit of future generations.

CAPPOQUIN BELONGS TO:

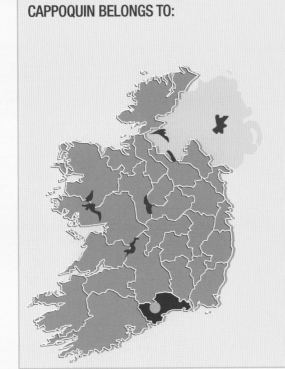

Rise Foundation

Friends of the Countryside

Activities & attractions

 Gardens
 Fishing

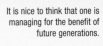 Historic private house
◯ Estate products

CONTACT DATA
Contact Person: Charles Keane
Cappoquin Estate
Cappoquin, Co Waterford
Ireland
charleskeane@cappoquinestate.com

Hardegg

Continental

Location: Seefeld-Kadolz, Hollabrunn, Lower Austria, Austria.
Surface: 2,792 ha.

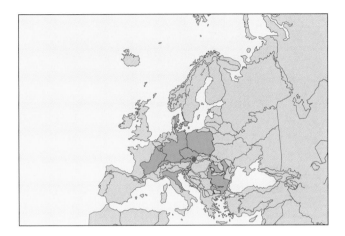

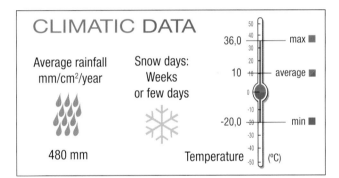

CLIMATIC DATA

Average rainfall
mm/cm²/year

Snow days:
Weeks
or few days

480 mm

Temperature (°C)

36,0 — max
10 — average
-20,0 — min

SUMMARY

The Seefeld Estate presently run by Dipl.-Ing. Maximilian Hardegg has been owned by the Hardegg family for many generations. The Estate is located in Lower Austria and shows a perfect balance between modern agriculture in the segments of farming, animal husbandry, wine production and sustainable rural development. Thanks to Seefeld's unique resources Maximilian Hardeggs' aim is to establish it as a role model for modern farming.

Hardegg Estate

Typical of the Austrian wine district are the rolling hills, beautiful vineyards and agricultural landscape surrounding Seefeld Castle.

Seefeld Castle, which was built at the beginning of the 18th century on the foundations of a medieval fortress, dominates the landscape.

HISTORY

The Family

The name Hardegg goes back to the 12th century. A nobleman from Bavaria, Luitold of Pleyn, built a fortress (25 km west of the present Seefeld castle) on a sharp bend ("harte Ecke"/"hard-eck") of the river Thaya and since then the landlords have carried that name and title.

The Hardegg fortress changed ownership frequently and eventually reverted back to the Emperor, Friedrich III of Habsburg in the 15th century. The Emperor struggled throughout his reign with financial, political and military issues and therefore loyal noblemen were in great demand. Amongst his closest supporters at that time were two brothers from a Styrian noble family, Sigmund and Heinrich Prueschenk. Sigmund was a close political and personal consultant to the Emperor and his son, the Imperial Prince Maximilan (Emperor Maximilian I), his younger brother Heinrich was mainly involved in business transactions and military camapaigns. Both Emperors rewarded the brothers generously with titles and large estates. On March 28, 1495, Emperor Maximilian I sold the Hardegg fortress to Heinrich Prueschenk and bestowed on him and his descendants the title of Count Hardegg. The present Count, Maximilian Hardegg, directly descends from Heinrich.

In the late 16th century the family fortunes declined. The Emperor lost faith in the Hardeggs, mainly due to their religious beliefs. The Hardeggs were at that time devote Protestants. This culminated in 1635, when Count Julius III, having inherited many debts from his father, was forced to sell the fortress .

Several years later two Hardegg brothers, Julius Adam and Conrad Friedrich, again reestablished the family fortunes by splitting the remaining properties and founding two family branches for which they built respective Baroque castles in Stetteldorf and Seefeld. The Stetteldorf branch of the family died out in 1945 and the younger branch remains in Seefeld to this day.

Seefeld Castle

Seefeld Castle, which was built at the beginning of the 18th century on the foundations of a medieval fortress, dominates the landscape. This Baroque masterpiece was build by Count Conrad Friedrich Hardegg and designed by the architect Johann Jakob Castelli, whose intention was to express the euphoria of the Baroque period as well as the landlord's importance in the region.

Cultural heritage is a responsibility Maximilian Hardegg takes very seriously, living in and supporting the castle to this day. Restored in the 1990s, Seefeld Castle has regained its former splendour.

Inside, a charming courtyard leads to the castle chapel featuring a fresco by Winterhalter and a marvellous ballroom with frescos inspired by John Baptist Wenzel Bergl.

The garden has also been restored according to Baroque plans as well as through advice from the National Heritage Association of Austria. Seefeld Castle is a private home, but the present owner, like his predecessors, opens it for selected events in order to promote culture in the Weinviertel.

DESCRIPTION

Seefeld Estate is situated close to the Austrian/Czech border approximately 80 km north of Vienna.

The continental climate produces hot and dry summers and cold winters, and early summer rains produce intense vegetation and high fertility. Cool late summer nights are favourable for the vineyards and the sugar beet, making the estate and its seasons exceptional.

Farming and crops

THE AVERAGE CROP DISTRIBUTION (TOTAL 2300 HA)	
Winter wheat	1,100 ha
Winter barley	180 ha
Spring barley	120 ha
Sugarbeet	190 ha
Maize	250 ha
Oilseed rape	130 ha
Potatoes	120 ha
Long term set-aside	70 ha
Wetland areas	100 ha
Hedgerows/beetle banks	40 ha
TOTAL	2,300 ha

Crop yields have increased significantly on the estate since the 1960s (e.g. winter wheat in the 1960s yielded 3 t/ha, compared with 5 t/ha in the 1990s) mainly because of improved farming techniques and soil improvement. High quality winter wheat is the crop that offers relative stability over the years and the farm management was able to establish good ties to customers within Austria (mills, traders) and abroad (Italy).

"Top quality wheat is our speciality" (M.Hardegg)

Today a well developed irrigation system has opened up new opportunities for crops such as potatoes. Since 2002 the farm has been the largest potato contractor for McDonalds in the country.

Another secret to success is the closed circle of nutrients, accomplished with the usage of the Estate's own organic fertilizer, produced by the pigs.

The Pig Breeding Unit

Animal welfare, animal health, food safety and the environment are some of the main factors the estate's pig breeding unit is constantly considering.

Hardegg Estate

With 1,000 mother sows Seefeld Estate is one of the biggest Austrian pig farms. The well-known farm uses the best management practices to ensure the well-being, quality and performance of its animals. The young breeding gilts (app. 5,000/year) are sold to Austrian farmers and abroad. The fattening pigs (app. 17,000/year) are sold to the local abbattoir. The real advantage in the competitive breeding market is the good health status, the uniformity of the animals and the availabilty of sufficient numbers from one origin.

The view from the Czech border over the Austrian plains.

Breeding gilts.

Hardegg Estate

Group Housing

The most radical change in pig keeping over the past decade has been the establishment of group housing systems to replace individual stalls for breeding sows during gestation. In 2013, under EU law, all pig farms have to transfer to the new system. In 2002 Hardegg established a state of the art group housing system for all its mother sows, having studied and visited various group housing systems worldwide. The Hardegg group housing is based on individual feeding systems, so each sow can have its own feed portion. Furthermore the necessary herd management is done mainly through the feeding station. The manager can control the daily individual feed intake and adapt it if necessary. As only sows with a good character are fit for group housing this has an immense impact on breeding.

Today, after six years of experience Hardegg has come to the conclusion that the breeding gilts known under its brand name "Austromax" have through the group housing system increased their

The 42 ha of vineyards have, since 2006, been managed organically.

Hardegg Estate

biostatistics in fertility, longevity, stability and food conversion.

Vineyards and Wine Production

The most traditional segment of the Hardegg Estate is certainly the wine production. As we know from history, Count Johann Conrad Friedrich had to choose between building the castle or the Baroque cellar and set his priority on the cellar which was built 10 years before the castle.

Graf Hardegg wines are well known in the world of wine-connoisseurs. The main varieties are Grüner Veltliner, Riesling and Pinot Noir as well as a sparkling Burgundy wine methode champenoise. The freshness and elegance of both whites and reds are due to the cool climate in which they mature. The cellars´ principle is to allow the wine to mature naturally.

The 42 ha of vineyards have, since 2006, been managed organically. Although this produces an additional risk the result of extremely individual wines allow us to appeal to new market segments.

Facts: average yield 2,500-6,500 litres/ha; annual sales over 30,000 cases; 35% export rate, mainly to the US, Germany, The Netherlands, Canada, Belgium, Scandinavia and Sitzerland; the varieties are Grüner Veltliner (45%), Pinot Noir (10%), Riesling (12%), Merlot (8%), Pinot Blanc (7%), Zweigelt (7%), Viognier (4%), Cabernet Sauvignon (3%), Chardonnay (3%) and Syrah (1%).

Sustainable management of a wild pheasant population in Austria

Seefeld Estate has one of the highest densities of wild pheasants in Europe and has been subject to a study published by the Game & Wildlife Conservancy Trust. Spring densities of over 100 hens/km^2 have been measured on areas of this ef-

The main varieties are Grüner Veltliner, Riesling and Pinot Noir.

Hardegg Estate

ficient and productive modern arable farming estate. Imaginative management of set-aside, game cover and field margins, combined with targeted predator control, have enabled an annual sustainable harvest of wild pheasants to be maintained. The annual harvest in the last 10 years has ranged from 16 to 54 birds/km^2.

Dr. **Roger Draycott** from The Game & Wildlife Conservation Trust in the UK has addressed a difficult question: "Can agriculture and wildlife coexist?"

1. Over the past 50 years arable farming across much of Europe has changed beyond recognition. Tremendous advances in crop production methods have led to dramatic increases in crop yields. We also now have farm landscapes that few who were farming in the 1950s would recognise today. The next 50 years are likely to prove just as challenging. World food demand is increasing, and the

LANDSCAPE AND WATER-MANAGEMENT

Award of the Belleuropa Prize

Maximilian Hardegg:

"The northern parts of Lower Austrian are among the driest farming areas in the country. Some 20 years ago, after suffering from severe droughts, we began to create irrigation systems and water storage facilities such as ditches and ponds. Completing this project took much time and effort. Today, we have a complete network of 25km² of wind breakers, water ditches, habitat zones and beetle banks for wildlife. There is a small river, the Pulkau, that runs through the estate for about 11km. We restructured the river, raised the river bed level and connected small woodlands and ditches to the river. Today we see the

benefits of this work in a favourable micro climate, improved flood prevention and a balanced water household."

"Belleuropa" is a yearly award promoting outstanding initiatives of land rehabilitation and biodiversity enhancement in EU rural lands. In 2008, the jury awarded the prize to Maximilian Hardegg, to whom it was presented by Corrado Pirzio Biroli, for the rehabilitation of the local river and the creation of wetlands and valuable habitats on Seefeld Estate.

Maximilian Hardegg was honoured that his and his fathers visions for land management had been recognised at a high level and pointed out that the project would not have been possible without Austria's EU membership and the availability of relevant funds for sustainable land management.

pressure on arable land from development and for growing non-food crops is higher than ever before. The effects of climate change may lead to some cropped land being unsuitable for growing crops in the future. It is inevitable that there will be increased pressure on the wildlife which lives and depends on farmland. We must ensure that wildlife can co-exist alongside productive, efficient farming systems of the future. Fortunately, there is a growing recognition by governments, farmers and the general public of the socio-economic value of wildlife and that farming systems in the future must not be to the detriment of wildlife.

2. It is widely recognised that a lot of wildlife was lost from farmland between the 1950s to the 1990s. Few species sum up the consequences of agricultural intensification over this period better than the fate of the Grey Partridge *(Perdix perdix)*. This bird is dependent on farmland and has been studied intensively by The Game & Wildlife Conservation Trust in the UK for over 40 years. In the UK it declined by 88% between 1970 and 2006. There were three main reasons for the decline: 1) the introduction and widespread use of herbicides and pesticides on cereals reduced the abundance and availability of both weed seed for adults and insect rich habitats for feeding chicks, 2) loss of

hedgerows and introduction of large blocks of intensively managed crops which reduced the amount of suitable nesting habitat, and 3) increased levels of nest predation. Significant declines in grey partridges have been observed across Europe (including Austria) and the factors responsible for their decline are likely to be implicated in the declines of many other species which depend on farmland.

3. Over the past five years a range of measures have been introduced throughout the EU from Cross Compliance to targeted grant aided habitat management to conserve and enhance the wildlife on farmland. Although it is too early to say what the effect of these measures will have on wildlife at landscape and regional levels, there are many examples of individual farms that show that farming and wildlife can co-exist and indeed thrive. Seefeld Estate is a fine example. As well as being one of the largest and most productive farming businesses in Austria, it also has amongst the highest densities of wild pheasants recorded in Europe. Count Hardegg and his family have been able to maintain a sustainable wild pheasant shoot at Seefeld by providing the habitats for pheasants to cover all aspects of their life history and by farming in ways which are sympathetic to game and wildlife. Winter game covers, permanent grass areas for nesting and brood rearing areas rich in insects are all provided alongside supplementary grain in a network of feed hoppers and a targeted predator control programme to reduce levels of nest predation. Careful monitoring of the pheasant population is undertaken to ensure that stocks are maintained and that hunting is managed at sustainable levels. Wildlife thrives on the back of this integrated farm and game management approach; bird surveys on the estate identified 76 different species, including 6 raptor species and several species designated as having unfavourable status across Europe on agricultural land including the grey partridge. The future of farmland wildlife is in the hands of landowners and land managers. There are many examples of how farming and wildlife can co-exist and there are now more opportunities to improve habitats under grant aided schemes. It is up to land managers to follow the lead of estates like Seefeld to ensure that farming and wildlife can prosper in the future.

Count Maximilian Hardegg.

Hardegg Estate

Biodiversity – a vital part
of modern farming.

OPTIONS AND CHALLENGES FOR THE LAND MANAGER

Does farming have a future?

Sometimes when meeting friends who are not part of the farming and land owning community it is difficult to explain what farmers do. Often I find myself in a defensive position where I have to explain to critical urban people that we are not destroying nature, spraying pesticides all over the place and ill-treating animals. There is a lot of prejudice, fear and a huge lack of good information.

It is unnecessary to point out that responsible landowners follow a stewardship idea with sustainable management schemes and therefore it is in their own interest to keep the resources in the best possible order. Only fertile land and well maintained animals perform economically.

Also there is a worldwide increasing demand in food and feed. The human population increases by almost 90 million every year – food demand will be one of the main future issues and the annual increase will be approximately 25 million tonnes of cereals due to the yearly consumption per capita of 300kg. Therefore global farming output has to increase 25% by the year 2020.

In addition to this we face shrinking farmland resources. All over Europe about 8 km² of land is being used daily for new building.

So the answer is YES, farming has a future and the future lies in sustainable production on an intensive basis. European farmers will play an important role, their land is very fertile with a temperate climate, and they have clear ownership rights and stable political systems that allow entrepreneurs to invest in agribusiness year after year.

The main opportunities and challenges

We have to face a service oriented society that is gradually losing the link to its rural origin and primary production. So we have to convince them of what we are doing and communicate on a continuous basis. The main challenge will be to face the fact that the average consumer is sceptical towards modern farming practices. They see farmers more in an old fashioned way (small, traditional). As consumers generally are quite conservative as far as their purchases are concerned, changes within the production sector (e.g. larger farms with modern equipment) are not yet popular.

The answer to this challenge can only be good work and good communication. Farm visits have almost always a positive response as the farmer or landowner himself can often show authority and trustworthiness. So why not intensify that and make communication on different levels a main entrepreneurial segment of each estate.

Another opportunity and challenge is the countryside itself, its landscape, fauna and flora. In German we use the word "Kulturlandschaft" and compare it with the untouched regions of the "Naturlandschaft". The difference is that in the one human beings have lived and worked for generations whereas in the untouched areas the human influence is very limited.

What we have not done sufficiently is to inform the public that the human influenced countryside is not a bad thing as we can combine, for example, modern farming practices and wildlife management. We can set aside boundaries and water reservoirs next to fields and make the landscape very attractive and varied both for the human eye and many wild species.

In fact through good land management the capacity and variation of wild species (insects, songbirds, game) per ha is often increasing. So the management of the countryside is an entrepreneurial necessity, but the benefits go far beyond the farming sector. Everybody participates in it and is a beneficiary – tourism, sportsmen, food industry, even the cultural sector promotes the landscape. It is both an opportunity and a challenge to convince opinion leaders and decision makers that the upkeep of the landscape is of national interest and that the ones who do the work should be supported both financially and morally.

Unfortunately the environmentalists and many decision makers are convinced that the beauties of the countryside are not there BECAUSE of farmers but DESPITE them. Legislation and administration are often ruled by irrelevant environmental influences and, as a result, scepticism and demotivation amongst farmers and landowners has increased substantially. The key for the future in the upkeep of the countryside will be to create a public budget and motivate the landowners to manage it according to the best practice schemes.

Hardegg Estate

Optimism through Principles

There are definitely sectors in the economy which perform better and faster than farming. The productivity and trading volume is limited and we very much depend on unpredictable influences such as the weather. The volatility in food and feed markets seems to increase as well. So there is risk with small profitability compared with the underlying asset of the land itself. Still the booming economy sectors quite often turn out to be bubbles and the whizz-kids disappear as fast as they have appeared.

As a farmer you my not become rich overnight, and most probably not in a lifetime, but you can follow your principles that lead you through life.

These principles are: thinking and planning over generations, frugality, steadfastness, humility and modesty.

As long as landowners do not turn away from these principles one can be optimistic that farming and land management will stay as it is – the most beautiful and passionate profession in the world for present and future generations.

Maximiliam Hardegg

Hardegg has been able to maintain a sustainable wild pheasant population on the Estate.

HARDEGG BELONGS TO:

Game Conservancy Trust

DLG (Deutsche Landwirtschafts - Gesellschaft - German Agricultural Society)

Friends of the Countryside

Belleuropa

CIC (The International Council for Game and Wildlife Conservation)

Activities & attractions

-  Birdwatching
- Shooting
- Cycling
- Educational activities
- Gardens
- Historic buildings
- Rural tourism
- Walking trails
- Wine
- Estate product

CONTACT DATA

Gutsverwaltung Hardegg
Guts- u. Forstverwaltung Maximilian Hardegg
Großkadolz 1 • A-2062 Seefeld-Kadolz
Tel.: (+43) 2943-2203 • Fax: (+43) 2943-2203-10
www.hardegg.at
office@hardegg.at • mhardegg@hardegg.at

157

La Garganta

Mediterranean

Location: Municipalities of Almodóvar del Campo and Brazatortas, Province of Ciudad Real, Castilla-La Mancha, Spain.
Surface: 13,289 ha.

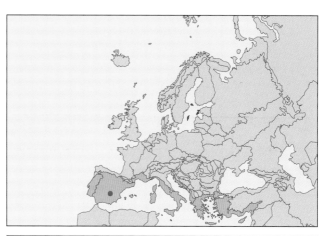

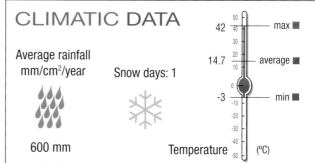

CLIMATIC DATA

Average rainfall
mm/cm²/year

Snow days: 1

600 mm

Temperature (ºC)

42 — max
14.7 — average
-3 — min

SUMMARY

La Garganta Estate has a surface area of 13,289 ha and is located in the south of the province of Ciudad Real, in the Castilla-La Mancha region in the southwest of the Iberian Peninsula. The estate lies at an average altitude of 669 metres above sea level.

The northern half of the estate is formed of a range of mountains and hills *(sierra)* where Pines *(Pinus sylvestris)* and Oaks *(Quercus spp.)* grow, whereas in the southern half the vegetation comprises woodland and open wooded pastures *(dehesas)* with isolated Holm Oak *(Quercus ilex)*, Olive *(Olea europaea)* and Eucalyptus *(Eucalyptus camaldulensis)*.

The estate is managed with two priorities in mind: conserving the indigenous natural environment and developing sustainable hunting. This policy has allowed the density of Red Deer *(Cervus elaphus)*, Wild Boar *(Sus scrofa)* and Roe Deer *(Capreolus capreolus)* to increase, along with the Red-legged Partridge *(Alectoris rufa)* and Rabbit *(Oryctolagus cuniculus)*, both of the latter being important links in the food chain of protected and valuable species amongst which are, for example, the Iberian Imperial Eagle *(Aquila adalberti)* or the Iberian Lynx *(Lynx pardinus)*.

The number of breeding pairs of Iberian Imperial Eagle *(Aquila adalberti)* remains stable at 11 pairs, although daily counts reveal the simultaneous presence of more than 26 different specimens of these birds hunting over La Garganta at the same time. Without counting the other innumerable predators that also live on the estate.

J.L. Rodríguez

HISTORY

La Garganta was born when the mining and metals company of Minero-Metalúrgica Peñarroya (better known as just "Peñarroya") absorbed another mining company by the name of Nueva Sociedad de las Minas de Horcajo in 1908. This latter property included an estate of 6,919 ha on which no mining exploitation was possible. Nevertheless Peñarroya decided not only to preserve the estate but also to add to it, purchasing other adjacent estates until a total of 15,052 ha had been acquired in the municipal districts of Almodóvar del Campo and Brazatortas (Ciudad Real), the entire land holding taking the name of La Garganta.

In 1912 the estate embarked on laying out its forestry, a task personally directed by Frederic Ledoux. Almost 4,000 ha were replanted with Eucalyptus in areas where the soils were poorest. The arable areas were ploughed by steam engines, hitherto unknown in the region. At the same time roads and tracks were laid down, dwellings were built, and a big reservoir was constructed to supply the population with water and to establish irrigation systems for crops, all of these in pursuit of the objective of turning La Garganta into a model agro-forestry enterprise. In 1914 a textile factory was established, designed to make sacks for packing organic fertilizer, and a timber business was started to take advantage of the wealth of wood. However these factories were subsequently sold in 1928, when firstly the First World War and secondly the progressive depletion of the mining strata were submerging Peñarroya in a crisis from which it would not manage to emerge, though it still remained present in the area for many years.

In 1968, the company ceded one part of the property (some 3,000 ha) to the Spanish National Forestry (Patrimonio Forestal) – later the Institute for the Conservation of Nature (ICONA) – and some years later the rest was transferred to the agricultural company Villamagna S.A., a subsidiary of Explosivos Río Tinto, which maintained it until 1980 when it was bought by the Wittelsbacher Ausgleichsfonds belonging to the Royal House of Bavaria and managed by HRH the Duke of Bavaria. In the autumn of 2002 the estate was bought by the sixth Duke of Westminster, Gerald Cavendish Grosvenor, and became part of the portfolio of rural lands belonging to the Grosvenor Estate.

In the last 30 years, the management and business plans have undergone an important change. They are now directed principally towards a model of sustainable agro-forestry, hunting and conservation, at the same time encouraging the maintenance and development of the rural population within the area.

The success achieved in all these different aspects means that La Garganta can be considered as one of the best European estates. Indeed the Wildlife Estates Project chose this property as a model pilot estate for the Mediterranean bio-region in Spain, as a site from which it can extract the information necessary to work out the demanding Specific Indicator Criteria, with a view to the evaluation of future hunting areas under the Wildlife Estates Label.

In the last 8 years natural grazing areas have been cleaned or formed on over 1,500 ha, creating the dehesa, a habitat typical of Mediterranean Spain which supports a great density of herbivores, especially red deer and rabbits.

D. Ateca

The flattest part of La Garganta, over 7,000 ha, has a central road known as the *autopista* (motorway), which acts as the backbone for communications in this area.

DESCRIPTION

La Garganta is located in the south of the province of Ciudad Real, bordering on Córdoba, and in terms of local administration belongs to the municipalities of Almodóvar del Campo and Brazatortas which are part of the Puertollano region known as the Valle de Alcudia

The estate is in an area of temperate Mediterranean climate with continental characteristics, which is to say strong contrasts in temperatures. With regard to its physical geography, La Garganta belongs to the eastern sector of the Sierra Madrona (1,300m) in the part known as the Sierra Morena and Valle de Alcudia, where the altitude varies between 585 m and 1,266 metres above sea level.

The profile of the estate on its eastern side is a succession of three *sierra* systems. The first comprises the hills known as Cerro de Postdata (945 m.) and Cerro de los Ladrones (935 m.). From these hills rises the stream of Arroyo de la Ribera, which crosses La Garganta from east to west for almost 15 km, forming one of the most beautiful and best preserved valleys with a magnificent Alder Grove *(Alnus glutinosa)* that borders the banks of the stream for over 11 km.

The second massif is that of the Sierra del Nacedero, with its high point of Aguzaderas (1,110 m.), and from which the stream known as Arroyo de la Garganta rises at the foot of the Cerro del Viento (1,190 m.).

The third *sierra* system, orientated north-west to south-east like the others, is Sierra de La Garganta whose highest point is the summit of Peñarrodrigo (1,266 m). From there, the slopes and foothills spread out towards the plain as far as the River Guadalmez, 9 km. to the south.

Numerous streams cross the estate, such as La Garganta itself, San Juan, La Rivera de Casillas, San Serafín, El Enebrillo and La Lentisca among others. Several small reservoirs have been built from them to make effective use of the water. The resulting ponds and marshlands are known as *pantanos*, and include the Pantano of La Garganta formed from the Arroyo de La Garganta in the south-eastern part of the estate deep in the *sierra* which bears the same name; the Pantano de D. Matías (also known as the Pantano Servanda) on the right bank of the Arroyo San Serafín; the Pantano del Olivar which is fed by the water of the Arroyo de la Garganta; the Pantano del Señor Duque fed by the Arroyo del Enebrillo; and the five *pantanos* in the area of Quintos de Brazatortas among others.

Vegetation

In La Garganta we can distinguish the following types of vegetation:

- On the siliceous soils, which are the principal forestry areas, appears the meso-Mediterranean series of Holm Oak *(Quercus ilex rotundifoliae)* accompanied by others such as Juniper *(Juniperus communis)*, Strawberry Tree *(Arbutus unedo)*, Lusitanian Oak *(Quercus faginea broteroi)*, Pyrenean Oak *(Quercus pyrenaica)*, Cork Oak *(Quercus suber)*, Heather *(Erica sp.)*, Rowan *(Sorbus aucuparia)* and Maritime Pine *(Pinus pinaster)*.
- Adjacent to the meso-Mediterranean holm oak series and in places in the north-eastern area where there are plants that grow well in

C. Otero

siliceous soils, species such as Heather *(Erica* ssp.) and Rowan *(Sorbus* ssp.) appear as a substitutional stage of the supra-Mediterranean Pyrenean Oak series *(Quercus pyrenaica).*

- In areas of major degradation and most impoverished soils, the groves of Holm Oaks have been replaced by scrubland where the Rockrose *(Cistus ladanifer)* predominates, accompanied by species which include the White Cistus *(Cistus monspeliensis),* Lavender *(Lavender stoechas)* and Rosemary *(Rosmarinus officinalis).*

- The most widespread use of the traditional livestock areas, where poor siliceous soils predominate, is still for livestock; the primitive woodland has been converted to traditional open shaded pasture by eliminating not only a good number of trees but also practically all the shrubs of the scrub layer.

- Of the Eucalyptus replanting undertaken in 1912 and destined for use in the mining industry, only a small proportion remains, due to the fact that since 1982 it has been progressively replaced either by restoring the land for cultivation purposes or by planting it with bushes and trees of various other species.

- There are also some small replanted areas of Maritime Pine *(Pinus pinaster)* which are traditionally accompanied by Cork Oak *(Quercus suber)* and Cedar *(Cedrus* spp).

- Finally, attention should be drawn to an interesting formation of riverbank vegetation in the Arroyo de la Ribera dominated by the Alder *(Alnus glutinosa).*

Use and utilization

Agricultural use

Annually 1,300 ha of cereal are cultivated as well as an additional area of slightly more than 20 ha of legumes which are sown in the open rows of the olive groves and the reforested areas.

This cultivation is done every third year, a system known in Spanish as al *tercio.* Every year 1,300 ha are cultivated, while another 1,300 ha are rested and a further 1,300 ha are left fallow. This costly technique is done more for ecological than economic or agronomic reasons.

The cereal is mixed with undersown clover to increase the quality and variety of the pasture. Furthermore, leaving the land fallow means that it is naturally enriched in organic matter and nitrogen.

The crops of wheat and oats produced (approximately 1,300 kg/ha/year) are not harvested.

C. Otero

They are eaten directly by the deer and smaller species, principally the rabbits, red-legged partridges, Iberian hares, wood pigeons, turtle doves and the other birds living on the plains, the small passeriform birds and the numerous small mammals which form the base of the food pyramid at La Garganta and which make up the generous provision of prey species. Simply of itself, this type of management would explain the spectacular results of the conservation initiatives, especially with regard to the Iberian Imperial Eagle *(Aquila adalberti)* and the Iberian Lynx *(Lynx pardinus)*.

Olive groves

There are 18,868 olive trees of two varieties, Hojiblanca and Picual, of which 10,473 are irrigated by a drip system. Average production is 30 kg/olive tree/year. The olive groves cover an area of almost 265 ha, with 22.06 ha in La Ribera, 30.41 ha in San Serafín and 212 ha on La Estación. The olives harvested (more than 566,000 kg) are destined for the production of olive oil in the mill in Almodóvar del Campo.

This enterprise is managed according to the EU directives for ecological agriculture.

Hunting

La Garganta is registered as a game reserve for both large and small game.

Large game species:

- Spanish Ibex *(Capra pyrenaica hispanica)*: 500 head.
- Red Deer *(Cervus elaphus hispanicus)*: 3,000 head.
- Wild Boar *(Sus scrofa)*: 2,500 head.
- Roe Deer *(Capreolus capreolus)*: 500 head.

Small game species:

- Red-legged Partridge *(Alectoris rufa)*.
- Rabbit *(Oryctolagus cuniculus)*.
- Iberian Hare *(Lepus granatensis)*.
- Wood Pigeon *(Columba palumbus)*.
- Turtle Dove *(Streptopelia turtur)*.

Research and development

As part of the National R&D Plan, the Institute for Research and Development of Hunting Resources (IREC), located in Ciudad Real and part of the University of Castilla-La Mancha, is developing

D. Ateca

a research project in La Garganta entitled "Predation and Recovery of the Rabbit in the central south of the Iberian Peninsular – Evaluating the Hypothesis of the Well of Predation". Technical staff from the IREC are taking part in this project, directly supported by staff from the estate.

Since 2006 another research project has been investigating ticks in the area, and an integrated tick control programme is now carried out which is compatible with ecological practices. At times, and depending on the climatology, some years produce an over-population of this mite which seriously harms the populations of rabbits, hares, roe deer and red deer. The most common species is *Hyalomma lusitanicum* and the research work is being done by the Veterinary Faculty of the Universidad Complutense in Madrid.

In addition there is permanent collaboration with the Council for the Environment of the regional government of Castilla-La Mancha.

On the low ground a series of management measures have been put in place which simultaneously favour high densities of both prey species and game species such as Rabbits, Partridges, Hares, Red Deer and Roe Deer. The density of Rabbits in this area accounts for incredible summer populations of almost half a million specimens. This explains the presence of over 200 birds of prey that "comb" this area every day.

Clearing and removing eucalyptus stumps is considered hard work... and very expensive! Currently stumps have been removed from over 200 ha, replanted with oak, cork oak and typical Mediterranean shrubs. The intention is to create new habitats for smaller species of wildlife.

C. Otero

The entire team at La Garganta: Ignacio Landaluce, Francisco Landaluce Sr, Francisco Landaluce Jr and Jose María Tercero with some of the more than 50 gold medal stags shot in the last rut. The six trophies in the foreground all scored over 200 CIC points.

La Garganta Estate

GUIDELINES DRAWN UP BY THE DUKE OF WESTMINSTER

Protected species

One of the priorities in our management model is the development of four species: the Iberian lynx, which is the most threatened feline in the world at the moment, the Iberian imperial eagle and black stork (both under threat of extinction) and black vulture (under threat). For this we have set the following objectives.

- The management of the lynx is based on the principle of "no trouble", in other words of not interfering. No artificial or supplementary feeding is practiced, and we do not look for their burrows. The lynx hunts the rabbits that are present in the territory in such abundant numbers, and moves about wherever it

Gathering the crop of cast horns each year is exhausting, as is the work of recognizing, classifying, pairing and recording them alongside the sets of cast horns recovered in previous seasons.

C. Otero

wishes, marking its territories, or in case of the young lynxes, colonizing new territories. These lynxes are neither an object of pursuit for scientific enthusiasts nor are they a principal motive for any television documentary. We all know that they exist and that they take advantage of the thousands of rabbits – among other things – that are at their disposal in this magnificent habitat, but nobody chases them nor bothers them. A very important part of managing the lynx is the control of foxes, for example. The foxes are removed by selective methods and live capture, and controlling them is one of the factors that allows such abundant numbers of rabbits and hares in this area.

- Maintaining a very high density of Iberian hares and Rabbits, in order to have an abundant and sufficient population of prey species to serve as food for the birds of prey and others like the Bonelli's Eagle *(Hieraetus fasciatus)* and the Short-toed Eagle *(Circaëtus gallicus)*, both of which are classified as threatened. This means that we have to forget of 14,000 specimens of both rabbits and hares every year. It also means that the pressure on other species and other protected small fauna is reduced.

- Creating feeding areas for the Black Vulture *(Aegypius monachus)*, Griffon Vulture *(Gyps fulvus)* and Egyptian Vulture *(Neophron percnopterus)*, supplying them with Red Deer which are hunted selectively. If the diet of these birds is improved throughout the year there is an increased likelihood that they will breed and therefore that their population will rise. All the viscera and remains of the deer, as well as the carcases of those which die of natural causes, are extracted to accessible places in order to be consumed by the three vultures that live on La Garganta. These measures are carried to extremes particularly during nest building time, even to the extent of sacrificing some deer if it is felt necessary.

- Imposing a total prohibition on all staff from carrying out any activity in the nesting areas of threatened species during the breeding period. We believe that by eliminating all possible disturbance to the nests, the productivity of the threatened species will increase.

Ecology

The estate must maintain and improve its environment, and we have therefore put in place the following action and management regimes:

- Not to use herbicides or insecticides on the crops, in order to permit the natural development of the populations of invertebrates and, therefore, some stable populations of game species – red-legged partridges – and protected species – Roller *(Coracias garrulus)*, Skylark *(Alauda arvensis)*, Stone Curlew *(Burhinus oedicnemus)*, Scops Owl *(Otus scops)*, Nightingale *(Luscinia megarhynchos)*, Swift *(Apus apus)*, Crested Lark *(Galerida cristata)*, Corn Bunting *(Emberiza calandra)* and many others. One of the first instructions given when we arrived in La Garganta was to convert the non-productive olive groves into biological (organic) cultivation. Although production has decreased, the ecological advantages are unquestionable: the grazing and feeding areas around the olive trees have increased and therefore the nesting potential for Red-legged Partridges and other birds; the risk of contaminating the ground water table is reduced; the number of treatments and therefore the presence of humans is reduced; and the quantity of insects is considerably increased.

- To encourage the breeding of the Black Stork *(Ciconia nigra)*. Each year about 10-12 small ponds are created, spread all across the estate. These ponds are a breeding area for frogs and small fish, and this extremely elusive species – under threat of extinction – finds easy food. The feeding areas and the opportunities for breeding are therefore increased.

- New wetlands continue to be constructed, and will be added to the eleven which already exist.

- A 220,000 volt high tension cable and several normal tension cables run more than 15 km across the southern part of the estate. There have been cases of Black Vulture *(Aegypius monachus)*, Common Stork *(Ciconia ciconia)* and Iberian Imperial Eagle *(Aquila adalberti)* colliding with these overhead cables. They also have a considerable adverse visual impact. Work is in hand to redesign the route and to mark the cables to make

La Garganta Estate

Iberian imperial eagle nests are checked and supervised by the game-keepers who prevent disturbance and interference.

La Garganta Estate

The black vulture colony has risen from zero in the 1980s to over 30 breeding pairs, with a daily presence of almost 100 birds.

La Garganta Estate

The presence of Iberian lynx had been denied by numerous official bodies and conservation groups. The policy at La Garganta has always been to exercise extreme care and total discretion, but in 2007 it was decided to show "officially" the presence of Iberian lynx. Automatic cameras were installed that recorded this photograph amongst others.

La Garganta Estate

Forestry

The desire is to conserve and improve as much as possible the forest and bush heritage of the estate. To achieve this, the following is in hand.

- To continue with the reforestation programme on the most open areas of the estate. In the 1960s, the plains on the estate were occupied by settlers working in agriculture and breeding livestock who had the right to cut wood. This produced deforestation which began to be corrected in 1997. So far these areas have only been replanted with cork oak, but we would like a greater variety of trees; gall oaks and evergreen oaks will be included.

- To create a screen of vegetation along the high speed train track which crosses the estate, in order to lessen its visual and acoustic impact.

- The residual area of eucalyptus has been reduced by more than 200 ha through cutting the trees and removing the stumps. Furthermore some 80 ha have been replanted with *Quercus* spp. and native shrubs. The sole purpose is to improve the capacity of these areas to shelter small game: Red-legged partridge, Iberian hare, rabbit and other associated species.

- To continue the traditional work of Mediterranean woodland areas, such as pruning, maintaining the shrub bushes, etc.

- The Pine forests on the estate will be cleared to encourage the development of shrub bushes. Presently, the density of pines is very high with little grazing growth possible due to the lack of light.

Since 2002 the quality of red deer trophies has improved considerably. The estate game book records over 1000 trophies of CIC gold medal standard, with glorious seasons of very favourable climatic and feeding conditions, such as that of 2007 in which a trophy of 230 CIC points and another 8 of over 200 points were shot.

them visible to the birds in conditions of poor visibility (dawn, dusk or days of fog).

- The planting of Tamarisk *(Tamarix africana)* in ponds and reservoirs encourages and protects ducks. Moreover it diminishes the visual impact of the walls.

The presence of Iberian Wolf *(Canis lupus signatus)* in the sierras of southern Spain has also been questioned frequently. Today its presence is a confirmed fact, demolishing the gloomy forecasts for the species made by the most prophetic "specialists".

Hunting improvements

The results of the estate's exceptional hunting management can be seen in the gallery of 1000 gold medal trophies of red deer – of which 150 exceed 200 CIC points. These animals are subjected to strict and precise selective hunting which is the key to improving the trophies and to adapting the number of animals grazing on the estate. No fodder is provided for the red deer; they eat only natural food, and the balance of sexes shows a commendable ratio of 1 to 1. The intention is to continue with this model. During the 2007 season the best red deer trophies in the history of La Garganta were obtained. Two deer were shot that reached 230 CIC points and there were eight trophies over 210 points. These are probably the best "unfed" deer that have ever been shot in Spain.

Also in 2007, a total of 8000 red-legged partridges were shot on the lower ground of La Garganta, driven and presented in the Spanish *ojeo* style, with 5000 of them shot in 11 *ojeos* in 3 days.

Alongside the supply of natural food, the best management tool by which we can obtain better deer trophies is by selective shooting. It allows us to delimit all the animals that do not meet the selection threshold, which is rising every year. During years of scant rainfall, we can be more demanding still and select more animals.

The annual number of wild boar hunted exceeds 600 specimens, which are hunted in the Spanish *montería* style, using dogs to drive the boar forward. The number of wild boar in the *sierras* of La Garganta is also on the increase, thanks to pruning of the oaks and cultivating the *dehesa* soils.

In the past two years, the two best *monterías* of wild boar in Spanish history have been held, performed in the traditional way, with only a few guns and at few shooting posts.

The density of roe deer has recovered to levels seen in the 1990s and it is very plentiful again on the low ground, where it coexists with red deer, red-legged partridge, rabbits and Iberian hares.

The Spanish ibex trophies have improved noticeably. The population is still growing and all ob-

jectives have so far been achieved; it is hunted selectively, with the focus on old infertile females and faulty bucks, and trophies of more than 258 CIC points have been shot.

It is important to highlight the importance of the role played in the management of the estate by Paco and Ignacio, the sons of Francisco Landaluce, not only in matters of hunting, in which they have vast experience in spite of their youth, but also in all aspects of the organization.

They enjoy my complete confidence and I consult them widely on all matters to do with the estate.

The Duke of Westminster

La Garganta Estate

LA GARGANTA BELONGS TO:

Friends of the Countryside   WE initiative   APROCA Castilla-La Mancha

Activities & attractions

- Research
- Olive Oil
- Birdwatching
- Hunting
- Shooting

CONTACT DATA
Finca La Garganta • Villamagna, S.A.
Villanueva de Córdoba • E-14400 Córdoba • Spain

Lulworth

Atlantic

Location: Dorset, United Kingdom.
Surface: 4,940 ha.

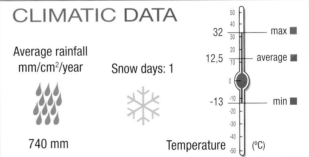

CLIMATIC DATA

Average rainfall
mm/cm²/year

Snow days: 1

740 mm

Temperature (°C)

32 — max
12,5 — average
-13 — min

SUMMARY

The Lulworth Estate is situated in the south west of England on the picturesque and dramatic coast of the county of Dorset. The estate extends to approximately 5,000 hectares incorporating rolling parkland, ancient deciduous woodland and chalk hills ("downland"). It also includes Lulworth Castle which is positioned a few kilometres inland of the iconic coastal landforms of Lulworth Cove and Durdle Door, part of the Dorset and East Devon Coast World Heritage Site (The Jurassic Coast). These unique coastal formations, together with the abundant and diverse local wildlife, mean that the area is of singular importance in the study of natural sciences.

The castle and estate have, since 1641, been home to successive generations of the Weld family, who continue to take a direct and proactive role in the management of the land and property. This includes the development of leisure and tourism-related enterprises as well as investment in more traditional sectors such as agriculture. The "home farm", Lulworth Castle Farms, accounts for half the agricultural portfolio of the estate. In total, across all enterprises, more than 200 people are employed.

The land use of the estate is mostly agricultural (3,600 hectares) with 320 hectares of woodland and forestry, 400 hectares let to the Ministry of Defence as a live firing range, the remainder being heathland, properties, tracks and buildings. The estate owns houses (170 units), commercial properties and buildings; more than 100 of these are listed - protected for their historical importance. In addition to farming, the estate operates a mobile-home Holiday Park at Durdle Door, coastal car parks and a number of retail and hospitality enterprises including the Weld Arms Public House in East Lulworth. In support of these enterprises, the estate includes building, gardening and landscaping departments as well as a substantial administrative office based in the 18th century stable block built by Thomas Weld.

Profitability balanced with sustainability forms the cornerstone of this approach, as the estate is focussed on balancing the conservation of the natural and historic landscape with commercial reality, visitor expectations and service provisions.

Lulworth Estate

The Lulworth Estate, situated on the coast of Dorset,
has been home to successive generations of the Weld family since 1641.

HISTORY

The origins of Lulworth Estate and Castle

Thomas Howard, younger son of the 3rd Duke of Norfolk, became a great landowner in Dorset by marrying the granddaughter of the last of the de Newburgh family, the original Norman owners of the Lulworth Estate and part of the Bindon Abbey Estate. Queen Elizabeth I made him Viscount Bindon and in 1575 he built a large country house on the site of Bindon Abbey. Thomas Howard was a wealthy man, holding important offices including Vice Admiral of Dorset in which his duty was to defend the coast and to suppress smuggling and piracy.

Thomas Howard was succeeded in 1582 by Henry, his son, who in the same year inherited the rest of the Bindon Abbey Estates from his aunt. When Henry died, his brother Thomas inherited and re-established the de Newburgh deer park and built Lulworth Castle as a hunting lodge to attract the King, James I, to hunt in Dorset.

The Howards owned Lulworth until 1641 when it was purchased by Humphrey Weld, the direct ancestor of the present owners.

The Weld family

Sir Humphrey Weld (1546-1610) did not inherit wealth but had to work for it. He was the 4th son of John Weld of Eaton in Cheshire and, aged 19, with no future at home, moved to London to seek for-tune. He became a prosperous merchant. When he died in 1610, Sir Humphrey had amassed a large family fortune and in 1641 his grandson Humphrey (1611-1685) purchased the Lulworth Estate.

Humphrey supported King Charles during the English Civil War. As a result, he returned to Lulworth to find his estate confiscated by the Parliamentarians, his house burnt to the ground and his hunting lodge (Lulworth Castle) stripped of its lead roof. Humphrey had to "re-purchase" his estate from Parliament in fines and, because of his Catholic sympathies, lost all his official positions. The ensuing financial hardship left him effectively bankrupt at his death.

William (1649-1698), Humphrey's nephew, inherited Lulworth in very difficult circumstances. Legal disputes concerning his uncle's debts and mortgages together with severe restrictions and taxes imposed on Catholic landowners plagued him for years. When he died, however, the estate was virtually free from debt.

William's son Humphrey (1680-1722) was only 18 when his father died. He came of age in 1701 and married Margaret Simeon of Aston in Staffordshire and Britwell in Oxfordshire. A beautiful illustration was drawn by Margaret in 1721 and shows the castle as a prosperous place surrounded by elegant gardens, a deer park and productive farmland.

During his time at Lulworth, Land Tax was raised on Catholic property and in 1717 the first Register

Thomas Howard built Lulworth castle at the beginning of 17th century. The Howards owned Lulworth until 1641 when it was purchased by Humphrey Weld, the direct ancestor of the present owners.

of Papist Estates was made. Humphrey, as a Catholic, had to keep his coach horses with his neighbours at Smedmore and Moreton.

Edward (1705-1761), like his father, inherited before he was 21 and enhanced the estate's prosperity. He commissioned a private Act of Parliament to allow the enclosure of the open fields and common lands and the removal of the old village. He employed Richard Woods to landscape the park, remove the gatehouse and courtyard in front of the castle and to redesign Humphrey's formal gardens. Edward (1741-1775) inherited from his father in 1761 and commissioned a survey of the estate (1769-71).

Agriculture was very profitable for large landowners in the late 18th century. Thomas Weld (1750-1810), who inherited Lulworth on his brother Edward's death, built many of the farms, which can be seen today. He also rebuilt the interior of the castle in the fashionable Neo-Classical style and continued his father's work by moving the village, building a new stable block and enclosing the park with the present wall and lodges.

Thomas left Lulworth to his eldest son Thomas (1773-1837) who, after the Catholic Emancipation Act of 1829, was appointed the first English Cardinal since 1536. In 1830 he moved to Rome and gave Lulworth to his brother Joseph.

Joseph Weld (1777-1863) was a well-known yachtsman. As well as being an original member of the Yacht Club, later the Royal Yacht Squadron, Joseph was also a talented boat designer. In 1837 he oversaw the creation of Lulworth Lake in order to test models of his yachts. His most famous yacht was the Alarm, which won the Kings Cup at Cowes in three consecutive years and also raced the schooner America in the £100 Cup, which in 1851 became known as the America's Cup.

Between 1863 and 1928 the estate was passed down in a series of successions, before being inherited by Herbert Weld (1852-1935), a noted explorer, in 1928.

Sadly, Herbert's time at Lulworth was tragic. His young beautiful young wife Theodora died in 1928 and in the following year the castle was completely destroyed by a fire which burned for three days. Herbert, who remained distraught, died childless and was succeeded by his cousin.

Colonel Sir Joseph (1909-1992) inherited an estate that had come through sixty years of crisis

Humphrey Weld (1611-1685).

but, through careful management and planning, he restored stability. After the Second World War, Sir Joseph took on several public appointments, and became the first Catholic Lord Lieutenant of Dorset in 1964. He was knighted in 1973.

Wilfrid Weld, the present owner, and his wife Sally remain involved in the management of the estate, although Wilfrid's son James oversees the day-to-day work. Ever since the fire of 1929, the family had ambitions to resurrect a principal family home in the park. In 1976 planning permission was granted for the construction of Lulworth Castle House. In 1998 the partial restoration of Lulworth Castle was completed and it was opened to the public.

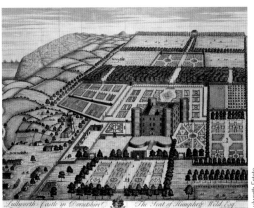

Lulworth castle by Margaret Weld.

Lulworth Estate

DESCRIPTION

The Lulworth Estate comprises 5,000 hectares, including some of the most beautiful coastline in England. Agriculture occupies 3,600 hectares and much of the remainder is managed to maintain the integrity of the landscape, conserving diverse habitats for wildlife. These include woodland, heathland, chalk downland, streams, lakes and coastal grassland. A further 400 hectares is leased to the Ministry of Defence for a tank firing range.

The stunning coastal landscape, complemented by the gently rolling unspoiled landscape, makes Lulworth a truly spectacular location. The 9 kilometers of estate owned coastline forms part of the UNESCO Dorset and East Devon World Heritage Site "The Jurassic Coast". The majority of the Estate is included within the Dorset Area of Outstanding National Beauty and there also several designated Sites of Special Scientific Interest incorporated within the boundaries.

Our understanding of the present type and distribution of the different habitats on the Lulworth Estate depends on the delicate interplay between the original spread of vegetation in the area, the influence of geology and climate, and man's subsequent interference and imposition of a new pattern on the landscape. The historical development of the vegetation has been related as far as possible to the soil types existing on the estate.

The estate

In the 21st century the ownership of an estate is a family business, and reflects every aspect of it. It must be managed in a business-like manner to enable it to survive, whilst at the same time preserving as far as possible the best of the old traditions and customs.

The estate is a self-contained entity but has always been, and continues to be, subject to changes and demands of the outside world. The objective is to maintain the best of the traditional rural practices, whilst embracing new opportunities presented by agriculture, tourism, education and conservation.

Through careful appreciation of the value or relative importance of the various elements of the estate's historic and natural landscape, it has been possible to ensure that the development of commercial interests does not erode the estate's heritage. Through survey and study, as well as the application of specialist skills and knowledge, the estate has been able to create a bed-rock of information to assist informed decision-making. The Historic Landscape Survey of the Weld Estate, published in 1987, forms the basis of the archaeological and historical information used extensively to ensure that decisions for the management and protection of the estate are the correct ones.

Lulworth Estate

GEOLOGY

The county of Dorset has a varied and interesting geology. The coastal region in which Lulworth is situated is known as an internationally important area for the study of Tectonic structures, geomorphology and Mesozoic rocks. The geology of the area in which the estate lies is composed of different clays, sands and chalk, such as London Clay, Valley Gravel, Portland Stone, Lower and Middle Purbeck, Portland Sand, Wealden Beds, Reading Beds, Upper Greensand, and Lower, Middle and Upper Chalk.

Coinciding in general with the geologic characteristics mentioned above, the area occupied by the estate is overlain by Brown Earths such as Almer, Downside, Gravelhill and Chiltern; Podzols such as Heath; Non-Calcareous Surface Water Gleys such as Holt; Non-Calcareous Ground Water Gleys such as Alluvium; and Grey Rendzinas such as Downland and Red Brown Rendzinas.

The Lulworth Estate is committed to the management of the coast in a balanced and environmentally sensitive way, constantly seeking initiatives to improve and enhance the property, in order to secure its conservation so that our children are able to enjoy the beauty and wonder of this, far into the future.

The Lulworth Estate Ranger Service was established in 1995 to maintain and enhance the coast for visitors and people who live or work there. The Lulworth Rangers provides and support:

- Access and recreation facilities, including footpaths, stiles and gates.
- Care of the countryside from hedgerows and dew ponds to grasslands.
- Field studies and education for all.
- Advice and liaison with the public and outside organisations.
- Reaction to everyday issues, from dolphin sightings to beach litter.

The medieval Deer-Park

In 1299 the de Newburghs built a medieval deer park by enclosing some 200 hectares with a 4 km ditch and bank which remains well preserved today. The park wall built by Thomas Weld at the turn of the 19th century tried to follow the route of the original deer park boundary as far as possible.

A detailed survey of the park at Lulworth was carried out in the 1980s, to identify features within the landscape, both lost and surviving, so that future management would take proper account of its historical past.

Forestry and woodlands

There are 320 hectares of woodland and forestry on the estate. The largest proportion, 265 ha, most of which has been planted within the last 50 years, is leased to the Forestry Commission. The remainder is in-hand, about half being coppice and the other half high and ancient woodland.

The Forestry Commission has most commonly planted Douglas Fir *(Pseudotsuga menziesii)*, some Norway Spruce *(Picea abies)* and Corsican Pine *(Pinus nigra)*, although replanting is restricted to natural regeneration of native deciduous varieties. The lease, which is for 200 years, mainly covers former woodland areas. At least half of the plantations contain evidence of old coppice, mainly hazel, sometimes oak and ash.

The castle and park today

Following the fire in 1929, the castle was left as a ruin until restoration by English Heritage returned the exterior to its original state. Today, more than 80,000 visitors are warmly welcomed to the castle and park. The wide open spaces, historic buildings and stunning landscapes have made it one of the most attractive visitor destinations in the south of England. The interpreta-

Today, more than 80,000 visitors are warmly welcomed to the castle and park.

Lulworth Estate

Lulworth **(United Kingdom)**

tion in the castle brings its history to life. It includes photographs of the interior from 1926 (before the fire), a children's activity room and magnificent views from the castle tower. The park has many popular features, such as the Animal Farm, picnic areas, children's adventure playground, and woodland walks.

The former stable block includes a café, for light meals and traditional English cream teas, and it's complemented by the Courtyard Shop which sells a wide range of gifts and souvenirs. The castle and park is an enjoyable destination for tourism and education groups alike.

Throughout the year Lulworth Castle & Park hosts a number of special events which are open to the public. These include re-enactments of medieval jousting and the English Civil War, music festivals, plays, concerts and several events raising money for charities.

The castle is also used extensively for private functions and is an ideal venue for weddings, celebrations, parties and corporate hospitality events.

World Heritage Status

Lulworth includes some 8 km of coastline which was granted World Heritage Site status in December 2001. This is England's first natural World Heritage Site and covers 150 km of dramatic coastline from east Devon to Dorset. It was designated by UNESCO for its exceptional geology and geomorphology, exposing 185 million years of the earth's history. This remarkable coastline attracts many thousands of visitors each year, who come for its clean beaches, to walk the coast paths and to enjoy its dramatic scenery.

Lulworth includes the unique coastal landforms of Lulworth Cove, Stair Hole (the Lulworth Crumple) and Durdle Door, which are studied by geologists, students and school children throughout the world.

The Lulworth Cove Heritage Centre was established by the estate as an interpretation venue. Inside are a number of displays which describe and recount the evolution of the coastline, together with its local and natural history. The centre supports a comprehensive education programme used by hundreds of school groups.

Lulworth includes some 8 km of coastline which was granted World Heritage Site status in December 2001. This is England's first natural World Heritage Site.

Lulworth Estate

The Lulworth Grassland Project

The Lulworth Grassland Project is an ecological project, funded entirely by the Lulworth Estate. The project aims to maintain diversity of habitats on the estate and to maximise the value of these habitats for as many species of flora and fauna as possible. A major research programme helps to identify species and to record the changes and differences in those species in grassland habitats.

The project is managed by the Ranger Service and employs four graduate ecological surveyors most summers. The coastal strip is largely composed of chalk grassland, parts of wich are uneconomic to farm and is now managed by the estate for the benefit of wildlife as part the Lulworth Grassland Project. Many wild flowers, including five species of orchid, are found every spring and summer.

In addition to the obvious wildlife advantages, this project has enabled the estate to be at the forefront of this branch of environmental conservation. Tourists and visitors have an increasing awareness of the environment around them ("green tourism"). The estate can also use the project to help educate future land and environmental managers in maximising the diversity of flora and fauna.

Lulworth Estate

The British Butterfly Conservation Society is based on the estate, occupying a refurbished 18th century buildings and yard in East Lulworth. The Society's aim is to conserve wild butterflies and moths and their habitats. Lulworth can boast the presence of 60% of British butterflies including its own, the Lulworth Skipper *(Thymelicus acteon)*.

The Lulworth Skipper *(Thymelicus acteon)* was first discovered in 1832 on a stretch of coast around the village of Lulworth in Dorset.

THE RURAL ESTATE IN THE 21ST CENTURY

Lulworth is traditionally agricultural in its origins, as are the majority of rural estates in Europe, and until recently continued to follow a countryside-inspired approach to many estate policies and management.

Located in the middle of the fascinating geological features of England's south coast, Lulworth slowly began to attract visitors in the early years of the 20th century. As transport became more available to the general population, numbers increased. This, in turn, led to the start of new enterprises based on the demands of visitors, and over the following 70 years the financial dependency on agriculture slowly reduced. During the latter years of the 20th century, the commercial activities at Lulworth expanded significantly, requiring increasing amounts of investment, management expertise and financial control.

Like many other estates, Lulworth had changed from a primary agricultural focus, into a diversified multi-million Euro business. Nowadays more than 65% of its revenue is generated from non-agricultural sources.

This change, as with so many changes in the world today, began many decades ago, but has over the years accelerated with improvements in communication and transportation. The 21st century has seen additional pressures on the countryside associated with greater visitor numbers and the expectations of society generally. There are also considerable challenges in respect to the meeting of those who live and work in rural areas. It is in this context that we need to consider how we manage and operate a rural estate for the benefit of future generations.

Coupled with this increase in tourism or, more probably, as a result of it, society's interest in having access to our countryside, our heritage, our environment and our conservation of natural habitats has also increased, so that now, after so many centuries of landowner management, everyone wishes to take part in the decision-making process of how our countryside is managed.

Lulworth's natural and built heritage is rich, and includes protected habitats, England's first natural World Heritage Site and over 100 protected buildings. Many of these produce little or no commercial return, but still need to be funded in both annual expenditure and longer-term capital.

Many estates like Lulworth are no longer entirely dependent on farming and agriculture, and increasing commercial operations have led to a need for increased skills to manage them efficiently and profitably. As multi-faceted, multi-million Euro business, how will future generations gain the skills needed to run a large estate successfully? Not every generation is blessed with the abilities needed and, on occasions, it may be necessary to buy these skills, perhaps in the form of a salaried and bonus-motivated Chief Executive Officer or Managing Director.

Lulworth has, over the last 20 years, worked hard to show how an active rural community can function succesfully both socially and economically. At the same time, increased interest in the countryside has resulted in demands for holiday and retirement homes, pushing the value of rural housing beyond the reach of those who live and work in our communities.

Courtyard. The estate's built heritage includes over 100 protected buildings.

As a result of expanding its business during the last 20 years, Lulworth now employs over 200 peo-

ple, rising to more than 230 during the summer months. Obtaining the right skills in the immediate locality can be difficult, but we have been able to find and recruit the majority of those we need. Our aspirations for future expansion will undoubtedly make this more difficult, and we will need to play to our strengths, particularly by providing a pleasant working environment and location.

Like many agricultural estates, all our farm employees traditionally received free accommodation and other benefits, such as continued occupation of their home after they had retired. As the proportion of our workforce employed in non-agricultural areas increased, we needed to review this, and we introduced a policy of charging a rent, albeit considerably below the full market value, for those properties occupied by non-agricultural workers, in return for a pension contribution from their employer.

One of the biggest difficulties with employment in the countryside is the availability of housing because of its relatively high value and scarcity, whether to buy or let. The ability to offer housing at affordable rents has certainly helped to attract and retain good staff, but the cost of providing this exceeds £500,000 (600,000 €) per year of lost potential revenue at 2009 values.

If we continue to expand our business, we will need to provide more housing within a short number of years. Therefore we are now following a policy of retaining all residential properties in order to make them available to our own staff when required, and we have a system of priority occupiers, beginning with our staff and other local people. After that, any surplus housing may be offered to the open market at a full rent. Current housing criteria in the UK does not class our estate housing as "affordable", even though in all respects it is; for the moment, therefore, we are unable to take advantage of more lenient planning laws in order to increase our housing stock, something which is an essential element to employment in the countryside.

As the population of the world increases, more and more people will inevitably live in towns. As the importance of the rural population decreases in political terms, it is obvious that new and revised regulations are designed with the urban resident in mind. Less and less attention is paid to the affects on the countryside and those that live and work there. Not only will we be expected to live under laws designed for the towns, but we will also see a reduction in available government funding for the country-side unless it is for the benefit of the wider population, most of whom live in towns.

Across Europe some traditional rural estates have been decimated by capital tax and inheritance laws, but those that have been able to survive, through sensible planning, good management or simply pure luck, are beginning to show what can be done in the countryside in the way of economic diversity, employment, housing, heritage, conservation and the environment. There is no doubt that the model of the rural estate is beginning to work to great effect and is again contributing substantially to the economic success and social diversity of the countryside.

Management of rural estates has always been driven by achieving a balance between competing priorities, and the future will be no different although more intense. Estates are no longer the "gardens" of the wealthy, but have now become competing businesses, whilst still retaining the best of the traditional values and particularly caring for all our assets in stewardship for all our children and future generations.

James Weld

Lulworth Estate

LULWORTH ESTATE BELONGS TO:

Friends of the Countryside

The estate includes a coastal zone which belongs to the Dorset and East Devon Coast World Site (The Jurassic Coast).

Activities

🏰 Historic building & sites of interest	🍴 Restaurant
🌳 Country Park	🚶 Walking trails
🏛 Historic private house	🚴 Cycling
⭕ Estate product	🐎 Equestrian
	📷 Rural tourism

CONTACT DATA
Mr. James Weld, The Lulworth Estate, Lulworth Castle, Wareham UK-BH20 5QS Dorset
Tel: +44 (0) 1929 400 352 • Fax: + 44 (0) 1929 400 563
james.weld@lulworth.com
www.lulworth.com

Postuero de Las Navas

Mediterranean

Location: Los Yébenes, Toledo, Castilla-La Mancha, Spain.
Surface: 7,800 ha.

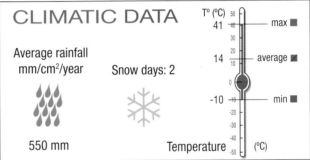

CLIMATIC DATA

Average rainfall
mm/cm²/year

Snow days: 2

550 mm

Temperature (ºC)

Tº (ºC)

41 — max ■
14 — average ■
-10 — min ■

SUMMARY

Postuero de Las Navas Estate is situated in the eastern part of the chain of hills known as the Montes de Toledo, in the region of Castilla-La Mancha, in the province of Toledo (Spain). It consists of four estates that have been acquired gradually over time by the Abelló family: Dehesa del Postuero de Las Navas (the principal estate, where the main house is located), Los Ballesteros, Quintos de Torneros and Quinto de la Sierpe.

The typical species found on the estate are determined by the presence of open glades and shady areas of the hills of Las Navas, in which the dominant vegetation is the typical woodland of the Mediterranean comprising Holm Oak *(Quercus ilex)*, mixed with Portuguese Oak *(Q. faginea)*, Pyrenean Oak *(Q. pyrenaica)* and Acers *(Acer* sp.*)*. The enterprises in Las Navas are a mix of agriculture, forestry and hunting, featuring extensive dry-land agriculture, the rearing of animals, woodland work, and hunting.

Many improvement measures such as cultivation, enclosures and creation of watering points have been implemented in Las Navas, in order to guarantee not only the development of the game species — Red Deer *(Cervus elaphus)*, Wild Boar *(Sus scrofa)*, Fallow Deer *(Dama dama)*, Roe Deer *(Capreolus capreolus)* and Moufflon *(Ovis musimon)* — so that they can be hunted in sustainable form, but also the conservation of species of special importance in the locality, such as the Iberian Imperial Eagle *(Aquila adalberti)* and the Golden Eagle *(A. chrysaëtos)*.

C. Otero

Aerial view of Las Navas Estate.

DESCRIPTION

Las Navas as a whole is made up of four separate estates: Postuero de Las Navas, Ballesteros, Quintos de Torneros and Quintos de La Sierpe. In total they account approximately 7,800 hectares.

The principal estate is Postuero de Las Navas, which has belonged to the Abelló Gamazo family since 1967, when they came to the area. This estate was acquired by D. Manuel Muñoz Aguilar in

October 1967. The other estates were incorporated later, firstly Torneros and La Sierpe in 1986, followed by Ballesteros in July 1990, to create what we know today as the combined estate of Las Navas.

Over the course of the years, many gamekeepers and staff have passed through the estate. At present the team is composed of gamekeepers who were born locally, and others from Andalucía, specifically from the provinces of Cádiz, where there is a great tradition of roe deer, and Jaén.

STAFF AT LAS NAVAS

Name	Years service	Full-Time/ Part-Time	Tasks
Diego Peña Romero	8	F.-T.	General Administration
Juan Alfaro	5	F.-T.	Head Gamekeeper
Carlos Ruiz	7	F.-T.	Gamekeeper
Juan José Maza	6	F.-T.	Gamekeeper
Justo Mercado	5	F.-T.	Gamekeeper
Ángel Almodóvar	4	F.-T.	Gamekeeper
José Cortés Vaquerizo	3	F.-T.	Gamekeeper
Miguel Molano	2	F.-T.	Gamekeeper
José Cortés	2	F.-T.	Gamekeeper
Christian Bodori	1	F.-T.	Gamekeeper – Tractor driver
José López	1	F-T	Gamekeeper
Oscar Ruiz	1	F-T	Assistant for various tasks
Juan Pedro Díaz	4	F-T	Assistant for various tasks
Maria José Borrego	8	F-T	Assistant for various tasks
Maria Flores Martín	4	F-T	Assistant for various tasks
Natalia Martín	1	F-T	Assistant for various tasks
Francisco Alfaro	6	F-T	Labourer
Julián Becerra	19	F-T	Machinery operator
Antonio Alonso Alonso	4	F-T	Machinery operator
Tomás Navarro	9	F-T	Tractor driver
José Fernández	3	F-T	Tractor driver
Esteban Garrido	17	F-T	Labourer
Manuel Cruz	2	F-T	Horseman

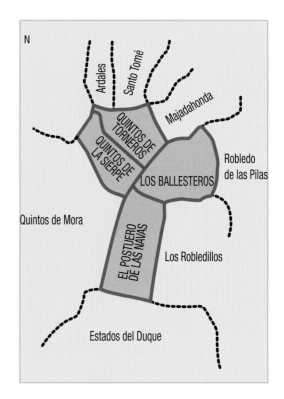

The gamekeepers are always one of the key factors of management. On them depends the threshold of stillness in Las Navas.

Situation and description of the hills and the landscape

These estates are in the eastern part of what is commonly known as the Montes de Toledo, and include a series of *sierras* of which the most significant are the Sierra del Pocito, Sierra del Comendador (or Las Guadalerzas) as well as the Sierras de Torneros y de La Sierpe. Hilly areas outnumber the flatter areas and valleys by a proportion of three to one.

The whole of the land comprising the combined estate of Las Navas belongs to the municipality of Los Yébenes. To the south of the estate there is the so-called *Umbría de las Navas* which borders on the province of Ciudad Real. To the north-east, Las Navas borders on lands of Retuerta de Bullaque, which also belongs to the province of Ciudad Real. The remainder, and neighbouring estates, belong to Los Yébenes (Toledo).

In terms of its mountains and hills, Las Navas is formed, on its southern side, by an area of shady ground *(umbría)* of approximately 4.5 km in length and covering 450 hectares. This comprises several hills, with heights that vary between 1,036 metres at the Cerro de La Cantera and 995 metres at the Cerro del Rufo. Going northwards, following the umbría, we come to the flatter land of Las Navas, which occupies some 1,700 hectares. This part is crossed from east to west by the Las Navas river, whose waters, together with those of El Milagro and El Bullaque, flow into the reservoir of Torre Abraham. After the flat land, the estate extends a little to the east, to take in the Ballesteros land, and to the north-west, which is the Torneros and La Sierpe land. From the orographical point of view, these lands comprise a succession of *sierras* and valleys, of which the most important are:

- The *umbría* and the range of Torneros and La Sierpe, of approximately 300 hectares, which in turn lead into a valley area before the succession of sierras and ravines starts again. It faces all directions, and is the most abrupt aspect of the combined estate. Its most northern part is where the highest peaks of the estate are located, reaching an altitude of 1,255 metres high at the top of the Cerro del Águila.
- Hills and ravines of Ballesteros. These are a combination of hills with an average height

of 1,100 metres, and valleys and ravines where the average height drops to more or less 900 metres.

On the slopes there are a lot of rocky outcrops where the rock is based on quartzites and slates, giving rise to very undeveloped soils, which in some cases can even be classified as Ranker in type.

The materials in the flatter zones are a result of sediments from flooding, composed of a high proportion by quartzite and clay-slate, so they are less developed soils with a high clay content that may belong to the kind of acid brown earth with Bt horizon. However, because they have been continuously used for growing crops they have changed, taking on the appearance of vertisols.

The predominant vegetation is the so-called quercinia forest, consisting of holm oak, portuguese oak, acers and pyrenean oak, with occasional Strawberry Trees *(Arbutus unedo)* and some Cork Oaks *(Quercus suber)* which are of little relevance.

This kind of vegetation is more noticeable in the shady umbrías and in the bottoms of the ravines and valleys, where the upper storey is more representative and where the coppice or under-storey is more varied. The latter consists principally of Rock-rose *(Cistus* sp.), Rosemary *(Rosmarinus officinalis)*, Heather *(Erica vagans)*, False Olive *(Phillyrea angustifolia)*, Thyme *(Thymus vulgaris)*, Terebinth *(Pistacia terebinthus)*, Hawthorn *(Crataegus monogyna)*, etc.

In the open sunny areas, the woodland is certainly more uniform in terms of the varieties of bushes and low shrubs. These form a tapestry

At night red deer, roe deer and wild boar leave the protection of the *sierra* and go down to the plains to feed. At daybreak they go back to their shelter.

Wild boar, red deer and roe deer are the game species *par excellence* in Las Navas.

greater continuity of the areas of holm oak and portuguese oak, particularly in the main estate of Las Navas itself, giving rise to more densely wooded areas where the holm oak is definitely predominant.

With regards to the fauna, it is important to highlight the presence of important species such as the Golden Eagle *(Aquila chrysaëtos)*, which breeds in the Quintos de Torneros, and the Iberian Lynx *(Lynx pardinus)*, whose population has been badly affected by the construction of the road linking Los Yébenes with Los Quintos de Mora. The Iberian Imperial Eagle *(Aquila adalberti)* and Bonelli's Eagle *(Hieraëtus fasciatus)* do not nest on the estate but they regularly hunt in the Valle de Las Navas.

There is an important population of both nocturnal and diurnal predators, amongst which we should highlight the Eagle Owl *(Bubo bubo)*, present throughout the entire region of Los Montes de Toledo.

Mammals present on the estate include the Otter *(Lutra lutra)*, the Weasel *(Mustela nivalis)* and the Hedgehog *(Erinaceus europaeus)*, as well as those of interest as quarry species, such as the red deer, roe deer, wild boar and fallow deer.

There are as many as 239 species of vertebrates catalogued and recorded in Las Navas.

usually of rock-rose, heather and rosemary, as well as isolated stands of holm oak, portuguese oak and strawberry trees, although these do not form big areas of woodland. On the flatter land there is a

Las Navas is a regular hunting ground for the Iberian Imperial Eagle *(Aquila adalberti)*.

LIST OF COMMON PLANT SPECIES AT LAS NAVAS

TREES AND BUSHES
- *Quercus ilex*
- *Quercus pyrenaica*
- *Quercus faginea*
- *Quercus coccifera*
- *Salix atrocinerea*
- *Pyrus bourganea*
- *Acer monspessulanum*
- *Arbutus unedo*
- *Pistacia terebinthus*
- *Rubus fruticosum*
- *Rosa canina*
- *Crataegus monogyna*
- *Prunus spinosa*
- *Genista hirsuta*
- *Cistus populifolius*
- *Cistus salvifolius*
- *Cistus ladaniferus*
- *Callunna vulgaris*
- *Erica umbellata*
- *Erica arborea*

- *Rosmarinus officinallis*
- *Lavandula peduncullata*
- *Thymus mastichina*
- *Thymus zygis*
- *Phillyrea angustifolia*
- *Daphne gnidium*

PASTURES
- *Agrostis* spp.
- *Anthosantum adoratum*
- *Arrhenatherum elatius*
- *Avena* spp.
- *Briza* spp.
- *Bromus* spp.
- *Cynodon dactilon*
- *Lolium* spp.
- *Stipa gigantea*
- *Vulpia* spp.
- *Trifolium* spp.
- *Lotus* spp. (crop)
- *Medicago* spp. (crop)

CONCEPTUAL DEFINITION OF THE ESTATE

Las Navas is an estate where the management model is the exploitation of agriculture, forestry, hunting and livestock.

Farming Aspect

The agriculture that is practised is basically that of extensive dry-land cropping where the varieties and areas grown are:

Varieties	Ha	Average yield
Vetch and Oats	180	6500 - 9000 kg/ha.
Cereals (Wheat, Oats)	70	800 - 1200 kg/ha.
Mix of Wheat, Barley and Oats	70	Not harvested
Meadows	130	
TOTAL	450	

The vetch and oats mix is the main crop. It is harvested green, with the grain half developed, and is used for feeding the cattle during the winter, up until the beginning of the next spring. It is also used as feed for the 40 pure-bred Cartujano horses that graze on the estate.

The wheat and oat cereal crops are harvested when fully ripe and are consumed on the estate, as much by the game quarry species as by the horses.

The cereal mixes are sown in specially prepared sites so that the animals can feed on them, either green at the beginning of winter or as grain at the end of the spring. We are converting these areas into permanent dry-land pastures, for better economic efficiency as well as for environmental benefits.

The meadows, with many varieties of clovers, grasses and some legumes, are protected from

The Golden Eagle *(Aquila chrisaëtos)* nests in the area of Ballesteros-Torneros, enjoying a rich and extensive hunting ground.

There is a herd of 40 Cartujano horses on the property.

avas Estate

The development of roe deer trophies has been surprising in the last years, and has produced exceptional records to date.

The rut usually begins with the first rains of September, going on well into the month of October.

the animals by electric fences, in order to avoid damage to the seed crops and to consolidate them as quickly as possible. They need a certain amount of fertilizer and cultivation to produce a better yield and to last for a longer period.

As we have just mentioned, all the crops are protected by electric fences in order to achieve appropriate yields, and to allow proper management of the animals, particularly the deer, so that they do not walk on the crops, or to allow them to have access at the right time.

The type of agriculture carried out is very basic, with fertilizer applied to the cultivated land, no herbicides, and harvesting done in daylight. The meadows are fertilized in early autumn and again in spring with superphosphate

Forestry

The estate's forestry is one of the aspects to which the most resources are dedicated, both economic as well as human. Anything related to woodland or trees is very easy to destroy, and takes a long time to rebuild. Because of this fragility, the decisions taken in respect of the woodland are the result of many, and long, conversations between all concerned, gamekeepers, management and owners, so that the decisions result from agreement after careful consideration of each and every possible impact.

This forestry work is directed towards correcting the excesses, from animals as well as from the agriculture of the past, and trying to balance, together with all the other variables that exist, both the woodland and the flatter plains where the trees are limited. Through measures such as reforestation, protection of certain zones or silviculture treatments, a major balance is sought between these two areas, to optimize both the capacity for diversity as well as the diversity that currently exists.

Of the various works that are undertaken, two types can be highlighted:

Reforestation and densification work. This applies in particular to the regeneration of the plain, on the main estate of Las Navas. This part of the estate, of about 1,700 hectares, is roughly divided into:

- 400 hectares of consolidated woodland
- 285 hectares of reforestation, where the principal varieties are the cork oak, the holm oak and the portuguese oak. The majority of this replanting has been done with the help of EU support for converting farm land into forestry.
- Multiple dispersed "corrals" of replanted pines, holm oak, cork oak and portuguese oak. These areas affect a total of some 100-120 hectares; they have the effect of creating "wooded islands" in the flat plains and have been located in areas where the density of trees was zero or very sparse. These corrals have, or will have in the future, the effect of creating dense zones in the flatter areas, and of reservoirs, to prevent the plain being devoid of trees. They are not usually

Las Navas Estate

very large in size; the biggest can be 10 hectares, but normally they are between 3 and 5 hectares. As well as these corrals, there are others that are even smaller, between 200 and 800 square metres, planted with the same varieties as previously mentioned, and whose end purpose is double, namely to ensure that large areas are not devoid of trees, and to serve as reserves so that more trees or under-storey shrubs can develop, given that all these corrals are protected from animals and from tractors at sowing time.

■ These corrals do not assume any great loss of arable hectares or natural meadows, and nevertheless they cloak the plain with trees, which otherwise could never have planted or developed.

A magnificent roe deer trophy from Las Navas.

■ Work to densify those areas where woodland coverage is not very thick, such as streams of little relevance or areas that cannot be cultivated. This is done in two ways: isolating the area so that the animals do not have access to it, so that the woodland regenerates naturally, or helping with the plantation of trees without disturbing the ground, by planting in individual holes.

Silviculture work. Where cover in the woodland is greatest, work such as pruning, thinning and clearance is carried out. These treatments bring about several effects, amongst which the following stand out:

■ Prevention of fire, given that such areas create firebreaks

■ Regeneration and health of the plot. Both older parts of the under-storey and branches of dry trees are removed, leading to greater production of acorns and better conservation of the site.

■ Benefit of feed resource; the acorns mentioned above, and new clearings in the under-storey.

■ Benefit from tree trunks and surplus branches, which are used as firewood in winter in the houses of the gamekeepers who live on the estate.

■ Aesthetic effect, keeping the woodland in proper order.

Hunting

One of the legs on which rich diversity depends is the maintenance of an appropriate style of hunting, which harmoniously brings together all the other aspects of the estate.

It is a question of trying to find the point of balance between the demands of the animals, the woodland, the plains and the land under cultivation. Throughout the whole estate of Las Navas, the particular conditions of each individual component estate are adapted to achieve a satisfactory result for hunting and shooting, without conflicting with the appropriate maintenance and balance of the different areas which make up each one of them.

The main quarry species of these estates are red deer, wild boar, fallow deer and roe deer. Amongst the other non-quarry species, which are important in terms of the richness of biodiversity, are the Griffon Vulture *(Gyps fulvus)* and the Black Vulture *(Aegypius monachus)*, the golden eagle, the Iberian imperial eagle, the eagle owl, etc.

In recent years, work has been undertaken to restore the roe deer, in order to increase the number of breeding animals and the quality of the trophies. Results to date have certainly been encouraging. The number of selective feeding points for this species have been increased, both for artificial (concentrates) and natural food, and in areas specifically reserved for them. In addition, areas within the woodland have been newly planted.

The combined estate of Las Navas is divided into three distinct hunting areas. In two of these, which include the estates of Torneros, La Sierpe and Ballesteros, hunting is mostly driven, using dogs, given the geography of the land, which is characterised by hills and wide deep ravines. In the other area, in Las Navas itself, where both the woodland and the flat plain land is undergoing regeneration, hunting is well below capacity, and the method of hunting best suited to this land is stalking. Furthermore, it is in Las Navas where the finest trophies can be had.

In order to enhance the rich hunting experience and the conditions of each individual estate, work is being done to improve some significant aspects:

- The creation of feeding points at typical sites, to allow resting places to be established in which varieties of cereal crops can be grown or meadows planted.
- The creation and improvement of watering points. This is a question of optimizing the land so that the water is distributed in the best possible way, and so that the water itself is in satisfactorily healthy condition. Tests are carried out on the pH of the water, to check that it is fit for consumption and to intervene at specific moments to correct it.
- Monitoring the health of the animals, for which there is a quick and efficient system of communication between the gamekeepers and a specialised veterinary surgeon.
- The combined estates of Las Navas is, with dedication and care, thus trying to ensure that the conditions of the natural world are the best that they can be, and is helping this by intervening as reasonably and rationally as possible in order to conserve, develop and implant the correct balance between everything that lives in the countryside.

LAS NAVAS ESTATE BELONGS TO:

APROCA Castilla-La Mancha

Friends of the Countryside

Rise Foundation

ASAJA

Fundación amigos del Águila Imperial

WE initiative

Activities & attractions

Shooting

Birdwatching

Hunting

Riding

CONTACT DATA
Postuero de Las Navas
C/ Fortuny, 1
E-28010. Madrid
fterry@torreal.com

'T Kristallijn

Atlantic

Location: Mol, Province of Antwerp, Belgium.
Surface: 200 ha.

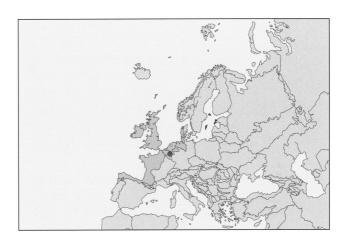

CLIMATIC DATA

Average rainfall
mm/cm²/year

Snow days: 15

805 mm

Temperature (°C)

31,7 — max ■
9,7 — average ■
-8,9 — min ■

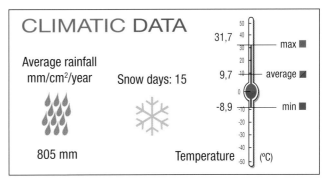

SUMMARY

At the end of the 19th century, hundreds of hectares where acquired in the vicinity of the village of Mol-Rauw in the province of Antwerp. The estate of 'T Kristallijn was bought for quartz exploitation. The unique quality of the quartz sand was discovered in 1845 when digging a canal. From 1869 authorisation was given for the quartz to be exploited. Because the sand layer was situated under the ground water table, the pits filled with water when the sands were being extracted. In the beginning extraction was done solely by manpower, but soon after the two world wars, as a result of evolving modern industrial techniques, research and development, the company started to produce new and innovative products.

The exploitation of quartz in 'T Kristallijn has now ended and the place has been returned to the nature. The company Sibelco continues to exploit quartz at other places in the vicinity. A basic philosophy that runs like a common thread through the history of the company and this estate in particular is the search for long term commitment in a framework of sustainable development. Long before the expression became a fashionable word, Sibelco and its several family shareholders had begun to search for a balance between economic prosperity, social responsibility and the environment.

'T Kristallijn Estate

In 1995 the decision was taken to renovate an old farmhouse
on the edge of the quarry, to play a social and cultural function.

BIRTHPLACE OF QUARTZ SAND EXPLOITATION IN THE CAMPINE (KEMPEN) REGION OF BELGIUM

To tell the story of this estate, one should first understand the story of the exploitation of quartz sand, as both are closely linked.

The story of quartz sand exploitation in Belgium began in a poor, rough, untouched and at first sight economically uninteresting landscape of the Campine, a region in the north-eastern part of Belgium. When digging the "Kempisch Kanaal" in 1845 in order to connect the Schelde and the Maas rivers, the unique quality of the quartz sand was discovered.

In 1862 the Ministry of Public Affairs gave authorisation for the quartz sand to be exploited. This original authorisation permitted sand to be taken from the sides of the canal, but on January 29th 1862 the Governor of the Province of Limburg asked his colleague in the Province of Antwerp to expand the authorisation to include that part of the canal located in the latter province. Several entrepreneurs set up in business, but it was on April 17th 1872 that King Leopold II confirmed by Royal Degree the official foundation of S.A. Sablières et Carrières Réunies. The company's goal was to exploit sand in the Campine "suitable for the production of glass and crystal". It was one of the first industrial companies in the Province of Antwerp and marks the birth of the economic prosperity of this region and of Flanders.

Because the layers of sand were situated under the ground water table, the pits filled with water when the sand was being extracted. In the early days, extraction was done purely by manpower, but soon after the two world wars, as a result of evolving modern industrial techniques, research and development, the company began to produce new and innovative products.

Having achieved its original goal, Sibelco then began activities in other countries, starting in the early 1950s, and successfully established its operations across the rest of Europe. In 1973 the company expanded into the USA, and in 1990 it started in Brazil. In recent years it has expanded to the Far East and Russia.

The small sand extraction company which started in the Campine in 1872 has grown today into a world player, active in 38 different countries, on 5 continents and with more than 10,000 employees.

The minerals produced by the company are used in products such as glass, castings, ceramics, abrasives, solar glass and other products which are in everyday use. As an example, about 100 kg of quartz sand is used in the production of one car.

View of the Wirtz garden that has been integrated into the landscape.

'T Kristallijn

THE ESTATE OF 'T KRISTALLIJN ON THE EDGE OF THE RAUW SAND QUARRY

At the end of the 19th century, hundreds of hectares were acquired in the vicinity of the village of Mol-Rauw in the Province of Antwerp. Under the land were large quantities of quartz sand. In 1896 the Stevensvennen sand quarry was opened, and was worked mechanically by means of a sand dredge.

From the early 1960s the company expanded its sand extraction towards the location of the estate, and the Rauw Quarry was started. This finished in 1997.

Over a period of 40 years, the landscape slowly evolved into what it has become today.

Sibelco has thus moulded a landscape, appreciated by so many people on a daily basis. Few of them realise that the landscape through which they walk or bicycle is totally man-made.

FARMHOUSE BECOMES SOCIAL AND CULTURAL CENTRE: 'T KRISTALLIJN

The management of the company understood that a society, however rich it is, is in fact poor when there is no richness of mind. They were convinced that art and culture are essential.

Art opens the mind to new things and enriches life emotionally. In today's fast-moving and stressful times, art enables reflexion.

In 1995 the decision was taken to renovate an old farmhouse (of the local district waterboard) on the edge of the quarry in order for it to play a social and cultural function. The building is available for cultural initiatives. It is in fact a social and cultural initiative to make art accessible for everyone. Local artists can show their works and the local community has the opportunity to see works of artists of other parts of the country and even the world.

The building is 435 sq.m. in size and consists of two parts: an entrance hall with orangerie decorated with tapestry by the famous Brazilian artist Colacco. From the orangerie there is a magnificent view across the garden and the lake.

The second part is an auditorium fully equipped with audiovisual technology that can

Postcard of Stevensvennen quarry.

be used as exhibition hall, concert hall and conference room.

The decoration has elements of an English cottage style and the building is surrounded by a beautiful garden of approximately 2 ha designed by the famous garden architect Wirtz. The garden is seamlessly integrated with the natural surroundings of the restructured slopes of the quarry. The high *Grassimilus miscanthus* grasses are prominent and sway in the wind to give the illusion of transferring the movement of water in the lake

Simulation of the evolution of the landscape in 4 steps: 1960 – 1964 – 1997 – 2008.

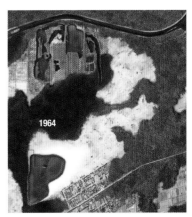
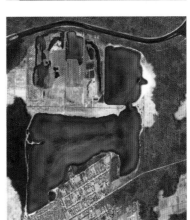

onto the land. The ancient stable building was retained and renovated.

The 'T Kristallijn estate opened in 1997 on the occasion of the 125th anniversary of the company.

The building lies at the crossroads of past and future, and represents the present and the philosophy of what the company stands for. The building, integrated into its surroundings, is an excellent example of sustainable development. On the eastern side an active quarry is still in operation and guarantees the future of the company and the estate. On the other side people can see the result of land restoration after quarrying, fully rehabilitated according to the principles of sustainability.

The 'T Kristallijn became a high quality attraction in the region. At every private view, opening or visit, people are impressed by its beauty and unique location in an exceptional landscape.

In June 2004 the company and family authorised the opening of an itinerary for walkers through the estate landscape. The itinerary was developed in conjunction with the local community, the locally active NGO and the Regional Landscape of the Basse Campine. As such the location is completely integrated into the tourist network of the region and is a highlight for the 2 million people who visit the region each year.

In 2007 another jewel was added to the estate: the Quartz Experience Centre. Again an old farm building comprising two small sheds was renovated, and now houses now an interactive exhibition explaining the story of the company, the wonders of the world of minerals and the after-use of the quarries. Each year the centre welcomes 10,000 visitors, free of charge. Schools appreciate the unique educational opportunities of the exhibition.

IT ALL STARTED 2 MILLION YEARS AGO

However strange it may seem, the story of this Estate started 2 million years ago. It was then that the quartz sand was deposited in this region.

During the Plio-Pleistocene epoch the configuration of land and sea was totally different from today. The Netherlands and the northern part of Belgium were covered by the sea. In the

Aerial view across the estate and its surroundings.

region where the estate is located, rivers – the "prehistoric Maas and prehistoric Rhine" – deposited sediments which they had collected in the Vosges and Ardennes mountain areas. The geological name for this deposit is "Sands of Mol Donk" or "Formation of Mol". They are unique in quality because of their high silica (SiO_2) content and their low contamination of iron and aluminium. This explains why they are the best sands for glass production.

The quartz sands settled in a delta-estuary of the ancient river in layers up to 25 m thick. After a certain time the sea drew back and the deposited sands came to the surface. Beautiful forests and swamps were formed, similar to existing mangrove forests today. Storms and floods took these plants and accumulated them in depressions in the landscape. This organic material was then covered by later deposits, so that layers of Lignite were formed. They were of crucial importance for the characteristics of the sand layers underneath; the humic acids leached the sands for many years and assured the extreme purity for which they are famous.

At that time the region was still tectonically active; faults were formed and the earth's plates moved. Such a fault line was formed about 300 metres from where the estate is located, known as the "fault line of Rauw". The land east of this fault

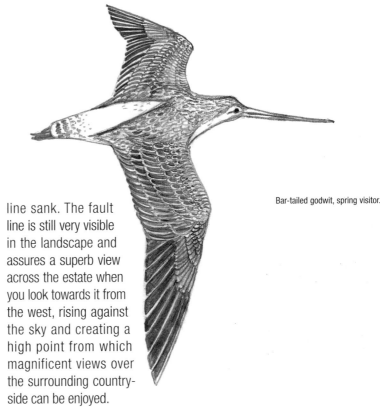

Bar-tailed godwit, spring visitor.

line sank. The fault line is still very visible in the landscape and assures a superb view across the estate when you look towards it from the west, rising against the sky and creating a high point from which magnificent views over the surrounding countryside can be enjoyed.

The eastern part which sank was later covered with a second layer of sand brought down by the rivers, with the result that, on this side, the deposit is up to 65m thick and again of extremely interesting quality.

Later, during the Quaternary period, known for its ice ages, the Mol Sands were covered by alveolic sands transported by the wind. These sands were of lesser quality and covered the treasures underneath, which took a long time to be discovered...

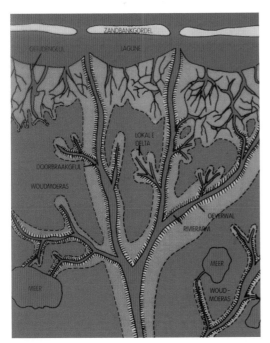

River delta.

Diagram of the geology of the region.

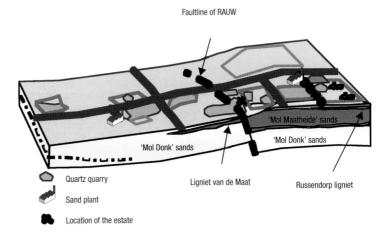

Faultline of RAUW

'Mol Maatheide' sands

'Mol Donk' sands

'Mol Donk' sands

Ligniet van de Maat

Russendorp ligniet

Quartz quarry

Sand plant

Location of the estate

Award-winning quarry Opgrimbie.

SIBELCO'S SUSTAINABLE DEVELOPMENT POLICY

Landscape with inspiration

The Board of Directors and the shareholders of SCR-Sibelco embody the philosophy of sustainable development and long-term management, which arose from their keen interest in mankind and nature.

A basic philosophy, running like a common thread through the history of the company and this estate in particular, is the search for long term commitment in a framework of sustainable development.

Long before the expression became fashionable, Sibelco, and in particular its several family shareholders, had begun to search for a balance between economic prosperity, social responsibility and the environment.

The first element – economic – is clearly a basic prerequisite for the guaranteed continuity of every company. The economic results of Sibelco are crystal-clear; over the decades the Sibelco group has grown from operating as a local sand extractor to becoming a world-wide market leader. This economic efficiency however is not sufficient in itself.

Indeed, there is a second factor, superbly demonstrated by the goal of the Kristallijn: providing people with opportunities. Artists in particular, but also society as a whole can discover itself in a broader perspective in this centre of social and cultural activities.

The third element, indisputably linked with Sibelco's activities, is the ecological factor. Its activities have an undeniable impact on the landscape. In the minds of many people, mining activities destroy the landscape and leave a permanent scar. The landscape of this estate, which is completely man-made, proves the contrary. In the example of the Kristallijn, three after-uses of an abandoned quarry are superbly demonstrated: nature, recreation and culture. The philosophy exceeds the scale of the rehabilitation of the quarry, and opportunities are explored to integrate it into the landscape and the community in which it is located.

The company's licence to operate means that it is pro-active in keeping a balance between these three factors.

One could also express it in the words of Elton John, in the song for the movie Lion King: "you should never take more than you give".

Quarries become locations of excellent biodiversity

In 2004 the Anders Wall foundation, in cooperation with Directorate General Environment of the European Commission, awarded a diploma for the

Bar-tailed godwit visits 'T Kristallijn during his travels on spring and autumn.

194

restoration of the Opgrimbie Quarry in Maas-
mechelen, Belgium.

A dam to raise the water level in the quarry and
the surrounding landscape, together with the creation of extra sandflats near the quarry slopes,
created superb ecotopes.

The quarry is now completely integrated into
the National Park of the Haute Campine, similar to
the example of the "Hoge Veluwe" in the Netherlands, and is home to species like nightjar, woodlark, natterjack toad, moor frog, sundew and other
endangered species of this type of habitat. This
restoration can be seen as evidence that, through
private initiative, landscape restoration can be
achieved hand in hand with commercial business
and can create beautiful landscapes, recreational
opportunities and biodiversity.

Natterjack Toad
(Bufo calamita).

Deviating a river to exploit a quarry: new opportunities!

In 2007 the Inbev Baillet Latour prize was
awarded for the successful deviation of a river
on one of their quarries. The river formed, and
still forms, the habitat of species protected by
Natura 2000, namely the Spined Loach *(Cobitis*

Dr. Alain De Vocht
(University of
Hasselt – Belgium) with
his students, monitoring
the deviated River Witte
Nete.

'T Kristallijn **(Belgium)**

Floating island: habitat for black tern.

taenia) and Sculpin *(Cottus perifretum)*. Sibelco decided to deviate the river in such a way that it reverted to the form it had previously had in 1877, namely a meandering river with excellent biodiversity. During the project intense coopera-

tion with local authorities, the local community and NGOs was established. The commitment surpassed the execution of the project but funds were also made available to allow monitoring for several years in conjunction with the

View of the deviated river.

University. The jury concluded that «this project shows that economical development can go hand in hand with nature conservation and development».

Smaller projects, such as building sand walls for Sand Martins *(Riparia riparia)*, rehabilitating an ancient electricity cabin as a site for the Barn Owl *(Tyto alba)*, creating floating islands as nesting possibilities for the Black Tern *(Chlidonias niger)* and Common Tern *(Sterna hirundo)* do not take much effort, but establish great results and demonstrate the company's commitment to its contribution towards biodiversity.

The curlew is easy to identify in flight, with its large size, very long curve beak, dun plumage and white rump.

Stonechat *(Saxicola torquata)*.

'T Kristallijn Estate

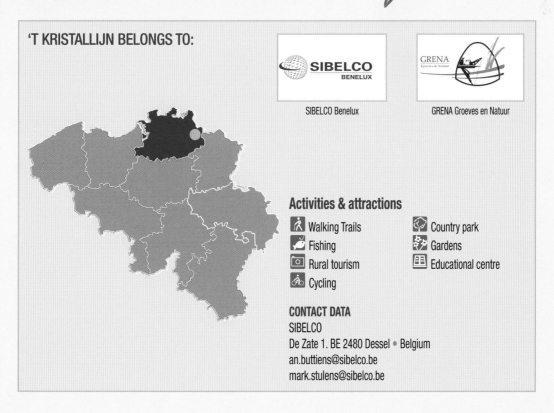

'T KRISTALLIJN BELONGS TO:

SIBELCO BENELUX

SIBELCO Benelux

GRENA Groeves & Natuur

GRENA Groeves en Natuur

Activities & attractions

- Walking Trails
- Fishing
- Rural tourism
- Cycling
- Country park
- Gardens
- Educational centre

CONTACT DATA
SIBELCO
De Zate 1. BE 2480 Dessel • Belgium
an.buttiens@sibelco.be
mark.stulens@sibelco.be

Theme 3

Fauna, flora and wildlife estates

FAUNA, FLORA AND WILDLIFE ESTATES

Carlos Otero

As the Commissioner for the Environment Stavros Dimas reminds us, *'The main challenge we are faced with is that biodiversity has been declining at an alarming rate, mainly as a result of human activity. Biodiversity is crucial to life as we know it. In 2001, the European Union set itself the ambitious goal of halting the loss of biodiversity by 2010. Important progress has been made and there are signs that the rates of loss are beginning to slow down. However, we also now have evidence that the 2010 target will not be achieved. This is a clear indication that more must be done'* [1]. Commissioner Dimas also underlines the importance of the EU Birds and Habitats Directives and the resulting Natura 2000 network as essential tools for halting biodiversity loss in Europe.

However, as Commissioner Dimas explains, it is safe to assume that the full implementation will not be sufficient to achieve this goal. Thus, achieving enhanced biodiversity requires the right balance between legal nature protection measures and sustainable human activities on the land, and the future of biodiversity lies, to a large extent, in the hands of land managers across Europe. According to Commissioner Dimas, hunting[2] can play a crucial role in this context as it is in every wildlife territory manager and hunters' interest to protect the habitats and diversity of species living on their territories. Commissioner Dimas therefore warmly welcomes ELO's **Wildlife Estates initiative** which promotes such synergies between conservation and sustainable land use.

The original **Pilot Wildlife Estates initiative (PWEi)** born in 2003 gave way in 2008 to the **Wildlife Estates initiative** which aims to establish a network of exemplary estates. The latter showcases the simple principles of good management and conservation of wildlife estates all over Europe, divided up according to its different **biogeographical regions**. Sustainable management is a very important feature of these exemplary estates, especially due to budgetary restrictions linked to the CAP reform, the lack of environmental funding and climate change which makes it necessary to develop much more sustainable behaviours.

Apart from a highly beneficial exchange of experience, the initiative also has considerable potential for society, both in socio-cultural and socio-economic terms: it provides an undeniable value to our common cultural heritage and it brings some added value to the common good of society. It will raise public awareness about the quality of wildlife populations, the necessary management, and crucially, it will be an educational tool for future generations. More concrete benefits of the initiative are for example the fact that it anticipates the implementation of the new Natura 2000 biodiversity strategies, it aids identification and communication of the activities of the Wildlife Estate managers and it creates a new network promoting innovative activities and techniques.

The exemplary estates, which comply with the previously mentioned principles of sustainable management and wildlife conservation, are rewarded (after a selection procedure[3]) by obtaining the **Wildlife Estate Label (WE Label)**. This Label has been developed to recognise and admit good management of hunting and fishing territories, rich in species and with abundant wildlife populations. In other words, if we apply a simple logic when looking for excellent administration of the natural, private territories where one hunts and/or fishes, we should look for its potential development into a Wildlife Estate.

The Label creates a system which ensures and demonstrates that the management and the use of natural resources on relevant estates respect

---

[1] *Wildlife Estates Booklet,* 2009. ELO Brussels.
[2] There are many wildlife and hunting estates across Europe that are part of the Natura 2000 network.

[3] See website for more details, www.wildlife-estates.eu

biodiversity and nature conservation principles. The Label aims to be flexible and is not a binding certification. However, a territory or an estate must complete two levels of assessments to receive the WE Label. On the first level it is a voluntary commitment to the 10 wildlife estate management principles of the **WE Charter**[4] and on the second level, a territory manager must fulfil the requirements of the **WE Questionnaire**[5]. Until now, the assessment methods for candidate properties have been supported by special questionnaires for the **Atlantic**, **Continental**, **Boreal** and **Mediterranean** biogeographical regions. It is important to note in this context that there are also 3 other major biogeographical regions in the European Union: **Macaronesia**, **Alpine** and **Pannonian**. WE aims at including at least one other biogeographical region in the future, e.g. the Alpine region.

As a conclusion we can say that the Wildlife Es-

tates is a logical progression for wildlife estate management. In other words, becoming a Wildlife Estate should be a logical aspiration for all hunting and/or fishing territories, which are, as previously mentioned rich in species and in wildlife populations. Firstly because this would demonstrate excellence in administration and sustainable, integrated usage. Secondly, the initiative aims to work within Natura 2000 and to pre-empt the upcoming strategy on biodiversity. Thirdly, WE allows land managers to make personal commitments to sustainable land use without having to rely on already stretched EU resources. It also gives them the opportunity to communicate with each other and to learn from the experience of others who find themselves in similar positions. Finally, successful WE application would prove that private rural actors are able to provide their own solutions to problems such as biodiversity loss. However, by applying to qualify for the WE Label, the territory managers already make a valuable contribution to biodiversity, whether they obtain the Label or not.

---

[4] *Ibidem.*
[5] *Ibidem.*

NATURA 2000 NETWORK – ITS BENEFITS FOR RURAL ENTREPRENEURS AND BIODIVERSITY

Ladislav Miko

The recognition of the need for nature protection because of severe losses of biodiversity dates back to 19th century, but in Europe the most serious problems emerged in connection with the post-war reconstruction of national economies in the early 1970s. The idea of cross-border site protection first materialised in EU 9 by the adoption of the Birds Directive in 1979, requiring Member States to classify so-called "Special Protection Areas" (SPAs) for selected bird species. However, even the theory of this concept was very weak at that time: no rules for either selection or management of sites in an EU-wide concept were provided.

It was only the 1992 Habitats Directive that introduced the concept of a real network of conservation areas for selected species and habitat types, incorporating SPAs as an inseparable part of the entire network, though by their character different.

The idea behind Natura 2000 was very progressive. In contrast to a national network of protected areas, focusing only on phenomena endangered or even close to extinction at the national level, the Directive selected a list of species and habitat types which are ecologically valuable but not always explicitly threatened (yet) in the whole EU, and has given Member States possessing such phenomena the obligation of designating conservation areas for them. Thus, Natura 2000 does not act as the "fire extinguisher" of last resort but as a real EU-wide network of areas managed in such a way that particular phenomena, rare in some parts of the continent, are still sufficiently protected everywhere, thus providing a big chance for long-term survival and possible future recovery.

However, there was no full political consensus about the real implementation of the network at the beginning, and in fact the decision about the first enlargement of the EU after 1989 acted as a big incentive for the implementation of the network in the "old" Member States. The arrival of EU 10+, soon followed by the accession of Bulgaria and Romania, has not only broadened the area of the EU in both geographical and political terms, but it has also seen the introduction of vast areas of natural heritage considerably "better" in terms of both quantity and quality when compared to the "old" EU, but perhaps potentially much more threatened. In most new countries, the high level of biodiversity was a factor of the low standard of living – and the biggest expectation of nations living under Communist regimes for decades was simply to reach the same living standards as "in the West".

But there was also another challenge emerging, especially in most of the new Member States, namely the low respect for owners' rights due to the suppression, on ideological grounds, of the basic principle of managing property. The establishment of Natura 2000 in the new Member States does not just represent a huge scientific exercise and a resulting mobilisation of substantial resources. It has tested the viability of the Natura 2000 concept. While the Directive, underpinned by rulings from the European Court of Justice, requires that sites are proposed only on the basis of scientific data, the issue of ownership has remained unresolved – and in any democratic regime it is impossible to establish a viable network of conservation areas against the will of landowners even if this has not been mentioned in European Commission law. Recognition of this fact has sometimes been very painful both for state administrations preparing Natura 2000 and for the landowners, who are confronted with requirements which once again put a burden on their property – often as soon as they have got it back after decades of totalitarian regime, under the so-called process of property restitution.

Lack of any inventory of natural resources in many Member States - both old and new - has often led to sites being "designated" in a quite "generous" way, without an ability to justify either their shape or their size (or both). Another challenge has been the fact that the Directive explicitly requires two stages of Natura 2000 designation, separate in time. Firstly, Member States have to report their proposed sites to the European Commission; if these proposals are approved Member States are obliged to designate them as Special Areas of Conservation within a period of 6 years. Thus there is a considerable time gap between the stages of proposing and implementing the sites (up to 8 years). However, during the first stage the state administrations were often unable to set future management rules for the sites. For their part, the landowners were, from the very start, only interested in those rules, when their consent was requested – but at that time administrations had no idea about this issue, being under huge time pressure because of politically set timescales for finalising their Natura 2000 proposals. These circumstances have in many cases created an atmosphere of mistrust between nature conservancies and landowners which has made the already very complex Natura 2000 implementation process even more complicated.

Last but not least there is one further uncertainty that has caused many difficulties so far. The Habitats Directive does not say anything about the quality of habitats included in the sites. This is usually not a problem in non-forest habitats. However, in forests the situation is different, namely how the requirement not to worsen the initial status of the forest habitat types is to be interpreted. Is it possible to fell and artificially replant trees there, and if yes, in which way and to what extent? Is it a requirement to have the same tree composition on the same plot forever, or must the approximate area of given habitat type be maintained within the entire site only? And what to do with those habitat types that are of anthropogenic origin and, if left to natural succession, will gradually be transformed into other habitat types for which the site has not been designated? These and many other sometimes very painful questions have been raised, discussed and argued during the process of establishing the Natura 2000 network in all Member States – and the responses start their life usually as a consequence of the in-field activities.

What is the role of landowners, and especially of those owning large properties, in the implementation of Natura 2000? In one single word: crucial. Why?

First, the list of habitat types and species for which Member States are obliged to designate sites contain both "natural" elements as well as those whose existence is determined by human interference – in other words, they cannot exist without human activities. To conserve them against the will and without the active care of the landowners is impossible. Even countries which started to design their Natura 2000 networks without the participation of landowners soon recognized that this approach is untenable. Thus, the first precondition of Natura 2000 success is the landowners' consent.

However, this is not always sufficient. Those habitats mentioned above need management. It is no coincidence that many of them are threatened to the same extent by both improper management and abandonment. It is no secret that big landowners manage their properties better than those who only own small plots. The reasons are partly economic – small owners cannot, for example, afford the same machines as the larger ones – but very often also emotional. Very often, big landowners have owned their property literally for centuries and feel a family responsibility for the proper management of their land. Nor are they so economically dependent on every acre of land or every single tree trunk. Many of them also have a sense for nature. Thus it was no coincidence that e.g. in the Czech Republic those who were negotiating new Natura 2000 sites, and who approached big landowners with a proposal to include their forests into the Natura 2000 network, were often asked the question: Why do you approach private owners with whom negotiation is always more difficult? – Why you do not draw the sites from the state-owned forests which cover 60% of the forested area in this country? The answer from the authorities in all such cases was the same: Because the quality of stands in your private forests cannot be found anywhere in the national forest. This was not just sweet talk but a matter of hard fact.

Thus, from the Government's perspective, the privately owned land in the Natura 2000 network cannot be substituted. But how can Natura 2000 benefit the landowners? Is it not simply a rather uneven relationship? A cold mathematician might perhaps conclude that. Usually there is hardly any direct benefit, especially monetary, for landowners who have property in Natura 2000 sites. It is of course obvious that any income loss or any extra work required by landowners in favour of Natura 2000 management should be adequately compensated. This is not yet always the case – sometimes due to cultural and legal constraints, sometimes for a very prosaic reason, namely lack of resources on the side of Government. Sooner or later this type of difficulty has to be eliminated, as this is not about benefits but about fair and normal relationships between Governments and the public.

But there are indeed ways in which landowners can benefit from Natura 2000 network. We will not continue to promote subsidies and policies and schemes derived from the CAP, as subsidies are not the right way to support sustainability. However, as long as they exist – sometimes focused on Natura 2000 sites – they should be mentioned here. Yet there is a kind of benefit of a non-monetary nature. In some Member States, Natura 2000 is becoming a brand, such as organic products are. In certain places one can detect the overlap of these two brands: organic products from Natura 2000 sites double their added value for certain circles of consumers. This issue is not only bound to food; there are growing examples of the Natura 2000 "label" being used for non-food products and also for services, especially in the field of tourism. Above all, this type of branding increases the prestige of certain landowners; consequently, it may mean direct economic benefit.

However, regardless of the form of ownership, one has to bear in mind that the main aim of the Natura 2000 network is to maintain, protect and conserve valuable natural assets for the benefit of all Europeans as well as for nature itself. If its presence is supported by landowners and if they feel that they not only own their property but also their Natura 2000 sites, the future prospects of the network will be good. Promising examples of this already exist. Hopefully their number will be growing.

Ladislav Miko and Petr Roth

Herdade da Comporta

Mediterranean

Location: Grândola, region of Carvalhal, Alentejo coast, Portugal.
Surface: 12,520 ha.

CLIMATIC DATA

Average rainfall
mm/cm²/year

Snow days: 0

539 mm

Temperature (ºC)

28.8 — max
16.8 — average
0 — min

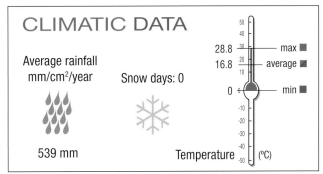

SUMMARY

Situated on the coast of the Alentejo, the Herdade da Comporta is one of the largest estates in Portugal, operating 12,520 hectares with an environmental and ecological heritage of inestimable value. The Espírito Santo family acquired the estate in 1955; they retain it today and their intervention has been essentially to develop the agriculture at the same time as supporting local communities.

The main focus of the Herdade da Comporta Estate is to develop high quality tourism, offering its visitors the experiences of leisure, sports and involvement with nature. Of the 12,520 hectares, about 920 hectares are being used to develop the infrastructure for leisure and accommodation. The seven villages comprised in the estate will be part of the tourism project, providing service centres and a restaurant. The development of this estate is based on the conviction that the economic success of the project is strongly linked to the preservation of the environmental and socio-cultural heritage.

The Herdade da Comporta is primarily a farm with agro-silvo-pastoral resources of great interest as well as a rich history and old agricultural traditions. Keeping these traditions alive, including the regional culinary traditions, is therefore of great importance in the development of the project. Its overall identity, strongly linked with a growing tourist industry, is only possible thanks to its landscape, its peace and tranquillity and its excellent beaches, as well as the local availability of high quality agricultural products.

The Herdade da Comporta brand includes a large number of environmentally friendly food products that meet current consumer demand in terms of health and quality food. The production methods apply principles of sustainability, already evident in the wine production.

Herdade da Comporta is situated on the estuary of the River Sado, 70 km from Lisbon. Covering an area of 12,520 hectares, it is one of the largest estates in Portugal. In the picture shows the new winery buildings.

Herdade da Comporta Estate

The chapel at Comporta, built in traditional architectural style.

G. Janssens

HISTORY

The Herdade da Comporta was acquired by the Espírito Santo family half a century ago. It is a place with a long history, spanning all the major periods from early prehistoric times to the present. The region has always been known for its considerable agricultural, industrial and commercial activities, motivated by the natural wealth of the land and its geographic location.

The Atlantic Company attempted to turn the farm into a model for rice production between 1925-1955. In 1955 the Espirito Santo family acquired the property.

G. Janssens

Pre-historic times - Alcácer was the political and commercial centre during the Bronze Age and the Iron Age.

Roman dominion (264BC-409AD) - Salacia (nowadays named Alcácer do Sal) was a major commercial and trading port of the Roman Empire from which it exported wine, olive oil and wool. Economic activity was driven by an emerging manufacturing industry (bricks, amphorae, lanterns). Near Grândola is one of the largest fish salting and preserving centres.

Visigoth dominion (409-711) - This is a poorly documented period, marked by recession in trade and urban life.

Moorish period (711-1217) - During the long period of occupation by the Moors, Alcácer returned to being an important centre of trade but also became a vital military base and shipyard, taking advantage of the extensive pine forest in the area. The town's name changed to Al-Qasr.

Presence of the Order of St James (1217-1550) - The Christians reconquered Alcácer under King Afonso II, with the help of the Order of St James. The town became the headquarters of the Order. The region of Grândola, in particular the riverside area, remained an important commercial centre until the late Middle Ages.

Modern Period (1550-1759) - The authority of the Order of St James gave way to the district council. In this period the export of salt, the main product of Alcácer, reached its peak. Much of the territory of the Herdade da Comporta was of low economic value during this time.

Emergence of the Lezírias Rice Company (1759-1925) - The Herdade da Comporta, which once belonged to the House of Aveiro, was incorporated into the royal *Casa de Infantado* and began to produce rice. Only in the 20th century however, when the *Companhia das Lezírias do Tejo e do Sado* (*lezíria* means marshland) was started, did it become the great economic engine of the area. The Herdade da Comporta was included as a result of the privatisation of national assets.

Atlantic Company (1925-1955) - The *Companhia das Lezírias* sold the estate to the Atlantic Company, which tried to turn the farm into a model for rice production. There was urban development and new settlements arose on the estate, namely those of Silchar, Torre and Carvalhal. The

The black-winged stilt nests in the marshy areas of Comporta.

©JNS

funds invested to increase soil fertility and for the construction of farm equipment exhausted the resources of the English company.

Acquisition of Atlantic by the Espírito Santo family (1955-1974) - In 1955 the Atlantic Company came into the possession of the Espírito Santo family. They began a process of improving the local standard of living which, to this day, has become integral to the development of the estate. They built 5 council neighbourhoods for working families, 3 schools, ensured weekly medical support, and extended the pinewood areas (by 822%), as well as the oaks and poplars.

Nationalisation (1974-1991) - In 1975 the estate was nationalised and the Atlantic Company was reduced to owning no more than some of the buildings. This resulted in reduced production of rice and a reduced local population. The process of returning the land to the Espírito Santo family took two years, from 1989-1991.

Recovery and development projects from 1991 until today - After removing the existing assets and reorganising the company, the process to recover and restore the natural heritage and urban and agricultural property began. In 2003 the estate became known as the "Herdade da Comporta, Actividades Agro-Silvículas e Turísticas SA". The aim was to develop a high quality tourism project and make the Herdade da Comporta a European benchmark.

DESCRIPTION

Brief overview and ecological context

The Herdade da Comporta estate lands include multiple ecological and environmental components that make it unique, in an area in which preserving high levels of conservation are a priority. It is no coincidence that land has been classified as a Natural Ecological Reserve, and part of it is included in the Natura 2000 network.

These different and connecting areas create a rich biodiversity of fauna and flora, some of them with characteristics unique to this region. For example, the estuary zone is rich in birdlife, including flamingos, ducks, herons and others; the dune structures contain several species of flora unique to this region, such as junipers; the waterside edges and wetlands are very fertile and are home to abundant migratory fish species especially along a ditch called Vala Real, formerly used for the transport of goods. In terms of forestry, the diversity of soil types means that there are Pine trees *(Pinus* sp.*)*, Willows *(Salix* sp.*)*, Alders *(Alnus* sp.*)*, and Oaks *(Quercus* sp.*)*, among others.

Environmental sustainability objectives:
- To preserve the fundamental eco-environmental balance;
- To encourage a balanced relationship between the local components of sustainabili-

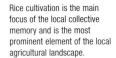

The flamingo is present in marshlands and rice-fields and is an indicator of ecosystem quality.

- Fishing, which despite the drop in catches, justifies the continuation of boats and harbours, one of them – the palaffite harbour at Carrasqueira – being of national heritage interest;
- The thatched cottages, of great ethnological significance, show the traditional Portuguese methods of constructing buildings with this kind of material.

Cultural sustainability objectives:

To strengthen the cultural identity and cultural traditions of the area, through:

- reviving traditional arts and techniques;
- reviving and maintaining festivities;
- increasing the number of thatched structures and exploiting their use;
- preserving traditional fishing boats and promoting their use;
- promoting cultural activities in the already refurbished Rice Museum.

ty: ecology, cultural heritage, cultural identity and land (in terms of transport, urbanisation and agriculture);

- To increase the quality of life of the resident population;
- To involve citizens in information and awareness raising programmes.

Most relevant cultural aspects

The cultural identity of the community of Herdade da Comporta reflects the ethnographic aspects that derive from leisure-time activities and daily work patterns. In an area whose history has been so marked by seasonal work and the passage of migratory groups, the most significant ethnographic elements are:

- The cultivation of rice, as an essential aggregator of the collective memory and as the most prominent element of the local agricultural landscape;
- The salt and the salt pans in the whole of the lower river area and the typical extraction technologies that characterised this practice;

Most relevant social aspects

About 3,150 people live on the Herdade da Comporta. According to a survey carried out on the estate, this population is aging faster than the Portuguese average, but is still younger than the average for the Alentejo. In fact, the farm has the youngest population of the municipalities of Castelo de Vide and Alcácer do Sal.

The population is mainly employed in the sectors of agriculture, livestock, trade and construction, but young people who complete their training can not find skilled employment in the region,

Rice cultivation is the main focus of the local collective memory and is the most prominent element of the local agricultural landscape.

The splendid beaches of Comporta are part of the sustainable development programme to make the estate into a renowned European tourist venue.

choosing to work in more distant places instead. Nonetheless, there is still a desire among the younger population to settle here, which is an important fact for the economic and cultural dynamism of the area. Besides, the residents recognise that they live in a "unique place" with strong potential for tourism, which, as long as it does not become overwhelming, can bring benefits to the population.

Social sustainability objectives:

- To contribute to the prevention of school drop-out rates.
- To encourage professional qualifications (technical courses for undergraduates).
- To promote varied training opportunities.
- To create jobs that, as a matter of priority, address the local population.
- To preserve the rural character of the area by improving farming and fishing.
- To promote the integration of tourists and new and existing residents.

Sustainable development programme

The Espírito Santo Group has proposed the creation of a Global Programme for Sustainable Development, to turn the Herdade da Comporta into a high quality tourist destination, capable of being a point of reference at European level. This tourism project is based on the integrated development of the economic, environmental and social aspects of the Herdade da Comporta, based on the latest trends from development models on sustainable tourism and UNEP recommendations.

This is possible thanks to the natural heritage of the estate: beaches and dunes, wetlands, forests, the estuary of the River Sado, and other spectacular landscapes which make this region unique in Europe and allow the territory to be classified as part of the National Reserve of the Sado Estuary, National Ecological Reserve, National Agricultural Reserve and Natura 2000. It is recognition that, in itself, points to a strategy of environmental preservation, demanding at the same time more responsible decisions about the future of this land.

The sustainable development is possible thanks to the natural heritage of the estate; beaches and dunes, wetlands, forests, the estuary of the river Sado and other spectacular landscape.

Sea salt, extracted by hand, was exploited at Comporta until the mid-20th century.

Herdade da Comporta Estate

The 64 hectares of grass are sold essentially to football fields and gardens.

G. Janssens

Economic activities

The economic and commercial activities on the Herdade da Comporta Estate are based mainly on agriculture, especially the production of rice and wine, meeting new trends by producing food in more environmentally friendly ways. The estate also plans to revive the production of salt, which is the last of the three major components of intervention to be implemented.

Meanwhile, economic activity resulting from the tourism project will provide the necessary conditions to sustain a strategy of conservation and natural heritage. Moreover it is worth remembering that, at national government level, tourism is considered one of the key factors for the country's economic development and the enhancement of its natural heritage.

1. Agriculture

- Turf grass production:

One example of an agricultural conversion is turf grass. Deployed in the former kitchen garden, the 64 ha of grass are essentially sold to football fields and gardens. The future purpose is to serve the tourism infrastructure of the Herdade da Comporta.

In terms of the use of water resources, turf production does not use a great quantity compared with other crops such as maize and it is suitable for the existing soil which is rich in water. In order to better rationalise surplus irrigation water, water is piped to a reservoir that serves the rice fields.

- The return of salt:

In order to restore a traditional activity in Portugal that is part of the estate's proprietary products, a plan is being launched to reactivate the salt pans which were created in this region in the 16th century. The project design envisages the recovery of the previous structure and the recruitment of local people to the art of salt-making.

- Revival of rice fields:

Rice production has featured throughout the whole history of the estate, and became the main crop in the 20th century. Since 1925 the estate has undertaken a programme to recover the areas adjacent to the river for rice cultivation, which increased from 7 hectares to 350 hectares.

From 1925 to 1950, a dam made of mud and plants was built to separate the rice lands from the river. However the estate has recently strengthened the wall and replanted it, since strong vegetation cover is essential to sustain the structure.

Today the estate produces 6,500 tonnes of rice annually, mostly the Carolina type, and is the second largest producer of rice in the country. Part of the production is delivered by 140 farmers, who pay rent and from whom the estate purchases the crop.

A proportion of the rice is marketed under the *Ceifeira* brand, since it has better distribution channels and is better organised. Nonetheless there is the possibility of creating a "Herdade da Comporta" brand.

- Certified wine production:

Since 2001, when the estate first began producing it, wine has become the emblematic product, contributing the most to the enhancement of the estate as a producer.

Occupying 30 hectares – 3 for white grapes and 27 for red – the Herdade da Comporta has taken great care over the establishment of its vineyards, not only through the selection of sites but also the selection of varieties, in order to qualify for wine of certified origin and to promote the quality wines from the district of Setúbal.

This regional wine from *Terras do Sado* appeared in 2003 under the *Herdade da Comporta* brand, since when production has not stopped. In its first year this certified wine was given an award by the Regional Wine Commission. One of the current objectives is to increase export sales, starting with Brazil and certain countries in Europe.

In terms of the protection of the vines and the vineyards, the Herdade da Comporta has opted for a regime known as Integrated Pest Management, which is applied to more environmentally friendly products and requires such things as the monitoring of rates of plant disease in order to enable more rational and timely interventions. Buildings have been upgraded in order to create a winery that can serve as a model in a region with only a few such installations. This new winery on the

G. Janssens

Herdade da Comporta is distinguished by its innovative style, architectural features and methods of production.

Built in the former estate offices, which date from 1930, the project has responded to one of the estate's main objectives: the rehabilitation of existing buildings. As such, the original design of the building remains, while inside it is both modern and bold. In energy terms, the winery offers means of minimising the use of energy. The building also includes a wine store and a room for wine-tasting and sales, and a restaurant will be built in another section. Award-winning wines and more environmentally friendly management are the hallmarks of this enterprise.

The new winery is distinguished by its innovative style, architectural features and production techniques.

Herdade da Comporta Estate

Occupying 30 hectares, the estate has taken great care over the establishment of its vineyards.

2. Forestry

Currently the forestry on the estate is dominated by the Maritime Pine *(Pinus pinaster)*, which is an introduced species and completely "artificial". In other words, it was the result of a consolidated forestry intervention of the last 50 years, since local memories and maps from earlier periods show that the area was once dominated by sparse shrubs.

Therefore, based on knowledge of the indigenous plant species in the locality, models covering the whole estate have been created and esta-

The regional wine "Terras do Sado" appeared in 2003 under Herdade da Comporta brand.

Herdade da Comporta Estate

There are 27 hectares of red grapes. The varieties has been selected to produce high quality wine and to promote the wine of the Setubal region.

blished in order to diversify the current forest cover, dominated by the monotonous and extensive Pine, with the ultimate goal of having trees and plants that suit the physical conditions and enrich local biodiversity.

These programmes have been implemented for the rural areas of the estate and provide for the continuous and gradual removal of non-native species in favour of indigenous varieties. In the future, in a programme covering the next 50 years, a dominant mix of Cork Oaks *(Quercus suber)*, Holm Oaks *(Q. ilex)* and other Portuguese native oaks,

Stone Pines *(Pinus pinea)* and Junipers *(Juniperus sp.)* can be expected, with some small areas of maritime pine remaining. In between, natural groves of coastal woodland will be re- established.

However, these natural formations – coastal pines and junipers – may require some appropriate human intervention. As an example, if there is no clearing work in the typical juniper woodlands, the species will be drowned by others due to the lack of light or competition for water and nutrients. Note that more than 90% of important species in Portugal result from human activity of some kind.

Cork oak woodland. The cork is harvested in a rotation of nine years.

The maritime pine dominates the forestry of the estate.

3. Real estate and tourism

The tourism industry is one of the engines of the Portuguese national economy and, as a service, represents a significant added value to the promotion of one of our most important natural resources - the climate and the environment. The richness of the Alentejo coast in its unique natural resources, associated with a requirement to preserve this heritage, allows high quality tourist services to be promoted and exploited.

Against a background of sustainable development, the current business initiatives are being developed on the basis of two models: those that are most appropriate to the natural environment, and those which take account of the social identity of local communities in terms of economic development, environmental balance and social progress.

The main tourist activities undertaken by the estate for the last few years have been to encourage greater supply in the sectors of accommodation, restaurants and shops. The efforts made to certify the beaches, the nature conservation mea-

sures and the rehabilitation of villages and buildings are also part of the reason why this region is increasingly sought after by tourists. There is therefore a real potential for tourism that deserves to be continued, based on the overall project aim.

An intrinsic part of the development strategy for tourism on the Herdade da Comporta is that it should be an engine for the economic promotion of the region through training and qualification of the local population, enhancing the provision of services and trade and the supply of jobs. As such, this project will have a large economic impact on the estate and adjacent areas.

The tourism project will be complemented with other measures that are either ongoing or are now concluded:

- restoration of the coastal zone and beaches;
- creation of parks, walkways and access to beaches;
- It should be noted that beaches at Pego and Comporta have Blue Flag status, have access for the disabled and have the Environ-

Herdade da Comporta Estate

- creation of the Rice Museum, which also aims to promote cultural initiatives;
- the reopening of the *Vala Real* which is now navigable once again;
- ecotourism and bird-watching;
- rehabilitation / redevelopment of the palafítte harbours at Carrasqueira and Comporta;
- walking, cycling and horse riding.

Another project on the estate was cleaning the beaches, done with the participation of children and inmates of the Pinheiro da Cruz Prison. These actions served above all to raise awareness and to support environmental education.

The rest of the work will be aimed at protecting, preserving and enhancing the environment.

Hydrological resources

The four ponds on the estate are the focus of rehabilitation projects that aim to combine environmental conservation with agricultural purposes.

The first of these is the Carrasqueira dam, which feeds the entire lowland area (cultivated riverside land that is flooded by water) and serves to irrigate the rice fields. Floating and marginal vegetation that was widespread across the water surface has been cleaned up. In addition, more trees have been planted and management measures have been taken to maintain an appropriate water level for the balance and enhancement of aquatic communities. It is also important to protect the peatbog, which is one of the fundamental resources of regional ecological study.

mental Certification ISO 14 001, which makes them unique in these respects along the Portuguese Atlantic coast;
- the reconstruction of 3 restaurants.

Main house of Comporta, built in typical Portuguese style.

G. Janssens

Wildlife management

The natural heritage is by far the most important element in the identity of the Herdade da Comporta, where the ecological richness has resulted in various environmental classifications. Furthermore, the local natural resources are factors of competitiveness and quality of life, especially for sustainable tourism.

Early on, the estate began a programme of comprehensive diagnostic work and implementation of environmental concerns, including:

- an inventory of biodiversity;
- an environmental assessment;
- the establishment of priorities and strategies for the conservation of all ecological components.

Surveys of the existing plant and animal species and the structure of natural habitats – mostly around urban areas – were carried out. At the present time the main drivers for conservation are known, but it implies continuous monitoring.

The region contains three different natural worlds, all of intrinsic value: the sea and the coast, the estuary, and terrestrial habitats bordering the rivers. These three systems have gradients that presuppose a structured management programme to maintain the natural habitats within.

To illustrate: the estuary is used by dolphins, flamingos and other birds and fish that also use the interior land for feed. Another example would be the fact that marine species also depend on the beach. There is a rich and varied gradient of plant communities from the beaches and dunes, home to flora of the region.

In terrestrial habitats, the inland sand in the more humid areas, along with the reservoirs and ponds, show a "peak" of rich biodiversity with characteristic vegetation such as Willow as well as reptiles and amphibians that use this area as a breeding site.

The riverside areas of transition, including the lakes and reservoirs, represent another remarkable point in biodiversity. In all this, physical assets overlap structures that may be less permanent and noticeable but are nevertheless essential to safeguard the biodiversity and the regeneration of internal areas. Examples of this are the corridors that link the different structural habitats.

One corridor serves the movement of migratory birds along the coast, on their journey between Europe and Africa; the fruits of plants in this area, such as Juniper and Crowberries *(Empetrum nigrum)* provide food. The second, along the rivers at Carvalhal and Vala Real, provides the link between the estuary and estuarine environments. These channels provide breeding sites for different species and promote the flow of energy sources, in the form of water and sediment.

Classification:

The estate's ecological and environmental assets are included in the following classifications:

- Natura 2000
- Natural Reserve of Sado Estuary
- National Ecological Reserve
- National Agricultural Reserve

The natural heritage is by far the most important element by wich the estate identifies itself.

G. Janssens

PRIVATE OPINION

The natural characteristics of the Herdade da Comporta are evident in the diversity of its country-side: the beaches and dunes, the cultivated fields, the forestry, the scrubland and the estuary of the River Sado. They make this estate a place of environmental qualities that are unique in Europe.

The investments and developments that have been made on the estate to date have been aimed at preserving and adding value to this heritage, in tune with the agricultural objectives and with the life of the local community in the seven villages that form part of the Herdade da Comporta.

We intend to continue to diversify the agricultural activity, in the way we have already started to do with rice and wine, embracing new trends in food production techniques that are more ecologically based. These initiatives, along with others that will be developed, will help to encourage the economy and business life within the local community.

For its part, the future tourism project is based on the integrated development of the whole estate across its economic, environmental and commercial aspects. The economic activity flowing from the tourism project will provide the necessary conditions to sustain a strategy of conserving and adding value to the natural heritage, but it will require large investment sums.

One of the pillars on which the future development of the estate relies is the involvement of the local community, through education, training and other incentives to create business activity and to develop the villages as trading centres and service centres all year round. One of the provisions of this project is to create over 6000 jobs over the next few years.

One example of the improved quality of life of the inhabitants is already under way. In 2001 the estate invested in a programme to refurbish the environmental and scenic qualities of the villages, through architectural work, providing basic infrastructure and tidying up the land.

On top of all this activity one must add the fact that the estate has been written deep in the life of a family for half a century, and that its development has been nurtured by their affection and desires over several generations. The investments made on the Herdade da Comporta to date have been the result of a series of objectives, including some of the least tangible - those that are born of dreams or are the result of the links created between the land and its people.

An important part of the dream is to bring this project to reality and to make it a reference point for sustainable development not only in Portugal but at world level too.

Manuel Fernando Espírito Santo

HERDADE DA COMPORTA BELONGS TO:

Friends of the Countryside

WE initiative

Associação Nacional de Proprietários e Produtores de Caça

Activities & attractions

- Birdwatching
- Shooting
- Hunting
- Equestrian
- Rural Tourism
- Historic private house
- Walking trails
- Hotel
- Restaurant
- Cycling
- Wine
- Estate product

CONTACT DATA
Rua de São Bernardo, 62 • 1249-092 Lisboa
Tel.: (351) 21 391 57 70 • Fax: (351) 21 395 20 08

Herdade do Zambujal Herdade Corte de Pão e Água

Mediterranean

Location: Locality of Águas de Moura, Palmela, region of Setúbal, Portugal.
Surface: 3,064 ha (1,719 ha Zambujal and 1,345 ha Corte de Pão e Água).

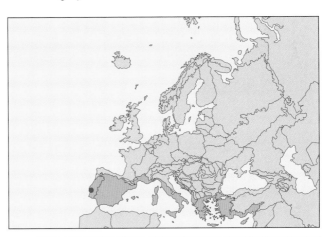

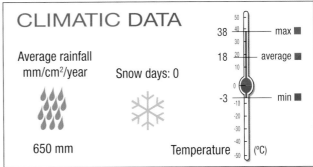

CLIMATIC DATA

Average rainfall
mm/cm²/year

Snow days: 0

650 mm

Temperature (ºC)

38 — max
18 — average
-3 — min

SUMMARY

Fifteen minutes from the city of Setúbal and 40 minutes from Lisbon, at the heart of the "Reserva Natural do Estuario do Sado" lies the Estate of Herdade do Zambujal, a privileged and magical place where nature is the basis of all social, economical, environmental and cultural activities and traditions.
Every human step forward is a fascinating experience, and reveals the exceptional values of natural, patrimonial and cultural heritage. Activities at Herdade do Zambujal are characterised by the breeding of horses and fighting bulls, rice fields, vineyards, wildlife conservation and hunting, and by the interesting combination of traditional white and blue Portuguese rural houses.

The original Main House was built at the end of the 16th century.
In 1755, was destroyed in the Lisbon earthquake. It was not until 1893 that the house was restored by the Vinhas family.

G. Janssens

HISTORY

The history of the place known today as Herdade do Zambujal goes back to Roman times, between the 1st and the 4th centuries AD. Indeed one can still see the remains of a site where pottery amphora were produced, used for transporting prepared fish (the famous Garum) back to Rome by sea. Even today there are still imposing and important examples of Zambujo Trees *(Olea sylvestris)* of over 2,000 years old, which gave the estate its name.

Historically, Zambujal was the property of the Portuguese royal house and later of the Cabedo family. It was the nobleman Jorge Cabedo de Vas-concelos who first built the mansion house in the 17th century. The building, nowadays a family house, was destroyed in the earthquake which devastated Lisbon in 1755. The only building left standing was the chapel, which shows evidence of having been a transit point on the pilgrimage to Santiago de Compostela. It had been previously rebuilt in 1719, highlighting the belief that the construction of the old house was prior to that date.

It was only after the acquisition of the property by the family of the current owners in 1893 that the work of recovery and restoration of the chapel and the residence began, according to what they believed to be the original lines before the earthquake.

Since its acquisition Herdade do Zambujal has been the home of the Vinhas family, and a meeting place for family friends and guests. Currently, the property is shared by two branches of the family, one belonging to the heirs of Manuel Vinhas and another belonging to Mário Vinhas, highlighting the fact that the property is still lived in today by the members of 6th generation of the same family.

About 40 years ago, before the property was divided, the estate represented more than 3,400 hectares of hunting area of very high quality, with records of small game shooting, rare in Portugal at the time, which were a result of several years work that included afforestation of 3,000 hectares of land with no previous tree cover. This is nowadays a forest of Stone Pine *(Pinus pinea)* and recognized as one of the best in the world in its production and quality of pine nuts. Currently steps are being taken to return to those golden days of hunting.

In the 1960s, as an innovative agricultural project, Herdade do Zambujal became the largest producer of peaches in Portugal, with approximately 125 hectares. France, England, Belgium and Brazil were the main export destinations, and the estate employed about 400 people, becoming a point of social reference within the "Região da Marateca". The social aspect has been evident since the 1940s, when the family streamlined the Herdade do Zambujal, introducing schools, a canteen, a doctor, and a ballroom, as well as other social aspects that remain to this day. Herdade do Zambujal is one of the few properties in Portugal which retains a population of current and former employees, with about 60 people living in a traditional village.

Currently hunting, rice production, the vineyards and the forests of maritime pine, eucalyptus and cork oaks, with a whole range of associated livestock, characterise the agricultural economy of the estate. The breeding of thoroughbred Lusitano horses and fighting bulls portrays the Iberian character of the family, linking land use to bullfighting traditions.

DESCRIPTION

LANDSCAPE: Feelings of tranquillity and harmony

Most of Portugal's landscape is worked by man, and agriculture is the principal activity responsible for the changes in the countryside. From the vineyards to the grasslands under the cork oaks, traditional human activities also play an important role in nature conservation. These unique ecosystems and landscapes combined with productive farmland offer unique and excellent management practices, allying quality, tradition, comfort and farming activities.

The landscape of the Zambujal Estate is heavily influenced by the serenity of the south, where the agro-forestry systems are the principal features, dominated by the Stone Pine *(Pinus pinea)* and Cork Oak *(Quercus suber)*. Elevations vary within the range of 2-50 metres. Herdade do Zambujal is characterized by an agro-silvo-pastoral mosaic landscape. The open and continuous nature of this landscape type is a result of the farming activities undertaken on the pastures and in the vineyards.

Supported by extensive forestry (stone pine and cork oak) and intensive forestry such as Eucalyptus *(Eucalyptus globulus)*, the property is also characterised by the overall presence of the Portuguese "montado". This is wooded pastoral habitat dominated by cork oaks, where growth of scrub and pasture is controlled and maintained by extensive rotational cultivation and/or grazing. It regularly supports more than 160 bird species and produces enough grass to breed horses and cattle extensively.

Uniquely in the Mediterranean region, visitors to Zambujal can go on to observe the salt marshes and rice fields, where it is possible to see another important group of birds, both resident and migratory, as well as fishing activities (molluscs, crabs, shrimps and sole).

Near the Sado river is the archaeological site dating from the Roman period. This was probably a site where pottery amphora, designed for transporting fish and agricultural products by sea across the entire Roman Empire, were made.

The **marshlands** are the estuary's major productive and biodiversity areas; these sites are breeding and feeding grounds for many marine and estuarine species. They are an interface between fresh and salt water, and between land and sea, where deposited alluvial soils are cyclically flooded by the tides.

Rice-fields are designated as a main food resource and habitat for a large number of species, and created an outstanding green landscape.

G. Janssens

The **salt marshes** *(salinas)* are artificial areas, but long used for the traditional exploitation of renewable resources and of great economic importance to the Sado Estuary. Although many are currently closed down, they are marsh areas that have retained some ecological characteristics of the converted biotope, meaning that they are still a habitat of fundamental importance for the majority of water birds.

The **rice fields** are strongly typical of the landscape surrounding the estuary. Although these are man-made areas, they serve a highly complementary function as food source for many species of birds.

Ecological context

Part of Zambujal Estate is classified under Natura 2000 and almost the entire estate is within the Natural Reserve of the Sado Estuary. This reserve covers the four municipalities of Setúbal, Palmela, Alcácer do Sal and Grândola, a total area of 23,160 hectares of which about 13,500 hectares are estuary. Although the region has high population concentrations and heavy industry between Setúbal and Mitrena/Praias do Sado, it nonetheless continues to preserve a large and complex variety of habitats of significant ecological value and productivity.

Diverse ecosystems, rich in flora and fauna, are thus created just a few kilometres away from Lisbon, the capital city, on the boundary with the city of Setúbal, where the urban setting quickly changes into rice fields, waterways, marshlands and successions of dunes and pine forests which briefly separate us from the Atlantic ocean...

The region is one of the natural areas of major ecological and landscape value in Portugal.

Situated in the central coastal area of the country, the region was inhabited from earliest times, when the fish salting trade was operated during the Roman period. The Sado is the second major estuary in Portugal and, in terms of aquatic birds, the Natural Reserve of the Sado Estuary is the third most important wetland site in the country.

Although extremely important for nature conservation, the region plays an equally important role in providing leisure and recreation for the inhabitants and visitors.

Natural heritage and wildlife

Generally speaking, the low intensity and localised nature of thousands of years of subsistence-style farming activities has had a profound effect on the landscape, creating a complex mosaic of alternating semi-natural habitats rich in wildlife. Zambujal Estate is extremely important as it represents a shelter for a variety of bird species, breeding grounds for many fish, and a place rich in vegetation.

Associated with its natural resources is the diversity of the landscape, which gives this region its character.

Over 100 species of vertebrates have been observed at Zambujal. Flamingos are very abundant in the Sado Estuary.

Herdade do Zambujal Estate

In the 1960s, Manuel and Mario Vinhas started once again to breed pure-bred Lusitano horses.

Herdade do Zambujal Estate

The "montado" of Zambujal Estate (explained above) is an ancient agro-pastoral farming system that strikes a delicate balance between productivity and wildlife conservation. Activities inland have resulted in a particularly complex vegetation structure which, combined with their dynamic management, provides a wealth of habitats and micro-habitats for wildlife. Golden Orioles *(Oriolus oriolus)*, Rollers *(Coracias garrulus)* and Hoopoes *(Upupa epops)* are a common sight throughout the year.

AMONG THE 100 SPECIES OF BIRDS FOUND IN THE RESERVE, THE MOST COMMONEST ARE:

SPECIAL SPECIES:
- Great Flamingo *(Phoenicopterus ruber)*
- Little Egret *(Egretta garzetta)*
- Black-winged Stilt *(Himantopus himantopus)*
- White Stork *(Ciconia ciconia)*
- Black-necked Grebe *(Podiceps nigricollis)*
- Purple Heron *(Ardea purpurea)*
- Glossy Ibis *(Plegadis falcinellus)*
- Red-breasted Merganser *(Mergus serrator)*
- Osprey *(Pandion haliaetus)*
- Purple Gallinule *(Porphyrio porphyrio)*
- Avocet *(Recurvirostra avosetta)*
- Bar-tailed Godwit *(Limosa lapponica)*
- Short-eared Owl *(Asio flammeus)*
- Lesser Spotted Woodpecker *(Picoides minor)*
- Water Pipit *(Anthus spinoletta)*
- Yellow Wagtail *(Motacilla flava)*
- Bluethroat *(Luscinia svecica)*
- Bonelli's Warbler *(Phylloscopus bonelli)*
- Penduline Tit *(Remiz pendulinus)*
- Hawfinch *(Coccothraustes coccothraustes)*
- Reed Bunting *(Emberiza schoeniclus)*

OTHER SPECIES:
- Cormorant *(Phalacrocorax carbo)*
- Cattle Egret *(Bubulcus ibis)*
- Snowy Egret *(Egretta thula)*

- Grey Heron *(Ardea cinerea)*
- Common Teal *(Anas crecca)*
- Black-winged Kite *(Elanus caeruleus)*
- Marsh Harrier *(Circus aeruginosus)*
- Coot *(Fulica atra)*
- Oystercatcher *(Haematopus ostralegus)*
- Kentish Plover *(Charadrius alexandrinus)*
- Lapwing *(Vanellus vanellus)*
- Grey Plover *(Pluvialis squatarola)*
- Redshank *(Tringa totanus)*
- Greenshank *(Tringa nebularia)*
- Common Sandpiper *(Tringa hypoleucos)*
- Wood Pigeon *(Columba palumbus)*
- Red-necked Nightjar *(Caprimulgus ruficollis)*
- Pallid Swift *(Apus pallidus)*
- Kingfisher *(Alcedo atthis)*
- Great Spotted Woodpecker *(Dendrocopos major)*
- Crested Lark *(Galerida cristata)*
- Sand Martin *(Riparia riparia)*
- Cetti's Warbler *(Cettia cetti)*
- Fan-tailed Warbler *(Cisticola juncidis)*
- Great Reed Warbler *(Acrocephalus arundinaceus)*
- Melodious Warbler *(Hippolais polyglotta)*
- Iberian Chiffchaff *(Phylloscopus ibericus)*
- Firecrest *(Regulus ignicapillus)*
- Nuthatch *(Sitta europea)*

- Crested Tit *(Parus cristatus)*
- Azure-winged Magpie *(Cyanopica cyanus)*
- Carrion Crow *(Corvus corone)*
- Cirl Bunting *(Emberiza cirlus)*

RARE SPECIES:
- Red-throated Diver *(Gavia stellata)*
- Great Northern Diver *(Gavia immer)*
- Marabou Stork *(Leptoptilos crumeniferus)*
- Greater White-fronted Goose *(Anser albifrons)*
- Green-winged Teal *(Anas carolinensis)*
- Bufflehead *(Bucephala albeola)*
- Surf Scoter *(Melanitta perspicillata)*
- Pintail *(Anas acuta)*
- Spotted Eagle *(Aquila clanga)*
- Crested Coot *(Fulica cristata)*
- Lesser Sand Plover *(Charadrius mongolus)*
- Buff-breasted Sandpiper *(Tryngites subruficollis)*
- Greater Yellowlegs *(Tringa melanoleuca)*
- Lesser Yellowlegs *(Tringa flavipes)*
- Marsh Sandpiper *(Tringa stagnatilis)*
- Spotted Sandpiper *(Tringa macularia)*
- Slender-billed Gull *(Larus genei)*
- Ring-billed Gull *(Larus delawarensis)*
- Iceland Gull *(Larus glaucoides)*
- Richard's Pipit *(Anthus richardi)*
- Olive-backed Pipit *(Anthus hodgsoni)*

Historical and patrimonial heritage

The garden

The garden is well integrated within the living area. The main house is considered to be part of the garden and vice versa, a living structure form where all kind of lianas transform the house into a living garden. The swimming pool garden is constructed on a former flooded area. Some emblematic *Platanus*, *Eucalyptus* and riparian trees border the garden and the river and exceptional views are to be glimpsed in between these trees that cast your mind towards the river. At one of the extremities, two well-proportioned ponds, irrigated by the river, reminds one of the natural beauty and the Natural Reserve that surrounds the park.

The farm and dependences

Considered as a small village, 60 persons live in estate houses all year round. Most of these are former or current employees and their families. All the houses are well maintained throughout the year and are of great interest because of their traditional architecture.

The village and houses at Zambujal Estate have the architectural characteristics of the Alentejo. The typical house of rural Alentejo is a house with large walls, to provide shelter from the summer heat, and painted with traditional colours. The houses of Zambujal Estate are painted with blue stripes. In others parts of Portugal these houses are commonly painted with grey or yellow stripes.

The thoroughbred Lusitano horses

In the 1960s, Manuel and Mário Vinhas restarted the traditional horse-breeding activity that existed at Herdade do Zambujal in their father's time, through the acquisition of all the mares belonging to João Coimbra and some belonging to Mendes Calado. The stallions used were "Guizo" (Veiga), "Firme" (Andrade), "Maravilha" (Veiga) and "Nilo" (Veiga).

In 1991, the descendants of Manuel and Mário Vinhas split the farm and the herd of mares into two different family brands. Consequently, Mário

Designed in a former flooded area, the garden once again shows off the charm of the property.

G. Janssens

Herdade do Zambujal Estate

Vinhas' stud farm started to select the horses along new lines, allowing better evaluation of the colt foals but more importantly an equal evaluation for the fillies.

With the stallions "Finório" and "Famoso" they assured the house's old blood line, and recently the two new stallions "Válido da Broa" (Veiga) and "Xisto da Broa" (Veiga) have brought a new impetus and an improvement in quality for the future.

The horses became internationally famous and a success not only in Europe but also in Latin America. They have shown their talent through bull fighting and sport, and have demonstrated that their development is going in the right direction because, apart from the morphological characteristics, they have been able to maintain the functionality and good temperament which is as characteristic as it is essential.

The private bullring (Praça de touros)

Essential in the breeding of fighting bulls, the bullring has undergone many transformations since 1946, the year that the brothers Mário and Manuel Vinhas started the family history of breeding fighting bulls.

Today, it is the place where the young females are tested while representing a traditional Spanish bullfight. This will show in some way their quality and bravery, which will ensure the future of the breeding programme and provide them a long breeding life.

This bullring has a long history, visited by some of the most important Spanish bullfighters, such as António Ordóñez, Paco Camino and Luis Miguel Dominguín among others, and almost all of the major bullfighters of Portugal, and also the setting for an interesting episode of one of the James Bond 007 movies, where a representation of a bullfight was made in our bullring.

The man-made palafitte harbour of Zambujal

During the late Neolithic period, about 5000 years ago, various fishing families settled on the estuary margins. In the Roman period, the business of salted fish reached its peak during the 2nd century AD.

According to archaeological research, pottery amphora for the salt industry were made at Zambujal, which is the site of the most famous Roman kilns.

We can see today that the traditional architecture still exists, despite the development of agglomerates, and that the types of construction are

Herdade do Zambujal Estate

distinguished either through the simplicity of form or through the use of local construction materials for restoration purposes.

Given the characteristics of its formation, implantation and vernacular design, the palafitte harbour with its handmade stilts is one of the defining features of the Sado region. Many fishing boats continue to be moored to the existing structure, which comprises hundreds of metres of board resting on fixed piles driven deep down into the water.

Zambujal Bridge

This is an old railway bridge converted to a road bridge when a new railway bridge was built a few kilometres away. This bridge crosses the "Ribeira da Marateca", a small river that goes into the Sado Estuary and connects Aguas de Moura to Zambujal.

DISTRIBUTION OF LAND USE

Irrigated pasture	57 ha
Vineyard	45 ha
Urban area & Gardens	15 ha
Eucalyptus	338 ha
Rice fields	33 ha
Montado and pine trees	1,231 ha

Extensive pasture land or montado

On flat and undulating land and in the plains, various forms of sustainable agro-silvo-pastoral farming systems have evolved that make best use of natural resources. The "dehesa" and "montado" of Zambujal is a prime example of a sustainable multifunctional agricultural system, capable of producing a whole range of different goods and services.

These open-wooded pastures cover 1,231 hectares of total land and are dedicated to meat breeds (Mertolenga) as well as the "Touro Bravo" or fighting bull, and the thoroughbred Lusitano horse.

The fighting bull is characterised by its aggressive behaviour with little or no provocation. They reach maturity slower than meat breeds as they were not selected to be heavy, having instead an "athletic" look and performance.

Far from aggressive, the **Mertolenga** is raised in an extensive regime with the objective of producing quality meat. The Mertolenga breed was historically used for its ability to work hard. It is a rustic breed well adapted to living outside all year round and to resisting the dry summer climate.

The estate also breeds **Lusitano horses**, considered as the classical Iberian war horse. The Lusitano is a very ancient breed, considered a warm-blooded thoroughbred. Archaeological evidence in the Iberian Peninsula, modern day Spain and Portugal, indicates that the origins of the Lusitano horse date back to at least 25,000 B.C. in the form of its primitive ancestor, the Sorraia horse.

In modern Portugal, the performance of the horse in the bullring is perhaps one of the most important factors in the breeding and selection process of the Lusitano. This factor has sustained the preservation of the characteristics of the classical Iberian war horse, so esteemed throughout the world over the ages. The Lusitano breed has been selected through dressage, war and bullfighting to become the most versatile riding horse in the world. Breeders at Zambujal are passionate horsemen and good riders.

Pine nuts

Pine nuts come from the Stone Pine (or Umbrella Pine) *(Pinus pinea)*, which has been cultivated for its nuts since prehistoric times. It is also a common horticultural tree, besides being cultivated for the seeds. The average harvests are 342,500 Kg/year.

Cork production

Cork Oak (Quercus suber)

The (noble) oak trees at Zambujal are used to provide cork which is mostly used to seal wine bottles. A cork oak tree will not produce any useful bark until it is 40 years old but from then on its bark can be stripped every 9 years with no ill effects. It will continue to produce bark for the rest of its life, which can be up to 200 years.

The cork industry is regarded as environmentally friendly. The sustainability of production and the easy recycling of cork products and by-products are two of its most distinctive aspects. Cork oak forests also prevent desertification and are the home of various endangered species. The average production is 112.500 Kg/year.

Rice-fields

The rice fields on the Herdade do Zambujal estate are still exploited by traditional methods and respect all the biological restrictions. Located in the heart of the Natural Reserve, by the river banks, they use river water to maintain the required flood area for the crop. That water attracts all the aquatic wildlife that gives the rice fields their designation as a source of food and habitat to a large number of species, and creates a beautiful green landscape sometimes visited by the beauty of pink Flamingos.

Vineyards

The Zambujal vineyards were established 12 years ago and are part of the quality controlled area of "Terras do Sado". The 45 hectares of vineyard are divided between six different types of grapes: Antão Vaz, Moscatel, Touriga Nacional, Aragonês, Syrah and Cabernet Sauvignon.

Regular annual production, which is hugely influenced by the climatic conditions, is 456 tonnes of grapes per year on the basis of optimum harmony between quality and quantity of the grape.

Sustainable wildlife management

The extensive pastures and general levels of production, combined with low mechanical activity in farming, make the estate of Herdade do Zambujal a perfect environment for exceptional wildlife management.

CORK PRODUCTION AT ZAMBUJAL ESTATE

Year	kg
1998	135,000
1999	35,355
2000	154,275
2001	132,000
2002	N/A
2003	90,000
2004	N/A
2005	130,620
2006	N/A
2007	107,250
2008	N/A

VINEYARD PRODUCTION AT ZAMBUJAL ESTATE

Year	Estimated Harvest (kg)
1998	N/A
1999	26.165
2000	76.270
2001	252.830
2002	368.510
2003	375.056
2004	414.120
2005	568.730
2006	404.080
2007	526.790
2008	456.400

Mario Vinhas with handlers from the horse-breeding enterprise.

The estate provides natural habitats for game and protected species, taking into consideration ecological principles such as capacity and general disturbance, and environmental conditions such as landscape, soil, hydrology, etc. The aim is to balance the needs of wildlife with the needs of economic activities.

Today, the hunting area of Zambujal goes beyond the limits of the property and represents a total of 3,275 hectares.

Concerned with the preservation and improvement of all habitats, the hunting season is planned according to game counts in order to preserve sustainable numbers. Nowadays Zambujal Estate excels in providing quality hunting for wild boar, red-legged partridges and woodpigeons.

The **HERDADE CORTE DE PÃO E ÁGUA**, an exceptional property of 1,345 hectares owned by the same family and could be considered the "oasis" of the entire region. The property is located in the municipality of Mértola and characterised by its cultural and natural heritage. The house recalls the Arab style and the delicate nature all around shows how important and necessary it is for there to be human presence. Even if it does not have the same proprieties and climatic conditions, all the land is managed in the same way as Zambujal, respecting and regenerating high natural and cultural values.

The Herdade Corte de Pão e Água is within the limits of the Natural Park of the Guadiana Valley. It has already been classified as a National Ecological Reserve, an Area of Nature Conservation, a Natura 2000 site and a Special Protection Area.

Land use plans establish schemes to safeguard natural resources and values, ensuring the permanence of agricultural systems and activities necessary for sustainable use, harmonisation and compatibility between human activities and the maintenance and enhancement of landscape settings. These schemes improve, year after year, the quality and quantity of wildlife and the economic development of the people living in the area. In terms of land use, uncultivated land is dominant, occupying about 515 hectares, followed by agricultural areas (about 397 hectares) and the areas of forested land occupying a total of 173 hectares. The purpose behind these activities is essentially to provide places for food and refuge for wildlife including wild game, thus providing important wildlife corridors and habitats. Uncultivated areas are retained, to be occupied by shrub or herbs of natural origin

The Herdade Corte de Pão e Água has established guidelines for the operational measures of its hunting resources, highlights of which are the efficient control of predators and the creation of enough watering and feeding points to boost the development of game species populations. It is worth stating that only one day's partridge shooting is organised per year. In other words, gamekeepers work hard all year round for one delicate day of recreation where quantity and exceptional quality is provided.

Herdade do Zambujal - Herdade Corte de Pão e Água (Portugal)

Herdade Corte de Pão e Água Estate is owned by the same family and upholds the same values in sustainable wildlife management.

Corte de Pão e Água Estate

HERDADE DO ZAMBUJAL BELONGS TO:

Friends of the Countryside

WE initiative

ICIMAD

Associação Nacional de Proprietários e Produtores de Caça

Ideas & Soluções Associadas

Instituto de Conservação da Naturaleza e da Biodiversdade

Cooperativa Agricola de Palmela

Activities & attractions

- Birdwatching
- Shooting
- Hunting
- Equestrian
- Rural tourism
- Historic private house
- Walking trails
- Hotel
- Restaurant
- Estate products

CONTACT DATA

Mário Vinhas
Herdade do Zambujal
2965 Águas de Moura
Tel: +351 265 912 256 ● Fax: +351 265 912 208
Antonio P. Soares
Tel: +35-939 443 335
antoniopsoares@herdadedozambujal.pt

Municipio Palmela

C. Otero

Herdades do Belo e da Raposa

Mediterranean

Location: São Sebastião dos Carros and Corte Gafo
Province of Mértola, Baixo Alentejo, Portugal.
Surface: 4,100 ha. (1,600 ha. Belo and 2,500 ha. Raposa).

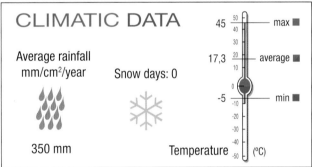

CLIMATIC DATA

Average rainfall
mm/cm²/year

Snow days: 0

350 mm

Temperature (ºC)

45 — max
17,3 — average
-5 — min

SUMMARY

The estates known as the Herdades do Belo e da Raposa, which have a total area of 4,100 hectares, are situated in the midst of the Serra de Mértola in the south-east of Portugal. The scenery is wild and very dry, and the soils are generally skeletal, with rocky outcrops of schist and deep gullies where the water is difficult to access. The region, of magnificent beauty, is crossed from north to south by the River Guadiana.

The Herdade do Belo was purchased in 1961 by António Champalimaud, father of the present owner, who took immediate steps to put in place a model of sustainable farm management, constantly taking into consideration the environment and conservation of natural resources, a policy which led to the rapid recovery of populations of small game species. In 1972 António Champalimaud also bought the Herdade da Raposa, a property that had been practically abandoned since the 1950s.

After the Revolution of 1974, in which all estates were taken over and devastated, the Herdade do Belo was officially recognised as a hunting estate (or game reserve) in 1989, followed by Raposa in 1990. In just a few years the game species had recovered exceptionally well thanks to the management efforts put into place, and in 1994 Belo achieved a result of 0.26 partridges per hectare. Thanks also to the hard work undertaken in restoring the habitat and in creating the ideal conditions for wildlife, such as planting crops for wild animals, creating water points and positioning drinkers, the estate's use as a hunting resource showed substantially improved results, and in 2005 a figure of 1.6 partridges per hectare was recorded.

The main house of Belo, built in 1961.
It retains the architectural style of the Portuguese Alentejo.

HISTORY

The Herdade do Belo Estate was acquired by António Champalimaud, father of the current owner, in 1961. The old farm was renovated and extended, conserving the architectural style typical of the Baixo Alentejo, namely white houses with whitewashed walls and blue boards which define the façade and windows. The design is based upon a spacious single floor plan, low-pitched roof with Arabian tiles, and interior courtyards which are cool in summer. In 1961 a new model of sustainable agriculture and environmental conservation management was introduced on the estate. It encouraged a rapid recovery of the small game populations. These included Red-legged Partridge *(Alectoris rufa)*, Rabbits *(Oryctolagus cuniculus)*, Iberian Hares *(Lepus granatensis)*, Black-bellied Sandgrouse *(Pterocles orientalis)*, Turtle Doves *(Streptopelia turtur)*, Stone Curlews *(Burhinus oedicnemus)* and a great collection of other related birds. At the end of the 1960s, there was an average of 4.5 partridges per hectare. This favourable situation continued until 1974, when the "Carnation Revolution" took place, and resulted in the disappearance of game reserves in Portugal. Within a few days, the wildlife was decimated and the estate physically occupied.

The Herdade da Raposa Estate was bought by António Champalimaud in 1972. It had been abandoned since the 1950s. The new owner had barely time to take possession before the 1974 Revolution took place. The estate was destroyed within a matter of days, and the populations of partridge, rabbit and hare which had slowly started to recover, disappeared. Both estates were at the mercy of the long and unsettled political situation, and it was not until 1988, the year in which official game reserves were re-established in Portugal, that João and Luis Champalimaud again took charge of both estates. Belo recovered its status as a game reserve that same year, and Raposa did so in 1990. With the unfortunate death of João in 1992, it was Luis, recently returned from overseas, who had to take over the responsibilities of running both estates at Belo and Raposa.

In just six years, in 1994, and thanks to the conservation management that had been re-established, shooting results showed 0.26 partridges per hectare at Belo. By concentrating on the preparation of special crops for wildlife, and on the creation of ponds and drinking troughs, 1.6 partridges per hectare per year were obtained in 2005 at Belo.

Herdade da Raposa has one of those landscapes, shaped and designed by the owner Luis Champalimaud, of which lovers of the red-legged partridge dream: deep valleys, indigenous vegetation, band cultivation, mosaic landscape design, thousands of rabbits, and many drinking points.

J. Carvalho

P. Maldonado

DESCRIPTION

Landscape

The region of Sierra de Mértola is a rugged landscape of low and eroded hills, with frequent outcrops of quartzite, deep gullies and hidden valleys. It is a magnificent region crossed from north to south by the Guadiana River, which to the south of Belo forms the border with the Spanish province of Huelva

Flora and fauna

The natural vegetation is characterized by significant degradation of the arboreal and bush species, resulting from centuries of goat grazing and charcoal manufacture. Only the steeper, wetter and rockier areas have retained the old trees, principally some Holm Oak *(Quercus ilex)* and Ash *(Fraxinus excelsior* and *Fraxinus angustifolia)*, and

continue to do so due to the policies and work of António and Luis Champalimaud.

A small Eucalyptus forest, planted on the island in the Grande do Belo reservoir by António Champalimaud is the home of Wild Boar *(Sus scrofa)*, thousands of Wood Pigeons *(Columba palumbus)*, many tens of thousands of Starlings (*Sturnus vulgaris* and *Sturnus unicolor*), perhaps 200,000 overwintering visiting birds, together with a good dozen Eagle Owls *(Bubo bubo)*, not to mention Black Kites *(Milvus migrans)* and Red Kites *(Milvus milvus)*, the Booted Eagle *(Hieraetus pennatus)*, Goshawk *(Accipiter gentilis)*, Sparrow Hawk *(Accipiter nisus)*, Black-shouldered Kite *(Elanus caeruleus)*, Barn Owl *(Tyto alba)*, Long-eared Owl *(Asio otus)* and many other nocturnal guests.

In 1994, the owner, utilising the Set-aside programme of the European Union's Common Agricultural Policy (CAP), reforested a total of 250

The red-legged partridges return results of 1,6 partridges/ha/year, under exemplary management.

J. Carvalho

The rivers that cross Belo, many of them even during the hottest summer periods, continue to support ponds, which become real oases when temperatures exceed 40 ºC.

hectares in Belo and a little more than 500 ha in Raposa with Mediterranean Stone Pine trees *(Pinus pinea)*. Today they offer wonderful protection for wildlife, and when they are lightly thinned will also provide a magnificent landscape, and is a good solution to protect the field from the erosion, and also to feed the ground water.

The much diversified grassland is composed of grasses and leguminous areas of great importance for small wildlife *(Trifolium* sp, *Echium plantagineum, Ornithopus compressus, Briza maxima, Avena barbata, Urginea marítima, Bromus* sp, *Raphanus raphanistrum, Dactylis glomerata, Ononis* sp, *Hordeum* sp., etc).

The entire food supply in Belo and Raposa, upon which so many predators live, depends on

Wildlife

- Horseshoe Snake *(Coluber hippocrepis)*
- Muzzled Snake *(Vipera latasti)*
- Eyed Lizard *(Lacerta lepida)*
- Large Psammodromus *(Psammodromus algirus)*
- Moorish Gecko *(Tarentola mauritanica)*
- European Pond Turtle *(Emys orbicularis)*
- Caspian Turtle *(Clemmys caspica)*
- Griffon Vulture *(Gyps fulvus)*
- Black Vulture *(Aegypius monachus)*
- Egyptian Vulture *(Neophron percnopterus)*
- Eagle Owl *(Bubo bubo)*
- Long-eared Owl *(Asio otus)*
- Tawny Owl *(Strix aluco)*
- Barn Owl *(Tyto alba)*
- Short-eared Owl *(Asio flammeus)*

- Little Owl *(Athene noctua)*
- Scops Owl *(Otus scops)*
- Golden Eagle *(Aquila chrysaetos)*
- Bonelli's Eagle *(Hieraëtus fasciatus)*
- Booted Eagle *(Hieraëtus pennatus)*
- Short-toed Eagle *(Circaëtus gallicus)*
- Red Kite *(Milvus milvus)*
- Black Kite *(Milvus migrans)*
- Black-shouldered Kite *(Elanus caeruleus)*
- Goshawk *(Accipiter gentilis)*
- Sparrow Hawk *(Accipiter nisus)*
- Honey Buzzard *(Pernis apivorus)*
- Buzzard *(Buteo buteo)*
- Peregrine Falcon *(Falco peregrinus)*
- Hobby *(Falco subbuteo)*
- Kestrel *(Falco tinnunculus)*
- Lesser Kestrel *(Falco naumanni)*
- Merlin *(Falco columbarius)*

- Great Bustard *(Otis tarda)*
- Little Bustard *(Tetrax tetrax)*
- Black-bellied Sandgrouse *(Pterocles orientalis)*
- Stone Curlew *(Burhinus oedicnemus)*
- Bee-eater *(Merops apiaster)*
- Great Spotted Cuckoo *(Clamator glandarius)*
- Cuckoo *(Cuculus canorus)*
- European Roller *(Coracias garrulus)*
- Kingfisher *(Alcedo atthis)*
- Azure-winged Magpie *(Cyanopica cyanea)*
- Wild Cat *(Felis silvestris)*
- Badger *(Meles meles)*
- Polecat *(Mustela putorius)*
- Otter *(Lutra lutra)*
- Mongoose *(Herpestes ichneumon)*
- Genet *(Genetta genetta)*
- Least Weasel *(Mustela nivalis)*

the very high density of rabbits, partridges and hares. Such densities would not be possible if the current model of habitat management was modified. Yet this model could be abandoned if certain sustainable uses such as shooting were prohibited or limited. Thus the current and future biodiversity and landscape of these magnificent estates are totally dependent on the hunting policies to support them.

The Raposa Estate is included within the Natural Park of Vale do Guadiana, and without doubt this is due to the considerable importance of the landscape, vegetation and wildlife which it contains. This park was created in 1995 and covers about 70,000 hectares in the districts of Serpa and Mértola, both in the Baixo Alentejo. Within the Natural Park there are already some restrictions on traditional uses, especially shooting, such as the prohibition of hunting on successive days and limitations on fox control. A conflict of policy is thus emerging which could put at risk the very environment upon which the Natural Park depends.

Agricultural activity at Belo and Raposa

There are currently about 40 arable field plots of 5 hectares in Belo, and another 80 in Raposa. In total, 600 hectares are cultivated annually, with a four-year rotation (one year of farmed and three lying fallow); the total farmed area is therefore 2,400 hectares. The dry land cereal crops are wheat (Barbelo variety), oats and vetch. The crop is not harvested but is eaten by the wildlife – rabbits, hares, red-legged partridge, wood pigeon, turtle doves, dormice, numerous passeriforms and some wild boar.

A vineyard has been established with the Cabernet and Syrah grape as test crops.

Olive trees have been established with the objective of reforestation rather than farming. The trees create small areas of shelter and food for the wildlife, and help to reduce the erosion of this dark-slated Mediterranean soil.

A small flock of sheep is run on the estate for the production of lamb.

There are three fundamental prey species in Belo and Raposa on which the whole wildlife structure depends: red-legged partridge, rabbit and Iberian hare. Without this extraordinary abundance the whole wildlife network would be reduced to nothing.

alho

Wildlife·Estates

BELO AND RAPOSA: MORE THAN JUST A GAME RESERVE

What would happen if some of the emblems and models of game reserves in Europe, for both large and small game, ceased to exist from one day to the next? What would happen if two Portuguese estates of Belo and Raposa disappeared overnight, for whatever reason?

The answer seems simple: For the owners it would mean significant economic disruption and a sentimental loss which would have to be classed as considerable. Doubtless within a few years, probably no more than ten, the owners would have found a new piece of land, in Portugal or Spain or perhaps even outside Iberia, in which they would have put into place a project that is vocational in character, in order to provide us with new but identical examples of "best practice" in managing nature.

If the authorities and the social demagogy of the new site had not bored the owner by then, it is certain that after ten years these wonderful achievements would have been repeated.

The reason is that the idea proposed and realised in these game reserves is indeed something … vocational. It is also certain that other game reserves would be constructed either close to or further away from the first. In other words, those affected would repeat their project out of sheer will and logic, and would put an identical model into place once again.

They already did so in 1988, if you recall …

But what would happen to the valuable and protected wildlife which depends to an extraordinary level on what is produced day by day at Belo and Raposa? What would happen to the dozens – I repeat, dozens – of eagle owls which live there now thanks to the thousands of rabbits which they catch on these lands? What would happen to the pair of golden eagles which depend on these rabbits, hares and partridges? What would happen to the ever-scarcer Bonelli's eagle for which Belo and Raposa is such an exceptional hunting ground? And the wild cats? And the otters? And the peregrine falcons? And the short-toed eagles? Or the booted eagles? Or the…?

The situation of loss faced by this hunting ground so full of prey would be catastrophic. Not catastrophic in the sense of shocking pictures of marine birds covered in oil, or genets burned to death in the summer fires. It would be catastrophic in the sense of … silence. The birds of prey would have to move away in search of other land where they could find abundant prey – an ever more difficult job – or, in the case of the golden eagle or the pairs of eagle owls. they would cease to breed, or raise fewer chicks each year, accentuating the decline of these species.

If they could, they would certainly talk to Luis Champalimaud to ask him to reveal the secret of the new site for his future project, to travel there and to be reborn, or at least to come close to someone like Luis who thinks about the future of the eagle owls and the large eagles and who is moved by the conservation of the natural values of the Alentejo which are so unique in this world.

There are plenty of other examples of places like Belo and Raposa amongst the almost 42,000 game reserves in Spain and Portugal. Valuable wildlife species have developed an interesting symbiotic relationship with well-managed game reserves. They live off the prey species which the estates produce, they clean up the sick or injured specimens – and in the case of vultures they clean up the dead ones as well – and they give such a high-profile value to the wildlife that they become a symbol of identity.

Cultivated strips of wheat alternate with hedges of xerophilous natural vegetation and with fallow. It is cultivated every fourth year so that natural food areas alternate year after year.

J. Carvalho

ng the landscape in Belo and Raposa reaches
vel of a work of art, a creative task that has taken
ars of tireless work.

The stone pines have been planted in linear form, bordering the cultivation strips.

J. Carvalho

The large eagle species, eagle owls, wild cat and otter are indicators of the quality of management on this reserve. As such, they have a wildlife value which it has been possible to quantify – in Euros – in many cases where it has been necessary to do so. To their traditional valuation processes – farming, forestry and hunting – the estates have gained another, which makes the figures of the former look very small.

The red-legged partridge population can reach almost 5 birds/ha and sustains a very dense population of predators. golden eagle, Bonelli's eagle, eagle owl, and up to 23 different species of raptor can be observed at Belo.

P. Maldonado

In other words, and as was defined in the ELO (European Landowners Organization) at one of the seminars held in Brussels in 2004 in the presence of official representatives of the European Commission: "Well-managed game reserves in Europe, thanks to the know-how and balanced management that is carried out on them, have become Wildlife Factories, in lands where results are not only measured in terms of red-legged partridges or grouse shot each year but also by the number of wildlife species that reside there and by the number of pairs of valuable species that breed there".

This conclusion opened up a new line of work for the specialists amongst us who were present, and it evolved into the definition of excellence for a game reserve that had achieved such a high level of management in conserving its natural values, in restoring its landscape and in promoting its biodiversity that it allowed the coexistence of game quarry species and at the same time – and at far more abundant levels than the former – of protected wildlife of incalculable worth. We decided to call this type of reserve a WILDLIFE ESTATE.

The next stage was the proposal that we develop a working protocol, using some simple indicators, by which we would be able to recognise whether a game reserve that was already well-managed could also be a Wildlife Estate and thus be awarded a label. It would then mean that this hunting and shooting estate would be recognised, by both society and public authorities at local, regional, national or European level, as an estate that is home to a large number of protected species and which in the face of devastating events or natural phenomena acts as a refuge and sanctuary for these valuable species.

Furthermore, in terms of the national heritage, they would acquire a value that could be added to other already established values (agricultural, livestock, forestry, fishing or hunting), to be known as the wildlife value, which in many cases, as I have mentioned earlier, makes the others look small.

The study group working on the Wildlife Estates Initiative has been developing a new line of work, namely the methodology for valuing Wildlife Estates in economic terms. Much thought has been given to this subject since 2002.

In order to identify Wildlife Estates across the length and breadth of the European Union, and to recognise their profile, we needed to have some

In Spring and Summer the female red-legged partridges bring their chicks twice a day to the water. At all times, the chicks remain exposed to continuous assault from all kinds of predators, who reduce the broods from 12 chicks per female in May down to 4 chicks in October. The less movement the better, and therefore the more drinking-troughs exist (up to 1 watering point every 5 ha) the more chicks survive. Belo makes use of every last drop of water, even the drinking-troughs existing in the main house, where the hares go too.

J. Carvalho

guidelines, criteria and reference values, and for this reason we selected various models of hunting and shooting estates to serve as Pilot Areas so that we could look below the surface at their secrets and provide a manual of their reference values.

Within the Mediterranean bio-region, the combined estate of Belo and Raposa in Portugal were chosen as model reserves. This estate offered a profile that could be analysed in depth thanks to the collaboration of the owner, the help of his manager, the transparent nature of his management methods, and by virtue of the successful results recorded on this land over the past 30 years.

Carlos Otero

HERDADE DO BELO E DA RAPOSA BELONGS TO:

WE initiative

Associação Nacional de Proprietários e Produtores de Caça

Friends of the Countryside

Activities & attractions

- Shooting
- Hunting
- Birdwatching
- Research

CONTACT DATA

Herdade do Belo e da Raposa
Rua Garret, 19 3ºA
1200-203 Lisboa • Portugal
l.m.ch@netcabo.pt

La Encomienda Mayor de Castilla

Mediterranean

Location: Villarejo de Salvanés, Madrid, Spain.
Surface: 1,710 ha.

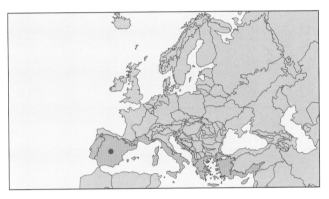

CLIMATIC DATA

Average rainfall
mm/cm²/year

Snow days: 2

447 mm

Temperature (°C)

38 — max ■
14 — average ■
-6,0 — min ■

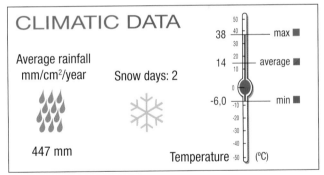

SUMMARY

La Encomienda Mayor de Castilla is a forested, agricultural and hunting estate located in the south-east part of Madrid, Spain, some 50 km from the capital. It has an area of 1,710 hectares consisting of Mediterranean woodlands of Aleppo Pine, Holm Oak and Kermes Oak interspersed with a mosaic of oak groves, pasture lands and plantations of dry land cereal (wheat, barley, and oats). This habitat represents the perfect place in which to hunt large game species such as red deer and wild boar and small game species such as rabbit, woodpigeon, red-legged partridge, etc.

The chief activities of the estate are hunting, agriculture, and conservation, with an additional focus on raising purebred Spanish horses, another outstanding and permanent feature of the estate. Comfortable accommodation facilities have recently been built which afford the visitor an agreeable stay.

The Estate of La Encomienda Mayor de Castilla is located 50km from Madrid in the south-east of the province. It has recently been awarded the Wildlife Estate label. Its main activities are forestry, agriculture, hunting and conservation.

T. Dorloodt

Wooded pastures of holm oaks and larges areas of cereal are crossed by the Valdepuerco, Barranco de Aragón and Balserón streams.

Encomienda Estate

HISTORY

Such *Encomiendas* were part of the jurisdictional territory of the medieval Spanish Military Orders, entrusted by the Master of the Order, and afterwards by the King of Spain, to a knight with the title of Commander. The person to whom the *Encomienda* was entrusted had jurisdiction over all its people, lands, and rights, and received whatever the goods and profits it produced. The *Encomienda* was the equivalent of a lordship for life, whose lord (the Commander) was responsible for its defence and its preservation. The primary purpose of granting such *Encomiendas*, therefore, was strategic. Because of the political power and life-long tenure that accompanied them, such grants were among the most valued dignities of the Military Orders.

The Commanders of the *Encomiendas* represented the authority of the Master of the Military Order in their territories, and only the Master had the power to hear cases brought against the Commanders.

The Military Order of Santiago had more than 84 *Encomiendas* spread throughout Castilla, León, Aragón and Sicily, all of them Spanish territories during the Middle Ages.

The origins of the *Encomienda* system date back to the period of the Reconquest, when the king and queen granted to the Military Order towns and estates, buildings and territories, as rewards for having helped them fight against the Moors. Little by little the Masters of the Military Orders gathered these rights and possessions to themselves until by the end of the 14th century the *Encomiendas* were permanently fixed as properties belonging to specific owners.

Commanders were required to reside for at least two months each year in the area of their jurisdiction, i.e. their *Encomienda*. If they did not do so, they were fined at a rate of 2,000 maravedíes for each man-at-arms under their command. This fine was to be collected by the rector of the church and the oldest magistrate.

In the last third of the 15th century, La Encomienda de Villarejo de Salvanés became the principal property in La Encomienda Mayor de Castilla.

In 1545 the Commander of La Encomienda Mayor de Castilla was Don Juan de Zúñiga y Avellaneda, the tutor and guardian of Prince Philip, son of the King Charles I of Spain, Emperor of the Holy Roman Empire. Prince Philip later became King Philip II of Spain.

Among the many properties of the Encomienda Villarejo de Salvanés village – which included a castellated fortress, the Commander's palace, storehouses, the church and the chapels – is a group of rural estates called *La Encomienda* minutely described in a document written on the occasion of the Encomienda's being granted to the heir to the Spanish throne, the Infante Don Fernando, by his father King Charles III in 1766.

The commander of the Villa to leave the greatest mark in history was Don Luis de Requesens y Zúñiga, Don Juan de Austria's lieutenant during the famous Battle of Lepanto, against the Turkish Empire.

After successive inheritances, the estate passed to the Sanz Vives family, which is how the current owner obtained it.

GENERAL DESCRIPTION

The estate is located in the municipal district of Villarejo de Salvanés in the south-east of Madrid, 50 km from the capital. The estate consists of a surface area of 1,710 hectares, of which 600 hectares are pastureland and groves of Holm Oak *(Quercus ilex)* spread among masses of Aleppo Pine *(Pinus halepensis)*, the Holm Oak subspecies *(Quercus ilex rotundifolia)*, Kermes Oak *(Quercus coccifera)*, Spanish Broom *(Retama sphaerocarpa)*, and Black Poplar *(Populus nigra)*.

The natural boundaries of the estate are as follows. *To the north* it is bounded by La Romera and La Nava, two places whose northern boundary coincides with the administrative division of the municipal lands of Belmonte de Tajo and Villarejo de Salvanés. *To the east* it is bounded by the estates of Valle Verde and La Matanza along a line that follows the bank of the Valdepuerco brook, a tributary of the Tajo River. *To the south* the perimeter of the estate follows the administrative boundary of the Regions of Madrid and Castilla-La Mancha (Province of Toledo). *To the west*, from south to north, the estate is bounded by the municipality of Colmenar de Oreja

La Encomienda Mayor de Castilla has a large amount of Aleppo Pine in good condition. The good land in the ravines and valley bottoms supports dry-land cereal crops. These wooded areas are ideal habitat for the red deer population.

T. Dorlodot

C. Otero

The highest areas of land are covered by a mixed woods of Aleppo pine and holm oak, cereal crops with scattered oaks and a pure oak forest.

and that of Belmonte del Tajo, known as La Romera.

Thanks to its extensive and well-distributed network of nearly 45 km of roads, the estate's game-keepers are able to maintain an excellent control over the territory and thus to guarantee a high level of tranquillity in the ecosystem which allows easier organization of hunts, more accurate tracking of game, and better management of other activities of the estate.

From the point of view of water management, the estate is part of the basin of the Tajo River, which flows immediately to its east. The presence and absence of water, which characterises mountainous regions, as well as the type of soil found there, form clearly differentiated vegetation areas. Thus on the eastern boundary of the property, defined by the Valdepuerco brook, one encounters formations of riparian vegetation such as French Tamarisk *(Tamarix gallica)* and Giant Cane *(Arundo donax)*. The brook is a source of water which can be pumped into a reservoir and distributed to various parts of the estate by buried PVC (plastic) pipe. Furthermore water from the brook can be pumped into large pools which serve as watering holes and bathing sites for

the animals. The area through which the Valdepuerco brook flows is at an altitude of 550 metres above sea level, the lowest part of the estate.

In the southern half of the estate, the woodland principally consists of Holm Oak *(Quercus ilex rotundifolia)* with a shrub and herbaceous layer in which Esparto Grass *(Stipa tenacissima)* predominates, together with mixed thyme plants (gypsophilous or not), calcicolous shrubs and a sporadic presence of Prickly Juniper *(Juniperus oxycedrus)* and White Broom *(Retama sphaerocarpa)*. The topography of this area is mainly flat and has two small seasonal streams: the stream of el Barranco de Aragón and the stream of Balserón, both culminating in the Estremera canal whose water flows into the Tajo River. The flow volume of these streams varies depending on climate conditions, but on numerous occasions, during the summer season the water remains in certain deep pools which are useful as watering holes for the various species of fauna that can be found in the area.

The northern half of the estate possesses a more variable topography, having hills and hillocks. The chief hill is El Cabrial (772 metres above sea level). The soil in this area is clayey and sandy and of very good quality because it has not been subjected to erosion. In this area the tree cover is mainly represented by Aleppo Pine *(Pinus halepensis)*, copses of Kermes Oak *(Quercus coccifera)* and Thyme *(Rosmarinus officinalis)*. In the highest part of this area, one can find a permanent spring that supplies drinkable water to the houses all year round.

The soils of the estate are strongly influenced by the nature of the limestone rocks, which predominate in the middle and lower parts. It can be said that, apart from those of an alluvial nature, the soils are formed in depressions between hillocks of limestone or chalky nature, with materials that come from the erosion of such hillocks. This fact gives the landscape a particular beauty.

Vegetation

The estate's vegetation surface is made up principally of areas of cultivation and of massive forests, as is shown in the following graphic:

Among the crops under cultivation are principally an abundance of dry land cereals, such as wheat, barley and rye, which take up an area of 600 hectares.

Other vegetation formations include:

DISTRIBUTION OF VEGETATION

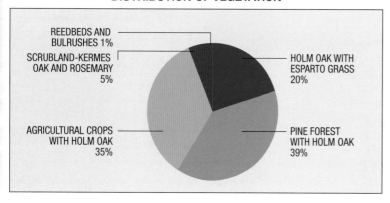

REEDBEDS AND BULRUSHES 1%

SCRUBLAND-KERMES OAK AND ROSEMARY 5%

AGRICULTURAL CROPS WITH HOLM OAK 35%

HOLM OAK WITH ESPARTO GRASS 20%

PINE FOREST WITH HOLM OAK 39%

- **Holm Oak:** This takes up half the estate. The Holm Oak *(Quercus ilex rotundifolia)* is situated in pastureland with a scrub layer formed by Esparto Grass *(Stipa tenacissima)* and White Broom *(Retama sphaerocarpa)*, with occasional Kermes Oak *(Quercus coccifera)* or Sageleaf Rockrose *(Cistus salvifolius)*, and, in the more humid areas, Tamarisk *(Tamarix africana)*.
- **Pine forest with Holm Oak:** Much of the surface is covered with a pine forest of Aleppo Pine *(Pinus halepensis)* with a scrub layer predominantly of Kermes Oak *(Quercus coccifera)* and Thyme *(Rosmarinus officinalis)*. In the pine forest there are also holm oaks that in some areas are as numerous as the pines. In some of the pine forests there are also other species such as Portuguese Oak *(Quercus faginea)*, Prickly Juniper *(Juniperus oxycedrus)* and sporadically Common Hawthorn *(Crathaegus monogyna)* and Ash *(Fraxinus angustifolia)*.
- **Agricultural crops with Holm Oak:** In many plots of agricultural land dedicated to the cultivation of irrigated cereals holm oak are present. Except for about 90 hectares in the northern and south-eastern part, the cultivated lands are open and the crops are freely eaten by animals. Nevertheless good yields are harvested here, especially significant amounts of wheat and barley – over 2,000 Kg/ha. Oats are sown earlier in the season so that they can re-sprout
- **Poplar area:** There is a small area of Poplar *(Populus nigra)* cultivation resulting from a plantation that was well used in the past. Nowadays it is not used.
- **Irrigation:** 15 hectares are for the cultivation of irrigated crops (maize and wheat) which are watered by sprinklers.
- **Scrubland - Kermes Oak and Rosemary:** On the hill of Cabrial there is a pine forest of Aleppo pine that suffered a fire 10 years ago affecting 40 ha. As a consequence the territory has been colonized by full-sun species that correspond to the substitution phases of this type of pines on limey soil, mainly Kermes Oak *(Quercus coccifera)* and Rosemary *(Rosmarinus officinalis)*. There are also other species such as Sageleaf Rockrose *(Cistus salvifolius)* and Spanish Gorse *(Genista escorpius)*. Because of its vegetation density, this area of the estate is a magnificent refuge for hunting, specially for wild boar, extremely abundant here.

A snow-white landscape is exceptional here. The snow stays for one or two days only. In the picture, wild boar and red deer search hard for acorns fallen from the oaks.

Encomienda Estate

■ **Reedbeds and Bulrushes:** There are vegetation formations associated with streams and flowing water made up mainly of Giant Cane *(Arundo donax)* and Common Reed *(Phragmites australis)*, Bulrush *(Typha latifolia, T. angustifolia)*, Lily *(Aphyllanthes monspelliensis)*, water-loving grasses, as well as French Tamarisk *(Tamarix gallica)*.

Fauna

In the denser pine forest areas one can observe birds such as the Red Kite *(Milvus milvus)*, Crested Tit *(Parus cristatus)*, Coal Tit *(Parus ater)*, Great Tit *(Parus major)*, and some nocturnal birds of prey such as the Little Owl *(Athene noctua)*. Among the birds of prey we can also find the Common Buzzard *(Buteo buteo)*, Common Kestrel *(Falco tinnunculus)*, Goshawk *(Accipiter gentilis)*, Sparrowhawk *(Accipiter nisus)*, Peregrine Falcon *(Falco peregrinus)* and Bonelli's Eagle *(Hieraetus fasciatus)* and Golden Eagle *(Aquila chrysaëtos)*. All of them are included in the catalogue of protected species of the autonomous region of Madrid and object of special attention following the model encourage by Wildlife Estate Label®.

The unmistakable noise of the Great Spotted Woodpecker *(Dendrocopos major)* Great Spotted in the trunk of the black poplar or in rotten wood creates a welcoming atmosphere on summer afternoons. This environment is enhanced at the end of springtime by the flights of White Storks *(Ciconia ciconia)* over the pine forests and cultivations of La Encomienda.

In the reed beds next to ponds and streams we can find other birds such as the Mallard *(Anas platyrhynchos)*, Grey Wagtail *(Motacilla cinerea)*, Reed Bunting *(Emberiza schoeniclus)* and Nightingale *(Luscinia megarhynchos)*. There are also mammals such as the South-western Water Vole *(Arvicola sapidus)*, Mole *(Talpa europea)*, Hedgehog

MORE IMPORTANT GAME SPECIES

- Red Deer *(Cervus elaphus hispanicus)*
- Roe Deer *(Capreolus capreolus)*
- Wild Boar *(Sus scrofa)*
- Rabbit *(Oryctolagus cuniculus)*
- Iberian Hare *(Lepus granatensis)*
- Red-legged Partridge *(Alectoris rufa)*
- Turtle Dove *(Streptopelia turtur)*
- Common Quail *(Coturnix coturnix)*
- Woodpigeon *(Columba palumbus)*

(Erinaceus europaeus), Least Weasel *(Mustela nivalis)*, Red Squirrel *(Sciurus vulgaris)*, and amphibians and reptiles such as the Jeweled Lizard *(Lacer lepida)*, Southern Smooth Snake *(Coronella girondica)*, Lataste's Viper *(Vipera latastei)*, Common Toad *(Bufo bufo)*, Natterjack Toad *(Bufo calamita)*, and Common Midwife Toad *(Alytes obstetricans)*.

In the more open areas of cultivation it is not unusual to find the European Bee-eater *(Merops apiaster)*, Pale Rock Sparrow *(Petronia petronia)*, House Sparrow *(Passer domesticus)*, Kingfisher *(Alcedo atthis)*, Swallow *(Hirundo rustica)*, and the Swift *(Apus apus)*. The Pin-tailed Sandgrouse *(Pterocles alchata)* visits the drinking throughs and ponds during the summer.

The scrubland and wasteland territories are inhabited by birds such as the Great Tit *(Parus major)*, Woodpigeon *(Columba palumbus)*, Northern Wheatear *(Oenanthe oenanthe)*, Subalpine warbler *(Sylvia cantillans)*, Dartford warbler *(Sylvia undata)*, and Rock Bunting *(Embericia cia)*. There are also mammals, especially rabbits, Iberian hares, and predators such as the fox. We can find reptiles from the Montpellier Snake *(Malpolon monspessulanus)* to the Ladder Snake *(Elaphe scalaris)*, in addition to the Large Lizard *(Psammodromus algirus)* and the Spanish Lizard *(Psammodromus hispanicus)*.

Main House and other buildings

The main house has recently been refurbished but the work has respected the original construction, with stonework, a concrete framework, and covered with treated wood and Arabic tiles.

It is a rectangular building that consists of two floors plus an attic. It has all the modern comforts with individual air conditioning, heating, wireless internet throughout the whole house, TV and audio connections in the communal and private areas, a swimming pool, a garden, etc.

Connected to the main building, houses for the game-keepers and some shaded arcades for cars have been refurbished. The total surface area of the construction is about 1,500 m².

Main economic activities of the estate

The estate is managed and directed towards its role as an important agricultural, hunting and tourism resource that will guarantee at all times the conservation of the environment and of the protected species that find their habitats there.

Encomienda Estate

Encomienda Estate

One of the immediate aims of the estate is to improve the standard of trophy of the Iberian red deer.

1. Hunting activity: Commercial hunting of Red Deer *(Cervus elaphus)* and Wild Boar *(Sus scrofa)*, as well as rabbit and partridges.
2. Agricultural activity: Mainly dry land cultivation of cereals.
3. Equine livestock: Purebred Spanish horses *(Pura Raza Española)*.
4. Public relations.

STAFF

Name	Qualification	Years of service
Alfonso García Morales	Hunting manager	6
Julio Gutiérrez	Tractor driver	6
Diamantino Santos	Gamekeeper	6
Adelaida Gouveia	Guardian	6
Álvaro Gutiérrez	Tractor driver	3
Julián Nitu	Gardener	1
Cristina Nitu	Domestic	1

J.L. Rodríguez

The pin-tailed sandgrouse is a valuable species present on the estate throughout the year. It is most often seen in summer when it goes to drink punctually each morning.

The population or red deer on La Encomienda Mayor de Castilla demonstrates the features of the Iberian sub-species *(Cervus elaphus hispanicus or angulatus)*, wich some authors uphold when describing the typical antler formations.

J.L. Rodríguez

With respect to the hunting activities, the territory has been divided into various smaller hunting units for better management. These units are commonly known as *manchas de caza*. The most important activity is the *"montería"*, which is celebrated one per *mancha* and per year. Other hunting activities are the stag hunting during the rutting season and by *"stalking"*. The red-legged partridge is hunted by the modality of driven partridge shooting.

MANCHAS DE CAZA

- La Romera (250 ha)
- El Tobar (250 ha)
- El Cabrial (250 ha)
- La Penosilla (280 ha)

Horses

On the estate there is a permanent herd of purebred Spanish horses for riding. They come from the breeding stock of the estate's own stud, the Yeguada Tres Cotos, which is located on the bank of the Alberche River in the province of Toledo, adjacent to the Autonomous Community of Madrid.

Agricultural activity

Agricultural activity is the main source of income for the estate (70%). One-third of the property is devoted to the cultivation and harvesting of wheat, barley and oats on dry (unirrigated) land. The agricultural department has its own buildings and facilities, such as sheds for storage and the housing of forestry machinery, a stable, houses for the tractor drivers, the agricultural and forestry workers and their families, and the main house.

The available machinery on the estate includes:
- Two four-wheel-drive vehicles.
- Two agriculture tractors of 150 HP with double wheels and front loader, and harrows.
- A bowser for irrigating, with a pressure pump.
- 2 trailers.
- 1 caterpillar-tracked machine of 120 HP with front blade.
- Tools: dumper, cultivators, fertilizer spreaders, disc harrows.
- Power saws and brush-cutters.

Public activity

Given its proximity to Madrid and Barajas international airport, the estate is ideal for the celebration of special events, such as high level courses, academic ceremonies, cultural events and musical performances, in addition to the selective hunting of high quality animals in small groups during the rutting season.

In the future we would like to offer the estate as a venue for the celebration of courses, academic occasions, events, etc.

GENERAL MANAGEMENT AND FUTURE STRATEGY

The administration of the property since its acquisition by the Corsini family six years ago can be summarized as follows:

1. Improving the forestry stock and fire prevention by the following actions:
- The creation of supplementary strips for fire prevention by clearing both sides of every track, which implies a surface area of 10.08 ha.
- Creating and reviewing firebreaks, a total area of 19.51 ha.
- Sylvicultural treatment: coppicing and pruning of 16.23 ha of leafy scrub vegetation (holm oak).
- Construction of two water tanks, one of 150,000 litres for watering gardens and supplying water for emergencies, and another of 50,000 litres for drinking water.
- Repairing two ponds each of 1,000 m^3.
- Sprinkler irrigation for cultivating of maize and wheat on 15 ha.

2. Improving the trophy quality of the big game quarry species that are present on the estate and specially of Iberian red deer.

3. Greater productivity in the cultivation of cereals, fertilizing more extensively with organic residues (purifiers) and burying the cereal residues (stubbles).

Tillage and other land operations on the estate always take slopes into consideration, in order to avoid erosion of the soil by rainwater run-off.

4. Fencing: The estate is fully fenced with high quality deer mesh complete with angled extension of 30°, 2.30 metres high and 24 km long. In some areas there are internal fences to protect sown crops.

The positive results obtained from implementing these measures, the outstanding suitability of the land for big game hunting, especially that of red deer and wild boar, as well as the presence of a mosaic of well distributed crops, woodland, scrubland and grassland will allow us to move forward to achieve big trophies of both species in a short time. Indeed in the last three years there have already been various gold medals for hunting obtained despite the fact that hunting has only been happening for such a short time. There has also been a significant increase in the population of the game quarry species.

At the same time, balanced management provides ideal conditions for a large number number of verebrate species, all of them protected, of wich the most significant are: wildcat, badger, genet, beech marten, polecat, golden eagle, Bonelli's eagle, peregrine falcon, eagle owl, scops-owl, pin-tailed sandgrouse, little bustard, great bustard, stone curlew, roller kingfisher, bee-eater, great spotted cuckoo, Thekla lark and red bunting, among others.

As has already been mentioned in the general description, the property has an extensive network of perimeter and internal paths and tracks that allow better control of the habitat and the fauna populations, and permit comfortable hunting activities in the most appealing periods such as the rutting season.

In the same way, the extensive network of paths, the cleaning and maintenance of the firebreaks and the creation of supplementary strips are all measures for the prevention of fires in this area, which has been so ravaged by fire during the summers.

Increasing the richness of the fauna (whether quarry species or not), improving agricultural production, increasing hunting activity by offering more commercial driven shooting and stalking for national and foreign clients, improving the development and conservation of the forestry, as well as the development of rural tourism are the main strategic objectives of the estate for the next five years.

J. Corsini

Much of the surface is covered with Aleppo pine and holm oak.

Encomienda Estate

Encomienda Estate

LA ENCOMIENDA MAYOR DE CASTILLA BELONGS TO:

Rise Foundation

WE initiative

Aproca Madrid

Activities & attractions

- Shooting
- Hunting
- Rural Tourism
- Cycling
- Riding
- Walking Trails

CONTACT DATA
Mr. J. Corsini
La Encomienda Mayor de Castilla
C/ Zurbano, 76 E-28010 Madrid • Spain
Tel.: +34 91 441 30 11
procorsa6@procorsa.com

Increasing the richness of the wildlife, improving agricultural production, marketing hunting opportunities by offering more commercial driven shoots, stalking, "monterias" and stag hunting in the rut, the improving and developing the forestry and conservation, and developing rural tourism and birdwaching: these are the main strategic objectives of the estate for the next five years.

La Jimena

Mediterranean

Location: Navas del Rey, Madrid, Spain.
Surface: 304 ha.

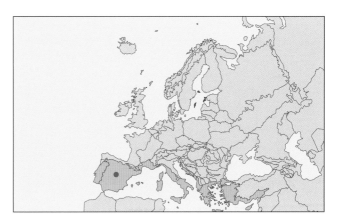

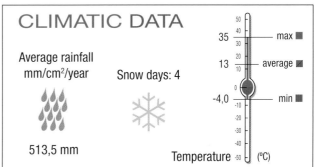

CLIMATIC DATA

Average rainfall
mm/cm²/year

Snow days: 4

513,5 mm

Temperature (ºC)

35 — max
13 — average
-4,0 — min

SUMMARY

La Jimena is located in Navas del Rey, in the northwest of the Province of Madrid (Spain). It belonged to the Peláez Quintanilla family for almost eighty years until it became the property of the Sociedad Dehesa La Jimena S.L. in 2006. Thanks to first class management, this company has succeeded in improving an *exhausted landscape* and converting it into a proper Wildlife Estate in less than eighteen months.

The estate extends to 304 ha and is included in the Natura 2000 network. It is an attractive place for numerous valuable species of wildlife to live and breed, thanks to the combination of typical Mediterranean woodland vegetation of Holm Oak *(Quercus rotundifolia)* and Umbrella Pine *(Pinus pinea)*, and areas of flat ground of optimum size for growing cereals and legumes. On top of this, there have been several improvements, such as the creation of arable fields, the establishment of grassland and the construction of warrens and refuges. All these natural characteristics and management practices have allowed the rapid recovery of small game species such as Wild Rabbit *(Oryctolagus cuniculus)*, Red-legged Partridge *(Alectoris rufa)* and Spanish Hare *(Lepus granatensis)*, and the settlement of numerous protected species such as Iberian Imperial Eagle *(Aquila adalberti)*, Golden Eagle *(Aquila chrysaetos)* and Black Vulture *(Aegypius monachus)* that find in La Jimena a perfect place for survival.

The key to this success, achieved within such a short period of time, has been the focussed management undertaken by the Sociedad Dehesa de La Jimena S.L., and it is a prelude to the remarkable improvements still to come.

J.L. Rodríguez

The presence of Iberian imperial eagle in La Jimena is constant, now that a population of wild rabbits has been re-established.

HISTORY

Between 1874 and 1883, D. José Martínez y Rino bought two properties from the State: La Jimena and Umbría de Barranco Lobero. In 1884 he sold the property composed by these two combined estates (281 ha), known as Coto San Fermín, to José Bernaldo de Quirós y Sevilla. He in turn sold the property in 1886 to D. Celedonio Rodrigañez y Vallejo, who kept it for 27 years and extended it, between 1886 and 1912, through the purchase of 31 small plots covering 44 ha, which lay within or adjacent to the boundaries and included Casa Carnero, Casa Nueva, Valdezate, Cruz del Pobre and Caja Nueva.

In 1913, his widow Dª Catalina Serrano Navarro inherited the whole property, extending it very slightly over the next two years. In 1915, she sold La Jimena to the Duke of Nájera, D. Leopoldo Travesedo y Fernández Casariego, who retained it until 1918 when he sold it to Dª Ángeles García Mauriño. At that time the property comprised 336 ha. Three years later, it was bought by D. Eduardo Peláez Quintanilla, who extended it with additional small pieces of land. In 2006, after 78 years, the three Peláez Avendaño heirs sold the whole estate (304 ha) to the Dehesa La Jimena company, which has owned it since then.

DESCRIPTION

La Jimena is a forest and agricultural estate located in the municipality of Navas del Rey, in the northwest of the Province of Madrid. It occupies 304 ha and it is included in the Natura 2000 network of protected areas. Specifically, it forms part of the Site of Community Importance (SCI) called "the Alberche and Cofio River Basins" (ES 3110007) and the Special Protection Area (SPA) for birds of "the holm oak woods of the Alberche and Cofio rivers" (ES0000056).

Its natural boundaries are: to the North with places called Las Caleras, Hoya Redonda and the Barranco Lobero track; to the North and West with M-501 road; to the East with Casa Carnero, La Lata and La Caseta; to the South with La Lata; and to the West, moving from south to north, with Tejadillo, Las Chorreras and the Valdezate creek.

Altitude varies between 575 m a.s.l. (corresponding to La Pita creek) and 796 m a.s.l. (corresponding to the hill where Casa Carnero is situated). The topography is markedly steep. There is large hill in the northern half, Cerro Monje, and another to the south of the M-588 road, where altitude increases from the road towards the place

Rabbit *(Oryctolagus cuniculus)*.

called La Carrasca. The dominant aspect is South-West.

The northern half of the estate is more topographically variable, due to the location of Cerro Monje at its approximate centre. The altitudes decrease towards the estate perimeter, delimited by the Valdezate creek, Barranco Lobero and the M-588 road.

The estate is located in the foothills of the Sierra de Gredos, very close to San Juan reservoir, and within the basin of the Tajo river. Creeks flow to the reservoirs at Picadas and San Juan. Both parts of the estate are located on hills which form the elevations of San Juan pass, between the towns of Navas del Rey and Pelayos de la Presa. The slopes are steep and, at the very highest part of the estate (the extreme north), there is an almost flat area.

The ground is composed of southern brown soils above igneous rocks.

The estate has a mild Mediterranean climate with a certain continental characteristics. According to the classification system of J. Papadakis, the humidity level is dry Mediterranean.

The potential vegetation of La Jimena corresponds to the Mesomediterranean faciation with *Retama sphaerocarpa*; the real vegetation of the estate is:

- Holm woods *(Quercus rotundifolia)* with individual Umbrella Pine *(Pinus pinea)* trees. The holm oak scrub layer is not very diverse, almost exclusively represented by Rockrose *(Cistus ladanifer)*, Rosemary *(Rosmarinus officinalis)* and the sporadic presence of Juniper *(Juniperus oxycedrus)*.
- Pine forest of Umbrella Pine *(Pinus pinea)*.
- Scrub with regeneration of Holm Oak *(Quercus rotundifolia)*.
- Rockrose Scrub *(Cistus ladanifer)*.
- Agricultural crops.

It is an interesting area for the conservation of the Imperial Eagle *(Aquila adalberti)* and Black Vulture *(Aegypius monachus)*. These two species are in danger of extinction according to the Madrid catalogue of endangered species. The commonest mammals include Wild Rabbit *(Oryctolagus cuniculus)*, albeit with very low populations, Squirrel *(Sciurus vulgaris infuscatus)*, Fox *(Vulpes vulpes)* and Wild Boar *(Sus scrofa)*, which are very abundant on the estate. It is important to stress the importance of this area as a residual area of the Iberian Lynx *(Lynx pardinus)*, in danger of extinction, although there are no current records of its presence. Nowadays the current distribution of this animal is a long way from this estate.

THE MOST REPRESENTATIVE SPECIES

REPTILE
- Turtle *(Mauremys caspica)*
- Common Gecko *(Tarentola mauritanica)*
- Redstart Wall Lizard *(Acanthodactylus erythrurus)*
- Ocellated Lizard *(Lacerta lepida)*
- Spanish Skink *(Chalcides bedriagai)*
- Horseshoe Snake *(Coluber hippocrepis)*

BIRDS
- Hobby *(Falco subbuteo)*
- Merlin *(Falco columbarius)*
- Black-winged Kite *(Elanus caeruleus)*
- Harrier Eagle *(Circaetus gallicus)*
- Booted Eagle *(Hieraetus pennatus)*
- Golden Eagle *(Aquila chrysaetos)*
- Iberian Imperial Eagle *(Aquila adalberti)*
- Sparrowhawk *(Accipiter nisus)*
- Goshawk *(Accipiter gentilis)*
- Griffon Vulture *(Gyps fulvus)*
- Black Vulture *(Aegypius monachus)*
- Barn Owl *(Tyto alba)*
- Long-Eared Owl *(Asio otus)*
- Tawny Owl *(Strix aluco)*
- Eagle Owl *(Bubo bubo)*

- Great Spotted Cuckoo *(Clamator glandarius)*
- Red-Necked Nightjar *(Caprimulgus ruficollis)*
- Roller *(Coracias garrulus)*
- Bee-Eater *(Merops apiaster)*
- Hoopoe *(Upupa epops)*
- Golden Oriole *(Oriolus oriolus)*
- Wryneck *(Jynx torquilla)*
- Great Spotted Woodpecker *(Dendrocopos major)*
- Green Woodpecker *(Picus viridis)*
- Wood Lark *(Lullula arborea)*
- Crested Lark *(Galerida cristata)*
- Thekla Lark *(Galerida theklae)*
- House Martin *(Delichon urbica)*
- European Swallow *(Hirundo rustica)*
- Red-Rumped Swallow *(Hirundo daurica)*
- Black-Eared Wheatear *(Oenanthe hispanica)*
- Wheatear *(Oenanthe oenanthe)*
- Subalpine Warbler *(Sylvia cantillans)*
- Provencal Dartford Warbler *(Sylvia undata)*
- Spectacled Warbler *(Sylvia conspicillata)*
- Sardinian Warbler *(Sylvia melanocephala)*
- Crow *(Corvus corax)*
- Azure-Winged Magpie *(Cyanopica cyanea)*

MAMMALS
- Pipistrelle *(Pipistrellus pipistrellus)*
- Kuhls' Pipistrelle *(Pipistrellus kuhlii)*
- Serotine Bat *(Vespertilio serotinus)*
- Greater Rhinolophus *(Rinolophus ferrum-equinum)*
- Median Rhinolophus *(Rinolophus mehelyi)*
- Lesser Rhinolophus *(Rinolophus hipposideros)*
- Mediterranean Rhinolophus *(Rinolophus euryale)*
- Squirrel *(Sciurus vulgaris infuscatus)*
- Wild Rabbit *(Oryctolagus cuniculus)*
- Spanish Hare *(Lepus granatensis)*
- Garden Dormouse *(Elyomis quercinus)*
- Fox *(Vulpes vulpes)*
- Weasel *(Mustela nivalis)*
- Marten *(Martes foina)*
- Polecat *(Putorius putorius)*
- Badger *(Meles meles)*
- Genet *(Genetta genetta)*
- Wild Cat *(Felis Sylvestris)*
- Wild Pig *(Sus scrofa)*
- Red Deer *(Cervus elaphus hispanicus)*

J.L. Rodríguez

Growing common oats
for wild animals.
Loma de la Casa.

C. Otero

FROM AN EXHAUSTED LANDSCAPE
TO AN ESTATE RICH IN WILDLIFE

When we took over at La Jimena in September 2006, we found a rather distressing panorama. Overgrazing by goats had had a clear impact on the landscape of Mediterranean vegetation and on the young shoots of holm oak in particular. Furthermore, part of the vegetation cover had been destroyed by previous forest fires.

The fields in which crops of cereals (wheat, barley and oats) used to be grown had been abandoned and invaded by pioneer colonies of Rockrose *(Cistus ladanifer)*, producing no natural grazing at all. The almond trees that adorned both sides of the main track (1,200 m) leading from the entrance gate to the impressive estate house were equally abandoned and dry.

In our first reconnoitre on foot, between the main house and Cerro Monje (800 m), we saw a single rabbit and some ringdoves that were easily startled. We found ourselves facing what we have come to call an *exhausted landscape*.

That distressing situation made us reconsider La Jimena's potential as a farming and forestry enterprise. Instead we defined and designed a more vocational profile for it. We decided that our management should focus towards wildlife and conservation, in accordance with the principles and the philosophy of the Wildlife Estates initiative (WEi), a project to which we were strongly committed at that time (early 2007).

As the first move, we decided to repair and restore the *threshold of quietness* in order to provide a basic prerequisite for achieving the WEi's objectives. A wiremesh fence 2 m in height was therefore built along the perimeter where overgrazing by goats, and poaching by humans, had been most serious.

bee-eaters are a splendid indicator of habitat quality. Their presence ates a high density of insects and a good degree of conservation.

257

La Jimena (Spain)

At the same time, 7 km of paths and tracks were built in order to allow adequate supervision and surveillance, and to provide rapid access in the event of a forest fire.

The main house at La Jimena, which had deteriorated considerably after years of abandonment, was consolidated, and a guards' house, a store and a garage were built on the same site. An off-road vehicle was provided, running water was installed from the water mains of Madrid's Isabel II canal system, and electricity was brought in.

Once the *threshold of quietness* had been achieved as a result of these fixed investments (perimeter mesh, Game Keepers's house, surveillance paths, and house), restoration of the former agricultural land began in September 2007.

As a first step, 35 ha of land were reclaimed in order to grow cereals. A wheat and oat mix was sown, purely for wildlife, and with no intentions of any productive harvest being taken.

The springs at El Enfriadero were cleaned and four water troughs were built at El Arrastradero, Barranco Lobero and Cerro Monje, due to the fact that water is, in this central part of Spain, an important limiting factor for wildlife in summer. The strategic distribution of water troughs and springs in the property guarantees the existence and survival of numerous prey-species, which is a key function of Wildlife Estates.

Little by little, the landscape started to change and to invigorate, thanks to the improvements introduced.

In winter 2007, the first reintroduction of 300 Wild Rabbits *(Oryctolagus cuniculus)* was imple-

Growing oats for wild animals.

C. Otero

mented. For this purpose we used branches and prunings from holm oaks and umbrella pines which were piled into artificial warrens and which are highly effective as refuges for rabbits. That spring, after the first litters were born, the wild rabbit population multiplied. Between the main house and Cerro Monje (800 m), where only a single rabbit had been seen in the previous year, we were able to count 48 rabbits.

Because of the increase in the population of wild rabbits, which is a key prey species in Mediterranean ecosystems and a basic species for a balanced food supply, there was a simultaneous increase in the populations of Spanish Hare *(Lepus granatensis)*, Red-legged Partridge *(Alectoris rufa)* and Squirrel *(Sciurus vulgaris)*. There was also an increase in the presence of mammalian predators such as Wild Cat *(Felis*

Grazing pine forest of umbrella pine.

La Jimena **(Spain)**

sylvestris), Genet *(Genetta genetta)* and Badger *(Meles meles)*, and numerous birds of prey that migrate to the southern plains to catch rabbits, such as Golden Eagle *(Aquila chrysaetos)*, Iberian Imperial Eagle *(Aquila adalberti)*, Eagle Owl *(Bubo bubo)*, Goshawk *(Accipiter gentilis)*, Buzzard *(Buteo buteo)*, Long-eared Owl *(Asio otus)*, Harrier Eagle *(Circaetus gallicus)* and Booted Eagle *(Hieraaetus pennatus)*.

In winter, flocks of several hundred Chaffinches *(Fringilla coelebs)* in the oats attracted the presence of two Merlins *(Falco columbarius)*. In addition, the summer hatching of the pine procession moth caterpillar attracted a pair of Hobbies *(Falco subbuteo)* that delighted in catching butterflies above the umbrella pines at sunset.

The sky at La Jimena is usually full of many necrophagous birds such as the Griffon Vulture *(Gyps fulvus)* from the forests of El Quexigal and El Endrinal, and the Black Vulture *(Aegypius monachus)* from the colonies in the neighbouring municipality of Cadalso de los Vidrios.

The improvements undertaken at La Jimena in 2008 were completed in the summer with three further projects: clearing 25 ha of rockrose infestation to establish more grassland for wild rabbits and red-legged partridges, sowing a plot of 45 ha with a wheat-oats-vetch mix, and establishing a small nucleus of wild boar and red deer from the neighbouring estates of Las Chorreras, Las Carboneras and La Carrasca.

The restoration process is not yet concluded, since pruning works, creating stone warrens for rabbits, constructing another five water troughs, and consolidating the populations of the larger game species (wild boar and red deer) remain to be done. Despite this we can say that, in a period of just eighteen months, we have managed to establish some truly emblematic species in La Jimena, such as imperial eagle, golden eagle, eagle owl, griffon vulture, black vulture and wild cat.

Carlos Otero

The entire team of La Jimena, from left to right: Marcos Frías, Carlos Otero, Alfonso García-Morales, Richard Luengo, Jesús Arribas, Carlos García-Morales and Juan Luis Frías.

R. Powell Poupa

Griffon vultures and black vultures in Cerro Monje, La Jimena.

LA JIMENA BELONGS TO:

Friends of the Countryside

Rise Foundation

WE initiative

APROCA MADRID

Aproca Madrid

Activities & attractions

Birdwatching

Equestrian

Research

Shooting

Wildlife Management

School

CONTACT DATA
Dehesa La Jimena S.L.
C/ Burgos, 107 - Urb. La Cabaña • 28223 Pozuelo de Alarcón
(Madrid) SPAIN
Tel: 00 34 91 799 05 20
renatur@arrakis.es

P. Maldonado

Las Ensanchas

Mediterranean

Location: Torre de Juan Abad, Ciudad Real, Spain.
Surface: 1,860 ha.

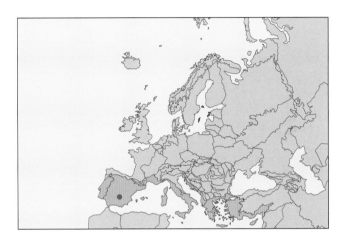

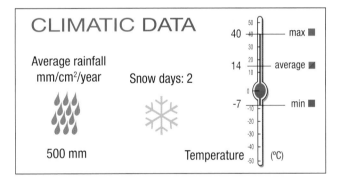

CLIMATIC DATA

Average rainfall
mm/cm²/year

Snow days: 2

500 mm

Temperature (ºC)

40 — max
14 — average
-7 — min

50
40
30
20
10
0
-10
-20
-30
-40
-50

SUMMARY

A hunting estate for both large and small game, located in the province of Ciudad Real (La Mancha) in Spain, with a surface area of 1,860 hectares, and renowned for its magnificent management. It is not hard to notice the mosaic of cereal crops, natural pastures in non-cultivated plots (known locally as *posío*), scrubland, meadows and humid areas. Imbued in this delightful Mediterranean landscape, we find wildlife of incredible richness: flocks of partridges run around the estate in the most natural way imaginable, hundreds of rabbits find a perfect place to live in the natural burrows, and protected species such as the Iberian imperial eagle, pin-tailed sandgrouse, black-bellied sandgrouse, etc. live in Las Ensanchas as if it were virgin land. The effort and care of Doña Patricia Maldonado, owner of Las Ensanchas, can be detected in every corner.

Las Ensanchas has been part of the entailed estate of Melgarejo family since 1757.

HISTORY

From 1757 Las Ensanchas was part of the property owned by the entailed estates of the Melgarejo family.

In 1895, the estate was one of the properties that made up the so-called Dehesa de las Terceras. The total size of this large estate, at that period, amounted to 8,000 ha, and belonged to His Excellency Don José Mª Melgarejo Enseña and to his wife and cousin, Her Excellency Doña Mª de Rosario Melgarejo Castilla Portugal, Dukes of San Fernando de Quiroga, who at that time owned as much as 48,000 ha in the province of Ciudad Real.

In further divisions of the property, and always remaining within the same family, Las Ensanchas, which is located in the Campo de Montiel, became a single and separate estate of 1,860 ha, its previous owner being Don Luis Moreno de Silva (husband of the current owner Doña Patricia Maldonado), who inherited from his maternal uncle Don Luis de Silva Melgarejo.

DESCRIPTION

The hunting estate of Las Ensanchas occupies a total area of 1,860 ha and is located in the municipality of Torre de Juan Abad, south-west of the agricultural district of Campo de Montiel, in Ciudad Real, a province in the Autonomous Region of Castilla-La Mancha.

The estate encompasses the typical landscape of La Mancha, where open flat plains and farming are the principal features amongst the geographical features and natural vegetation. Most of the estate is located on slightly sloping ground of less than 5% inclination; however in Cervalera and Cabeza de Buey the slopes are steeper, at 15% and 30% respectively. Both names refer to two elevated features covered by natural vegetation. While Cervalera is a small hill situated in the northern part of the estate, rising to an altitude of 905 m, Cabeza de Buey is a southern geodesic vertex and is the highest point of the whole area, at 1,155 m. The bulk of the estate lies at an altitude of between 790 and 840 m, corresponding to

At the end of summer male red-legged partridges form into groups known as *toradas*.

P. Maldonado

the central plains, and because of that, Cabeza de Buey presents a difference in height of between 315 and 365 m.

The estate belongs to the hydrographical basin of the Jabalón river, a tributary of the Guadiana river which flows immediately north of the estate. There are only intermittent water courses on the estate, with poor flows; these are mostly in the form of fountains, springs, run-off lines and creeks.

In terms of watering points, 29 ponds are distributed evenly across the estate, and there is a marsh of 7,000 m^2 in the north-west section. Less than half of the ponds are artificial, and were installed to meet the needs of the population of the various quarry species. The ponds vary in size between 200 and 1,000 m^2.

The landscape of the estate shows the typical characteristics of the region of Castilla-La Mancha; Mediterranean forest which appears to be in its most degraded form, with Rockrose (*Cistus*), Gorse (*Calicotome spinosa*) and pastures, a consequence of the livestock farming activity practised in the area for ever.

Vegetation

The vegetation of Las Ensanchas is clearly divided into two separate areas:

- The most southerly part of the estate is defined by the presence of plant communities of natural origin.
- Small areas and strips of vegetation are interspersed among the arable fields in the central and northern parts of the estate.

The southern part of the estate corresponds to the mountainous area of Cabeza de Buey, in which we find slopes covered mainly by Gum Rockrose *(Cistus ladanifer)*, Kermes Oak *(Quercus coccifera)* and Holm Oak *(Quercus ilex ballota)*. The kermes oak is also abundant on the hill at Cervalera, while in the more open areas both it and the holm oak are equally dominant. This latter broad-leaved tree features in all the estate's plantations, including the areas where cereals are cultivated, where it is scattered across the open pasture landscape known as the *dehesa*. The stocky appearance of these holm oaks is the same as we find in other holm oak areas in La Mancha. While the densest rockroses on the estate hardly permit other plants grow, holm and kermes oaks alternate with other types of plants. Amongst the smaller ones, many of

P. Maldonado

Male red-legged partridge on one of the shelters built to protect them from birds of prey.

them aromatic and less than one metre high, we can highlight: Thyme *(Thymus vulgaris)*, Rosemary *(Rosmarinus officinalis)*, Lavender *(Lavandula latifolia)*, French Lavender *(Lavandula stoechas sampaiana)*, Sage *(Salvia officinalis)*, Camomile *(Santolina chamaecyparissus)*, Lavender-leaved Sunrose *(Helianthemum syriacum)*, Wild Asparagus *(Asparagus acutifolius)* and Blackthorn *(Rhamnus lycioides)*. Of the larger shrub plants, the important ones are: Retama sphaerocarpa, Shrubby Hare's Ear *(Bupleurum fruticosum)*, False Olive *(Phillyrea angustifolia)*, White Spanish Broom *(Cytisus multiflorus)*, Scorpion's Thorn *(Genista scorpius)*, Dog Rose *(Rosa canina)*, White-leaved Rockrose *(Cistus albidus)*, Hawthorn *(Crataegus monogyna)* and Hairy Broom *(Genista hirsuta)*.

Over the entire surface of the estate there is hardly any bare soil to be seen, because in the clearings in the tree and bush plantations natural communities of herbaceous species grow: *Agrostis castellana, Poa bulbosa, Stipa tenacissima, Brachypodium distachyon, Trifolium glomeratum, Bellis annua, Bellis perennis,* etc.

Las Ensanchas (Spain)

All reforestation at Las Ensanchas is done with native Mediterranean tree species. Each young tree must be protected from the rabbits.

Apart from the vegetation previously described, there are small areas where species associated with more humid environments flourish. Some Reed Bed *(Typha dominguensis; Scirpus lacustris)*, Wild Raspberry *(Rubus idaeus)* and Sedge *(Carex paniculata)* grow next to the ponds, springs and small rivers on the estate.

Fauna

The most surprising feature of Las Ensanchas is the tremendous biodiversity, which one can almost breathe as soon as one crosses the entrance to the estate; groups of wild partridges run here and there, rabbits appear in dozens, and on the ponds it is not uncommon to see mallard, coots, moorhens and even sparrows enjoying their daily dip. That this biodiversity exists is thanks to the constant and painstaking efforts of the owner, Doña Patricia Maldonado, who is so deeply passionate about the natural world.

Of all the fauna present on the estate, the main protagonist is the wild Red-legged Partridge *(Alec-*

P. Maldonado

Male Little Bustard *(Tetrax tetrax)* in breeding season. Between the months of March and May the males have very territorial behaviour and regularly mark their breeding area.

BIRDS OBSERVED AT LAS ENSANCHAS BY TOM GULLICK

- Litle Grebe *(Tachybaptus ruficollis)*
- Great Crested Grebe *(Podiceps cristatus)*
- Night Heron *(Nycticorax nycticorax)*
- Cattle Egret *(Bubulcus ibis)*
- Litle Egret *(Egretta garzetta)*
- Grey Heron *(Ardea cinerea)*
- Black Stork *(Ciconia nigra)*
- White Stork *(Ciconia ciconia)*
- Gadwall *(Anas strepera)*
- Teal *(Anas sp.)*
- Mallard *(Anas platyrhynchos)*
- Pochard *(Aythya ferina)*
- Black-shouldered Kite *(Elanus axillaris)*
- Black Kite *(Milvus migrans)*
- Red Kite *(Milvus milvus)*
- Egyptian Vulture *(Neophron percnopterus)*
- Griffon Vulture *(Gyps fulvus)*
- Short-toed Eagle *(Circaetus gallicus)*
- Marsh Harrier *(Circus aeruginosus)*
- Hen Harrier *(Circus cyaneus)*
- Montagu's Harrier *(Circus pygargus)*
- Goshawk *(Accipiter gentilis)*
- Sparrowhawk *(Accipiter sp.)*
- Common Buzzard *(Buteo buteo)*
- Iberian Spanish Imperial Eagle *(Aquila adalberti)*
- Golden Eagle *(Aquila chrysaetos)*
- Booted Eagle *(Aquila pennata)*
- Bonelli's Eagle *(Aquila fasciata)*
- Osprey *(Pandion haliaetus)*
- Lesser Kestrel *(Falco naumanni)*
- Common Kestrel *(Falco tinnunculus)*

- Merlin *(Falco columbarius)*
- Eurasian Hobby *(Falco subuteo)*
- Peregrine Falcon *(Falco peregrinus)*
- Red-legged Partridge *(Alectoris rufa)*
- Common Quail *(Coturnix coturnix)*
- Common Moorhen *(Gallinula chloropus)*
- Common Coot *(Fulica atra)*
- Little Bustard *(Tetrax tetrax)*
- Great Bustard *(Otis tarda)*
- Black-winged Stilt *(Himantopus himantopus)*
- Avocet *(Recurvirostra avosetta)*
- Stone Curlew *(Burhinus oedicnemus)*
- Little Ringed Plover *(Charadrius dubius)*
- Lapwing *(Vanellus vanellus)*
- Little Stint *(Calidris minuta)*
- Common Snipe *(Gallinago gallinago)*
- Redshank *(Tringa totanus)*
- Greenshank *(Tringa nebularia)*
- Green Sandpiper *(Tringa ochropus)*
- Wood Sandpiper *(Tringa glareola)*
- Common Sandpiper *(Actitis hypoleucos)*
- Black-headed Gull *(Chroicocephalus ridibundus)*
- Yellow-legged Gull *(Larus michahellis)*
- Black-bellied Sandgrouse *(Pterocles orientalis)*
- Pin-tailed Sandgrouse *(Pterocles alchata)*
- Rock Dove (domestic) *(Columba livia)*
- Stock Dove *(Columba oenas)*
- Woodpigeon *(Columba palumbus)*

- Collared Dove *(Streptopelia decaocto)*
- Turtle Dove *(Streptopelia turtur)*
- Great Spotted Cuckoo *(Clamator glandarius)*
- Cuckoo *(Cuculus canorus)*
- Barn Owl *(Tyto alba)*
- Scops Owl *(Otus scops)*
- Eagle Owl *(Bubo bubo)*
- Little Owl *(Athene noctua)*
- Long-eared Owl *(Asio otus)*
- Red-necked Nightjar *(Caprimulgus ruficollis)*
- Common Swift *(Apus apus)*
- Bee-eater *(Merops apiaster)*
- Hoopoe *(Upupa Epops)*
- Wryneck *(Jynx torquilla)*
- Green Woodpecker *(Picus viridis)*
- Great Spotted Woodpecker *(Dendrocopos major)*
- Calandra Lark *(Melanocorypha calandra)*
- Short-toed Lark *(Calandrella brachydactyla)*
- Crested Lark *(Galerida cristata)*
- Thekla Lark *(Galerida theklae)*
- Woodlark *(Lullula arborea)*
- Skylark *(Alauda arvensis)*
- Sand Martin *(Riparia riparia)*
- Crag Martin *(Ptyonoprogne rupestris)*
- Swallow *(Hirundo rustica)*
- Red-rumped Swallow *(Cecropis daurica)*
- House Martin *(Delichon urbicum)*
- Tree Pipit *(Anthus trivialis)*

- Meadow Pipit *(Anthus pratensis)*
- "Yellow" Wagtail *(Motacilla flava)*
- White Wagtail *(Motacilla alba)*
- Wren *(Troglodytes troglodytes)*
- Alpine Accentor *(Prunella collaris)*
- Robin *(Turdus migratorius)*
- Nightingale *(Luscinia megarhynchos)*
- Black Redstart *(Phoenicurus ochruros)*
- Redstart *(Phoenicurus phoenicurus)*
- Whinchat *(Saxicola rubetra)*
- Stonechat *(Saxicola torquatus)*
- Northern Wheatear *(Oenanthe oenanthe)*
- Rock Thrush *(Monticola saxatilis)*
- Blackbird *(Turdus sp.)*
- Song Thrush *(Turdus philomelos)*
- Mistle Thrush *(Turdus viscivorus)*
- Cetti's Warbler *(Cettia cetti)*
- Fan-tailed Warbler *(Euthlypis lachrymosa)*
- Great Reed Warbler *(Acrocephalus arundinaceus)*
- Melodious Warbler *(Hippolais polyglotta)*
- Dartford Warbler *(Sylvia undata)*
- Subalpine Warbler *(Sylvia cantillans)*
- Sardinian Warbler *(Sylvia melanocephala)*
- Orphean Warbler *(Sylvia hortensis)*
- Garden Warbler *(Sylvia borin)*
- Blackap *(Buteogallus anthracinus)*
- Chiffchaff *(Phylloscopus collybita)*
- Firecrest *(Regulus ignicapillus)*

- Spotted Flycatcher *(Muscicapa striata)*
- Pied Flycatcher *(Ficedula hypoleuca)*
- Long-tailed Tit *(Aegithalos caudatus)*
- Blue Tit *(Cyanistes caeruleus)*
- Great Tit *(Parus major)*
- Short-toed Treecreeper *(Certhia brachydactyla)*
- Golden Oriole *(Oriolus oriolus)*
- Southern Grey Shrike *(Lanius meridionalis)*
- Jay *(Garrulus glandarius)*
- Woodchad Shrike *(Lanius senator)*
- Azure-winged Magpie *(Cyanopica cyana)*
- Magpie *(Pica pica)*
- Chough *(Pyrrhocorax graculus)*
- Jackdaw *(Corvus monedula)*
- Raven *(Corvus corax)*
- Spotless Starling *(Sturnus unicolor)*
- House Sparrow *(Passer domesticus)*
- Spanish Sparrow *(Passer hispaniolensis)*
- Chaffinch *(Fringilla coelebs)*
- Serin *(Serinus serinus)*
- Greenfinch *(Carduelis chloris)*
- Goldfinch *(Carduelis tristis)*
- Siskin *(Carduelis spinus)*
- Linnet *(Carduelis cannabina)*
- Hawfinch *(Coccothraustes coccothraustes)*
- Cirl Bunting *(Emberiza cirlus)*
- Rock Bunting *(Emberiza cia)*
- Corn Bunting *(Miliaria calandra)*
- Brambling *(Fringilla montifringilla)*

The power lines are responsible for considerable losses amongst the birds or prey such as black kite, imperial eagle, etc.

P. Maldonado

P. Maldonado

Agriculture and Livestock

Ten years ago there were three traditional activities on Las Ensanchas: crops, livestock and hunting. At that time the decision was taken to eliminate the livestock and to maintain crop cultivation, but to subordinate it to hunting. For this reason, the farming activities carried out at Las Ensanchas have an ecological rather than a commercial interest, as they are carried out in order to maintain and improve the population of the quarry species.

At the moment there is no livestock activity on the estate. Ten years ago, herds of goats fed on Las Ensanchas, but they were eliminated when it was considered that they competed with the quarry species, both in terms of food and space. The only livestock present today is the old gully where cattle graze.

Forestry Activities

There are two types of forestry activities on Las Ensanchas. On the one hand, there is the pruning and cutting and selection of leading branches of the Holm Oaks, as a function of the estate's game management. On the other hand, there are fire-breaks, constructed in areas where the natural vegetation is dense, such as Cabeza de Buey, as a preventative measure and to aid the extinction of forest fires.

Game and Hunting Activities

The estate is registered as a private reserve under registration number CR-10.205. Both large and small game are hunted and shot. In the latter category, the quarry species, in order of their economic importance, are: Rabbit *(Oryctolagus cu-niculus)*, Red-legged Partridge *(Alectoris rufa)*, Woodpigeon *(Columbus palumbus)* and Iberian Hare *(Lepus granatensis)*. Big game is represented by the Wild Boar *(Sus scrofa)*.

The estate is divided into two zones, as a function of the game management carried out in each; around Cabeza de Buey there is a fence for big game, the fence also serving as the southern boundary of the estate, while the fence erected for small game shooting marks the remainder of the boundary. The public road bisects the small game area and is protected by two fences, placed each side of the road and parallel to its axis. The small game area represents 76.54 % of the total surface of the estate. The game and hunting activity at Las Ensanchas is divided into eight separate beats:

The tradition of hunting and shooting on Las Ensanchas is very old, and for the last 10 years has been guided by the management directives laid down by Doña Patricia Maldonado, the owner, and by Tom Gullick who works as technical advisor. The remainder of the people engaged in managing the estate are the manager, the gamekeeper and his assistant, two tractor drivers and various labour teams for specific tasks.

Red-legged partridge are shot under conditions known as driven shooting, but only on three days in each annual season. This means tremendous peace and stillness for the wildlife on the estate during most of the year. Other measures that allow high densities of red-legged partridge to be maintained are the extraction rate, which is no more than 30%, and care of the habitat.

Las Ensanchas (Spain)

For birds of prey recovered in Castilla-La Mancha, this is an excellent estate for re-release into the wild. In the picture, Mr. José Barranquero, Head Game-keeper at Las Ensanchas, with a recovered immature Iberian imperial eagle.

P. Maldonado

Olive groves, grassland, crops and *posíos* are the hunting grounds of more than 23 species of avian predator, thanks to the abundance of prey available.

P. Maldonado

LOOKING AFTER WILD HABITATS TO PRODUCE BIODIVERSITY ON LAS ENSANCHAS

Inheriting or receiving a property entails the obligation of improving the inheritance with the intention of building a better future for future generations. It involves assuming a responsibility which commits us for the rest of our lives.

If the land has come to us through a family legacy, the commitment is double (and morally it forces us to consider it as a "loan from our children"). It will be necessary, initially, to get to know it, observe it, and look for its best purpose in what it has offered hitherto.

We will then be able to evaluate its future possibilities, and to work to consider which management policy would best achieve profitability, another of our biggest obligations. And to ask ourselves if what was done before our arrival has been appropriate, taking into account the fluctuations in markets and times.

When the assets are established and quantified, everything is translated into money. Our management will have exceeded that of previous generations if the property currently produces more and is of greater value.

There is a moment of real loneliness and decision. It is when the real facts appear in front of us and tell us what we must and can do. Afterwards there is the temptation of not doing anything, or maybe the temptation of trying out new and risky things which entail, of course, enormous investments that are never exempt from risk and doubt.

They say that every newcomer to estate management thinks that he (or she) is going to discover America. One's head is in danger of getting too full of livestock numbers, enormous warehouses, huge machines, free-flow irrigation in places where the most traditional dryland agriculture reigns, and lots of other endless adventures.

But above everything else the most arduous thing in this new job is the long wait: in the countryside, the only certainty is the long time things take to bear fruit, if indeed they do bear fruit. It has long been said that land will go on accepting improvements until its owner is completely ruined. And we must never forget the phrase my father always used: "whose idea was it to create a business in the outdoors?"

Slowly you start to understand that you are the owner of great natural richness that has nothing to do with the riches you keep in the bank and that your passage through this place (brief, always, in relation to its history) can be decisive. In other words, the maintenance of this natural treasure and its future survival will depend on how you perform.

In spite of the dozens of laws that suffocate us each year, and in spite of the fact that we need licences for everything, even, as an old manager once sarcastically remarked, "to stroke your dog", and because our business suffers from brutal interventionist policies, and also because public bodies insist on treating us as "alleged criminals", most of us know that to destroy Nature you need very little time and that most of the time such destruction is irreversible. That is, when it is the Administration itself that is not destroying it in the sacred name of developing "the interests of society".

It was after I had considered all these factors that I chose to care for habitats and wildlife. From that moment a love story began, between "Las Ensanchas" and me. And to be more precise, this was an estate considered, in agricultural terms, to be "very bad, poor and full of slate", and about which one of my sons once asked his father "Who was it who put so many stones here?"

Yes, stones…, and holm oaks, rockroses, kermes oaks, olive trees at the foot of the hills. Partridges, huge numbers of rabbits, predators working by day and by night (even the most emblematic of them breed here), pin-tailed and black-bellied sand-grouse, little bustards, stone curlews, ringed plovers, little ringed plovers, coots, moorhens, lapwings, black-winged stilts, song-thrushes, ducks, grebes, pigeons and doves. All of them live together in this natural area that I undertook to protect, entering it voluntarily in NATURA 2000 Network.

"What do I miss?" my friends sometimes ask me. The support of an Administration that is brave enough to admit the contribution that a lot of people like me make to maintain a natural world, magnified by everyone when it coincides with their own interests.

Meanwhile, the Iberian imperial eagles keep growing and eating the rabbits that breed on our estates.

Patricia Maldonado

The month of February marks the start of the red-legged partridge mating season in La Mancha. The males are famous for their fights.

P. Maldonado

LAS ENSANCHAS BELONGS TO:

APROCA
Castilla-La Mancha

Friends of the Countryside

WE initiative

Fundación amigos
del águila impreial

SEO

Activities & attractions

 Hunting

 Shooting

 Birdwatching

CONTACT DATA
Doña Patricia Maldonado Vidal
Estate Las Ensanchas, s/n,
Torre Juan Abad,
E-13344, Ciudad Real. Spain
Tel.: + 34 (0) 926 694 005

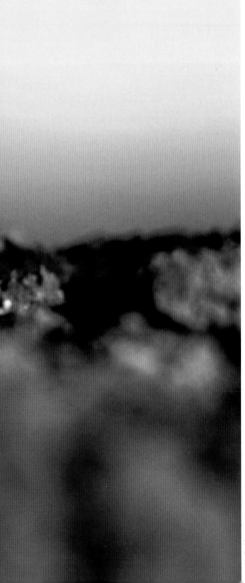

Orán

Mediterranean

Location: Pozohondo, Albacete, La Mancha Region, Spain.
Surface: 3,500 ha.

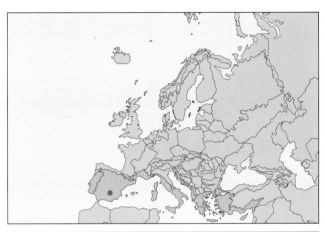

CLIMATIC DATA

Average rainfall
mm/cm²/year

Snow days: 3

500 mm

Temperature (ºC)

max
average
min

40
13,5
-10

SUMMARY

The Orán Estate, extending to 3,500 ha and located in the region of La Mancha, has been in the Sánchez Lodares family for three generations. It is one of those rural businesses that produce a return on capital of approximately 1%, and which, based on hard work, dedication, vocation, love, and making sure that debts are avoided, has improved from generation to generation.

With an eye permanently on improving the results of the mixed farming of the estate, the previous generation of owners put 700 hectares of dry land under irrigation, set aside 1,000 hectares of woodland for hunting, and left approximately 1,800 hectares for crops grown in dry land and for the Red-legged Partridge (*Alectoris rufa*), in all a total of 3,500 hectares of land.

On the altar of the ecology and biodiversity of the estate, the owners rejected the construction of a large wind farm on the estate, for the sole purpose of conserving one of the best known remaining areas for the Red-legged Partridge in Spain. For their work and innovations in agriculture they have deservedly received the Medal of Agricultural Merit, awarded by the Spanish State, and general recognition for conserving traditional hunting and shooting, deeply rooted in the culture, in natural surroundings which encourage the conservation and promotion of numerous protected species of wildlife.

Orán is an authentic genetic reserve
for the indigenous Red-legged Partridge.

J.L. Rodríguez

Mateo Sánchez, father of the current owner leading a partridge shoot. Orán, October 1958.

HISTORY

The name of the Orán estate probably originates in the coastal city of Orán on the Mediterranean coastline of Algeria. It probably comes from the Arabic "Ouahran" ("cut"), referring to the broken relief of the coastline. Orán (Algerian) belonged to Spain for three centuries (from 1509 to 1708, and again from 1732 to 1790), and was a city of considerable influence during the French occupation from 1831 to 1962. In fact, the estate immediately to the north of Orán is called Bujía, from another city in Algeria (Bougie) which also was under Spanish rule during those periods. Hence the poetry of Luis de Góngora: *"He served the King in Orán"*. Both properties probably acquired their names in this era.

Partridge shooting in La Losa and Orán, October 1958. *Secretarios* picking up the partridges after the first drive. This shoot, like many others, was held in honour of D. Francisco Franco, a good friend of the Sánchez Lodares family.

As far as ownership of the estate is concerned, it only needs to be said that one of greatest landowners of Albacete was Mateo Sánchez, who began selling his wares to local townships and ended up by building an empire which is nowadays a leader in many aspects of farming. Among the properties owned by the family, the one which stood out was the estate at Orán, situated on the road from Albacete to Pozohondo, the favourite hunting estate of D. Francisco Franco during the 1950s, '60s and '70s, who came to shoot the driven indigenous red-legged partridge. The son of Mateo Sánchez, Alejandro, who is the current owner, inherited the vast majority of the land. Initially he shared the land with his sisters, but ended up by buying back most of the properties and, further, increased his farming area through other investments. He has thus become the largest landowner in Albacete, both in terms of area as well as the quality of his products, installing irrigation and achieving magnificent levels of production across all his farms.

DESCRIPTION

The Orán estate is situated in the centre of Spain, in the region of La Mancha, 20 kilometres from the city of Albacete; it covers 3,500 hectares. The adjoining estates are Bujía to the north, Torre Mahiques to the east, Los Llanos to the west and smaller farms to the south.

There are numerous water points distributed across the estate. Forty of them are man-made, although there is one natural pond at *La Losa de Minuto*.

Orán is set in a semi-arid area, with an average altitude of 750 metres above sea level and with relatively shallow soils of average texture but abundant calcium carbonate. The characteristic vegetation is the Kermes Oak forest *(Quercus coccifera)*, with all its cohort of sclerophyll companion species, such as the Holm Oak *(Quercus ilex)*, Rosemary *(Rosmarinus officinalis)*, Esparto Grass *(Stipa tenaccisima)*, which is a magnificent nesting place for partridges, hares and rabbits, Buckthorn *(Rhamnus alaternus* and *Rhamnus lycioides)*, and a few examples of Spanish Juniper *(Juniperus thurifera)* and Common Juniper *(Juniperus communis)*, which after the disappearance of the holm oak may increase their biomass

as a result of growing in garrigue shrubland, a stage down from oak forest. There also are a mass of Pine trees *(Pinus pinaster)*, which were planted by the owners in the 1960s and '70s, forming isolated copses and giving a special element to the landscape.

The development model reflects a profile of four elements: crop production, livestock, hunting and conservation, with strong emphasis placed on all four of these elements, given the vast area of land and its livestock enterprise.

Cereal cultivation on dry ground (900 ha of barley) coexists alongside the most modern irrigation technology producing high yielding crops (800 ha). The farming system has practised direct sowing since 1999, for non-irrigated crops as well as for irrigated crops. Cereals and legumes are the predominant crops, with yields between 1,000-1,500 kg/ha for barley grown on dry ground, 40,000 kg/ha for irrigated onions and 9,000-11,000 kg/ha for irrigated maize. The estate also grows crops of Poppy *(Papaver somniferum)*, with yields of 1,500-2,000 kg/ha.

As far as livestock is concerned, it is not uncommon to see the flock of 1,300 sheep from La Mancha breed grazing the stubbles at Orán. They produce around 1,200 lambs every year.

The most famous partridge shoot dates to 1965-1966, a season in which 2,072 partridges were shooted. On that occasion, as every year, Francisco Franco attended, invited by Mateo Sánchez. The room in which the *Generalísimo* (as Franco was known) usually slept is still kept intact.

The population density of red-legged partridge in Orán has dropped from a figure of nearly 2.0 birds/ha/year in recent decades to 0.6 birds/ha/year at the present time, after all the changes that have been suffered: mechanisation of crop production, change of cropping regime, introduction of irrigation systems and the excessive increase of opportunistic predators. Until the mid-1980s, the annual production in Oran was around 6,500 birds.

Red-legged partridge density has decreased progressively because of several factors, as just stated. Amongst these are the changing agro-social profile in the countryside of Albacete, the abandoning of certain types of crops and the creation of extensive areas for irrigated crops. In addition, the creation of equally extensive areas for big game hunting – where the Red Deer *(Cervus elaphus)* is abundant but where the Wild Boar *(Sus scrofa)* is kept at bay – and the excessive increase of some predators like Fox *(Vulpes vulpes)*, Magpie *(Pica pica)* and wild boar. Nevertheless the zeal and vocation of Alejandro Sánchez Lodares in retaining the purity of the indigenous red-legged partridge, without ever resorting to restocking, led him to sacrifice shooting for three consecutive years in order to achieve a population density that would permit a sustainable basis. At present, the annual harvest of 100% wild red-legged partridge – in the years in which Alejandro shoots – is around 1,200-1,500 birds.

At the beginning of the 1990s, the results obtained in Orán were still close to 2 partridge per hectare per year.
In the photograph, the impressive result of the first shoot of the 1990-1991 season, with the assistance of His Majesty the King of Spain.

J. Belda

Mateo Sánchez speaking with his gamekeepers during the first partridge shoot of that season. Orán, November 1968.

J. Belda

ORÁN: GUIDE TO THE NATURAL MANAGEMENT OF THE RED-LEGGED PARTRIDGE *(ALECTORIS RUFA)*

At a time that now seems to us to be almost historic, namely the 1960s and 1970s, two partridges per hectare per year were produced in Orán.

Management then was focused primarily on the production of an incredible quantity of birds, reaching the astronomical number of 11 birds / ha in June, then falling and stabilizing at 6.5 birds / ha during the first days of October.

This abundant population formed the basis for shooting in correct and appropriate proportion, but at the same time its fine-tuned management created ideal conditions in which populations of associated wildlife could thrive – Rabbit *(Oryctolagus cuniculus)*, Iberian Hare *(Lepus granatensis)*, Quail

ORÁN ESTATE. STAFF LIST

Worker	Position	Age
Anastasio Gregorio Martínez	Honorary Head Game Keeper	76 years old
Anastasio Gregorio Torres	Game Keeper	31 years old
José García Gómez	Tractor driver	61 years old
Francisco Sánchez Martínez	Tractor driver	51 years old
José Antonio Martí García	Shepherd	44 years old
Antonio José Gómez García	Shepherd	62 years old
José Manuel Martínez García	Shepherd	44 years old
Manuel Montañés Ibáñez	Farm manager	61 years old
Mateo Alejandro Sánchez Pina	Manager	39 years old

(Coturnix coturnix), Turtle Dove *(Streptopelia turtur)*, Woodpigeon *(Columba palumbus)*, Pin-tailed Sandgrouse *(Pterocles alchata)*, Black-bellied Sandgrouse *(Pterocles orientalis)*, Little Bustard *(Tetrax tetrax)*, etc...

This overabundance of prey species was a fantastic opportunity, exploited by the many predators which, in amazing quantities, enjoyed such generous offerings.

But what are the guidelines for the management of the red-legged partridge that have been followed in Orán for 60 years?

1. Threshold of stillness

An effective team of gamekeepers, such as exists in Orán, provides the basic threshold of stillness.

The two main characteristics that each member of the keepering team should have are motivation and knowledge.

The threshold of stillness can be defined as the level of normality that should reign in a territory so that the basic interchanges and interactions between the fauna and its surroundings can occur; thus, not only is an ecological equilibrium guaranteed, but also the ecosystem retains its Capacity of Response and Capacity of Recuperation necessary to confront natural crisis situations. (C. Otero, 2008).

In other words, the wildlife present on the estate, whether prey or predator, should coexist in natural harmony, each one playing its role in the ecological network. Furthermore, prey species should be able to recuperate their population levels quickly, following the guidelines determined by the "r strategy" or *reproductive strategy*.

The *threshold of stillness* is also achieved by complementary measures other than the presence of a professional and effective team of gamekeepers, such as: rides and paths to provide satisfactory vigilance, vehicles and surveillance equipment, communications equipment, deterrents such as signs and posts, boundary fences, gates and security systems.

These systems, together with the gamekeepers, would prevent the pressure of human activities: collection of nests and chicks, poaching, the presence of wild dogs and cats, uncontrolled cattle, excessive human presence, and others. Consequently, they will provide a level of *quietness* to the ecosystem, allowing its inhabitants to preoccupy themselves solely with reproduction, rearing, eating and not being eaten. That is, they will be protected from external disturbance indirectly related to interactions with other fauna or meteorological phenomena. For these two situations, all the natural species present in Orán can count on their own resources and their ability to react, which have been tuned, adjusted and treasured as a result of thousands of years of evolution in this same ecosystem.

2. Water troughs, springs and water points

Much has been spoken about places to drink – both natural or artificial – but the basic *Orán doctrine* can be easily explained. On the plains of La Mancha, in the parched landscape of the centre of Spain, between the months of May and October, water is a *scarce resource*. Fauna, in the literal sense of the word, is completely dependent on water during these months. The more access to water – that is, the more water points – the higher the survival rates and, therefore, higher productivity and more abundant populations.

Note that we do not say "more water, more fauna", but "more water points, more fauna." The

spatial distribution of the places to drink should take priority over the amount of water.

Furthermore, there is one other question of great importance that must be considered. The majority of young partridge chicks hatch after the 10th of May. From that date, each female partridge goes to drink twice a day (on average). In so doing, she follows a path that leads from her feeding area to the water point... four times a day, followed by her chicks. During these movements, the partridge chicks are over-exposed to the eyes of predators, and during the first thirty days of life the coveys are literally decimated if the routes that they have to follow, and therefore their *overexposure time* to predators, are very long.

One method to reduce losses (although we will apply other complementary methods that we will explain later, such as setting up shelters for wildlife) is to shorten the distance to the drinking point and thus the *overexposure time* to predators, by placing drinkers every 4 ha. Thus each partridge and its chicks have to travel 100 m, at worst, which is a more reasonable distance.

When we refer to drinkers, we are talking about water points that are accessible to partridge (and their associated fauna) – whether it is watering troughs, fountains, natural springs or artificial drinkers.

Orán, November 2008. Agriculture at Orán has advanced with modern techniques adapted to the model of agriculture-with-hunting-with-conservation. In the photograph we can see barley being sown directly.

The black- bellied sandgrouse is the most common of the two species which exist at Orán. In summer it is completely dependent on water points which it visits diary.

3. Farming techniques favourable to partridges

The practice of biennial cultivation used in the Spanish Mediterranean (known in Spanish as "año y vez") guarantees the existence of stubble and brash full of fallen grain both before and after the harvest as well as green shoots during autumn; in addition, the land lying fallow for 12 months guarantees plenty of insects and their larvae, too.

The type of crops grown in Orán, historically in cereal fields spread across the property and creating a wise mosaic which depended on support of irrigated crops that produce extra food in the summer months, was perfectly adequate for the region. Other techniques were used, such as leaving 8 metres on the edge of the field unsown, direct sowing, and harvesting 3 or 4 days after the correct date in order to allow part of the grain to fall to the ground, which would then be avidly consumed by the partridges and would leave a good mantle of straw on the ground.

The combine harvesters, all of them equipped with chains to alert the birds to their presence, leave the stubble at a height of 35-45 cm, thus leaving enough cover for the chicks.

In other words, if barley were harvested early, partridge chicks aged 5 weeks old on the 20th of June, and scarcely capable of flight, would suddenly lose their natural cover and would be defenceless in the face of aerial predators.

However, if the predominant crop is wheat, this period of *canopied skies* will last an extra 30 days, by which time the partridge chicks would be 9 weeks old and would already be capable of flight. Additionally, wheat harvested at 35-45 cm gives them enough cover to defend themselves from the Montagu's Harrier *(Circus pygargus)*, Booted Eagle *(Hieraetus pennatus)*, European Magpie *(Pica pica)*, Common Raven *(Corvus corax)* and White Storks *(Ciconia ciconia)*.

4. Food

Food is abundant in Orán, and never lacking. Even so, when there is not enough food, we put wheat in special feeders to avoid it being eaten by wild boar, which, as an aside, do not enjoy an ideal habitat in Orán. Any wild boar that comes there soon regrets its arrival. In fact, one of the reasons for fencing the big game area was to limit the entry of wild boar to the rest of the property. The wild boar is no friend of partridges.

The agricultural techniques of cultivating every second year and of direct sowing, as we have explained before, are two methods that guarantee the existence of green shoots, grains and enough insects and larvae for partridges and their chicks.

5. Cover and shelter

Barley, wheat and irrigated crops represent 72% of the total area of Orán. There are an additional 1,000 ha (28%) of fallow land and coppiced forest that offer enough cover and shelter all year round.

Harvesting techniques guarantee that once the crops are harvested (between the 20th and 30th of June), stubble of sufficient height is left to help protect the birds and other wildlife.

Other measures carried out in Oran are to leave an 8-metre strip of land unsown, and to build specific shelters which are constructed in two ways:

- Huts are built, at a density of 1 per hectare. These are constructed from branches of olive trees, oaks, pines or vines, although any other materials that are to hand could be used.
- Natural scrub and thicket could be planted – Rosemary *(Rosmarinus officinalis)*, Giant Reed *(Arundo donax)*, Retama *(Retama sphaerocarpa)*, Esparto Grass *(Stipa tenacísima)*, Spanish Broom *(Spartium junceum)* and Common Broom *(Cytisus scoparius)* etc. – in plots of 5 x 20 metres next to the rides, which would then substitute natural shelter.

6. Promotion of other prey species

Correct management of partridge territory requires – and this is mathematically and biologically exact – that both biodiversity and populations of other prey species, and accordingly of their predators, are encouraged.

In La Mancha there is a saying: *if you want a lot of partridges, you have to have a lot of rabbits.* This tells us that a good density of rabbits (10 per hectare) or a high density (25 per hectare) encourages an increase in other prey species (see Point 7) and automatically, in a cause-and-effect reaction that can last between 3 and 5 years, a spectacular growth in the number of birds of prey and predatory mammals.

7. Control of opportunist predators

A delicate but absolutely vital point. Predators that affect partridge populations (and which can be legally controlled) are wild boar, fox, rat, wild dog, wild cat, magpie, Carrion Crow *(Corvus corone)*, all of which must be controlled in order to keep them at adequate densities so as to guarantee the survival not only of the partridge population, but also of equally valuable associated species.

Oran has 1,300 heads of La Mancha's sheep.

C. Otero

GOOD AND EFFECTIVE MANAGEMENT OF THE RED-LEGGED PARTRIDGE (AND ASSOCIATED FAUNA) AT ORÁN PRODUCES AN INCREASE IN BIRDS OF PREY AND PROTECTED CARNIVOROUS MAMMALS, SUCH AS:

BIRDS
- Honey buzzard
- Black kite
- Red kite
- Black-shouldered kite
- Egyptian vulture
- Black vulture
- Short-toed eagle
- Hen harrier
- Montagu´s harrier
- Northern harrier
- Northern goshawk
- Sparrow hawk

- Buzzard
- Iberian imperial eagle
- Golden eagle
- Booted eagle
- Bonelli's eagle
- Lesser kestrel
- Kestrel
- Merlin
- Hobby
- Peregrine falcon
- Barn owl
- European scops owl
- Eurasian eagle owl

- Little owl
- Tawny owl
- Long-eared owl
- Short-eared owl
- Shrikes (3 species)
- Raven

MAMMALS
- Wild cat
- European polecat
- Badger
- Common genet
- Stone marten

FAUNA ASSOCIATED WITH RED-LEGGED PARTRIDGE THAT BENEFITS FROM THE MANAGEMENT OF THE BIRD'S HABITAT AND THE CONTROL OF OPPORTUNIST PREDATORS AT ORÁN

- Red-legged partridge
- Quail
- Rabbit
- Spanish hare
- Pin-tailed Sandgrouse
- Black-bellied sandgrouse
- Stone curlew
- Little bustard
- Great bustard
- Rock dove

- Stock dove
- Woodpigeon
- European turtle dove
- Eurasian collared dove
- European nightjar
- Red-necked nightjar
- Kingfisher
- European bee-eater
- European roller

- Hoopoe
- Sand martin
- Crag martin
- Swallow
- Red-rumped swallow
- Blackbird
- Skylarks (8 species)
- Other small birds (21 species)
- Small mammals (11 species)

Control techniques must be highly selective and practical. Recently, the European Commission has recognised the technique known as **Alares** as the most effective in capturing foxes.

Wild boar are controlled by direct hunting. Wild dogs and cats, aside from using **Alares**, can be controlled with cages – selective traps – which is also applicable to magpies and crows.

8. Sustainable Exploitation and Shooting

Traditionally, the basic norm is to conserve the "mother population", from which, notwithstanding predictable meteorological phenomena or extrac-

tion by shooting, population recovery is guaranteed. In standard breeding conditions, it is accepted that 30% of partridge population can be extracted in the first days of October. If more than 30% is taken, there is a risk of severely damaging the *level of the mother population*.

And if partridges breed badly in a certain year... well, hunting is put off. There is no other solution when considering the real natural partridge, the Orán partridge.

It is the same situation that wine growers face when the yield is low or the quality of grape is under par. Bad wine cannot be sold under the first label of the company. The same situation is also faced by Spanish breeders of fighting bulls if the animals are not of sufficient bravery... the bulls are sacrificed.

No one has ever said that breeding wild partridge is an easy task... nor that many thankless hours do not occur.

Carlos Otero and
Alejandro Sánchez Lodares

Stone warrens for rabbits. Typically *manchego*, and efficient in guaranteeing a good population density. In the background is the natural pond called "El Minuto".

The Renatur model of cage trap is specially designed for controlling foxes. The number of foxes captured is about 1 per trap per month, with traps placed every 200 hectares.

C. Otero

Orán has traditional driven partridge shooting. This is the "Collado de la Mota" drive. The screens, built of limestone, also serve as shelter for wild animals.

ORÁN ESTATE BELONGS TO:

Friends of the Countryside

Rise Foundation

APROCA
Castilla-La Mancha

WE initiative

Activities & attractions

 Country

 Hunting

 Shooting

CONTACT DATA

D. Alejandro Sánchez Lodares
Campillo de las Doblas S.A.
Finca Orán
Campillo Doblas, • ALBACETE 02511 SPAIN
Tel.: 0034 967 58 00 32 • 696 484 180

Theme 4

Forestry

IN SEARCH OF A EUROPEAN POLICY FOR THE CORK OAK WOODLANDS. TALKING POINTS

Paulo Casaca

Chairman the Land Use and Food Policy Intergroup (LUFPIG) in the European Parliament, Member of the European Parliament

According to Aronson[1] – which is the most recent and comprehensive assessment on cork oak woodlands, and is the reference for the following paragraphs – although cork oak most likely originated in Asia, it is currently concentrated in the western Mediterranean basin. Widely used since early civilisation as a stopper for amphorae, material for shoes, housing material or as a floater for fishing gear, cork and the cork oak woodlands from which it is produced have been a central element in our civilization.

More resistant to droughts and fire than to freezing temperatures, cork oak evolved as a unique symbiosis of "nature and nurture" (Aronson, *op. cit.*) both in semi-natural woodlands developing into forests and in the open woodlands known as "montado" (Portugal) or "dehesa" (Spain).

Cork oak woodlands record one of the highest rates of biodiversity in the number of plants per unit of surface area, including endemic species, and in particular plants listed in the IUCN Red List of Endangered Species. In terms of animals, it is the habitat for such endangered species as the Iberian lynx in the Iberian Peninsula, the Iberian imperial eagle in Spain and the highly endangered Barbary deer in the Maghreb. Moreover it provides the habitat for nearly one hundred other animal species listed in the annexes of the EU Habitats and Birds directive that are rarely found elsewhere.

However, the most peculiar characteristic of this treasure of nature is that it has been able to develop "nurtured" by humans instead of being ravaged as is the case in most of existing ecosystems.

The noblest use for cork from early civilisation to the present day has been as stoppers, either in amphorae, wooden barrels or glass bottles of wine. Its use was critical in keeping sparkling wines under pressure and fundamental in ensuring the healthy breathing process that allows wines to age but not turn to vinegar.

Production of cork, reflecting the density of cork oak woodlands, is highly concentrated in the north-western tip of the Mediterranean basin, with Portugal representing 55% of the production and Spain 25%.

The *montado* and other existing cork oak woodlands have been widely used throughout history not only for the cork, but as a complex agricultural-forestry-pasture system. Cereal production has been occasionally developed, usually in intervals of many years, amongst open woodlands, whereas local breeds of pigs – highly valued by the market today – graze the fields mainly to eat the oak acorns, and sheep graze the grass. Mushrooms, honey, aromatic and medicinal plants are also occasionally produced.

The European Union's policy for the conservation of its internal biodiversity – namely its two most important tools, the Habitat and the Birds directives – covered some of these woodlands in Europe, including parts of them in the Natura 2000 network and confirming, for the most part, pre-existing national legal protection statutes.

In North Africa, where "almost all cork oak woodlands are state owned and managed by forestry directorates" (Aronson, *op. cit.*) conservation problems are more acute, as the local communities use the land for most purposes – access to grazing and acorn collection are free and not regulated – but the cork is a state owned product.

In spite of the existing regulatory framework, cork oak woodlands are decreasing and under threat, especially in the southern shores of the Mediterranean but also on its northern side.

The most important and recent threat has come from plastic stoppers and metal screw-tops used in cheap wine and in most of the increasing

[1] Aronson. 1968. The Tragedy of the Commons, *Science*, Vol. 162, n. 3859, pp. 1243-1248.

quantity of wine coming out of the New World. This tendency has led to the collapse of the price of cork and therefore to a serious threat to the sustainability of the whole ecosystem.

Wine cork stoppers are by far the most economically valuable product from cork oak woodlands. In effect, they work as the most important cross-subsidising tool supporting this most valuable and fragile ecosystem.

Regarding the quality of wine itself, it is important to take into consideration that research has proved there is no biological contamination effects on the wine caused by the cork: whenever biological contamination exists, this is due to a deficiency in the wine making process.

Furthermore, for those of us who appreciate wine as a living matter, plastic or metal stoppers, which prevent the wine from breathing, are really killing its soul. It is my firm view that a consumer buying a bottle of wine is entitled to know what this bottle contains, and he should be clearly warned before opening it if he is going to find plastic or metal in the place of a proper cork stopper.

Regarding North Africa, I am convinced that whenever property rights and responsibilities over scarce natural resources are blurred, the "Tragedy of the Commons", that is, the personal incentive to over-exploitation, is the most likely outcome.

In spite of its popularity, Garrett Hardin's famous article in Science continues to be ignored even in the heart of the supposedly most developed world.

I have been arguing for a long time that the European concept of "exclusive competence on the maritime biological resources" in the Common Fisheries Policy coupled with the general principle of free-access to them is a typical example of the "Tragedy of the Commons".

It is also necessary to keep in mind that all of the cork oak woodlands in the Maghreb face pressure from an ever increasing population boom.

So, even if European Union practice is not the best of examples, the truth is that our neighbours in the south would gain immensely if they could reform the property system relating to their cork oak woodlands.

Turning back to our shores, the main outstanding problem – that is, after the war against cork-stoppers – remains the different views regarding the epidemics devastating large portions of cork-oaks in the area where it is currently concentrated (southern Portugal and south-western Spain).

For most of the specialists this seems to be the sole consequence of overgrazing and poor management practices, while most of the forest owners see this as a pest that is difficult to control.

The Habitats directive (92/443 Council), in its article 8, had foreseen the creation of a financial framework to allow its implementation:

"1. In parallel with their proposals for sites eligible for designation as special areas of conservation, hosting priority natural habitat types and/or priority species, the Member States shall send, as appropriate, to the Commission their estimates re-

lating to the Community co-financing which they consider necessary to allow them to meet their obligations pursuant to Article 6 (1)".

In the context of this financial framework the European Commission nominated an expert working group, which estimated that an annual European budget of between €3400 m and €5700 m was required in order to implement the directive. The financial means used under the Life instrument are quite modest and certainly not able to address the issues under consideration.

However, the European Commission never followed this recommendation with the corresponding proposal, as would have been expected, arguing that the Council would never accept it. According to its recent communication on biodiversity ("A mid-term assessment of implementing of the EC biodiversity action plan" COM (2008)864), the European Commission acknowledges the failure of the planned objective of halting the deterioration of biodiversity by 2010.

Notwithstanding, the European Commission document fails to mention the most obvious reason for the action plan having failed: the lack of a coherent and significant financial framework to finance the Natura 2000 network as foreseen in article 8 of the Habitats directive.

Furthermore, the document does not even mention the cork-oak woodlands – or the green-oak forests that face perhaps even bigger threats – and fails to properly address the most significant biodiversity challenges of the regions with which I am more in contact (outermost regions and west Mediterranean).

We cannot understand the full challenge to the survival of the cork-oak forests without placing them within the Common Agricultural Policy (CAP) perspective. The CAP was organised into Common Market organisations, where each agricultural product is seen as a specific policy issue, and in that perspective it only viewed cork-oak forests as part of the "forest sector" (out of the CAP domain, according to the EC Treaty), never as a unique mix of semi-wild nature, forest, agriculture and animal production.

In relative terms, the application of the CAP to the Iberian peninsula favoured specialised modern agriculture to the detriment of complex systems like green-oak and cork-oak open lands.

However, whenever confronted with all of these criticisms, the European Commission always argues that the CAP rural policy should have corrected all of these problems.

Commission official positions forget several important factors, such as:

- (1) the most important agri-environmental tools, however positive, do not impact on these forests; they simply correct some of the excesses of modern intensified agriculture;
- (2) Subsidies available to plant these forests exist, but they have not been significantly different from other subsidies for more profitable forests with no biodiversity value;
- (3) Several of the measures, such as subsidies for low density cattle grazing, also have a considerably negative impact, as a European defined low density corresponds to high density for these forests, and actually encourages the replacement of well-adapted animals, such as local breeds of pigs, by cattle.

This is why I believe the main challenge ahead of us is to correct the under-financing of the Habitats directive and to reform fundamentally the existing CAP in the context of the next policy revision.

The purpose of the recently agreed "Health Check" was to simplify the Single Farm Payment (SFP) and improve its effectiveness, realign the CAP with global market realities and to adjust the CAP to the so-called "new challenges": climate change, renewable energies, water management and biodiversity in the context of rural development policy.

The Council decision on the "Health Check" may be seen as a step in this direction, but it is nonetheless a very modest one, equating to a shift of approximately €1.3 billion from conventional farm supports (which amount to about €36bn.) to the "new challenges". Most of the work remains to be done to ensure that the CAP post-2013 emerges as one truly fit for the 21st century.

Talking points

The Land Use and Food Policy Intergroup (LUFPIG) is a unique MEP-led intergroup of politicians that interacts regularly with the agri-business community. For nearly 20 years LUFPIG has brought together MEPs from across the European Parliament whose work is affected by the operation of agriculture and food policy.

Our aim is to provide a forum for debate for those players in the various policy areas who do not normally interact with politicians. As an intergroup on the boundaries of Parliamentary Committees dealing with issues from budgets, to international trade, development, the environment and consumer issues, in addition to agriculture, LUFPIG is well placed to do this.

It was created to bring together MEPs from different policy areas who, whilst not all agricultural specialists, could see the impact of the Common Agricultural Policy on the issues in which they were involved. At the outset, the debate was centred around the funding of the CAP, with MEPs insisting that it be cut. However, the consensus opinion soon emerged that issues other than money would form the crux of successful reform and the Intergroup's remit broadened quickly to encompass areas relating to external trade, development, environment, food policy and consumer issues.

In advance of the 1992 Agricultural Reforms, LUFPIG commissioned a study from six leading European agricultural economists, led by Professors Tangermann and Marsh. They concluded that agricultural production must be de-coupled from subsidies and they suggested the introduction of an 'income bond scheme' for farmers to replace production subsidies. These ideas are still at the forefront of Commission thinking on CAP reform and formed the basis for the recent reform introducing decoupled income payments across Europe.

Agricultural reform has advanced considerably since the Tangermann/Marsh report was written. It is now generally recognised that despite the successes of the CAP, many of its subsequent problems are inherent to its success and require further reform. The basis of the Intergroup's philosophy remains that European agricultural policy should be economically viable, transparent and environmentally sustainable. This is still to be achieved in full.

LUFPIG has continued to address these issues in the Parliamentary term 2004-2009. The emphasis of reform however, has now shifted from the CAP in general to its application in terms of trade, development, environment and food policy. It is therefore in these areas that LUFPIG is focussing its attention.

The creation of intergroups has become an increasingly popular activity. At the last count, it was estimated that there are over 80 cross-party groups of MEPs which refer to themselves as intergroups. Some, like ours, maintain a high level of transparency and although industry-sponsored, continue to be MEP-led and independent in the formation of our work programme and activities.

One of the reasons why intergroups have grown in number over recent years is that they enable MEPs to form cross-party coalitions on specific issues of interest, which can foster wider political friendships and consensus building within the European Parliament. Another reason for the proliferation of cross-party groups in the European Parliament is that political parties are weakly developed on the EU level. The party groups in the EP being far more heterogeneous than parties in national parliaments, MEPs are more likely to seek alliances across parties around specific issues and interests.

Faced with a vast workload due to their expanding policy-making mandate, for the 785 elected MEPs, the pressure is on. Much of this work involves highly technical issues with often far-reaching social and environmental impacts. Given this situation, MEPs often seek the input of stakeholders such as industry experts, environmental NGOs and trade associations to help inform their opinions. Our intergroup helps bring this collection of people to MEPs for an exchange of views similar to those which take place in think tanks.

Brussels & Strasbourg, February 2009

Baroniet Adelswärd AB Estate

Baroniet Adelswärd AB

Boreal

Location: Åtvidaberg, Östergotland county, Sweden.
Surface: 21,740 ha.

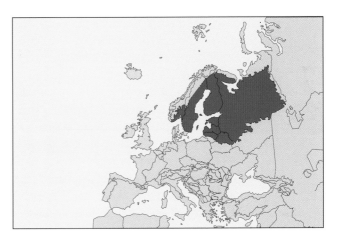

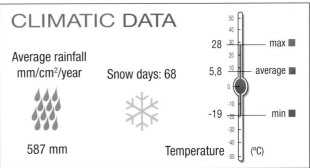

CLIMATIC DATA

Average rainfall
mm/cm²/year

Snow days: 68

587 mm

Temperature (°C)

28 — max
5,8 — average
-19 — min

SUMMARY

"Tradition, Know-how and Quality" is what characterizes this property and family business.
Baroniet Adelsward AB is a forestry and farming estate based in Åtvidaberg, in the county of Östergötland in Sweden, with four main activities, a common business idea and historic traditions.
The estate, founded in 1782 by Johan Adelswärd (1718-1785), the production of copper then being its main activity, is today a company based on forestry, farming, real estate and wildlife management.
13 people are employed today. Services for forestry and for buildings.
"We face the future management of Baroniet with the ambition to make it continuously prosperous and profitable", says the former owner Johan Adelswärd.

Adelsnäs Manor and Park.

HISTORY

The original motive to establish the estate was the ambition to resume the copper mining, which had been closed for centuries. The founder of the estate, Johan Adelswärd, applied in 1782 to King Gustaf III to make it an entailed estate. The acquisition of forests guaranteed the supply of charcoal for energy for the smelting-works.

The barony at that time represented a typical Swedish production structure where in certain regions a unique natural resource was abundant, in this case copper ore, central and dominant for its population. The capital required for its mining and processing was invested by entrepreneurs who settled in the place, exercising leadership and power. The Swedish term for this is "brukssamhälle" which may be translated as "manufacturing estate".

The landowner and his family had a great impact on the local region, the forming of the industrial village, its social institutions and workers' dwellings.

The mining of copper and to some extent iron ore was the main industry in the estate until 1903 when it was discontinued because of diminishing yield and competition from higher quality mines.

The entailment has, through the generations, kept the estate undivided due to the right of primogeniture. At the turn of the century Theodor Adelswärd (1860-1929) was challenged with the task of finding new lines of production for the redundant work force. Now the timber was to be refined in saw mills and an electric power company was formed for local distribution of power. Other industries were started: office furniture, manufacture of wheels, and a dairy farm.

The original timber production was located in eight different so called "forest ranger districts" and was centralised in 1946 when a sawmill company was formed by Eric Adelswärd (1909-1986) and one central sawmill was built on the estate.

DESCRIPTION

In 1963 a Swedish law was passed to discontinue the entailed estate system, to open it to democratic inheritance. Due to this, the barony was then made a limited company. Since then, two generational transfers have been carried out, the family estate still in one piece and undivided. This was achieved as a result of capital funds emanating from the selling of the power company in 1997 and the sawmill company in 2007.

The present estate is a forestry and farming enterprise still in the hands of the family, owned and managed by the tenth descendant, Gustaf Adelswärd, after a generational transfer in 2005 by his father Johan Adelswärd.

The Adelsnäs mansion was built in 1914-1920, replacing an older manor from the 18th century.

Across the lake
is the town of Åtvidaberg.

Baroniet Adelswärd AB Estate

General infrastructure

The Adelsnäs mansion was built in 1914-1920, replacing an older manor from the 18th century. With the new mansion, there was a subsequent change in the structure of the premises including farm buildings, stables, garages, dwellings, gardens and park.

Theodor Adelswärd took the initiative to build a manor for his family and for representational purposes. The mansion is beautifully set on a peninsula surrounded by an English style park. The mansion has ca. 50 rooms.

The architect Isac Gustaf Clason was commissioned for this building, which is one of the latest private houses of its kind in Sweden. Across the lake is the town of Åtvidaberg. The mansion is today the residence of the present owner, Gustaf Adelswärd and his family.

The Orangerie next to the main house was built in 1860 for the cultivation of exotic fruits. It was renovated in 1994 partly with government subsidies and is now used for art exhibitions in the summer.

The little museum at the entrance of the park represents the history of the park, the two mansions and the family.

The farm buildings: The barns and stables are maintained in good condition and in use for breeding heifers. Sheep are also kept for rotational grazing.

A bio-mass boiler was built in 2007 for the general heating of the numerous dwellings, office, manor house and grain storage. The boiler is fed with wood chips and a continuous hot water system circulates through pipes, 3km in length.

Staff

During the last 40 years, the number of personnel and staff employed at the estate has drastically decreased. The diversification of activities within the barony stemming from a tradition of managerial self-sustainability has been replaced by a concentration of the main resources in forestry, farming and building maintenance. In the 1960s, around 150 people were employed. Today, 13 qualified employees are working in management and production.

Forestry

The forests of the barony originate from the demand for charcoal for the copper works. Since the beginning of the 20th century, forestry has been the estate's main activity. A forest management firm takes care of the 17,000 hectares of productive forest and some external forests. The forest has been

DISTRIBUTION OF LAND-USE

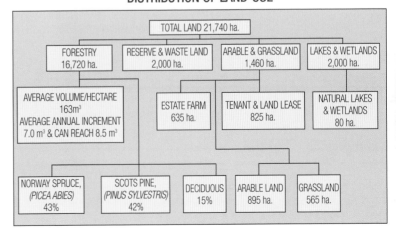

A programme has been started to preserve the oak stands in the estate.

Baronet Adelswärd AB Estate

managed for almost a century with high ambitions in forest culture and the production of high quality raw materials for the wood industry.

The forests are managed on a long-term basis according to defined production and environmental policies. All forestry operations, from planting to final felling, are carried out by contractors. This implies flexibility, as different logging equipment is needed according to the varying nature and topography of the terrain.

From the 1950's, modern logging development gradually replaced the horses and manual work force. One could roughly describe this change by stating that 50 years ago the annual work by 100 employees equates today to 10 qualified foresters with 2 modern machines.

Around 80% of the estate is covered by conifer forests interspersed by deciduous forests and lakes, at an average altitude of 100 metres above sea level. 240 kilometres of forest roads provide for convenient transportation of personnel and timber.

Since the sale of the sawmill company, the forestry management now focuses on the marketing of felled timber as well as standing timber. The demand for bio-energy products is increasing.

The felling quantities are set according to the market situation and limited by the annual increment (growth) and the objective of good silviculture safeguarding a balanced age distribution of the growing stock 280,000-350,000 conifer plants are set out annually.

The mean felling quantities during the last ten year period amounted to a total of 88,100 forest m³. Of this, final felling accounted for 45,600 forest m³, and thinning produced 42,400 forest m³.

All forest products delivered are certified according to PEFC and FSC, promoting sustainable forest management.

The estate owns a part of the largest stand of Oak *(Quercus* spp.*)*, unique in the region and designated as being of national interest.

Within the barony, a total of 180 hectares are under the EU Birds and Habitats Directive under Natura 2000.

Farming

The farming centre is in Adelsnäs, on the outskirts of Åtvidaberg. 1,460 hectares are divided into 565 hectares of grassland and 895 hectares of arable land. Wheat, triticale, barley, oats, rye and rape are the main crops produced.

Until 2007 about 600 hectares were worked in order to produce high quality milk. In spite of skilled and committed personnel, healthy livestock, neat pastures and fields and a well controlled feeding chain, delivering over 9,000 kg per cow (1.8 million kg annually), the dairy farm was closed down in 2007 due to economic loss. A new model of production is now being tried, namely the contracted breeding of heifers: 150 weaned calves are bought annually, raised for two years and sold in late pregnancy to a dairy farm. This production is already under way, on an ecological inside-outside extensive farming plan. 192 hectares of grazing land have been restored for this purpose and sheep are kept for interchanged grazing.

Tenant farms have decreased by 60 units over the last 50 years. This land was subsequently afforested. Now there are only two tenant farms and some 20 land lease contracts

Real estate management

The houses of the barony are situated in the countryside around Åtvidaberg. In total the estate owns and manages 50 permanent houses and 120 holiday houses and some 100 grants of residential leases.

These real estate assets are continuously renewed and developed according to a plan that also includes the selling off of houses too expensive to develop. There is an awareness of the impor-

tance of taking care of historical values of the buildings that are characterized by farming, mining and the manor culture. Tenants mainly originate from Åtvidaberg and surroundings, but the weekend houses attract tenants even from southern Sweden and northern Europe.

Restoration of a large mosaic pasture / A sustainable project

Old pastures have become overgrown with Birch *(Betula pendula)* and Aspen *(Populus tremula)*, and the Oaks have not regenerated because of the competition from the more shade-tolerant species.

In cooperation with the County Administrative Board the management has recently started a conservation programme for preserving the oak landscape at Adelsnäs.

Around 80% of the estate is covered by conifer forest interspersed by deciduous forest.

Baroniet Adelswärd AB Estate

Baroniet Adelswärd AB **(Sweden)**

The capercaillie is a rare bird on the estate. Predators like badger threaten its reproduction.

Overgrown areas have now been cleared leaving oak and Hazel *(Corylus avellana)* to grow more successfully. Some rocky areas with birch and aspen are also left without too much clearing. The general idea is to create a mosaic landscape. The sites are Woodland Key Habitats and the clearance was done purely to benefit nature conservation and to provide grazing, thus combining preservation and production and not forgetting the recreational values.

Long-term solutions for the land use at Adelsnäs have to take both ecological and economic matters into consideration. There has to be a concern over biological and natural values as well as over the yield for forestry and farming. The fact is that the restoration project is already financially viable.

Restoration is a partnership between the landowner and the nature conservation advisors.

Sustainable wildlife management

The Elk *(Alces alces)* is the most important species. Its population has to be controlled because of grazing damage to new trees, especially to Scots Pine *(Pinus sylvestris)* plantations. Regional plans are set up with a common ambition to promote quality in the elk population. The Fallow Deer *(Dama dama)* is very abundant and the Wild Boar *(Sus scrofa)* is expanding, while the Roe Deer *(Capreolus capreolus)* has decreased in number.

The Capercaillie *(Tetrao urogallus)* and the Black Grouse *(T. tetrix)* are rare, as is the Quail *(Coturnix coturnix)*. Predators like the Badger *(Meles meles)* threaten their reproduction.

In 1982 organised marketing of elk, fallow deer and roe deer shooting was started and this has become a developed activity. A total of two weeks of sold shoots are offered. Shooting is also let on contract. About a third of the total area is still used for private hunting. Lakes are also let for fishing on contract for Pike *(Esox lucius)*, Perch *(Perca fluviatilis)*, Zander *(Stizostedion lucioperca)* and Crayfish *(Pacifastacus leniusculus)*.

A gamekeeper administers the hunting and fishing and is the guide at all shooting events. Hunting and fishing has become a profitable business. The basic management principle is to shoot and fish according to the carrying capacity of land and water.

PRIVATE OPINION

I clearly remember the moment when I understood that I had an important task ahead of me, something that would bring me both joy and a great challenge. I was eighteen and my father Johan and I were out in the forest to shoot Elk. Suddenly they were there; a cow with calf came trotting straight towards us. I aimed, listened to my father's brief advice to wait until the calf reached the fence and to shoot as it stopped to jump. The calf did stop, I squeezed the trigger... and nothing happened. The mechanism had jammed. My disappointment was great. My father looked at me and said: "Do not be disappointed; you have a lifetime ahead of you in our forests".

Today the forest is the most valuable asset of the barony. It is essential to manage the forest both effectively and with perseverance and in order to create a financial basis for investing in the future, as well as maintaining the houses on the estate and its environment. Furthermore, without such active forest and agricultural management, it will not be possible to maintain this diversified Swedish landscape. My family and I face the challenge of not only tradition but of change and adaptation to new techniques and products.

The future requires increased efforts to produce energy from the forest. Energy can be produced by the extraction of biodiesel, biogas and firewood. The product development of sawn timber and pulp evolves at a much slower pace and is more influenced by cyclical market fluctuations than energy products. The forest also offers leisure and recreational experiences (trekking, mountain biking, walking and so on) and the willingness to pay for these experiences is slowly growing.

Farming in the forest-dominated part of southern Sweden where the barony is situated, limits the agricultural yield. The area of each field is modest and configuration is irregular which makes efficient cultivation hard. The yield is also adversely affected by grazing by wild animals. That, combined with high operating costs, means that subsidies from the European Union are essential.

Sweden together with Finland has Europe's largest and purest fresh water resources. The EU Water Directive is to ensure and improve water quality. To maintain and develop these resources, economic incentives will be needed to generate production and distribution of water to Europe.

As the owner of a family estate in the tenth generation, the transfer to the next generation is an important challenge. Thus the allocation of capital from the annual profits from farming and forestry goes to other investment areas in order to facilitate capital freedom and rural entrepreneurship for the next generation. The long term desire is to keep the estate and the family undivided, and there are some important aspects to safeguard this vision.

Sustainability

The estate with its assets creates a platform for innovative steps in farming, forestry and water management. The arable land is already arranged for contracted breeding of heifers. The grazing land includes the promotion and protection of the oak landscape. Forests are managed according to the Swedish law of forest management as well as to the certification standards of PEFC (Pan European Forest Certification) and FSC (Forest Stewardship Council). The freshwater lakes are a future resource yet to be protected, managed and utilized.

Organisation

The organisation of the company must be executed for the benefit of the company. The importance of well-coordinated professional leadership with the owner present but not necessarily at the helm in daily operations, and contracting of production, is a warrant for efficiency and flexibility. But we cannot ignore the fact that the next generation must be prepared for the ownership responsibility and corporate governance.

Emerging business opportunities

Wind power prospecting is continuing, whilst new forest products are being offered to the market and new uses for wood fibre are being assessed. The management of deciduous forests

The fallow deer is very abundant and the wild boar is expanding, while the roe deer has decreased in number.

Baroniet Adelswärd AB Estate

The Estate owns and manages about 50 permanent houses and 120 holiday houses.

Baroniet Adelswärd AB Estate

may offer a field of future possibilities. Preservation of water may offer the single most important business opportunity in the future considering Southern Europe's drought and Central and Eastern Europe's struggle with water quality. Tourism, shooting and fishing is an obvious branch for development.

I am a strong supporter of the European Union, but I also believe that the less legislation and detailed regulation we have to follow and the more incentives we are given, the more we can, and will create. For my wife Malin and me the main purpose is to create an environment where our children can understand the management of the estate, to appreciate rural values and finally and hopefully give them the joy to manage farm and forest.

Gustaf Adelswärd

BARONIET ADELSWÄRD BELONGS TO:

PEFC
Programme for the Endorsement of Forest Certification

Friends of the Countryside
Friends of the Countryside

FSC®
FCS (Forest Stewardship Council)

Activities

- Hunting
- Birdwatching
- Product Estate
- Fishing
- Historic private house
- Walking trails

CONTACT DATA
Gustaf Adelswärd
Baroniet Adelswärd AB, Box 256, 597 26 Åtvidaberg, Sweden
Tel.: 0120-858 00 • Fax: 0120-858 10.
gustaf.adelsward@baroniet.se
www.baroniet.se

"...ay the forest is the most valuable ...t of the barony", G. Adelswärd.

Breme Estate

Breme

Continental

Location: Breme, Pavia, Lombardy, Italy.
Surface: 803 ha.

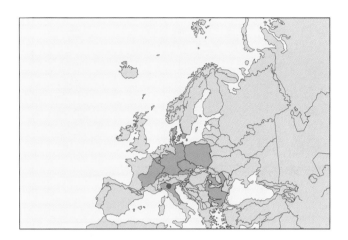

CLIMATIC DATA

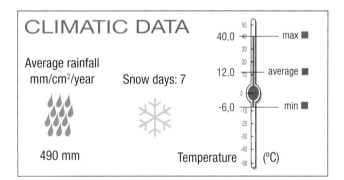

Average rainfall
mm/cm²/year

Snow days: 7

490 mm

Temperature (°C)

40,0 — max

12,0 — average

-6,0 — min

SUMMARY

Owned by the Noble House of Visconti since 1400, Breme is characterized by its ricefields, poplar trees for timber production and a rich biodiversity of fauna and flora species, thanks to the floodplains (known as *golena*) of the River Po. It is located in the northwest of Italy, 60 km northwest of Pavia, between the provinces of Alexandra and Pavia (Lombardy region).

It is a perfect place to watch species of birds linked to marshlands, including significant concentrations of the Common Cormorant *(Phalacrocorax carbo)* during the winter.

The main initiative carried out by the owners is the programme to conserve and recover the fluvial ecosystem of the *golena* of the Po, thus avoiding events like those that occured in 1994 and 2000, when the River Po devastated crops, forests, etc.

The old Manor House of Breme is now integrated in the town with the same name.

Breme (Italy)

The estate has another building, the Torre d'Isola, on the right bank of the River Po.

Breme Estate

Coat of Armas of the House of Visconti, depicting the "biscione", a serpent who appears to be swallowing a human.

DESCRIPTION

What do we find in Breme?

The Visconti Agricultural Estate has a surface area of about 800 ha across Piedmont and Lombardy, on both sides of the River Po. Current land use is 70% agriculture and forest (cereal crops, plantations of Poplar and broadleaved tree plantations) and 30% natural habitats (mainly riverside forests, river channels and gravel beds). The tree plantations are concentrated inside the golena (floodplain) area and the crops outside. The traditional crop in the area is rice.

The estate has been owned for many centuries by the Noble House of Visconti, whose coat of arms can be seen on the central estate buildings in Breme (Pavia, Lombardy), on the left bank of the River Po.

Main buildings

The main house is a building attached to a typical Lombardy farmstead (dating back to the 18th century). The farmstead has two sections, one for resident estate workers, the other for the rice pickers (these were traditionally women, called *mondine*) who came from other regions especially for the rice harvest and needed accommodation. Today the section used by resident workers is still used for housing purposes. As the *mondine* gave way in recent decades to mechanised harvesting, their section has been divided into workshops and storehouses.

The estate has another main building in the little village of Torre d'Isola (Valmacca, Piedmont) on the right bank of the River Po. It is a magnificent example of rural architecture, and was restored in recent years to fulfill purposes of both agriculture and nature observation. It possesses a tower that, in the flat landscape of the area, was used as an observation post during the Second War of Independence of Italy (1859). The farmstead is close to

The River Po and the Alps provide magnificent scenery at Breme.

Breme Estate

the very course of the river; within the *golena* there are no rural buildings as such.

Staff

The estate is managed by Consolata Visconti and has a permanent staff composed of a farmer (Luciano Righetti) and three workers, with the advice of forestry consultants *"ForTeA studio associato"*, which developed the re-naturalisation programme of the estate, the first of this kind in Italy.

Fauna, flora and ecosystems

The fauna and flora in Breme are diverse. The migratory species that frequent wet areas, such as herons, ducks, terns and plovers, are very abundant on the estate. The biodiversity is determined by the intermix of different environments present on the estate: the river habitat, consisting of the River Po, its banks and its intricate channels; the forest habitat, formed by the leafy riverside forests and by the tree plantations which occupy up to two thirds of the total area; and the agricultural system, formed by crop fields (mainly rice).

In these habitats ducks, Coot *(Fulica atra)*, Moorhen *(Gallinula chloropus)*, Little Grebe *(Tachybaptus ruficollis)*, Cuckoo *(Cuculus canorus)*, Golden Oriole *(Oriolus oriolus)*, Carrion Crow *(Corvus corone cornix)* and Purple Heron *(Ardea purpurea)* thrive without problem.

On the left bank confluence of the River Po with the River Sesia, and on the islands wich adorn the course of the river, there are extensive gravel beaches. These seemingly bare areas are indeed the habitat – and nesting area – for several species of bird, such as Little Ringed Plover *(Charadrius dubius)*, Stone Curlew *(Burhinus oedicnemus)*, Common Sandpiper *(Actitis hypoleucos)*, Nightjar *(Caprimulgus europaeus)*, Common Tern *(Sterna hirundo)*, Little Tern *(Sterna albifrons)*, Black-headed Gull *(Larus ridibundus)* and Yellow-legged Gull *(Larus michahellis)*. In this habitat evolution gave bird eggs a very useful cryptic appearance. For instance, the eggs of the Little Ringed Plover *(Charadrius dubius)*, laid in groups of 3-4 on the ground like black-spotted chestnuts, are easily mistaken for pebbles.

The Kingfisher *(Alcedo atthis)* is abundant along the River Po itself and its redundant channels, where it carves holes for its nest in the steep earth banks.

In recent years, significant winter concentrations of Common Cormorant *(Phalacrocorax carbo)* as been observed in Breme.

The meanders and old branches of the Po have particular importance to the fauna, as they remain flooded alongside the bankside vegetation under a canopy of trees which form the riparian woodland. These are based on Poplars *(Populus nigra, P. alba)*, different species of Willows (mainly *Salix alba*), Ash *(Fraxinus excelsior)*, Alder *(Alnus glutinosa)* and outspread trunks of Oaks *(Quercus robur)*.

In the forest, field borders and in the most recent tree plantations the Hawthorn *(Crataegus monogyna)* is abundant. This thorn shrub, which can eventually grow to become a little tree 5 metres high, provides food and shelter to many species of birds.

Big old trunks of oaks, willows and poplars are very important for biodiversity and as outstanding elements in landscape. They provide nesting sites for bigger tree species such as Great Spotted Woodpecker *(Dendrocopos major)*, Green Woodpecker *(Picus viridis)*, Long-eared Owl *(Asio otus)* and Tawny Owl *(Strix aluco)*. The great spotted woodpecker also depends on the larvae of wood-boring beetles.

The meanders and old branches of the River Po have particular importance to the fauna, as they remain flooded alongside the bank side vegetation under a canopy of trees wich forms the riparian woodland.

Breme Estate

Breme Estate

A hunting day in Breme Estate.

The birds of prey, apart from owls, are represented by Buzzard *(Buteo buteo)*, Hobby *(Falco subbuteo)*, Osprey *(Pandion haliaetus)*, Marsh Harrier *(Circus aeruginosus)*, Sparrow Hawk *(Accipiter nisus)* and Red-backed Shrike *(Lanius collurio)*.

In isolated and quiet areas the herons establish colonies, called *"garzaie"*, were Grey Heron *(Ardea cinerea)*, Little Egret *(Egretta garzetta)* and Great White Egret *(Egretta alba)* breed. The outer part of the estate hosts the protected *"Garzaia del Bosco Basso"*, where there is a good colony of herons. The vegetation upon which this colony lives is typical of the riparian forest of the River Po. Black poplar is the dominant species with white poplar, elm, ash, alder and oak trees. In the undergrowth, there is a dense vegetation of reeds and willows. The colony is surrounded by extensive rice fields which constitute a magnificent hunting area for the 6 species of heron which are present. The grey heron is the species which occupies the earliest colony, becoming established at the end of January. The second species which arrives is the Nightheron *(Nycitorax nycitorax)* which has a breeding nucleus of about 45 pairs. The third species to become established is the Little Egret with about 70 nesting pairs. The Purple Heron *(Ardea purpurea)* with about 10 nests and the

Garzaia del Bosco Basso
Riserva naturale
Sito di importanza comunitaria

The outer part of the estate hosts the SIC "Garzaia del Bosco Basso", where a good colony of herons exists.

Breme Estate

Squacco Heron *(Ardeola ralloides)* do not join this breeding group until April. Among the undergrowth, in the reed beds, nests the Little Bittern *(Ixobrychus minutus)*.

The rice fields constitute the man-made habitat which replaces the old marshes, which in historical times covered the fertile alluvial soil and seasonal pools of the Po flood plain. The masses of marsh plants (*Typha* sp. and *Phragmites* sp., mainly) and flood meadows have given way to rice crops, but the habitat has proved to be ideal for numerous ducks which breed or winter here. The Mallard *(Anas platyrriynchos)*, Teal *(Anas crecca)*, Pintail *(Anas acuta)*, Shoveler *(Anas clypeata)*, Gadwall *(Anas strepera)*, Wigeon *(Anas penelope)* and a multitude of waders, plovers and Snipe *(Gallinago gallinago)* find here a magnificent place to shelter during their annual migrations. Moreover it is the marsh harrier's chosen nesting area.

Occasionally, Breme is visited by the rare Black-Winged Stilt *(Himantopus himantopus)* searching for food in the rice fields and shallow waters.

In recent years, significant winter concentrations of the Cormorant *(Phalacrocorax carbo)* have been observed. They arrive here from coastal and continental areas of northern Europe.

Among the mammals (mainly rodents, Red Fox *(Vulpes vulpes)*, Badger *(Meles meles)* and Beech Marten *(Martes foina)*, the Wild Boar *(Sus scrofa)* has increased its presence. The Wild Boar is a major problem for cultivated fields. A "Plan of Wild Boar demographic control" is under way by the River Po Park Organisation. In recent years the timid Roe Deer *(Capreolus capreolus)* has returned to the area from higher regions, moving along the river Orba.

A striking feature in the Po river environment and well represented in the estate is the mixed presence of indigenous and exotic species of fauna and flora. Alongside the original forests of willows, poplars and alders (the oak forest, farther from the river for ecological reasons, has given way long ago to cultivated fields), we can find the Black Locust *(Robinia pseudoacacia)*, imported from America about 250 years ago, that by now forms widespread forests in the Po basin. Another intruder is the Desert False Indigo *(Amorpha fruticosa)*, a bush imported for use in the dyeing industry. Two newcomers, Japanese Knotweed *(Reynoutria japonica)* and the Oneseed Burr Cucumber *(Sycios angulatus)*, both quick-growing shrubs, have been found to be very dangerous for the renovation of indigenous tree species.

The European Hare *(Lepus europaeus)* shares the estate with the Eastern Cottontail *(Silvilagus floridanus)*, apparently without adverse effect on the former, which shows wider habitat range. The latter – introduced into Europe from North America many years ago – is now declining in Italy but is still present in numbers in the Po basin.

The Coypu *(Myocastor coypus)*, is a South American species, perfectly adapted to the river and marshland habitat. It is widely spread throughout central Europe. The population along the River Po is kept under control by trapping in order to contain damage to plantations and fish stocks.

In the rivers, declining numbers of indigenous fish species are faced by newcomers from the Danube area. For instance, Northern Pike *(Esox lucius)* and Marble Trout *(Salmo trutta marmoratus)* have suffered from the spread of the big Wels Catfish *(Silurus glanis)*.

Among the indigenous frogs, toads and salamanders, the North American Bullfrog *(Rana catesbeiana)* and Eastern Golden Frog *(Pelophylax plancyi)* – from China – have been observed.

The presence of exotic species and their possible effect on indigenous ones is a matter of concern for farmers, local officers and scientists, and has been the subject of careful study by Universities and the River Po Park Organisation.

The two most serious floods of the River Po happened in 1994 and 2000. In both cases the river devastated crops and woodland formed new banks and beds, and changed the landscape.

The River Zones Management Plan includes, amongst other objetives, the conversion of poplar plantations and agricultural crop areas to mixed native trees and shrubs.

Protected areas on the estate

Piedmontese

The Piedmontese part of the estate lies inside the area of the *"Regional System of the Protected Areas of the River Belts of the Po - Natural Park of the Po and the Orba"*, which was protected in April 1990 by a Regional Law.

It is a nature protection area with an area plan which requires different kinds of protection according to the predominant regional land-use, either agricultural or natural.

The land of the Visconti Estate (involving the areas of Lotto Chiodo, Isola dei 41, Isolotto, Panigale, Isola dei Rossi, Isolone) lies partly in the area of a Special Natural Reserve with a special protection system, whilst the remaining area is in the Protected Area (a partial protection regime, which includes all agricultural activity).

Lombardy

In the Lombardy part of the estate, a part of the land (about 12 ha) lies within the Protected Area known as *"Garzaia del Bosco Basso"* – the Heron colony described above, which was protected in March 1986 by a Regional Law.

Golena (Floodplains)

Within the *golena*, the estate has had particular obligations imposed on it in terms of farming and future development initiatives. The special environmental values require conformation with regulations and criteria to protect the river flow, habitat conservation and the landscape.

The Inter-regional Agency for the Po River (formerly River Po Basin Authority), with its offices in Parma is the body responsible for the management of the Po basin. It has drawn up numerous planning tools and management plans of the river areas, among which is the River Zones Management Plan, which subdivides the territory into three zones A, B and C, according to the frequency of the flooding.

In zones A and B, the area most affected by river dynamics (in which almost all the land of the estate lies) the only developments allowed are those directed towards the maintenance and extension of flood control areas, the reactivation and the reconstitution of wetlands, the restoration and extension of areas of natural vegetation, and river maintenance work.

Since 1999 the estate has undertaken a programme of re-naturalisation of the area of the River Po in the reach under its responsibility, in collaboration with the Park Organisation and the Inter-Regional Agency for the River Po (former River Po Basin Authority). The programme foresees the re-conversion of agricultural cultivation to forestry, the renovation, extension and management of the riverbank forest, and the improvement of the waterways within the golena. The objective is to encourage the reconstitution of the traditional river

environment and provide an example of management of the golena area that is totally in balance with the river's natural regime.

The operative phase of the programme is under way. Fauna and flora benefit from the above, including:

- Conversion of poplar plantations and agricultural cultivation to plantations of mixed indigenous trees and shrubs (whose fruits are greatly enjoyed by many bird species) and managed in longer cycles;

- Reduction of fertilizers and other chemical products for plant protection in crop fields;
- Renovation, extension and management of riverine and areas of wet woodland, including control of invasive exotic species (e.g. *Sycios angulatus, Reynoutria japonica*);
- Maintenance of existing hedges and small wooded areas among cultivated fields, or the creation of new ones, all with indigenous species.

Breme has two main houses, Breme and Torre d'Isola, each on a different bank of the River Po. The estate has been owned by the Noble House of Visconti for many generations, and is located in the *golena* of the River Po.

Breme Estate

Plantations of poplar clone are mostly grown for the production of fibreboard. Breme has 359.37 ha of the poplar clone I-214, certified under the PEFC system.

Breme Estate

Breme Estate

The rice harvest is an important element for the estate.

PRINCIPAL OBJECTIVES OF MANAGEMENT

Breme is an estate where the sustainable development of natural resources present in the property is carried out: rice-fields, forests, a unique landscape and important species of fauna and flora that must be protected.

The rice crops are an important element of the estate's economy. Breme depends on small embankments and channels to maintain the land submerged in 20-40 cm of water. Production is approximately 6 tonnes/ha. The harvested rice is stored on farm and sold into the market.

Plantations of poplar clones are grown mainly for the production of fibreboard. Breme has 359.37 ha of the Poplar clone I-214, certified by the PEFC system. Annual production is 3,000-4,000 tonnes of timber.

With regard to landscape conservation, the main objectives, included in *"Programma di gestione dell'area fluviale del fiume Po fra la confluenza dei fiume Po fra la confluenza dei fiumi Sesia e Rotaldo volto alla ricostituzione e valorizzazione dell'ambiente fluviale tradizionale"*, are:

A.- Recovery of natural environment and management of the territory:

- Creation of a natural band, as a natural filter, between the flooding zone and the most productive lines of poplars, so that the more productive area is inside.
- Conservation of natural areas (forest, shrub and grasslands), improving their physical and eco-

Reducing fertilizers and other chemical products guarantees that rice production is more respectful of the environment.

Breme Estate

logical stability, and strengthening the natural functions by the control of invasive species, reafforestation with indigenous species, etc...

■ Environmental recovery of degraded zones.

B.- Improvement in Agro-forestry Economics:

■ Introducing techniques and looking after stands in ways that are eco-compatible with the cultivation of Poplars, through eco-certification.

■ Studying new forms of energy, through burning products derived from the Poplar industry.

■ Management to obtain the fishing rights in the River Po.

C.- Improvements in rural activities developed on the property.

■ Creation and recuperation of natural paths for riding, cycling or walking.

■ Recovery and restoration of buildings for accommodation.

■ Temporary or permanent exhibitions.

■ Educational activities.

BREME BELONGS TO:

Friends of the
Countryside-Meta

ELO

Rise Foundation

PEFC

WE initiative

Activities & attractions

 Birdwatching   Rural tourism

Hunting   Walking Trails

 Shooting   River navigation

 Historic buildings   Riding

CONTACT DATA

Breme

Az. agricola Visconti di E. Visconti & C. S.a.s.,

Via Visconti, 4 • 27020 Breme • (PV), Italy

Tel.: +39 027 208 81 • Fax.: +39 027 208 83 00

GSM: +39 (0) 335 21 39 08

gvisconti@portalevisconti.it

Herdade da Agolada de Baixo

Mediterranean

Location: Municipality of Coruche, district of Santarém, province of Ribatejo, Portugal.
Surface: 1,530 ha.

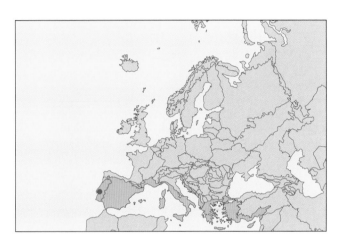

CLIMATIC DATA

Average rainfall
mm/cm²/year

Snow days: 0

650 mm

Temperature (°C)

38 — max ■
18 — average ■
-3 — min ■

SUMMARY

A Mediterranean estate of approximately 1,530 ha located in the province of Ribatejo (Portugal). The property has belonged to the Sommer D'Andrade family for many years.
Its principal features are agriculture – maize and rice – and forestry, especially cork and wood for pulp production.
It has an excellent herd of Lusitano horses as well as some animals of the Sorraia breed. The estate also provides opportunity for hunting.

Agolada Estate

The Main House of Agolada de Baixo is framed by more than 60 ha of rice.

Growing rice in the rich lowland area of the Agolada river.

HISTORY

In the middle of the 19th century, as a result of the Civil War in which D. Pedro II and D. Miguel, the two sons of the king D.João VI, fought for succession to the throne, and also as a consequence of the French invasions by the Napoleon army, the kingdom of Portugal suffered one of the most serious financial crises in its history, and was obliged to sell considerable properties belonging to the younger members of the royal household in order to face up to the debts deriving from the war.

It was at this point that the great-grandfather of the current generation of the Sommer family acquired the estate of Herdade da Agolada. At the time it extended to more than 5,000 hecta-

In the 1950s Luis de Sommer adepted the lowland and river area of Agolada to create 70 ha of irrigated crops, mostly rice.

res, which were mostly used to graze herds of goats and to produce logwood for the production of charcoal. The cork oaks were also exploited, both for wood and for cork, a raw material which was starting to be valued as a result of the evolution of Port Wine, which was at that time the principal national agricultural product of high added value.

With the turn of the century, and with the industrial revolution in full swing in Europe, the son of Luis de Sommer, also called Luis, a man of great knowledge and vision, started experimental work with the aim of trying to manufacture pulp from eucalyptus, in partnership with the cellulose industry based in Sweden to which he sent samples of different varieties of eucalyptus planted in small areas on the estate.

The fruit of this research was the decision to plant a forest of eucalyptus, almost exclusively of *Eucalyptus globulus*, commonly known as White Eucalyptus, and *Eucalyptus rostrata*, the Red Eucalyptus, which was of lesser industrial use but was good for firewood and charcoal, and which, because it thrived in wet conditions, was planted next to watercourses.

It was the largest clearance of land and forestry plantation ever undertaken on private property in Portugal, the area of ground covered by eucalyptus having reached over 3,000 hectares and thereby constituting, for decades, the greatest eucalyptus plantation in the whole of Europe.

The rotation period for eucalyptus being about 10 years, the date of the first harvest of wood destined for export for the production of pulp coincided with the start of the Second World War, which, for obvious reasons, prevented the business from being completed. There was a general fuel crisis as a result of the war, which led the Government to confiscate and reserve all the timber of harvestable age for use by the Portuguese Railway Company in its trains, a situation that lasted until 1945.

From that time onwards, the eucalyptus forests of Agolada have never ceased to produce wood for cellulose, as well as the oil derived from distilling the leaves, a secondary product of the forestry industry manufactured in two production units on the estate itself and in a third on the Quinta da Cardiga, another family property at Golegã next to the River Tagus.

On his estate, the entrepreneurial and innovative Mr. Luis de Sommer also developed an extensive programme of adapting his land to irrigation, in order to grow rice. He built dams and channels, he levelled ground, and he devised an ingenious scheme to capture and re-use irrigation water, in order to maximise its use and reduce losses. The system is still functioning today, and on Agolada de Baixo alone is responsible for irrigating and producing 70 hectares of rice and other crops.

With the passage of time and the development of agriculture, the property is nowadays divided amongst the heirs of the fourth generation, and has become a showcase of important forestry products such as cork, timber from eucalyptus and pine, pine nuts and resin. It produces rice, maize and livestock, in particular purebred Lusitano horses and Sorraia horses, the latter being a passion of Luis de Sommer's brother-in-law, Dr. Ruy D'Andrade, who is the grandfather and father-in-law of the current owners of the Herdade da Agolada de Baixo, Josefina Maria D'Andrade and Maria Emília D'Andrade de Oliveira e Sousa.

DESCRIPTION

The estate is surrounded by other forestry properties consisting principally of cork oak, stone pine and eucalyptus, and is situated in the Vale do Sorraia, one of most important areas of irrigation in the country, where large areas of rice, maize and tomatoes are grown. It is also close to rural housing areas where residents cultivate small vineyards, orchards and vegetable plots in order to supplement their main income from their work.

The property is crossed by two small streams: the Ribeira da Agolada and the Ribeira do Paul de Coruche. These join together on the estate and form the start of the Ribeira do Cascavel, flowing down to the dam at the Barragem de Magos, and from there into the Tagus river. In 1935 a dam was constructed on the estate in order to supply water for irrigating the rice; the resulting volume of water is about 500,000 m^3 and covers an area of 20 ha. To stabilise the left-hand bank, some 50 ha of Stone Pine *(Pinus pinea)* were planted. This soon became an important roost for Wood Pigeon *(Columba palumbus)*, which rest there on their return from feeding in the surrounding area.

The D'Andrade de Oliveira e Sousa family have maintained the property since the late 19th century. In the picture we can see three generations.

Agolada Estate

Herdade da Agolada de Baixo (Portugal)

Agolada Estate

Cork is havested in the month of July, every 9 years.

mic shallow sandstone soils, and non-hydromorphic podzols with allioz (VT + Ppt). In the valley, which crosses the estate, the soils are hydromorphic, of light and medium texture, poorly drained and cold (Cal + Ca). There are still some small areas of non-humic psamitic regosols (Rg). On account of the characteristics of these soils, farming is only possible in the valleys, where the principal crop is rice. The whole of the remaining area is forested, divided into smaller blocks according to the species present, the main one being cork oak (over 750 ha) and eucalyptus (approximately 500 ha). The remainder is occupied by pine groves, fields for forage, open spaces, etc.

Activities developed

The main activity on the estate is forestry, and in particular the production of cork, which is destined for transformation into natural cork, stoppers, as well as eucalyptus wood for pulp. In addition, the estate produces pinewood and resin, and pine cones from which pine nuts are extracted. In terms of farming, the main crop is rice that is produced by means of Integrated Production.

Forestry

Throughout the "montado" area (a Portuguese word that refers to open landscape covered with cork oaks or holm oaks), there are Maritime Pines *(Pinus pinaster)*, from which resin and timber is harvested, and Stone Pines *(Pinus pinea)*, for the production of seed cones of pine-nuts.

The main forestry product is cork, followed by eucalyptus. The secondary products, as well as trees which have dried out or species of lesser importance such as acacia or Red Eucalyptus *(Eucalyptus rostrata)*, are for firewood.

Linked to the reservoir, an extensive combination of channels and recovery ditches for discharged water was developed, maximising the use of the stored water available, and enabling the irrigation of about 70 ha of different crops, principally rice, maize, fruit and vegetables. In the 1970s, before the Revolution, the estate used to export fresh strawberries to the United Kingdom, grown in 5 ha of glass-houses.

The geology of the estate is Pliocenic, the majority of the land being composed of non-hu-

The importance of the economic activities is:

1) Cork
2) Eucalyptus wood
3) Rice
4) Maize
5) Pine-nuts and resin
6) Horses
7) Country sports
8) Honey

STAFF

Name	Qualification	Years of service	Full-time/Part-time	Tasks
Joaquim Custódio	Farm management	19	Full time	Overall responsibility
Clarisse Teles	Secretarial	14	Full time	Administration
Alberto Silva Arroz	Tractor driver	18	Full time	Machine operator
Leonel Goginho	Gamekeeper	18	Full time	Game keeper
AntónioJosé	Tractor driver		Full time	Machine operator
João Martins	Rider	6	Part time	Groom
João A. Fernandes	Trainer	1	Full time	Training horses
Adélia Arroz		12	Full time	House Keeper
Maria Custódio		12	Part time	Farm worker

314

Agolada Estate

Cork harvesting is the most
productive forestry activity
in this estate.

Horses

Although in times past the estate was grazed by herds of beef cattle and fighting bulls, the only livestock enterprise at the present moment are the horses. The name D'Andrade has been a symbol in breeding the Lusitano since the early 20th century, and a nucleus of mares and horses lives on the estate, forming the well-known "Coudelaria S.A." Both Lusitano and Sorraia horses are bred.

The Sorraia horse is an animal whose origin goes back to the pre-history of the southern part of the Iberian Peninsula. It was discovered by chance by the biologist and equine expert Dr. Ruy D'Andrade, while hunting near the river Sorraia. He acquired all the animals that were roaming in that area, in semi-wild condition, and succeeded in establishing a small herd which he kept on his properties, giving them the name Cavalo de Sorraia, as it was beside this river that he had first glimpsed them.

Today the breed is in serious danger of extinction and subject to strict protection measures, constituting as it does an important genetic and historical legacy in the evolution of the horse in the Iberian Peninsula. It is thought that horses of this

Agolada Estate

The Lusitano is the main breed
of horse at Agolada,
but the endangered Sorraia
breed is also bred..

Eucalyptus wood has been extracted since the start of the last century.

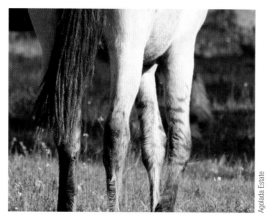

The Sorraia breed has a black dorsal stripe, black-tipped ears and sometimes even zebra stripes on its legs and shoulders. This characteristics is know as *zebruras* in Portuguese. When the portuguese explorers of the 15th century first discovered strange wild horses with a black dorsal stripe in Africa, the named them *zebras*.

type were transported by Christopher Columbus to America and then abandoned, thus becoming the basis of the Mustang and the South American Criollo breeds.

The horse has particularly unique characteristics, such as a mane of two colours and with dark stripes, especially on its front legs, similar to those of the zebra. These stripes are known in Portuguese as *zebruras*.

Indeed it is a curious fact that Portugal has many settlements with names related to the word *zebra*, such as Vale do Zebro, Zebreira, etc. These relate to the historical presence of animals marked with these stripes. It was because of this that, when Portuguese navigators landed in Africa and first saw wild "horses" covered with these *zebruras*, they called them *zebras*.

Agriculture

As already stated, the main crop produced is rice, grown in some 60 ha and whose irrigation is assured by the water stored in the reservoir built on the estate. Because of the soil type in the valley, where the water table is close to the surface, the land is not cultivated during the winter and thus forms an important wetland area that becomes a real habitat for wildlife, especially birds, which spend the winter in this country.

The winter population of the Common Snipe *(Gallinago gallinago)* on the rice fields reaches very large numbers.

The main species are ducks, snipe (common and jack snipes), Moorhen *(Gallinula chloropus)*, Sandpipers (*Tringa* sp.), Lapwing *(Vanellus vanellus)*, Cattle Egrets and Little Egrets (*Bubulcus ibis* and *Egretta garzetta*) and even the White Stork *(Ciconia ciconia)*, as well as mammals such as the Otter *(Lutra lutra)* which finds both food and shelter there.

This ecological balance is threatened, however, as a main highway is in the process of being planned, similar in characteristics to a motorway, with one alternative route being to cross the area of ground described.

Forage crops for the horses and mares are also grown, as is maize which is grown for feed for ornamental and sporting birds such as Racing Pigeons.

Hunting and fishing

The whole estate is designated as a Hunting Reserve. The main species are Rabbit *(Oryctolagus cuniculus)*, Red-legged Partridge *(Alectoris rufa)*, and Wood Pigeon *(Columba palumbus)*, with ducks and snipe in the wet areas.

In the wooded areas, the only large game species is the Wild Boar *(Sus scrofa)*, which is either shot in drives or is stalked on moonlit nights.

The only fishing in the reservoir is for sport, with the principal catch being the Black Bass *(Micropterus salmoides)* and Carp *(Cyprinus carpio)*.

The rabbit is a fundamental part of the zoological structure of Iberian ecosystems. It is present at Agolada in large numbers.

Agolada Estate

MAIN OBJECTIVES FOR THE MANAGEMENT OF THE PROPERTY...

Taking account of all its characteristics, its component soils, and the vegetation present, the estate will surely continue to be worked for forestry purposes. In view of the way in which the modern world is developing, concerns about the environment, and the energy crisis, it is highly probable that producing products for energy will provide an alternative to current uses. Biomass, new varieties of trees, and ground improvements are examples of possible future projects in the region.

Parallel to this, it is certain that the environmental tourism sector will continue to develop, as much through observation and contemplation as through country sports activities. Livestock breeding may evolve into the production of other species such as outdoor pigs to maximise use of the acorns, and the horses will remain. The family has instilled into the next generation the responsibility for continuity, as well as a love of the countryside and the activities linked to it. This has been fully and successfully achieved, and for this reason we do not envisage any problems when the estate is passed on.

THE BIGGEST CHALLENGES FOR YOUR ESTATE IN THE FUTURE...

Related to Environment and Climate:
Because of climatic change we are seeing profound changes in relation to "normal" years, such as the pattern of rainfall, for example. A further cause for great concern, possibly also as a result of the same problem, is the index of mortality in species of Quercus, in this case the Cork Oak *(Quercus suber)*, which constitutes the estate's core business.

Related to Economical issues:
Globalisation is a fact of life today. Its effects on agricultural economics, especially in small countries such as Portugal, cause enormous volatility and vulnerability in this sector of the economy, and constitute a level of apprehension which, in turn, means that great care must be taken in management and in decisions for future investment, choice of crops, etc., in particular when these crops are world commodities such as rice.

Related to Policy and Legislation issues:
Agricultural policy, both European and national, is not always synonymous with stability and confidence in the sector. The role of farmers and landowners has been very distorted, and they have unjustifiably been accused of causing great damage and harm in so-called civil society. What has not been properly recognised is their role as guardians of the natural world, as producers of food, as promoters of biodiversity, all of which are the fruits of farming and forestry. Issues of taxation have been, and still are, badly handled by politicians, who do not recognise the sector as being of strategic importance, nor attribute to it a specific policy which takes account of the vulnerability of its activities and the period required for a return on investments, especially as far as forestry is concerned.

Eduardo Oliveira e Sousa

Growing some flowers under irrigation, with Eucalyptus plantations in the background.

Agolada

Agolada Estate

Collecting resin from the
Maritime Pinus
(Pinus pinaster) at Agolada.

HERDADE DA AGOLADA DE BAIXO ESTATE BELONGS TO:

Associação Nacional de
Proprietários e Produtores
de Caça

Associação dos Agricultores
do Ribatejo

Friends of the Countryside

APFC
Associação dos
Produtores
Florestais de Coruche

Associação Internacional
de Criadores do Cavalo
Ibérico de Tipo Primitivo
"Sorraias"

Associação Portuguesa
de Criadores do Cavalo Puro
e Sangue Lusitano

Associação Portuguesa
de Criadores
do Cavalo Puro e
Sangue Lusitano

Activities & attractions

- Equestrian
- Shooting
- Hunting
- Birdwatching
- Rural Tourism
- Fishing
- Walking trails
- Cycling

CONTACT DATA

Apt. 69, 2104-909 CORUCHE • Portugal
Tlf: (+ 351) 243 66 00 22 • Fax: (+ 351) 243 66 00 23
agoladadebaixo@sapo.pt • www.natureinaction.com
www.coudelariaSA.com

Herdade da Machoqueira do Grou

Mediterranean

Location: Coruche, Tagus Valley region, Portugal.
Surface: 2,423 ha.

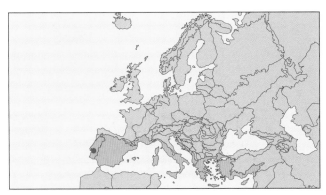

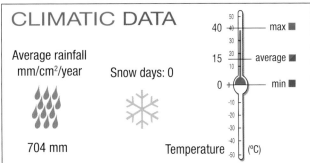

CLIMATIC DATA

Average rainfall
mm/cm^2/year

Snow days: 0

704 mm

Temperature (°C)

40 — max ■
15 — average ■
0 — min ■

SUMMARY

Machoqueira do Grou Estate is located in Coruche (39,116ºN-8,352ºW), in the Tagus Valley region of Portugal at the heart of the Western Mediterranean cork oak forest.

With a total area of 2,423 hectares, Machoqueira do Grou is part of a large landscape unit, which also includes the "Cabeção" Natura 2000 site.

In Portuguese the word "machoqueira" means a place with a lot of newly sprouted cork oaks or "machocos", and that is the main feature of the estate: a flourishing cork oak forest.

Naturally cork oak would occur in mixed forests, sharing the arboreal stratum with other evergreen oaks or pines, but here we talk about its cultural derivative, an open woodland or anthropogenic savannah, of selectively maintained and carefully cultivated trees, a multi-functional agro-silvo-pastoral farming system, in Portuguese called "Montado".

Cork oaks *(Quercus suber)* produce cork, which are mainly used for the closure of wine bottles. Cork and wine represent a successful and symbiotic relationship that has existed since the Benedictine monk Dom Perignon first used cork to stop champagne bottles in the 17th century and which is still current.

In cork oak woodlands, cork production lives alongside wood production from Maritime Pine *(Pinus pinaster)*, Eucalyptus *(Eucalyptus globulus)* and other non-wood products such as pine nuts from Stone Pine *(Pinus pinea)*, grazing land where cattle are reared and other products such as game and mushrooms, in a complex multi-functional system of immense biodiversity value.

Cork oak woodlands are characterised by their occupation of large areas of low resilience soils either in mountain regions near to desert areas or in the sandy soils of the Mid-Pliocene period in the western Mediterranean.

They are of paramount ecological importance as they play a key role in ecological processes such as water retention, soil conservation – protecting against erosion and halting desertification – and carbon storage as well as being high biodiversity areas.

The main feature of Herdade da Machoqueira
do Grou is a flourishing cork oak forest.

N. Calado

HISTORY

Machoqueira do Grou Estate has belonged to the Cunhal family since the beginning of the 20th century. The estate was bought by Alfredo Augusto Cunhal, great-grandfather of the current owners.

The family's first contact with the estate was as tenants and began in 1875, firstly with a 25 year contract, followed by a 99 year one. In 1903 Machoqueira do Grou was bought in a deal referred to by the first owner as being the "worst of his lifetime". History proved he was wrong, and the estate has already been the source of work and passion for five generations of the family. Since the 1940s the management approach has been directed towards a common desire: safeguarding the cork oak woodlands.

This management history was interrupted in 1976 when the estate was expropriated by the Portuguese government during the "hot summer" that followed the 1974 Portuguese Revolution. The estate was returned to its owners, by right, in 1981, but partial compensation was only paid in 2000, in a process that represented one of the biggest attacks on private landownership in Europe in modern times. During this five year period the estate was run as a Soviet-inspired cooperative. In the specific case of Machoqueira do Grou, little harm was done to the productive system, mostly because of the courageous behaviour of a former chief employee, who was called in for management duties by his fellow workers. Against all the odds, he was able to maintain basic management guidelines and did not allow the disruption of the productive systems which characterised that period and which brought Portuguese agriculture to a stop for so long.

A management practice aimed at endorsing cork oak woodlands helped to improve Machoqueira do Grou's total cork production, which rose from 150 tonnes in the first decade of the 1900s, when the first register was held, to 1800 tonnes – sufficient to stop 90 million bottles of wine – in the first decade of 2000.

The management practices encompassed innovation, adaptation and production to the needs of the market. Since 2008 Machoqueira do Grou has been one of the first FSC certified cork oak woodlands. In that year, a long-term commitment

Since 2008 the estate has been one of the first FSC certified cork oak woodlands.

N. Calado

The Main House located in a privileged situation, gives a global view over the estate.

Z. da Quinta

to responsible management, based on known economic, environmental and social principles and criteria set by the Forest Stewardship Council was subscribed, audited and approved.

The multi-functional farming system that characterizes cork oak woodlands has an important agricultural component that has been constantly evolving over the last one hundred years. With a rare capacity to adapt to successive macro-economic cycles, the agricultural component of the system was sequentially based on beans, wheat and maize, rice, stone fruits and seedless grapes, and cattle production.

This was possible for two main reasons: the financial umbrella assured by cork production and a focused internal investment programme that resolved one of the main weaknesses of the Mediterranean biogeographical region, namely the lack of water during summer. Between the 1940s and the 1970s five dams were constructed to provide irrigation to the agricultural areas of the estate.

The reservoirs of these dams and the surrounding areas are also biodiversity hotspots as their margins have developed riparian galleries that are nowadays managed for biodiversity purposes.

Knowledge is the seed of evolution. Machoqueira do Grou is a door always open to the new paths of knowledge. Free access to the forest stands is provided for researchers of relevant fields, either from university or applied science, making the estate part to the most up-to-date findings and incorporating them in its management approaches. This was one of the 10 sites covered by the book *"Cork Oak Woodlands on the Edge"* edited in 2009 by the Society of Ecological Restoration International.

The human side of the cork oak woodland farming system is of utmost importance. The cork oak landscapes were shaped by man in friendly relationship with nature, through the "montado", a farming system of high biodiversity levels, higher than its natural site, and an important source of human presence in these remote landscapes.

Machoqueira do Grou is fifteen kilometres from the nearest villages and has a population of 12 people, who live in two residential areas. The main house, located in a privileged situation, gives a global view over the estate. The farm provides work for 20 to 25 workers all year round, some of them living on the farm with their families, the others living in nearby villages. The other inhabitants of the farm are retired workers and their families to whom free housing is provided.

A balanced presence of man, as shaper, as steward, as direct or indirect user and as visitor, is the secret for the future of these landscapes.

G. Lopes

Machoqueira do Grou,
in an old fresco on a chimney
of the main house.

DESCRIPTION

At Machoqueira do Grou the bio-climate is considered sub-humid, with an average rainfall of 704 mm per year over the period 1955-2002. Annual average temperature is 15ºC, with winter minimum close to 0ºC and summer maximum over 40º C.

This climate has winters of high rainfall, mild springs and autumns and very hot summers. The high risk of fire during summer is one of the main features of this climate zone.

The entire watershed is on deep Miocene sands and altitudes range from 79 to 173 m, with slopes between 0% and 5% and, exceptionally, up to 35%. The main soil types include fluvisols, leptosols, and podzols. Soils are characterised by residual levels of organic matter, low levels of nitrogen and phosphorus, medium levels of potassium, and pH of < 5.5.

This is a mesa-type landscape with U-shaped gullies, valleys, and occasional sandstone outcrops. The area has mainly forest capability with the exception of the cultivated valley floors.

Despite the high fire risk level of this Mediterranean bioregion, no big fires have been reported in the last 100 years. A small fire occurred in the 1980s, caused by illegal fishermen, at a time before hunting and fishing rights were regulated and consigned to the landowner.

Over the past most of the cork oak woodland has been managed to maintain or increase tree crown cover. In areas where a decrease in tree cover has occurred, due to natural mortality, active restoration is being pursued through improvement

of conditions for natural regeneration, combining cattle management modifications and reduced soil disturbance during shrub control. Wherever symptoms of tree decline are showing, restoration activities are implemented including fertilisation and active afforestation.

Farming is a living system where people, including managers, workers and users, interact with nature to produce food, fibre and environmental goods. This is an unquestionable truth, and strongly so in Mediterranean farming systems as the cork oak woodlands, which are characterized by a humanized, low intensity, multi-purpose approach to farming in a network of uses that in a complementary way respect the basic principles of nature. Machoqueira do Grou is a good example of that.

The economy of Machoqueira do Grou is driven by its forestry, which occupies more than three quarters of its landscape. Agriculture, cattle production and other activities such as hunting or mushroom gathering are components of the system managed, nowadays, towards the main purpose: the production of quality cork on a sustainable basis.

At Machoqueira do Grou four main forest species are found: cork oak, stone pine, maritime pine and eucalyptus.

Cork oak and stone pine have colonised the estate naturally because of sympathetic management, with low intensity grazing and shrub control, which has allowed forest cover to grow from less that 40% in the early 1940s, to the present 55%. Maritime pine and eucalyptus were introduced to cover areas where, due to soil constraints, the cork oak would not grow spontaneously. At the beginning of this century some agricultural land was planted with cork oak and stone pine under EU funded programmes.

The evolution of the tree crown cover and the presence of young age classes has led to a substantial change in the livestock component of the system, which once included ewes, goats and cows grazing on the pastures, to a cattle operation that is fed mainly in the colluvial valleys that divide the cork oak woodland.

Cork is Machoqueira do Grou's main product, the cork oak woodlands being the estate's main natural and ecological asset. Cork woodlands cover almost 1500 ha, with 30% of the area in mixed stands with stone pine. It is a young forest with

The stone pine forest is subject to careful and special pruning to form the tops of the tree into a shape that increases nut production.

more than three quarters of the trees belonging to young age classes or full production classes.

Stone pine produces pine nuts. The mixed stands provide one of the characteristic stamps of these landscapes, with *Pinus pinea* filling the blanks were the cork oak does not manage to develop. New techniques such as grafting and mechanised harvesting are important developments and important strengths for the competitive future of pine nut production.

Pinus pinaster and *Eucalyptus globulus* are the two types of wood produced on the estate. They produce wood for sawmills and for the pulp industry respectively. Commercial plantations of eucalyptus occupy areas where cork woodland would not grow naturally. *Pinus pinaster* is a pioneer crop whose areas will be colonised in future by cork oak. Eucalyptus grows at 12-15 m³/ha/year and will be ready for felling in 10-12 years. Maritime pine will grow at about 5 m³/year and optimum felling will be after year 60.

The forests on the estate are separated by agricultural areas of colluvial valleys. These areas, apart from their agricultural value, have a very important function for fire protection, being natural firebreaks.

The richer soils of the agricultural areas are cultivated as natural or improved pasture lands, based on *graminea x leguminosae* mixes, where local cattle breeds are bred. The total suckler cow herd is 200, which represents a density of one cow per six hectares of total pasture land.

Conflicting interests that arise from the livestock grazing component can affect the natural regeneration of cork oak trees. Interventions and adjust-

ments to promote natural regeneration and active afforestation (e.g. fencing combined with shrub control) have been included in the management plan over the last 5 years. This, combined with low intensity of cattle pressure, assures minimum damage to the natural regeneration of the cork oak and that the shrubs and grass level under the trees is satisfactorily controlled, thus reducing the fire risk during summer.

The right balance between the needs of the forest on one hand, and the intensity of agriculture and cattle breeding on the other hand, is the key factor in the management of this agro-silvo-pastoral farming system.

Hunting and angling are two complementary activities of the estate. The main natural game species are Wild Boar *(Sus scrofa)*, Iberian Hare *(Lepus granatensis)*, Red-legged Partridge *(Alec-*

The annual production of pine nuts is one of the complementary components of cork oak woodland.

The forest of the estate is separated by agricultural areas of colluvial valleys that work like natural firebreaks.

Z. da Quinta

toris rufa) and wild Rabbit *(Oryctolagus cuniculus)*. Apart from wild rabbit, which is of high conservation value, all the others are exploited for commercial purposes based on a careful species monitoring programme. Woodcock *(Scolopax rusticola)*, Mallard *(Anas platyrhynchos)* and Wood Pigeon *(Columba palumbus)* are also present, the latter being the iconic species of the estate.

The estate's four main reservoirs are pleasant fishing zones. One of the reservoirs is of free access to local fishermen and it is possible to fish by permit on the other three.

The natural production of mushrooms is also a component of cork oak woodlands. It is also a delicate issue as fungus mycelium is an important inductor of regeneration of cork oak. This activity is more expressive in years of heavy spring and autumn rainfall.

Gathering mushrooms was free until 2007. Since then a harvesting programme involving the former collectors has been implemented, to monitor and manage a sustainable programme for this activity.

The natural value of cork oak woodlands arises from the great variety of species, both flora and fauna, which they support. The habitat heterogeneity and its complex horizontal and vertical structure give the woodlands a high conservation value through the agro-silvo-pastural farming system. Patches of shrub land mixed with pastures, and greater or lesser tree cover, configure exceptional characteristics for shelter and feeding of several animal species. The different microclimates, related to the changes in vegetation, promote floral biodiversity.

At Machoqueira do Grou, management assures this heterogeneity and promotes conservation of species and habitats. Several areas are identified as special zones where different ecosystems are preserved and promoted.

Fire risk is a major management concern and managing for conservation means finding the ideal

Reservoirs	Water areas with riparian vegetation boundaries that concentrate species of flora and fauna distinct from the ones in the forest, contributing to species richness in the whole area.
Water courses	Water courses with classified habitats within Natura 2000 – riparian galleries of Willows *(Salix alba)*, Poplars *(Populus alba)* and Ashes *(Fraxinus angustifolia)*. Well preserved, these water courses and the associated vegetation are fundamental to regulate the infiltration and runoff of water, preventing soil erosion.
Mediterranean Shrubland Patches	The Mediterranean shrublands present at Machoqueira do Grou, such as the Strawberry Tree *(Arbutus unedo)* and Hawthorn *(Crataegus monogyna)* provide food for several birds and small mammals during the autumn. In terms of shelter, the shrubs protect a key species in the ecosystem – the wild Rabbit *(Oryctolagus cuniculus)* – prey of several protected birds of prey. Also relevant is the presence of Gall Oak or Lusitanian Oak *(Quercus lusitanica)*, a small evergreen oak, some patches of which are classified within Natura 2000.

C. Otero

Antonio Gonçalves Ferreira doing a *formative* pruning in a *machoqueira* of stone pine.

level of shrub control. Shrub control is done within a rotational scheme of patches which promotes an adequate decrease in fire risk, safeguarding the maintenance of areas with conservation characteristics.

External aspects, such as soil protection, biodiversity conservation or carbon storage, are a very important component of the cork woodland ecosystem. Governments and society in general do not yet value these external features fairly. At Machoqueira do Grou this is already a reality, based on a private carbon payment contract with the national energy company (EDP), as a result of the estate's soil pro-

tection policy. Carbon sequestration by cork oaks is also being monitored in a research project led by the Technical University of Lisbon (ISA-UTL).

Machoqueira do Grou's remote location, more than fifteen kilometres away from the nearest village, gives it a wilderness status that is not common in cork woodlands nowadays. Not many years ago Wolves *(Canis lupus)* would live there, the last one being seen in 1973.

The quietness of night and the brightness of the stars or the moonlight are, at Machoqueira do Grou, a unique pleasure and, who knows, something to value in the future.

PRINCIPAL FEATURE AND FUTURE MANAGEMENT

Cork oak woodlands and cork production are Machoqueira do Grou's main feature. They are also its principal economic and natural asset.

The cork oaks across the estate have been tended, pruned, selected and shaped by five generations of landowners from this family, creating a type of landscape that has evolved over centuries as a unique mix of nature and nurture that is the very heart and soul of the Mediterranean region.

Cork oaks can survive adverse conditions of both human and non-human origin. They support cutting, grazing, prolonged drought and fire, but not extreme cold.

Each year cork oak trees produce a new layer of suberized cells forming annual rings as happens in wood. When enough cork has accumulated, harvesting can take place. Cork stripping must be done when phellogen or cork cambium is active, in late spring and early summer.

Harvesting is done manually by very skilled workers who use an axe to make incisive cuts on the bark of the tree. Like a tailor cuts a piece of cloth, they make it possible to strip the outer bark of the cork oak, in planks, without harming, damaging or cutting the tree. This delicate intervention is made every nine years, the time necessary for cork to grow again to sufficient thickness to be able to punch a cork stopper from it.

Cork oaks are heavily protected by national legislation. Legally the first cork harvest can occur at 25 to 30 years of age. Cork oaks can live for more than 200 years and be harvested more than 15

times. The longevity of this species is one of the main contributors to the stability of its ecosystem.

Investment and management of cork woodlands is done over a long term perspective, as the economic results will only be directly seen one or two generations in the future.

The cork planks, harvested during the stripping season, are then piled together and transported to a local processing plant, where they are boiled and normalized according to a quality grid. The best quality cork planks are used to make natural cork stoppers. The remaining product is transformed into one of the other numerous uses of cork, which include construction and architecture, the automobile, aeronautical and aerospace industries, design, and the pharmaceutical industry, to name only the most relevant.

Natural cork stoppers are excellent clousures for bottled wines. They provide consistent quality for the function, guaranteeing that wines to drink in the short run maintain all their characteristics and in the long run gain from an interesting biochemical relationship that only cork allows.

Cork production for natural cork stoppers is the value-added component of this fragile agro-silvo-pastural farming system and the feature that allows a low intensity use of the other components, including agriculture and livestock, creating the right conditions to enhance the ecological value of cork oak woodlands.

The cork industry also provides a case study for environmental performance by assuring the maintenance of an ecosystem considered throughout the world as a biodiversity hotspot, as well as providing the best option for wine closure in terms of non-renewable energy consumption, greenhouse gas emissions, contribution to atmospheric acidification, contribution to the eutrophisation process of superficial waters and total amount of solid residues produced.

The added value of cork results from its use as the wine industry's closure of first choice. Maintaining this relationship is the main challenge of the cork industry and the best insurance for the future of cork oak woodlands.

Commonly, wine consumers have a pro-cork altitude that associates cork with quality, and that is definitely true. Delivering balanced information to the consumer market is a challenge nowadays, as well-informed consumers will surely prefer cork as the closure for their wines. A responsible supply chain will try to meet the consumers' demand.

The main objective of the estate management team, seen from the perspective of the family business, is to pass this asset to the next generation with a greater value than it was received from the previous generation, and doing it in a sustainable economic, environmental and social manner. The cork woodland is to be preserved for the future.

Sustainable economic, environmental and social management is possible if the estate management plan ensures effective protection of the soil and water resources. They are the basis of the productive function of forests and in this specific case the perfect symbiosis with cork oak woodlands. Cork oak cover protects the soil and better soil means more resilient woodlands.

Aiming for a sustainable development path means tackling and getting results at economic, environmental and social levels, although constrained by evolving political frameworks.

In the last two decades (1989 to 2009) precipitation levels have fallen 50 mm, from an average 700 mm/year to less then 650 mm/year. Even if it is not yet fully assumed, major climate disturbance is under way. Tackling it, adapting the production patterns of the cork oak woodlands to this new reality, is the estate's main environmental challenge.

The economic focus is the basic challenge, as businesses have to be economically viable and competitive if they want to stay alive. Owners will only maximize their asset if, in the long run, this represents a competitive alternative in terms of investment.

Competitiveness has to be achieved based on two pillars: the economic performance of cork products and of the complementary components of the cork oak woodland economics – pine nuts, wood production, cattle breeding, hunting,... – and fair reward for the environmental services – soil and water protection, biodiversity conservation and carbon sequestration.

European taxpayers and consumers, who include farmers, expect European governments not to forget the strategic role of farming, both as food and fibre producer and as steward of nature and European landscapes.

Political agents should ensure and compromise for a fair-trade globalized economic world, where European products can compete with the same level of exigency. The European Union should defend European products and industries from unfair competition and must implement and endorse a legal framework where environmental services are rewarded on an acceptable basis.

Closures for the wine bottling industry have a market leader, the cork industry. This European industry is the international market leader and a clear example of something we find, most of the time, difficult to demonstrate – namely sustainability. The cork market chain uses a natural product, in an environmental friendly process, adding value at the same time as it strengthens nature.

An ethical individual intervention is a characteristic of mature societies. By purchasing wine closed with natural cork stoppers, individual consumers are contributing directly to a better world, defending cork oak woodlands, promoting biodiversity, tackling desertification and halting climate change.

The future of cork oak woodlands and landscapes depends on the landowners, as they must guarantee responsible use of these landscapes and the sustainability of cork production. European citizens will certainly help with their ethical and informed approach to consumption and their clear pro-cork attitude.

Work towards these goals is the best tribute to all those that in the past have contributed to what Machoqueira do Grou and cork oak woodlands are today, an example of sustainable management. If we make it ... our ancestors will be proud and our children will thank us.

Herdade da Machoqueira do Grou

During the first 2000's decade 1,800 tonnes of cork was harvested in Machoqueira do Grou, enough quantity to put the top on 90 millions of wine bottles.

Herdade da Machoqueira do Grou

Herdade da Machoqueira do Grou

HERDADE DA MACHOQUEIRA DO GROU BELONGS TO:

Associação Nacional de Proprietários e Produtores de Caça

Friends of the Countryside

FSC 100%
From well-managed forests
FSC
SA-FM/COC-001873-009

unac
União da Floresta Mediterrânica

União da Floresta Mediterrânica

Activities & attractions

- Birdwatching
- Shooting
- Fishing
- Hunting
- Rural tourism
- Walking trails
- Estate products

CONTACT DATA

António Alberto Gonçalves Ferreira
Herdade da Machouqueira do Grou
Horta de Santa Luzia
2100-047 Coruche • Portugal
aferreira.machoq@sapo.pt

Forstgut Hintere Seifrieding

Alpine

Location: Mössna/St. Nikolai im Sölktal, Styria, Austria.
Surface: 1,139 ha.

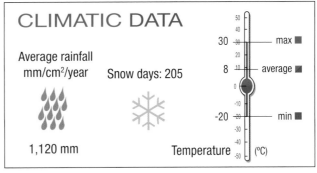

CLIMATIC DATA

Average rainfall
mm/cm²/year

Snow days: 205

1,120 mm

Temperature (°C)

30 — max
8 — average
-20 — min

SUMMARY

The Hintere Seifrieding Estate lies in the highest part of an Alpine valley in Austria. The mountainous environment and harsh climatic conditions are mirrored in the landscape. In summer the scenery ranges from steep forest-covered slopes to Alpine grasslands. The uppermost part ends in rocky ridges enclosing a barren landscape. In winter the valley is covered in snow making it inaccessible for many months. Undisturbed by mass tourism, Hintere Seifrieding offers amazing scenic impressions and unforgettable wildlife experiences. Enthusiastic of high mountain hunting go after red deer, chamois, marmot, black grouse, and in the lower parts of the valley roe deer. Furthermore, the Seifried river provides excellent trout fishing opportunities. Alpine forestry is a challenging enterprise: the geological features complicate timber harvesting and climate changes are visibly impacting on the forests. The present owners are deeply committed to conserving this Alpine paradise for future generations.

M. Miller-Aichholz

Morning view from the upper part of Hintere Seifrieding Estate.

HISTORY

Ownership

In 1907 the Saxe-Coburg-Gotha family sold the property of the Herrschaft Mössna in Upper Styria (Obersteiermark) to the Feltrinellis, an Italian industrial family who owned forests and saw mills in several countries. Upper Styria refers to the mountainous parts of the north-western part of the Austrian federal state of Styria. The estate, in the valley known as the Großsölktal, was extended by further purchases of forests and mountain pastures.

When the property was split up in 1979, it encompassed approximately 8,400 ha. While the Feltrinelli successors kept their part of the property, other relatives sold their shares, among these the

Christoph Amonn, father of the present owners, Thomas and Magdalena, developed the family property "Hintere Seifrieding".

lower and middle part of the Seifrieding (Seifrieding valley).

The late Christoph Amonn, father of the present owners Thomas and Magdalena, inherited the upper part of the Seifrieding called Hintere Seifrieding. Christoph Amonn started an arrangement with the buyer of the middle part of the valley over hunting and game-keeping, which is still maintained today. Most of the forest road infrastructure of Hintere and Mittlere Seifrieding was developed from the early 1980s onwards. The combined estates together cover about 2,000 hectares.

A cultural and natural heritage

Massive mountain ridges covered in green divide the valleys and give the whole region its character. More than 60% of Styria is covered by forest consisting predominantly of spruce. Meadows, lush pastures and orchards complete the picture. Viewed from the air, the landscape shows many folds made up of myriad hues of green. It is this greenery of the summer landscape that gave Styria the subtitle of "die Grüne Mark" (the Green March). Many wooden farmhouses with adjoining barns dot the landscape and make up the nostalgic charm of this Alpine region. The peasant culture of old still lives on today and old customs are specifically being revived.

The Sölk area is composed of two valleys called Großsölktal and Kleinsölktal. The Großsölk valley stretches from the Sölk pass to the Enns valley. It contains the municipalities of Großsölk and St. Nikolai, which constitute the middle and upper reaches of the Großsölk valley. The village of Mössna lies at the crossing of the opening of the Seifrieding valley and the Großsölk river.

From prehistoric times onwards the Sölk pass was frequently used to transport salt from the area of Hallstatt down to the south. During the flourishing of the Hallstatt Culture (from the 8th to 6th century BC) and later, the Sölk valleys were under the influence of the Celtic kingdom of Noricum in Carinthia. The region continued to be influenced by the succeeding Romans, who ruled over all of present day Austria for three centuries, and then by the Slavs who had established a dukedom in Carinthia. In the 12th century Styria became a crown duchy of the Habsburg dynasty and remained such until the end of the Austro-Hungarian monarchy in 1918.

G. Janssens

In the early 19th century, a predominantly agrarian Upper Styria benefited greatly from the Habsburg Archduke Johann's furthering of industrial development. The Großsölk valley lagged behind in economic development due to its remoteness. Changes in farming and timber harvesting affected the local economy and the traditional farming methods. The ensuing abandonment of farms and mountain pastures thus increased the areas of regenerative re-growth of forests, radically changing the landscape. Old property maps still feature names and places of abandoned mountain farms and pastures. The old designations are still used locally today, even though often only ruins of the old farmsteads are left. Not until the 1970s were proper roads built leading northwards to the Ennstal. The municipality of St. Nikolai saw its population decrease over the years. Nowadays only 508 people live in an area of 135.38 square kilometres. Today, besides commuting, some villagers continue to eke out a living by farming cattle. Peasants earn additional money taking forestry and hunting related jobs too. A little bit of soft tourism has developed in the valley.

Amonn Family Archive

View of a typical wooded Alpine slope in summer: European spruce forest at the treeline.

Christophorus Hütte – Main hunting lodge in Hintere Seifrieding Estate.

DESCRIPTION

General overview

Location

The estate is located near Mössna, part of the municipal area of St. Nikolai im Sölktal, which is in the district of Liezen, in the region of Upper Styria, part of the federal state of Styria, Austria. The Großsölk valley stretches from the Sölk pass to the Enns valley (Ennstal).

Description

Hintere Seifrieding comprises the upper part of the Seifrieding valley. The surface area of the Amonn property amounts to 1,139 ha. The lowest point is about 1,450 m above sea level, the highest point being the peak of Melleck at 2,365 m. The forestry at Hintere Seifrieding consists of 132 ha of coniferous forest, of which 80 ha are categorized as protective forests (natural defences against avalanche and torrent, which must be maintained by law). The rest is mostly made up of Alpine and barren landscapes (523 ha + 477 ha). Forest roads take up 6 ha. There are two hunting huts on the property as well as a hunting lodge.

Organisation

Forstgut Hintere Seifrieding is involved in a joint forestry, hunting and game-keeping cooperation with the neighbouring Forstgut Mittlere Seifrieding estate (843ha), which belongs to the Kernmayer family and which forms the middle part of the Seifrieding valley.

Geology

Tectonically and geologically speaking, Seifrieding is part of the Schladminger, Rottenmanner and Wölzer Tauern. This range bedrock is mainly composed of layers of mica slate and gneissoid rock banded with feld spar and quartz. This geological area also features lime, dolomite and quartzite deposits. Having been a glacial throughway, there are also remnants of recessional moraines and within the debris cones one can find the typical unconsolidated glacial debris collected through time. An assumed phreatic faultline extends across the Seifrieding valley.

Sustainable wildlife management

The Hintere Seifrieding offers excellent chamois, red and roe deer hunting opportunities and unforgettable wildlife experiences. Keeping up

Red deer at the winter-feeding in Mittlere Seifrieding. Game would starve in harsh winters if not fed additionally.

S. Konrad jr

an excellent shoot requires feeding game in winter, creating and maintaining infrastructure in the hunting territory, intensive hunting ground management, and sound biotope care. Quality service entails prudently looking after hunting customers; this greatly enhances the shoot's reputation. A well-planned system of installations such as hunting lodges, stalking trails, shooting boxes and winter feeding points consolidates the market value. Correspondingly, our shoot produces and guarantees venison and trophies of the highest quality.

A balanced relationship between game stock (especially cloven-hoofed game) and food supply shows in the availability of specific plants preferred for browsing, whereas the lack of such plants combined with a predominant occurrence of spiny, thorny, bitter, poisonous or browsing-resistant plants characterises oversized game populations. Adhering only to commercial interests would result in unnaturally high game populations with disastrous consequences for the forests. Attuning the hunting strategy to forestry needs at the Alpine timberline reduces unnecessary eco-physiological stress sources and damages caused by game. Until the 19th century, red deer used to migrate seasonally in winter down into the Enns valley, returning with the coming of spring. Nowadays this is impossible due to community sprawl and intensive use of land for traffic, tourism or agriculture. Therefore, depending on the first snows late in autumn, red deer are fed in a fenced enclosure of 50 ha in the Mittlere Seifrieding, until the snows melt late in spring.

Thus the destructive influence of game on vegetation, consisting of food intake (grazing, browsing, bark peeling) and fraying of velvet as well as beating of antlers, is kept low. The present game warden of the Mittlere and Hintere Seifrieding has devised a sound long-term game-keeping strategy and shooting plan, which accommodates timber and hunting interests very well. This shows in the negligible statistics on damage caused by game animals.

GAME TO HUNT IN HINTERE UND MITTLERE SEIFRIEDING

- Alpine Marmot *(Marmota marmota)*
- Black Grouse *(Tetrao tetrix)*
- Chamois *(Rupicapra rupicapra)*
- Red Deer *(Cervus elaphus)*
- Roe Deer *(Capreolus capreolus)*

Sustainable Alpine forestry management

Alpine regions were more subject to man induced changes than generally expected: man already roamed the Austrian Alps looking for food more than 10,000 years ago. Man has engaged in pasturage in the Alps for more than 6,000 years. Thus, man transformed and shaped the Alpine forest regions through intensive cattle farming reaching heights of 2,000 metres and more. Local peasants intensively engaged in pasturage in the whole valley until long after the Second World War. These activities shaped vegetation communities greatly. Mountain forests usually respond more sensitively to man's forest and pasturage interventions and are more seriously endangered by irreversible processes than commercial forests outside the Alps.

An Alpine forest undergrowth community can consist of various ferns, mosses, lichens and grasses. All these combined indicate good soil properties. Strategic timber removal guarantees biodiversity.

M.Miller-Aichholz

M.Miller-Aichholz

A fine specimen of Fleckvieh cattle grazing on a verdant alpine pasture in Seifrieding.

The bluish-green colour and the radial needle structure distinguish Engelmann spruce from the dark green colour and more flattened needle structure of the European spruce.

M.Miller-Aichholz

The alpine tree line and eco-tone are a fascinating ecosystem: flora and fauna have to adapt to very challenging climatic conditions to survive. Plants and animals are pushed to their adaptive limits in long and harsh winters. The snow cover and mantles in Hintere Seifrieding can have a depth of more than 3 metres. In winter avalanches constitute a grave danger, in summer torrents and landslides another. Trees growing in that zone need to be frost hardy, possess excellent soil and water management qualities and endure changing temperatures over the year. Furthermore, being in high altitudes constrains growth periods and capacity for plants on the one hand and the carrying capacities of the soils on the other.

All these factors affect Alpine biodiversity. Mountain pasturage boosts biodiversity too: a surprising side-effect which is now under intense scientific scrutiny. However, the testing eco-physiological factors and the ever-present hazard of erosion, in turn, govern the commercial extent of timber production viability and game-keeping. The opening up of forests by forest roads and the use of fully or partly mechanised forest machinery on steep grounds (mountain harvesters) would impact on the ecological structure of forests and therefore only low impact machinery is used. The intensity of forest management in the Alpine area is still strongly determined by orographic features such as accessibility, slope gradient and remoteness. Increased production costs for road infrastructure, tree harvesting and silviculture significantly constrain effective mountain forest management, compared to more favourable production areas in the accessible lowlands. Therefore the Amonn and Kernmayer families have entered into a forest management cooperation to keep forestry costs low and increase timber productivity when felling. Hintere und Mittlere Seifrieding mostly harvest European spruce.

Cautious timber removals from the mature forest balance the given arboreal age groups since age gaps are found due to unsystematic felling strategies in the first half of the 20th century. Decreasing intensity of cattle grazing and pasture conservation caused abundant natural tree regeneration. Climatic stress and an increased frequency of storms have led to extensive damage, mainly uprooting spruces.

This in turn intensifies the spread of bark beetles, which constitutes a serious problem throughout Austria. The concurring incidences of windthrow, snow break and frost drought result in the spruce's susceptibility to all kinds of infestation. The increased recurrence of bark beetle outbreaks can be seen as a possible consequence of climate and local weather changes. Spruce in the Alpine timberline reacts to these multi-factorial developments by throwing seeds annually instead of every four to seven years. Forests can be compared to people habitually on an imbalanced diet: increasing in weight but at the same time decreasing in overall fitness.

The repeated infestation of *Chrysomyxa rhododendri*, a fungus infesting mainly the European spruce, is supposedly evoked by climatic stress. Another factor could be the increased return of the Alpine Rose *(Rhododendron ferrugineum)* due to reduced conservation of mountain pastures. The alpine rose acts as vector for fungal spores of *Chrysomyxa rhododendri.*

Fortunately, the Engelmann spruce populations planted in Hintere Seifrieding have not yet been affected. These were introduced from the early 1980s onwards and so far they have done exceptionally well. This tree, mostly associated with its North American origins, was in fact an indigenous plant in Central Europe before the glacial Würm period (115,000 to 10,000 BC) ended.

A quick and efficient removal of felled timber helps contain the spread of bark beetles. High quality forest roads are needed to transport big truck-loads of timber off the property.

TREES OF THE ALPINE TIMBER LINE ECOZONE IN HINTERE SEIFRIEDING

- Mountain Pine *(Pinus mugo)*
- Juniper *(Juniperus communis var. alpina)*
- Swiss Pine *(Pinus cembra)*
- European Larch *(Larix decidua)*
- Norway Spruce *(Picea abies)*
- Engelmann Spruce *(Picea engelmanni)*
- European Silver Fir *(Abies alba)*
- Black Alder *(Alnus glutinosa)*
- Grey Alder *(Alnus incana)*
- Silver Birch *(Betula pendula)*
- European Rowan *(Sorbus aucuparia)*
- Sycamore Maple *(Acer pseudoplatanus)*

The owner Thomas Amonn in conversation with Siegfried Konrad Senior, the game keeper who developed the Mittlere und Hintere Seifrieding hunt.

View of the lower reaches of the Seifrieding valley with the Größsölk valley further down.

CHALLENGES IN
THE ALPINE ENVIRONMENT

Today's low timber prices and high labour costs gravely affect income possibilities. As long as this development continues, we will be forced to concentrate on game-keeping. Income generated from timber largely depends on the quality of the wood, and any timber thrown by winds or infested by beetles is greatly diminished in value. Due to increased climatic pressure on the European spruce, we have begun to introduce adaptive trees like the Engelmann spruce, as well as promoting pronounced growth of European larch and Swiss pines. These reforestation concepts are designed to enhance biodiversity, soils and the water regimen. The reforestation measures ought to prevent erosion and thus stave off avalanche and torrent occurrence. Responsible and sustainable alpine forestry can only be practised productively if long-term ecological strategies spanning more than one generation are adopted and applied.

A means to boost local biodiversity is to resume alpine pasturage on a larger scale. Such measures prevent scrub encroachment. Pasturage enhances grazing potentials meaning high quality forage for both cattle and deer. Landowners and agro-industrialists have completely different objectives: while agro-industrialists are mainly intent on maximising earnings, landowners adhere to the concept of good stewardship. This concept calls for a responsible and sustainable handling of available resources over generations. Responsible stewardship as practised by landowners is synonymous with sustainable and ecological land-use.

Between 1977 and 1983 the Sölk valleys were integrated in a natural park (Naturpark Sölktäler). In 2006 the Sölk valleys were declared Natura 2000 areas. Thus far, this procedural development has not materially affected the forestry and hunting activities of the Seifrieding. No striking disadvantages have accrued, since Austrian laws on hunting and forestry already in place covered most sustainability issues. Nevertheless, an example of clashing European guidelines and present national law is given by the black grouse *(Tetrao tetrix)* rulings: in order to protect the birds

Small sample of biodiversity enhancers in Seifrieding: predators and pollinators clockwise: 1.- Cross spider; 2.- Hover fly; 3.- Bumble bee and fly feeding on a thistle; 4.- Wasp attacking fly.

M. Miller-Aichholz

throughout Central Europe the shooting plan regulations reduced the number of grouse to be shot. Yet this particular fowl has always thrived in abundant numbers in Seifrieding. This kind of intervention proves to be an impediment for estates dependant on income from hunting.

To meet growing future challenges, any regulatory environment must accommodate climate change developments, thus allowing landowners to adjust to these altered economic and ecological conditions. Landowners conserving ecosystems and ensuing ecosystem services in climate change challenged areas should be rewarded by a system of measures ranging from tax easements to topical subsidies.

ECOSYSTEM SERVICES RENDERED BY HINTERE SEIFRIEDING:

- Moderate weather extremes and their impacts: *Up-keep of protective forests.*
- Disperse seeds: *Sustainable hunting & pasturage & reforestation.*
- Mitigate drought and floods: *Protective forests & natural riverbed retention. Water retention cycle.*
- Cycle and move nutrients: *Preventing human interventions impeding organic processes.*
- Protect stream and river channels from erosion: *Protective forests & natural riverbed retention.*
- Detoxify and decompose wastes: *Polluted air & rain detoxification via surface vegetion.*
- Control agricultural pests: *Intact edible environments and food-chain integrity.*
- Maintain biodiversity: *Pasturage and reforestation.*
- Generate and preserve soils and renew their fertility: *Pasturage & reforestation.*
- Contribute to climate stability: *Mature forests sequestrating CO_2.*
- Purify the air and water: *Sustainable forestry management plan implementation.*
- Regulate disease carrying organisms: *Toads, wasps, ants etc.*
- Pollinate crops and natural vegetation: *Frequent presence of bumble bees, hoverflies, butterflies, birds etc.*

Ecosystems are fundamental and conditional to all life. An ecosystem is a community of animals and plants interacting with one another and their physical environment in a given habitat. Ecosystems include physical and chemical components, such as soils, water, and nutrients that support the organisms living within them. These organisms may range from large animals and plants to microscopic bacteria and fungi. People, too, are part of ecosystems. The health and well being of human populations depend upon the services provided by ecosystems. These ecosystem services are natural processes by which the environment generates resources that we very much take for granted like clean water, pollination of native and agricultural plants, and habitats for fisheries.

The United States Environmental Protection Agency (EPA), for example, has calculated the financial value of pollination services for all of the U.S. "Over 100,000 different animal species – including bats, bees, flies, moths, beetles, birds, and butterflies – provide free pollination services. One third of human food comes from plants pollinated by wild pollinators. The value of pollination services from wild pollinators in the U.S. alone is estimated at four to six billion dollars per year".

Accordingly, the public should appreciate landowners' efforts to conserve and preserve an ecosystem's integrity and functionality, since most of these hidden services rendered are not locally restricted and benefit society and nature as a whole. Any forestry, farming and game-keeping regulation should avoid "one size fits all" solutions, which simply do not concur with anything natural.

Thomas Amonn,
Marysia Miller-Aichholz

FORSTGUT HINTERE SEIFRIEDING BELONGS TO:

Activities & attractions

🌲 Forestry
🦌 Hunting
🐟 Fishing

CONTACT DATA
Magdalena Amonn, Thomas Amonn
Mössna 84
A-8961 St. Nikolai im Sölktal
Tel: +43 (0) 368 93 29

Koskis Gård

Boreal

Location: Salo, Varsinais-Suomi/Egentliga Finland, Finland.
Surface: 1,389 ha.

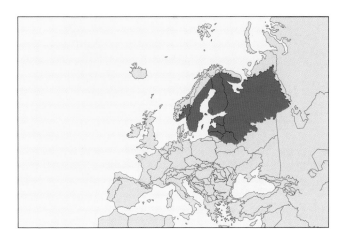

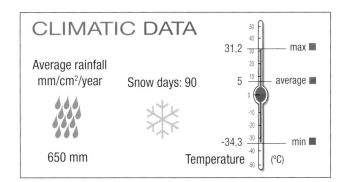

CLIMATIC DATA

Average rainfall
mm/cm²/year

Snow days: 90

650 mm

Temperature (°C)

31,2 — max ■
5 — average ■
-34,3 — min ■

SUMMARY

Nature conservation through active management methods is at the forefront of the management of the Koskis Estate. "Preserving the old – keeping up with the present" is a motto that lies behind many of the aims of the current owner and how he is managing his estate.

Behind the changes in the management towards organic farming and beef production, re-establishing wetlands, conserving grazing areas of high biodiversity value and establishing renewable energy lies the fact that the world has to be changed and that it is changing towards a more sustainable way of consuming. Koskis Estate is a perfect example of how the past, present and future of rural living can be combined.

Koskis Gård Estate

The main house in autumn. The house was built in 1731 although its present appearance dates from 1924.

HISTORY

Koskis, from ironworks to a modern agriculture and forestry enterprise

Koskis is situated in the south-western part of Finland in a district where 12 ironworks were founded in the 17th century, all within 50 km of the estate. There was enough waterpower and wood in the locality to satisfy two of the basic conditions for the iron industry. Some ore deposits had also been found, although they appeared to be insignificant. Therefore ore for the ironworks soon had to be imported from Sweden.

The Koskis ironworks were founded in 1679 and, with a few interruptions, remained in use until 1890.

From 1780 to 1830 the Orijärvi copper smelting plant also operated in Koskis. With the Kisko river running through the entire estate and the forest providing the necessary firewood, iron and copper smelting were made possible.

Some of the different buildings associated with the iron and copper smelting industries continued to be in use until the 1950s. In the small village you can still feel traces of an old industrial community. As a memory of the industrial epoch of Koskis, there is a small electric water power station by the river. Built in 1909 it is the second oldest in Finland and still in operation.

The founder of the Koskis ironworks, Daniel Faxell (who took the name Cronmarck when he was raised to the nobility), was from Sweden. During the 18th century the ownership changed rapidly. The squire of the Wefverstedt sold Koskis in

Miniature of the old building where iron was made.

1738 to John Montgomery, the owner of the Fiskars works. For over a century afterwards, Koskis was a part of Fiskars, the owner of several industries and estates in the district.

In the family since 1822

In 1822 Johan Jakob (John) Julin (von Julin after his ennoblement) bought Fiskars including the Koskis and Antskog ironworks and the copper smelting in Kärkelä as well as the Coppermine in Orijärvi. The total area was 35,000 hectares. Since then Koskis has been in the same family.

John Julin, who was a pharmacist, achieved great progress in all respects. He developed his industry, took part in cultural and economic efforts of the time and was also a pioneer in the educational system and in agriculture. At Antskog and Koskis he built the first two floodgates in Finland in 1824-26.

After the death of John von Julin, his second son Albert von Julin inherited Koskis in 1869, an estate including 8,000 hectares and a blast furnace with associated industry. Big investments were made in agriculture and a cow shed and a piggery were built. As building material, by-products from the ironworks were used. During this period more than 500 people lived on the estate, which had over 100 employees.

The next generation to own Koskis were Albert von Julin's two sons, Albert Jr. and Jacob Sr. Together the two brothers made detailed plans for their estate. By the time Finland achieved its independence from Russia in 1917, the future looked bright. However Albert Jr. was tragically killed in 1918 during the civil war. Everything was changed and his brother Jacob von Julin Sr. became the sole owner of Koskis.

The first owner of the estate, Johan Jakob Julin, ennobled to von Julin.

Jacob von Julin Sr. made his career in the forestry industry, living with his family in Helsinki. He continued with the plans which he and his brother had made, and started renovations at Koskis. It has been said that during his time, in the early 1920s, Koskis was changed from a regular farm to an estate. The farm buildings close to the Manor house were pulled down and a new stable was built further away from the Manor to make room for a new garden with grass lawns, flowerbeds and a tennis court.

Changes in the law meant that several tenanted farms and crofts had to be sold in 1919-1922 and the area of Koskis was reduced to 6,500 hectares.

Jacob von Julin Sr. died in 1942 and Koskis was divided by his children when his estate was distributed. The transfer of land to people who had to leave their farms in Karelia after the Second World War also meant a further reduction in the land area.

Jacob von Julin Jr. and his mother Elsa von Julin were the new owners of Koskis, now with 3,000 ha of which 150 ha was arable land. Elsa von Julin moved to Koskis from Helsinki and lived there until her death in 1981. Jacob von Julin Jr. was, like his father, involved in forestry and other industries but he was also very interested in improving agriculture and the forests at Koskis. To meet new demands, farms in Finland had to be modernized and big investments and reforms were made during the 1960s. The dairy herd was sold in 1964 and horses were replaced by tractors and new agricultural machines. In 1968 the first Hereford beef calves were born at Koskis. Suckler cows and beef breeds were something quite unknown in Finland at that time, but suitable for the type of landscape represented at Koskis.

Koskis Hereford was one of the first herds in Finland and turned out to be a "life's work" for Jacob von Julin's daughter Mariana (1943). Mariana, who together with her husband Franz von Limburg Stirum began farming Koskis in 1974, became owner after the death of her father in 1987. When the estate was distributed, Koskis was again divided and the total area of the estate was reduced from more than 3,000 hectares to around 1,200 hectares.

During late 20th century and during the first years of the 21st century several buildings related to beef cattle breeding and other agricultural activities were constructed. Additionally many existing build-

Koskis Gård Estate

ings were renovated and later passed on to the next generation in excellent condition. Cropping at Koskis became organic in 2002 and the cattle in 2005.

Transporting goods in the Kisko River, 100 m from the main house, in the early 20th century.

Koskis and the von Limburg Stirum family

Franz von Limburg Stirum (1943), the father of the current owner, was born in Flatow, West Prussia. In 1944, due to the Soviet offensive at the end of the Second World War, the family had to leave their estate in Rattay, West Prussia and escaped to relatives in Sweden. Franz grew up in Västervik, Sweden and moved to Finland in 1973 where he married Mariana von Julin, daughter of the owner of Koskis. Franz is the current head of the house of Limburg Stirum. The von Limburg Stirum family took its name in the 12th century from the castle of Limburg an der Lenne (Today Hagen-Hohenlinburg) in what is now Germany. The family descends from the Ezzonen dynasty in the 9th century, making it one of the oldest families in Europe.

The church was originally built in the 17th century, 30 km from Koskis. It was moved to Koskis Gard in its entirety in 1785, along with 1208 horse carriages.

Koskis Gård Estate

Re-establishing wetlands at Koskis has created great interest among land management experts.

The Church, the cultural treasure of Koskis

The first church at Koskis was built in 1686 but fell into very bad condition during the wars of the time. The owner, Bengt Magnus Björkman, decided to move his other church which had been renovated in 1766. This church was situated in Antskog, 30 km away. The church was transported in 1208 horse-drawn carriages during the winter of 1785-1786. Since then only the old altarpiece, now on the side wall, has been exchanged. The current altarpiece and pulpit (from 1694) were bought in 1800 at Forsmark in Sweden. Koskis had its own priest and parish until 1869. Of the old burial place only two iron crosses remain. Koskis Church is one of the three privately owned churches in Finland. The church has room for 250 people and is used for services 3-5 times a year by the nearby parish of Perniö. The church is also used for private occasions such as weddings and concerts.

KOSKIS TODAY

Koskis handed over to the 6th generation

In 2007 Fredrik von Limburg Stirum (1974) became the owner of Koskis. He is the 7th owner in the family and represents the 6th generation. Fredrik graduated as Master of Agriculture and Forestry at the University of Helsinki in 2004. As his main subjects he studied wildlife management and agricultural economics. After his studies he worked as a project manager with the Finnish Hunters' Association. Before taking over the estate, he also worked for the Ministry of Agriculture and Forestry and was involved in several projects related to wildlife management which were financed by the EU.

As owner of Koskis, he both manages the estate and lives on it. Besides he is involved in different projects and organizations outside the estate. Together with some well-known Finnish business leaders he established a foundation for game and

Fredrik von Limburg Stirum, owner of Koskis.

nature management in 2006. For the first three years Fredrik was the manager of this foundation and is now a member of the board. The foundation's main task so far has been to work for the recovery of the Grey Partridge *(Perdix perdix lucida)* which has suffered from intensive farming and disappeared from large areas. In 2009 they started their second project together with the Baltic Sea Action Group. The aim of this project is to combine agricultural methods that promote biodiversity and reduce the amount of nutrients escaping into the Baltic Sea. Additionally Fredrik is a board member of several companies related both to real estate and other businesses. In the future he hopes to be able to use most of his time to develop profitable, interesting and sustainable businesses on his own estate.

LANDSCAPE MANAGEMENT AND ACTIVE NATURE CONSERVATION

Nature conservation through active management methods is always at the forefront of the management of the estate. The different management methods cover various aspects such as conservation and promotion of biodiversity, landscape and game management as well as care of the waterways, and are all important aspects in caring for nature at large.

Hereford cattle at Koskis Gård keep the landscape open and keep groves and meadows in very good condition. Pasturing cattle is important both for preserving the landscape and for promoting biodiversity. The meadows bordering the Kisko river remain open and they are the habitat of several species of birds. Semi-open meadows where cattle also graze provide a habitat for several species of plants on the decline. One-third of all the threatened species in Finland occur in agricultural areas even if those areas cover less than 10% of the country. These red-listed species are totally dependent on how these areas are managed.

Creating small marshes in various parts of the estate has restored a valuable living environment that had disappeared as a result of land drainage. These marshes are excellent habitats not only for ducks, waders and other wetland birds, but also for bats, Swallows *(Hirundo rustica)* and many other organisms which find abundant food in the wetlands. Furthermore, properly created wetlands purify the water that runs through them, before it reaches the ditches, the Kisko river and finally the Baltic Sea. The Baltic Sea is regarded as one of the worst polluted marine areas in the world. Because of its shallowness and its "low salt degree", the Baltic Sea is extremely sensitive to the input of nitrogen and phosphorous from all kinds of human activity in the area.

To show their commitment to nature conservation Koskis joined the Countdown 2010 network, the first partner in Finland to do so. The aim of the IUCN Countdown 2010 network has been to halt the loss of biodiversity by the year 2010. It is obvious that this work has to be continued and intensified in Europe, and all over the world, after the year 2010, in order to be able to reach the goal some time in the future.

ECONOMIC ACTIVITIES

Cattle Breeding

The estate started breeding Hereford cattle in 1967. The original purpose was to improve the exploitation of fields and riverside land that was less suitable for efficient grain growing, as well as to keep open the landscape around the old ironworks. For centuries the Hereford has been bred for the efficient transformation of fresh grass, straw and hay into prime quality beef. Hereford cattle are undemanding and peaceful. The estate's experience of this breed has been nothing but positive since the cattle arrived here more than 40 years ago.

"Koskis Hereford" is the oldest herd of Hereford cattle in Finland. During the last 40 years more than 2,000 calves have been born at Koskis. Cattle-breeding originally started as a hobby and as a side-line to growing grain but is now, alongside forestry, the most important business. The estate has about 70 breeding cows and heifers. The present size of the herd is about 150 head, including breeding bulls and calves. They graze from May to October on fields, in forests and in recently cleaned groves.

The Herefords are effective landscape and biodiversity managers, in addition to producing beef and income from the sale of breeding animals. When cattle-breeding at Koskis originally started, the owners at the time had no idea that they would eventually be protecting and saving traditional biotopes, which nowadays are considered so important for nature conservation.

In 2005 the Hereford herd at Koskis was approved for monitored ECO-production (organic farming). In winter time the cattle are fed with organic silage from privately owned fields.

The world's best grazing cattle and most efficient beef producer

Over the long term, cattle-breeding at Koskis Gård has produced good results. The precise objectives of the herd are based on information and breeding both from Finland and the world at large, as well as on practical experience from the estate's own activities and from other breeders. The estate appreciates and endeavours to improve reproduction, growth, meatiness and successful calving. It also greatly appreciates the ease of caring for these cattle, their calm character, low demands and good capacity to process fodder and exploit meadows.

Beef products, with different added values

In recent years food safety and environmental issues have been constant topics, not only in Europe but in the whole world. The managers of Koskis strongly believe in their products, which have many added values. The estate guarantees quality and safety. The meat can be traced all the way to the farm where the calf was born. The management believes that consumers in the future want to know where and how their beef, as well as food in general, has been produced. Quality is something more than just taste and tenderness. Care of the animals, their feeding and well-being, as well as correct handling of the meat, are all parts of the production process for ensuring prime quality.

The stamp of the old ironworks used today on meat products sold by the estate.

The estate started breeding Hereford cattle in 1967.

Koskis Gård Estate

Cattle grazing is important for biodiversity and landscape management.

Agriculture and Grassland

Organic farming is a form of agriculture that relies on crop rotation, green manure, compost, biological pest control and mechanical cultivation to maintain soil productivity and control pests, excluding or strictly limiting the use of synthetic fertilizers and synthetic pesticides, plant growth regulators, livestock feed additives and genetically modified organisms. *(Directorate General for Agriculture and Rural Development of the European Commission).*

The estate's production from all of its arable land – 200 hectares plus 60 hectares of natural grazing meadows – follows the rules, regulations and standards of organic farming. Of the 200 ha, 120 ha is grassland for hay/silage and the remaining 80 ha are mainly rye, oats, barely and rape. In addition some extra land is dedicated to gamecrops to promote game and biodiversity in general.

Organic farming at Koskis is based on crop rotation and manure from the cattle. With correct crop rotation and good timing in all activities, it is possible to produce high yield and good quality crops with less negative and more positive effects on the environment.

Organically produced silage and grain

Prime quality organically produced silage is sold in round bales. Silage is suitable for feeding both cattle, sheep and horses. It uses no artificial fertilizers and no pesticides, which gives more variable and diversified species of plants than on normal cultivated fields. Organically produced silage is therefore also eminently suitable for feeding game. This kind of fodder is very close to the natural food of deer and hares.

Rye and some oats is sold to businesses for use in bakeries etc. In the future the estate plans to develop its own branded products similar to how the meat has been developed. Part of the oats and the barley is fed to the cattle. The rape is sold to a company that produces organic rapeseed oil and the by-products can be brought back as protein fodder for the young bulls.

Hereford beef is renowned for its great taste and tenderness. Marbled meat is a special quality of the Hereford breed. The estate has long experience of appropriate feeding and of choosing the correct moment for slaughter. The proportion of Omega-3/Omega-6 fatty acids is ideal in animals fed only on grass. Most of the meat is sold directly to private customers, restaurants and supermarkets in the area.

There is even more added value than just the wellbeing and correct handling of the animals. An important part of the added value for the customer is the fact that the production methods at Koskis minimize the negative influences on the environment and maximize the positive ones. By grazing, the cows promote the conservation and management of areas of high nature value. The farming methods used minimize the negative effects on climate, waterways and biodiversity. These are all facts that can be added to the product information as well as to the price for consumers that have a level of awareness.

Forestry

The forests at Koskis are typical of the boreal region of southern Finland, with mixed coniferous and deciduous forests. The total forest area is approximately 1000 hectares. The main species are Norwegian Spruce *(Picea abies)* and Scots Pine *(Pinus*

The mother of the current owner holds one result of more than 40 years of succesful cattle breeding.

sylvestris). Deciduous forests, mainly of Birch *(Betula pendula)*, account for less than 10% of the forest area. There is also a presence of Oak *(Quercus* sp.*)*, Ash *(Fraxinus* sp.*)* and Elm *(Ulmus* sp.*)* closer to the fields, within 1 km of the main house. Total annual cut is around 4,500 m³. The total stock of growing forest on the estate is around 140,000 m³ and the annual growth is around 6 m³/ha.

The forestry is based on a management plan made every 10 years. On each occasion an inventory is made and the different forestry figures and plantations are dealt with depending on the urgency. Forestry work is done on contract by a regional partner who handles all the work from planting trees to thinning out young plantations and harvesting complete areas.

The forestry in certain sensitive areas close to waterways and important habitats is regulated by law. The forests at Koskis are certified by the PEFC scheme, which is the most common in Finland.

In addition the owner of Koskis has taken special action along the edges of the forest. The goal has been to create a semi-open transition zone with mainly deciduous trees between the fields and the forests, where many species can find suitable habitats. These areas also produce a lot of suitable fodder for big game like the elk and the white-tailed deer, which keeps them away from the more important young forests. The transition zones are kept open regularly and the trees cut are used for energy purposes.

Most of the wood (both log and pulp) is sold to one of the big Finnish forest companies but some of the high quality logs of pine, birch, elm and oak are sold to a local saw-mill for furniture and design articles. Branches and some of the low quality wood are sold for energy purposes to nearby towns, and some is used on the estate to heat its own buildings. In the future it is likely that an even greater part of the wood that today is used for the pulp industry will be used to heat local towns and villages.

The management of the estate sees climate change and some political risks as the main threats for sustainable forestry in the future. The risk of storms and new devastation is increasing as temperatures rises, and the effects have already been seen. On the political side there is a risk of new protection areas in southern Finland in the future. This should, according to the owner, be seen both as a risk but also as an opportunity to safeguard biodi-

Koskis Gård Estate

versity for future generations. As long as the protection areas are fully compensated and the protection plans are set up in cooperation with the owner, it is acceptable and indeed preferable that new protection sites are established to safeguard biological diversity. If the owners are not compensated, these sites can be a major risk to sustainable forestry, as the owner of the estate sees it. He also thinks that in protected areas in general it should be possible to utilize game, fish etc. sustainably.

Biomass Energy

Some 500 m³ of woodchips are consumed every year to heat all the farm buildings, the manor and surrounding stables and houses. A decision to replace the old oil furnace was made in 2004. The investment was well-timed and profitable. It was calculated that the payback time on the investment would be around 10 years, but, mainly because of the rising price of oil, the payback time now looks to be reduced to around 6 years.

The capacity of the new woodchip furnace is 250 kW, and it is capable of heating 8 houses and 5 other buildings. The wood used is mainly low quality Spruce, a by-product of the high quality logs and timber for pulp. The chipping is done on contract 2-3 times a year. The owner sees the fur-

Spruce, pine and birch are the most important species in the forestry at Koskis.

347

Koskis Gård Estate

The European Elk *(Alces alces)* is the biggest game species at Koskis.

sive and sustainable nature tourism on the estate. At present Koskis has 15 houses or apartments for rent. About half of the houses are used all year around and the rest only for weekends and holidays. Over two-thirds of the 60 roofs on the estate have been renovated during the last 20 years.

Hunting and Fishing

The estate supports the motto of "Conservation through sustainable use" established by the CIC (International Council for Game and Wildlife Conservation). It is important for the conservation of nature and quality of life of landowners and people living in the countryside all over the world to be able to utilize game and fish in a sustainable way. Sustainable hunting and fishing does not conflict with nature conservation, it gives an added value and increases the motivation of the people involved. At Koskis a census of different game animal populations is done annually. Annual exploitation never exceeds natural reproduction.

nace as a good investment for the estate and also from a wider perspective as a way to take part in the move to reduce fossil fuels and increase renewable energy. By the time this book is printed, Koskis might have taken the first steps towards producing electricity through windpower, solar and manure from its own cattle.

Real Estate and Tourism

Real estate and tourism is an area of great potential at Koskis. The combination of beautiful nature, ongoing active management work, interesting history and old buildings make it exclusive. At the moment the estate can already offer exclusive hunting and fishing for companies and there is an ongoing project to identify the potential for exclu-

Koskis Gård sells a limited number of hunting and fishing packages. At present, they offer elk and white-tailed deer hunting, as well as pike and pike-perch fishing in the Kisko river. Today, quality commercial hunting is organised mainly for companies and their guests. The addition of 3 adjacent estates brings the total area to about 4,500 ha.

Elk are hunted on corporate hunts usually with 8-12 hunters and a few doghandlers using Norwegian elkhounds or similar. Hunting for white-tailed deer takes place either from high seats in the evening or by stalking in suitable areas. They are also hunted during the daytime, mainly with dachshunds. The white-tailed deer was introduced into Finland in the 1930s and today the annual cull is over 20,000 animals.

The white-tailed deer was introduced into Finland in the 1930s and is common at Koskis.

In the future there are also plans to sell commercial wild duck shooting, thanks to the re-established wetlands. In a few years time, these wetlands will produce hundreds of wild waterbirds annually, which can provide a sustainable annual cull.

In 2009 Koskis Manor, together with a local operator, started to offer pike and pike-perch fishing in the Kisko river. This is a former trout river and there are plans to build fish passes around the existing hydro powerstations to let the trout come back. This will make Koskis a really interesting fishing destination.

Koskis Gård Estate

Koskis Gård Estate

Meat products

In addition to the Hereford meat sold directly to customers, you can buy elk and white-tailed deer venison directly from the estate from October to January. Since the regulations on handling game are not as strict as they are for beef, the meat can be further processed on the estate. Most of the meat is sold directly to private individuals, but in recent years elk and white-tailed deer venison from Koskis has also been offered in top restaurants in Helsinki. The owner of the estate is concerned that the provisions and regulations are becoming so strict that small processors of game cannot fulfill the demands set up by the authorities without major, and unprofitable, investment. If this development continues there is a risk that safe and small-scale local food will be replaced by unknown products from mass production units on the other side of the planet. This trend has to be stopped.

GAME SPECIES

Big Game

The most common big game species in the area are the White-tailed Deer *(Odocoileus virginianus)* and the European Elk *(Alces alces).* The elk is a native species whereas the white-tailed deer was introduced to Finland around 1930. No harm to native wildlife has been documented as a result of this introduction. There is also a small population of Roe Deer *(Capreolus capreolus)* in the area. The population of roe deer is very low, mainly because of the large population of European Lynx *(Lynx lynx).*

The european lynx is the only common big predator in the area, and is present in the area all year round. In addition Wolves *(Canis lupus)* and Bears *(Ursus arctos)* or their tracks are observed each year. The big predators are principally protected, but some licences for lynx have been issued in southern Finland in recent years.

Small Game

In the forests of Koskis Gård, you can find small game species like Capercaillie *(Tetrao urogallus),* Black Grouse *(Lyrurus tetrix),* Hazel Grouse *(Bonasa bonasia)* and Mountain Hare *(Lepus timidus).* In the lakes and rivers you can find several species of ducks. The most common are Mallard *(Anas patyrhynchos),* Teal *(Anas crecca)* and Goldeneye *(Bu-*

cephala clangula). The population of European Otter *(Lutra lutra),* which is not a huntable species any more, has been increasing over recent years.

Closer to the fields, you can find the European Hare *(Lepus europeus),* Wood Pigeon *(Columba palumbus)* and very rarely nowadays the Grey Partridge *(Perdix perdix lucida).*

The small predators present in the area are the Red Fox *(Vulpes vulpes),* Racoon Dog *(Nyctereutes procyonoides),* Pine Marten *(Martes martes),* American Mink *(Mustela vison),* Badger *(Meles meles),* Stoat *(Mustela erminea)* and Weasel *(Mustela nivalis).*

Protected wildlife

Among the protected species of birds breeding in the area, the Osprey *(Pandion haliaetus),* Red-throated Diver *(Gavia stellata),* Black-throated Diver *(Gavia arctica)* and Dipper *(Cinclus cinclus)* should be mentioned. The population of the national bird of Finland, the Whooper Swan *(Cygnus cygnus),* is increasing throughout the country as a whole as well as at Koskis.

The most impressive bird in the forests of Koskis. The capercaillie needs special attention in areas of intensive forestry.

The national bird of Finland is the Whooper Swan *(Cygnus cygnus).* It is present at Koskis in large numbers.

Koskis Gård **(Finland)**

CHALLENGES AND OPPORTUNITIES THOUGHTS OF THE OWNER

"Preserving the old-keeping up with the present" is a motto that lies behind many of the aims of the current owner and how he is managing his estate. Behind the changes in the management towards organic farming and beef production, re-establishing wetlands, conserving grazing areas of high biodiversity value and establishing renewable energy lies the fact that the world has to be changed and is changing towards a more sustainable way of consuming. For the current owner his strategy is a mix of economic optimization at present and what he thinks is right and required to make both production and consumption more sustainable in the future. In the long term he believes that he can generate an economic profit as a forerunner in sustainable food production. Koskis will be a leading estate in sustainable solutions in primary production in the 21st century.

Today the estate is, like many other farms in the country, too dependent on subsidies from the EU. But the strategy of the owner is to use them as much as possible, as long as they are still there. It is also possible to use current subsidies to create future businesses. It is likely that after the year 2013 the production-related subsidies will be cut even further and the income will have to come from products sold. EU money will most likely be used more to support sustainable food production and different environmental services than to support farmers to produce as much as possible. Therefore at Koskis the subsidies are being used to create landscapes and biodiversity, which will attract people in the future. Exclusive tourism and different services for people from the cities could be an important part of the business at Koskis in the future. With the advantage of being a forerunner in biodiversity and landscape management, and having the interesting history of the estate, the owner believes he can create interesting new businesses. Commercial fishing and hunting for selected customers is already a part of the business. In general the owner believes that the opportunity for the countryside is not only to produce food for people in the cities. Sevices for stressful people from the cities is a growing opportunity.

Even if some of the future businesses are more service related, the owner is also planning to produce high quality added-value food products in the future. Farmer- controlled businesses is something the owner studied during an advanced course in agricultural business management in England in 2007 and he believes in some good ideas that could be turned into practice in the future.

As key factors in long-term survival, the owner sees the task as being to combine the focus on the right businesses and to still keep other "doors open" when the world is changing. He will be careful about making big investments on the estate that have no alternative use. The change of agricultural policy in the future will always be a risk. This is especially true in Finland, where natural circumstances make it difficult to compete with the rest of the world, at least in quantity of food production. Of course, climate change can and probably will alter the situation, but taking into consideration all the negative consequences forecast, this cannot be regarded as a positive change.

What climate change also brings is the opportunity for an estate like Koskis to produce energy for people living in the towns. The threats have to be turned into opportunities. Preserving nature also provides opportunities for future generations to utilize it in a sustainable way. For Koskis, as for every other estate, the main task for the future is to preserve the old and keep up with the present.

The Kisko River flowing through Koskis Estate.

ård Estate

KOSKIS GÅRD BELONGS TO:

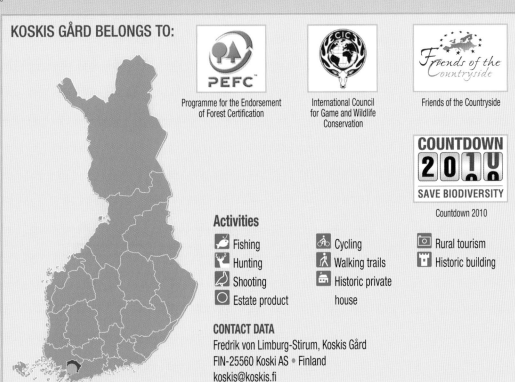

PEFC
Programme for the Endorsement
of Forest Certification

International Council
for Game and Wildlife
Conservation

Friends of the Countryside
Friends of the Countryside

COUNTDOWN 2010
SAVE BIODIVERSITY
Countdown 2010

Activities

- Fishing
- Hunting
- Shooting
- Estate product
- Cycling
- Walking trails
- Historic private house
- Rural tourism
- Historic building

CONTACT DATA

Fredrik von Limburg-Stirum, Koskis Gård
FIN-25560 Koski AS • Finland
koskis@koskis.fi

Marzale

Continental

Location: Madignano, Cremona, Lombardy, Italy.
Surface: 380 ha.

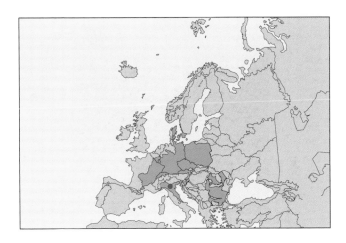

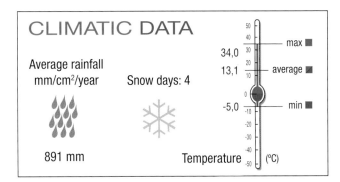

CLIMATIC DATA

Average rainfall
mm/cm²/year

Snow days: 4

891 mm

Temperature (°C)

34,0 — max
13,1 — average
-5,0 — min

SUMMARY

Within the region of Lombardy, and 50 km from the centre of Milan, the Marzale Estate lies nestled in a superb remote and unique area of wetlands, where wildlife, including rare seasonal migratory species, can rest and find shelter. Marquise Emilia Bonzi Dal Pozzo's oasis of woodland is surrounded by flat flood-plains characterised by an abundance of water and irrigated arable land.
The Estate has a museum dedicated to Leonardo Bonzi and an ancient sanctuary called the Sanctuary of Marzale dating from the 16th century.

Marzale Estate

The River Serio makes Marzale an excellent point of attreaction for migratory birds and wildlife.

Marzale Estate

HISTORY

In very early times the area surrounding both Cremona and Crema was the scene of conflict between the two towns over possession of the Isola Fulcheria, the area between the rivers Serio and Adda which until medieval times formed a lake known as the Lago Gerundo. The lake no longer exists, but was famous for the legend of a dragon named Tarantasio, whose favourite diet was small children. The drying out of the lake is said to have been due to various possible causes, including the dragon's defeat by Saint Christopher or by Frederick Barbarossa. Another popular belief is that the dragon was killed by the founder of the Visconti family, who then adopted the snake-like beast, complete with a child in its mouth, as the coat of arms for his family. In reality it is likely that the waters of the lake subsided as a result of drainage, land improvements, geological movement and later the creation of the Muzza canal.

The town of Crema was divided between two factions, the Ghibellini who were supporters of the Visconti family of Milan, and the Guelfi who supported the cause of Venice. From amongst the latter, a man emerged who would become very important in the town's history: Fachino Bonzi, the founder of our family. Fachino knew Venice well, and built up a successful business transporting goods along the Serio, sailing down the Adda and Po rivers and proceeding to the lagoon of San Marco in Venice. He became an important and loyal servant to the Venetian Republic, and in September 1449, following the capture of Crema, the Doge Francisco Foscari granted the Bonzi family the exclusive rights to fish in the Serio River. This fishing right extended to 31 km, from the border of Mozzanica to the outlet of Boccaserio in the Adda, and made the family rich and powerful.

The family house of the Bonzis dates from the year 1685 and is located in the small village of San Michele. It was restored by Count Giiuseppe Ignazio Bonzi in 1870 and passed on to his children, Aldo, Febo, Clito, Enzo, Iro and Ercole.

DESCRIPTION

The Marzale Estate is situated south of Crema, in the province of Cremona.

The property has a surface area of 380 ha, based in four municipalities (Madignano, Ripalta Arpina, Ripalta Cremasca and Ripalta Guerina), and lies within the River Serio Regional Park. The Marquise Emilia Bonzi Dal Pozzo and her son Leonardo, the present-day landowner and manager, believe that they can contribute towards, and achieve, something of great mutual interest to both private and public sectors, and can promise a great future for their flourishing protected area.

The Marzale Estate lies an average of 75 m above sea-level. The property has the typical flat landscape of Lombardy, composed of floodplains. The majority of the land is irrigated by a well-arranged water suply.

On one side of the property, very close to the river, the land is tending to become more and more damaged and indeed lost due to powerful water action. The eternal problem lies in the transition of the fundamental level of the floodplains and the river bed. Without important investment in riverbank work, there is no long term solution. In this area, known as the "costoni", no agricultural cultivations are practised nor are there any plantations.

The same situation is repeated in many parts of the Estate and it has been transformed into a remote but beautiful reserve where wildlife finds a perfect ecosytem and natural habitat.

The presence of the river Serio has contributed on one hand to the formation of flat and flooded parcels of land but, on the other hand, because it has evolved in itself over the decades, the water has generated a very closely connected hydrographical landscape and excellent shelter for migratory birds and for wildlife.

The main buildings were developed into a fine estate, surrounded by gardens and grassland. In the early 20th century, Count Leonardo Bonzi rearranged the buildings and the estate, purchasing land on both sides of the river Serio in the locality of Ripalta Vecchia. Over time, this became the game reserve of the present-day Marzale Estate.

The main house is about 2 km from Marzale Estate. It is a typical large family house based in the middle of the Cremasca countryside. Simple in its entirety and improved by decorative details and adornment from the 17th century, the house today is a warm, welcoming and stately country home.

The other buildings on the estate consist of a typical Lombardy farm with a square courtyard and a central farmyard comprising two hunting lodges, offices for managerial staff, barns, and other facilities. Away from the farm buildings, the keeper's house is located near the cages where wild duck and pheasants are reared.

Special Focus on Conservation and Ecotourism

The income of the estate comes mainly from forestry, crop production and hunting, and provides just enough profit for the estate to be self-sufficient and to survive. Nowadays, however, ecotourism is considered as the main focus point for the Marzale Estate. The owner is considering a plan to lead school groups, tourists and other selected participants into the forest to teach them about nature and wildlife, and from there to organise visits to the well-known Sancturay of Marzale as well as the recently inaugurated "Leonardo Bonzi Museum".

Decorative details of facade, from 17th century.

Marzale Estate

355

C&M Bru

Lake in June covered with Lotus flowers *(Nelumbo nucifera)*.

Their PASSION: Environment, Nature, Agriculture, Forestry and Shooting

How is a shooting and wildlife estate born?

One way of trying to answer this question is to look at what the lawmakers have done. Specifically, a hunting and wildlife estate in Lombardy is only possible where suitable natural and habitat conditions for wild animals exist. The management of such a place must be carried out by a manager who operates within the law and who, rather than simply go hunting, tries constantly to improve the estate.

The exploitation and use of the territory is restricted by regional law, whose aims are to conserve and improve wild animals and flora. In following this aim, the measures that have been put in place in Marzale are:

- Diversity of crops alternating with woodland, poplar groves, fruit trees, vineyards, crops, hedges, fallow land and wetlands, over a minimum area, in this case not less than 20% of the estate's total surface area.
- Presence of crops (sorghum, maize, sunflowers, barley, wheat, etc.) used exclusively for game species, and distributed like a mosaic across the estate.

- During winter season, the estate retains green cover on at least 40% of the area (wetlands, the woodland, poplar groves, orchards, winter cereals, fallow crops, crop stubbles, etc.).
- In the alluvial zones, the presence of reedbeds and areas of perennial shrubs ensure that migratory waterbirds can rest and breed.
- At least 1.8% of the estate's area is set aside to allow a refuge for wildlife and a place for it to develop, and no hunting of any kind is allowed.

Some important considerations, and one question, arise immediately from these measures:

Firstly, an estate which is used for hunting must depend upon agricultural land, and thus is a farm in every respect.

Secondly, the typically fragmented landscape of rural Italy is characterised by an average farm size of 7.5 – 10 hectares. This fragmentation necessarily leads to intensive agriculture, based on high inputs into a low surface area.

Finally, the legal requirements mentioned above must be taken into account.

That said, one must ask whether it is possible to manage such a farm with economically sound

356

criteria and methods, compatible with modern agriculture.

The answer is yes. It is achieved by intelligence, far-sightedness and management capacity, coupled with unquestioned economic effort and sacrifice.

The measures mentioned above are precisely those which, from the 1960s, have led Count Leonardo Bonzi, the Marquise Emilia Bonzi Dal Pozzo and her son Leonardo, and Claudio and Alberto Gaffuri – owners, creators and managers of the present estate – to understand that in order to achieve a turn-round it was necessary to change the priorities. In other words, from agriculture to nature.

Twenty five years later, in 1985, when the River Serio Natural Park was created, the whole of the estate of Marzale was included within it, and it remains to this day one of the most precious natural sites.

As mentioned already, all of this is the result of economic and environmental decisions and choices.

Growing Poplars

Initially, the estate decided to specialise in planting and growing poplars. More than 130 ha are dedicated to poplars, *populus x euroamericana*, clone I-214. This clone is characterized by the lightness of its wood and its white colour, both characteristics being very highly valued in wood working. It took some experimentation before this variety of poplar was proved to be the best for the climatic and soil conditions of this estate.

The production cycle is 9-10 years. We start with poplars of 2 years old and a commercial diameter of 14-17 cm, planted in squares of 6m x 6m, to give a density of 275 plants per hectare. Yield is variable, based on the climatic and soil conditions during the cycle. Generally, we can estimate a loss of 10% due to wind and parasites, and therefore end up with 250 plants per hectare, each weighing 0.7-0.8 tonnes.

The total area dedicated to poplars is organised in rotation, each plot being 10-15 hectares in size. This allows us to cut a good number of poplars every year in the 10 year cycle.

The poplars, whose principal use is in the production of panels rather than paper pulp or chips, are sold "standing", so the estate does not become involved in felling.

Why the poplar?

The importance of poplar is not exclusively economic. Indeed quite the opposite. Wood production on agricultural land reduces the pressure on natural forest, both in Italy and in other countries. It contributes towards improving the benefits to the landscape and environment that have always been priority objectives in forestry. Emilio Sereni, in his book *Storia del Paesaggio Italiano (The History of Italian Landscape)*, indicates that the poplar is a typical element in the flat landscape of the River Po. Wood production implies reducing CO_2 from the atmosphere, responsible for global warming. Planting poplars means using pesticide amounts of between 2 and 15 times less than alternative agricultural crops.

Growing a crop of trees for 10 years or more enriches the land with nutrients, from the leaves which the trees drop each year onto the land and which are then absorbed at depth by the roots. The poplar plantations also benefit hunting in Marzale in other ways. The poplars enable the estate to comply with the legal requirement in terms

The total area dedicated to poplars – clone I-214 – is managed on a 10-year rotation cycle.

Marzale Estate

of both woodland cover and permanent vegetative cover on the land. As a result, in contrast to normal agricultural cropping patterns typical of this district, with crops such as maize, wheat and barley, we never see an empty space. The poplars, in their rotations, alternate with the crops just mentioned, like a mosaic. Wildlife can therefore always find food and shelter during the winter months when other crops are not present. Throughout the year, farming operations and in particular the cleaning of the land are carried out so as to avoid creating large bare spaces devoid of vegetation.

Finally, from the economic point of view, we should note that although the price of a poplar tree was between € 6-7 per quintal (100 kg), standing, in the early 1990s, the price has performed worse than other agricultural commodities in recent years. With respect to the above, unfortunately, it shoud be noted that the European Union's new regulations on rural development for the period 2007-2013 have taken the option of insisting on a period of two years before poplars can be replanted on land from which they had been remove, instead of one. This is the absolute opposite sense of other environmental options adopted, and causes economic hardship for the estate.

Water

Marzale is characterised by the presence of a dense hydrographic network. It is traversed by the Serio river, whose bed and channel have evolved over the centuries, leading to the creation of a system of small pools of water as "morte" or "lanche". These once formed the river bed, which has now moved elsewhere, and they have become exhausted, hidden, and in some cases dried out.

In spite of this, the efforts by Marzale to improve the environment have led to the creation of a network of small channels to irrigate the agricultural land and to supply these pools of water.

Taken as a whole, this constitutes a permanent undivided system of moving water that covers an area, excluding the river, of 11.5 ha.

As well as existing by itself, this system needs to be maintained by human activity, so that the pools do not become buried or completely dried out. These tasks include clearing the pools and channels of mud, logs, branches and grasses, and checking the flow rate and the break-up or collapse of the banks.

This attentive and wise management ensures proper and efficient use of the water for irrigated lands but, above all, it has enabled the fishlife and birdlife to develop and the flora to flourish.

Fish

The river Serio is an excellent habitat to shelter species as the Common Carp *(Cyprinus carpio)*, Tench *(Tinca tinca)*, Northern Pike *(Esox lucius)*, European Eel *(Anguilla anguilla)*, Chub *(Squalius cephalus)*, Common Rudd *(Scardinius erythrophthalmus)*, Pumpkinseed *(Lepomis gibbosus)* and the Channel Catfish *(Ictalurus punctatus)*. The stretch of the river that crosses the estate has been destined a fish restocking area, with the undoubted benefits upstream and downstream of the river.

The Angelo Bruni Angling Association, to whom the Bonzi family has rented the fishing rights since the Second Word War to the present day, works closely with the estate to control, conserve and research the fish stocks.

Aquatic birds

For a long time the presence of aquatic species of birds, migratory, seasonal or annual has constituted a great richness for Marzale. The main species are: Grey Heron *(Ardea cinerea)*, Little Egret *(Egretta garzetta)*, Great Egret *(Egretta alba)*, Black-crowned Night Heron *(Nycticorax nycticorax)*, Little Bittern *(Ixobrychus minutus)*, Cormorant *(Phalacrocorax carbo)*, Mallard *(Anas platyrhynchos)*, Common Teal *(Anas crecca)*, Garganey *(Anas querquedula)*, Gadwall *(Anas strepera)*, European Water Rail *(Rallus aquaticus)*, Common Moorhen *(Gallinula chloropus)*, Common Snipe *(Gallinago gallinago)*, Eurasian Woodcock *(Scolopax rusticola)*, Common

Northern Pike
(Esox lucius).

Marzale has a dense hydrographic network in which there is an important duck-breeding station. Shooting is also offered.

Kingfisher *(Alcedo atthis)*, Litle Grebe *(Tachybaptus ruficollis)*.

Flora

The constant presence of water is the source of a richly developed tree and shrub flora; Within the species present in Marzale, we can highlight: Alder *(Alnus glutinosa)*, Narrow-leafed Ash *(Fraxinus angustifolia)*, Aspen *(Populus tremula)*, Alder Buckthorn *(Frangula alnus)*, Bird Cherry *(Prunus padus)*, European Hackberry *(Celtis australis)*, Cornelian Cherry *(Cornus mas)*, European Cranberrybush *(Viburnum opulus)*, Dogwood *(Cornus sanguinea)*, English Oak *(Quercus robur)*, Wych Elm *(Ulmus campestris)*, European Spindle *(Euonymus europaeus)*, Field Maple *(Acer campestre)*, European Ash *(Fraxinus excelsior)*, Grey Willow *(Salix cinerea)*, Purple Willow *(Salix purpurea)*, Common Hawthorn *(Crataegus monogyna)*, Common Hazel *(Corylus avellana)*, Hornbeam *(Carpinus betulus)*, White Mulberry *(Morus alba)*, Manna Ash *(Fraxinus ornus)*, White Poplar *(Populus canescens)*, Black Poplar *(Populus nigra)*, Oriental Plane *(Platanus orientalis)*, European Privet *(Ligustrum vulgare)*, Rowan *(Sorbus aucuparia)*, and White Willow *(Salix alba)*.

Particular mention should be made of the surface of the lake during the month of June, which is partly with flowers of Lotus *(Nelumbo nucifera)*.

Birds and Mammals

The richness of the existing flora and its integrity over the last fifty years is an object of study by the Serio Natural Park. This has singled out the fact that Marzale is one of three areas in which the vegetation has evolved naturally over this period of time. Periodically, a botanist from the Museum of Natural Sciencies of Milan visits the property to study the flora. The results are published in scientific journals.

Obviously, this type of habitat, with excellent flora, crops and grazing, constitutes a suitable place for the conservation and protection of non-aquatic birds, such as: Hoopoe *(Upupa epops)*, Green Woodpecker *(Picus viridis)*, Great Spotted Woodpecker *(Dendrocopos major)*, European Bee-eater *(Merops apiaster)*, Common Buzzard *(Buteo buteo)*, Peregrine Falcon *(Falco peregrinus)*, Grey Partridge *(Perdix perdix)*, Common Quail *(Coturnix coturnix)*, Common Pheasant *(Phasianus colchicus)*, Wood-Pigeon *(Columba palumbus)*, Eurasian Collared Dove *(Streptopelia decaocto)*, Barn Owl *(Tyto alba)*, Little Owl *(Athene noctua)*, Tawny Owl *(Strix aluco)*, Long-eared Owl *(Asio otus)*, as well as all members of the Passeriformes family.

Amongst the mammals, there are European Hare *(Lepus europaeus)*, Red Fox *(Vulpes vulpes)*, European Badger *(Meles meles)*, and Least Weasel *(Mustela nivalis)*.

Shooting

Hunting in Italy remains a much debated and controversial theme. The estate has never wanted to become lost in futile talk and argument. As far as we are concerned, we have understood for decades what others don´t understand, which is

that hunting is only possible where there is a healthy environment. This once again confirms our efforts and our priorities in maintaining the conservation of nature and the protection of the environment. Hunting is an opportunity granted by the environment itself.

Leonardo Bonzi Museum

Inaugurated on the 4th June 2006, the Leonardo Bonzi Museum is located in San Michele di Ripalta Cremasca and houses a collection of several objects that characterize the life of Leonardo Bonzi (1902-1977), a versatile personality keen on travel and who continuously experienced new adventures. In the Bonzi family's farmstead, the accurate restoration of the small stable building has freed up a large exhibition space - between the ground floor and the balcony along the perimeter. The objects, documents, personal recollections and pictures, tell of an adventurous life. The events follow one another, each leaving a sign: his travels, the sports he played at high level and not only in his youth (alpinism, tennis, bob-sleighing – for which he took part in the first Winter Olympic Games in Chamonix in 1924, carrying the nation's flag), explorations in eastern countries (Afghanistan, Persia, Morocco) and in the far north (Greenland), the war period (his 2000 flying hours, a gold medal at aeronautics, 4 silver medals, a bronze medal, the Iron Cross). The passion for aviation accompanied Bonzi throughout his life and culminated in the famous «Angelo dei Bimbi», a non-stop flight across the Atlantic in a small plane to Buenos Aires in 1948 to raise public awareness for the thousands of mutilated children and war orphans of South America. Bonzi also had a deep passion for the cinema: he became a producer of documentary films: *Lettera dall'Africa*, *Magia Verde*, *Continente Perduto* and *Muraglia Cinese*, and won several prizes at the festivals in Cannes, Berlin, Taormina and Venice.

Marzle Estate

Leonardo Bonzi Museum,
inaugurated on the 4th
of June, 2006.

The museum of Leonardo Bonzi
contains objects, documents,
personal collections,
pictures and stories of his
adventurous life.

Marzle Estate

Sanctuary of Marzale

Several variations of the name Marzale have appeared on historical documents: Marxale, Marzalo, Marzale and Marsale. The place which gives its name to the Sanctuary is certainly very old, and not easy to interpret. The most credible interpretation dates from the early 18th century, when the principal church festival celebrated was that of the Annunication of the Virgin on March 25th. The interior of the church contains a painting of the Annunciation on the remaining wall of the high altar. The second interpretation of the name is that it comes from the old word Sale, referring to the long coastline which begins in Rivoltella on the right bank of the River Serio and ends at the Mar-Sale (salt sea). A third interpretation suggests that it derives from Mark (a Lombardy name meaning "border") and Sale.

The Sanctuary of Santa Maria del Marzale dates from 1041-1046, although the first appearance of the Virgin is said to have occurred some centuries later. The church of Marzale was for very many years the centre of the deep-seated wars between Cremona (imperial, and supporters of the Ghibellini) and Crema (democratic, and allied to the Visconti of Milan).

In 1202 Santa Maria del Marzale acted as the focus of a truce between the two warring parties, which was to last five years. In fact, the truce lasted for eleven years, and led to this sacred building becoming a symbol and shrine in our history, on account of the intervention of the Virgin who is worshipped here, having appeared to console a young shepherdess in her misfortune.

In January 1985, three tombs were uncovered beneath the church floor, dating from the late medieval times (8th/10th centuries AD) but constructed of Roman bricks. Further studies are still in progress.

Recently the "Scala Santa" (Holy Stair) has been restored, which leads from the chapel below to the space adjacent to the church.

G. Janssens

The Santuary of
Santa Maria del Marzale
dates from 1041-1046.

G. Janssens

Crops, poplars and natural forest.

THE FUTURE AND THE CHALLENGES...

For a hunting estate like Marzale this is a strange question. Why? The future and the challenges are always the same. They are as they were on the first day, when the journey began that led us to the present levels and standards of our environment. It is a journey and a challenge that never ends.

It is a love affair with nature itself; one that offers amazing sights. At the same time it is a struggle against the elements of nature that often frustrate our efforts (river floods, tornados, etc ...).

It is a challenge against the imposition of laws, often written hundreds of kilometres away from Marzale and without knowledge of how delicate environments shoud be maneged.

Sometimes, the very institutions which are responsible for the protection of sites like Marzale, such as the Natural Parks, are a challenge. The first phase of park management in Italy has led to the creation of living museums, which are untouchable, and is therefore slowly leading them to degradation instead of improving them and enhancing their value.

Another challenge is the progressive urbanization of the surrounding region, which makes Marzale a green lung on the edge of the town of Crema.

It is a challenge that tries to transmit the culture of protection and respect for the natural environment to the people who visit Marzale, even if just for a walk. Often a lost battle.

OUR PRIORITY IS "NATURE":
CONSERVATION AND PROTECTION OF THE ENVIRONMENT THAT FOR EVERY CITIZEN CONSTITUTES A NON-RENOUNCEABLE DUTY NOW IF WE WANT TO GUARANTEE AND PRESERVE FOR FUTURE GENERATIONS THE RIGHT TO A TOP QUALITY OF LIFE.

In the past, Count Leonardo Bonzi and Claudio Gaffuri succeeded in achieving this.

Today, the Marquise Emilia Bonzi Dal Pozzo, her son Leonardo, and manager Alberto Gaffuri are harvesting the heritage of the past, certain of being able to face the numerous challenges that will always lie ahead and which have so far made Marzale one of the oldest, noblest and most beautiful wildlife estates in Lombardy.

Marzle Estate

MARZALE BELONGS TO:

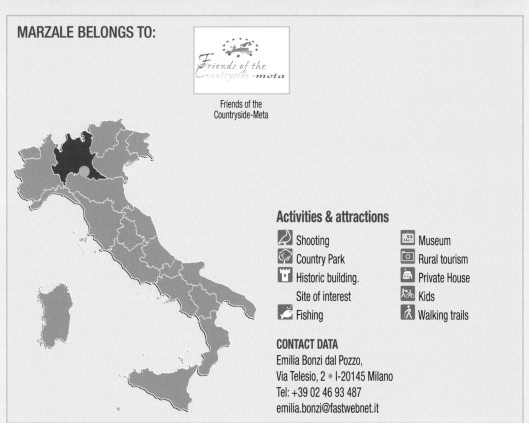

Friends of the
Countryside-Meta

Activities & attractions

- 🦆 Shooting
- 🌳 Country Park
- 🏰 Historic building. Site of interest
- 🐟 Fishing
- 🖼 Museum
- 📷 Rural tourism
- 🏠 Private House
- 🚴 Kids
- 🚶 Walking trails

CONTACT DATA

Emilia Bonzi dal Pozzo,
Via Telesio, 2 • I-20145 Milano
Tel: +39 02 46 93 487
emilia.bonzi@fastwebnet.it

Scy Sanssouci

Atlantic

Location: Communes of Hanois, Province of Namur, Region of Wallonia, Belgium.
Surface: 750 ha.

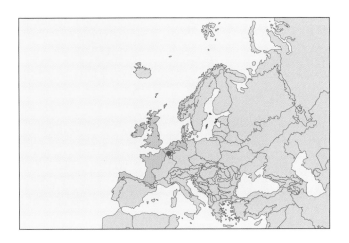

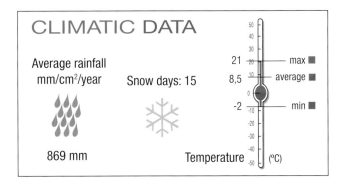

CLIMATIC DATA

Average rainfall
mm/cm²/year

Snow days: 15

21	max ■
8,5	average ■
-2	min ■

869 mm

Temperature (ºC)

SUMMARY

Scy Sanssouci is a large estate composed of different types of both coniferous and hardwood forest, arable land and grassland, ponds and marshes, which all combine together in one whole. Its achievements are remarkable, for biodiversity is at the forefront of management, and it can rightly be regarded as a point of reference. The property extends to 750 hectares which are divided as follows: 430 hectares of woodland, 300 hectares of arable land, 10 hectares of wetlands and ponds, and 10 hectares of park.

Scy Sanssouci Estate

The plans for the castle were guided by a desire to integrate the building into the parkland.

Scy Sanssouci (Belgium)

Count Charles Cornet d'Elzius (1922-2006).

HISTORY

An ancient property of the Dukes of Bourgogne and the Kings of Spain, the Scy Estate was sold in 1671 by Charles, King of Castile. It was sold again in 1767 by the Counts of Beaufort-Spontin, to the Viscount de Propper and subsequently transferred through inheritance or donation down to the present owner. A remarkable fact is that, in 1940, Count Ludovic d'Espiennes, having no descendants and concerned about the future of his estate at Scy, adopted the three sons of Count Cornet d'Elzius, his neighbour at Saint-Fontaine.

As the family estate of Saint-Fontaine passed to the eldest son, Scy was left to the younger son, Count Cornet d'Elzius. Despite a political career spanning more than 40 years, both at local level, as major of Scy and the town of Ciney, and in the Belgian parliament, as deputy, senator and minister, Count Cornet d'Elzius's imprint upon the management of Scy from 1950 until 2006 is unmistakeable. An experienced forester, he anticipated the risks in the estate's profitability by diversifying the forestry, planting the poorer land with species that were faster-growing, such as Douglas fir, which very soon came to prove itself as the species best adapted to the Famenne region. He continued his predecessors' policy of acquiring land and in 2002 left, to his daughter Elisabeth and her three children, one of the largest estates of the Condroz region. A rare thing in a country which applies the Napoleonic Code, and where the law of primogeniture is unknown, is the fact that the estate of Scy, which has doubled in size since 1767, has known neither division nor break-up except for the inevitable compulsory sales for public utilities or the sale of the occasional building plot.

View from the house.

soucci Estate

The castle of Scy Sanssouci built in 1993.

DESCRIPTION

The property consists of 750 hectares which are divided as follows: 430 hectares of woodland, 300 hectares of arable land, 10 hectares of wetlands and ponds, and 10 hectares of park.

The area is characterized by relatively cool, wet summers and mild, rainy winters. There are, however, some notable exceptions, which are not without their effect on the woodland because of its long age cycle. For example, the exceptional droughts of 1921, 1947 and 1976, or even the tornado of 1963 and the storms of 1984, 1990 and 2007 caused considerable damage from wind-blow in the woods.

The dominant winds come from the southwest. The average wind speed is between 2 and 4 m/s. The maximum wind speed exceeds 30 m/s. The air mass brought in is mild and moist when the wind blows from a southerly or westerly direc-

Scy Sansoucci Estate

The castle and park in 1860.

Scy Sanssouci (Belgium)

tion, unstable and cool between west and north, and more or less dry but cold from north to south, which moderates the formation of layers of mist and moist air in winter.

The landscape of the region of Condroz, in which the property lies, is formed by the hills of the Upper Famennien (limestones, nodulous schists) alternating with the schistous depressions of the Lower Famennien. In general, the depressions are in grassland, and the plateau is in arable cropping; the woodland covers the slopes and the edges of the plateau adjacent. Scy Sanssouci Estate is located at a height of between 280 and 320 metres above sea-level. The soils are silty and sandy-silty, slightly acid (pH between 4.2 and 7), and capable of filtration and leaching. As far as water and hydrology are concerned, the estate does not have a river of any importance, but some springs, streams and wetlands are present at the bottom of small valleys. The river Bocq, an important collecting point for

water supplied to the Brussels area, has its source in the park at Scy. Some ponds and wetlands have been developed or restored for recreational fishing and wildlife.

The landscape of Condroz is formed by the alternation of wooded and agricultural plateaus (with crops), ribbed by small valleys with wooded slopes and grassland in the valley floor.

The forest consists of a mix of hardwood stands of diverse ages, with diverse species to suit the purposes of landscape, ecology and shooting, and coniferous blocks of equal age whose purpose is essentially commercial but which are managed as high forest, a policy which benefits both flora and fauna. Where the slopes are important features of the landscape, straight lines and right angles are avoided. The restoration of the woodland edge in the case of the current coniferous blocks is done progressively, as and when new plantings or regeneration is carried out.

Farm renovated in 2005 and converted into dwellings and estate offices.

The Castle and surrounding buildings

Designed in 1992 by the architect Emmanuel de Callataÿ, the plans for the castle were guided by a desire to integrate the building into the parkland setting by giving the impression that the park was laid out to emphasise the building and to give the landscape greater depth for the enjoyment of its owners. An expert and a lover of antiquarian books, Eric Speeckaert has put together a library of his collection of works and engravings on the history and architecture of the gardens, the farming and forestry.

Conscious of the importance of diversifying sources of income on the estate, the owners have implemented a policy of residential letting by acquiring and refurbishing property, amongst which are three sets of farm buildings that were no longer in use. Two have been modernised and were converted into dwellings in 2000 and 2005. The buildings opposite the castle contain the estate office and three lodgings. The granary was transformed in 2004 into a reception hall for shooting parties, family celebrations and social and cultural events. The buildings on the third farm, where the agricultural activity has been taken back by the owners, are undergoing renovation.

Park

"...the gardener is called the goldsmith of the earth: because the gardener surpasses the simple farm labourer as much as the goldsmith the common blacksmith..."

Olivier de Serres, *the theatre of agriculture and mesnage of the fields*, 1600.

Olivier des Serres' book is a work of great importance, and the parkland at Scy is a practical application of this, in its evolution towards a living "landscape".

The aim of the landscape architect Benoît Fondu is to re-dynamise the park by achieving the best possible harmony with the surrounding countryside without harmful visual effect for the village of Scy, and a wish to bring an intimate link between *"this nature made art"* and its environment. It is what was called, in bygone days, *"la coulée"* (a single casting) – with grassland space acting as the mould – an "agricultural and scenic" park; at the same time both beautiful and productive. A very simple way of linking the useful to the enjoyable.

Scy Sansouci Estate

The principal characteristic of this type of park, such as here at Scy, is the desire for an intelligent cohabitation between, on the one hand, conservation (a orchard), research (Scy will soon have its own geographic arboretum of conifers), and a large pleasant open space in which are scattered a few follies inspirited from the 18th century and specimens of rare trees in the immediate vicinity of the castle. All this is achieved by respecting the surrounding countryside and in perfect harmony with the rural appearance of the village. The apparent simplicity of the composition, however, requires time, research and very detailed work in modelling the ground and choosing the specimens, so that all these efforts appear, from afar, to have vanished into the natural surroundings which were once grazing land for livestock.

One of the sources of the River Bocq flowing out of the park at Scy.

Eric Speeckaert
and Léon Wauthoz.

Scy Sansouci Estate

LAND MANAGEMENT

Sylviculture

By surface area, forestry is the main source of income for the estate. It retains the full attention of the owners, who devote themselves to it with a passion and who perpetuate the economic policy implemented in 1950 whilst at the same time adapting it to the current objectives of ecology and sustainable development.

The first move achieved after the death of Count Cornet d'Elzius was the award of PEFC certification (Programme for the Endorsement of Forest Certification schemes) in 2006. The project established within this framework has allowed the owners to reflect on the future management of their forest capital with a view to improving it by taking into account the forest's multiple functions.

With the collaboration of engineer Leon Wauthoz, a former director of the Department of Nature and Forests of the Walloon region, a management plan has been prepared.

DIAGRAM OF THE WOODLAND LAYOUT

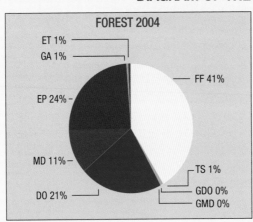

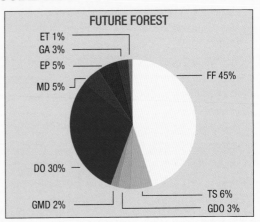

Domaine SCY						
			Forest (2004)		**Future Forest**	
Surface (ha)			425		425	
Distribution	Forest	Abbreviation	Percentage %	Surface ha	Percentage %	Surface ha
HARDWOODS	High forest	FF	41%	174,25	45%	191,25
56%	Scrubland	TS	1%	4,25	6%	25,5
	Group of Douglas	GDO		0	3%	12,75
	Group of Larchs and others	GMD		0	2%	8,5
SOFTWOODS	Douglas	DO	21%	89,25	30%	127,5
40%	Larch	MD	11%	46,75	5%	21,25
	Spruce	EP	24%	102	5%	21,25
AUTRES	Pasture	GA	1%	4,25	3%	12,75
4%	Wetlands	ET	1%	4,25	1%	4,25
Total			100%	425	100%	425

Timber production

The principal aim is to produce quality timber from the various different species.

The purpose of the renewal programme is considered from a long-term perspective, and implies a study of the future composition of the forest in equilibrium with the environment, and the cost of periodic renewal programmes in light of current knowledge of forestry economics. In applying the programme, one must always bear in mind the current make-up of the forest and the sylvicultural management to which the plantations have been subjected.

The density of the current softwood plantations is quite high, the corollary of which is that the trees are of smaller than average girth and consequently have a higher felling age. Their management today is more dynamic and has the effect of considerably lowering the age at which they can be exploited at the equivalent girth stage.

According to studies by Léon Wauthoz, controlling the density and radial growth of the plantations is an essential component of the profitability of the estate. It can increase the average profitability of one hectare of softwood by 25%.

Overall management is directed towards a mixed forest where hardwood stands are dominant (approximately 50% of the total forest area), treated as coppice and high forest, diversified and of multiple age. Coppice will cover approximately 10% of the entire space, in order to help meet the demand for wood from the rural population, for nutritional and shelter requirements of the wildlife, and to encourage natural regeneration (oak, ash, wild cherry and maple). This treatment meets all the ecological interests defined by the Walloon region simultaneously.

In the hardwood areas, some dead trees are preserved, along with other distinguished specimens which do not present any environmental risk. Care is taken in maintaining those supporting species which promote biodiversity (elder, rowan, birch, hornbeam, aspen, etc). However, attention must always be paid to how these species interact in terms of plant health.

For the softwoods, the aim is to achieve regular plantations covering approximately 46% of the total area and consisting of mixed stands [of Douglas fir and spruce] and of pure stands of Douglas and/or larch, on the sandy-loamy grounds of the plateaus. Management of the mixed stands will favour the best Douglas.

The transition of the current forest to the future forest is progressive and any brutal intervention is out of the question.

Obtaining a balanced structure of the age groups is essential in conserving the heritage and developing it in a sustainable form. Costs associated with renewal should be as regular as possible.

When preparing the scheme, if the average life of hardwood species is about 100 years, it is advisable to regenerate 1 percent of the total forest every year. Softwoods being divided into 8 cuts, with the cuts being 8 years apart, renewal is an average of 8% of the total area planted.

Priority is given to natural regeneration whenever the seed-bearing trees are of sufficient number and quality.

For the sake of completeness, attention should be drawn to ten hectares of arable land which have been converted into forestry and rented for the production of Nordmann Fir Christmas trees.

Sales of standing timber are arranged by tender and are organised twice a year (October and December) by the Socofor, an owners cooperative. Dependent on the state of the economy, the crowns are either sold along with the bark or are given to local woodcutters and to the people working on the estate as well as to the inhabitants of the village, to whom coppice wood is offered as a

Scy Sanssouci (Belgium)

Wet area restored in 1996.

Scy Sanssouci Estate

priority. Average sales each year amount to 4000m³ or 10m³ per hectare.

Ecological Objectives

The concerns of "nature-friendly forestry practices" preached by the European movement *Pro Silva* is broadly applied here. The goal is to increase profitability whilst reducing costs, by minimum intervention in plantation work, weeding and thinning. The result is diversified forestry of different species and structure which leads to better resistance to risks posed by climate, health and game damage. This choice of forestry management also addresses the risks presented by the state of the economy, and the fashion and taste in the conversion of the timber from these plantations. The contribution made by this type of

forestry management to protection measures for soil and water should not be overlooked.

Environmental aims

Since 1995, the Walloon Foundation for Habitat Conservation has collaborated with Scy Estate essentially to conserve natural and semi-natural areas, which include many wetlands. The area surrounding the source of the river Bocq deserves special attention. The property is managed according to the principles of reasonable or "wise use", recommended by all the international nature conservation authorities, and aims to avoid degradation or exhaustion of vital natural resources, such as soil and water, fauna and flora. Scy Estate is thus part of the vast movement safeguarding the resources of our planet.

The principal objective of the Walloon Foundation for Habitat Conservation, founded in 1993, is to conserve and restore natural and semi-natural habitats in Wallonia in private ownership (an exactly similar foundation exists for Flanders). By the end of 2008 the Foundation was collaborating with some twenty landowners, covering a total of over 6,400 hectares of private land in Wallonia.

Scy Sanssouci is a large estate composed of different types of both coniferous and hardwood forest, arable land and grassland, ponds and marshes, which all combine together in one whole. Its achievements are remarkable, for biodiversity is at the forefront of management, and it can rightly be regarded as a point of reference for the Foundation by virtue of the aims which it pursues.

To achieve this result, the understanding and collaboration of all who occupy the area, primarily the owners, but also the tenants and managers, whether they be foresters, farmers, hunters, fishermen, hikers or naturalists, is essential. It is in this spirit that

the owners and managers of Scy Estate have subscribed to an agreement on signposting, which authorises public access, subject to a code of behaviour which safeguards its biological potential and respects the rights of the owner.

To encourage others to follow the example of Scy Sanssouci, the Foundation for Habitat Conservation awards an important environmental prize every year, thanks to the patronage of the Inbev-Baillet Latour Fund. About fifteen owners have seen their efforts rewarded in this way.

Finally, Scy Sanssouci is still characterized by its built heritage; the castle and its outbuildings integrated into the landscape of Condroz provides added value. The happy marriage between nature and culture provides the original feature and the richness of the landscapes of Europe.

Baron Edgar Kesteloot
Chairman of the Foundation

EDUCATION AND TRAINING

In collaboration with the owner, who has placed the estate at its disposal, the Walloon Foundation for Habitat Conservation offers, on request from FOREM (the Walloon Public Service for Employment and Training), a training programme on sustainable management for foresters in Wallonia who wish to practice in Flanders. Practical hands-on training on the ground in studying and exploiting Douglas fir are available with the Royal Forestry Society of Belgium.

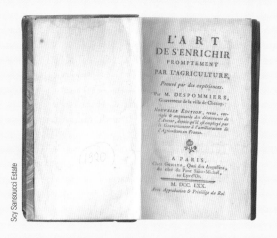

Reproduction of the book, *L'art de s'enrichir, promptement par l'Agriculture*, 1770.

Research

In 2009, an arboretum specialising in coniferous forestry species will be set up.

Library

Forming the most important private collection in Belgium in the field of the history and architecture of gardens of the 18th and 19th centuries, the old books and iconographic documents which constitute it are the object of consultation by researchers or are loaned for exhibitions. Two other sectors are just as developed: forestry and agriculture.

Agriculture

Composed of many small to medium-sized family farms rented from the Estate, local farming practices have changed profoundly with the general developments in the agricultural world since 1960. The progressive disappearance of farms of less than 50 hectares and the younger generation's choice for less constraining professions have enabled the owners to gradually take land back in hand and to cultivate themselves.

The owners have nevertheless always been concerned to pass on tenancies only to direct descendants of farmers whose relation to the Scy estate goes back several generations. Their presence maintains the rural character and life of the village, in which there is no longer any other activity. At the present time, of the 300 hectares of arable and grassland owned by the estate, 150 are managed by the owner who has the status of farmer and is helped in her management by a company called Agriland. The remaining 150 hectares are rented to 7 farmers in individual plots ranging from 5 to 60 hectares.

Looking at the long term, the owners also maintain a policy of acquiring vacant or tenanted arable land in the locality.

The surface area farmed is about 150 ha, including 100 ha under plough and the remainder in grassland. The part under plough consists of equal areas of 3 crops (rape, wheat and winter barley) and approximately 8% in agri-environmental schemes.

The potential yield on the arable land is 35 quintals (3.5 t/ha) from rape, and 80 or perhaps 85 quintals (8.0-8.5 t/ha) from cereals (according to rainfall). The roles played by Agriland SA are many, and are to help the owner in managing her farm:

- 1) **Technical Support:** rotation, varieties, soil improvement, treatments, plant health
- 2) **Management:** implementing policy for purchase of inputs and sale of outputs in the owner's interest.
- 3) Following the crop throughout the season, from sowing to harvest.
- 4) Relationships with the different ministries in dealing with the formalities of CAP and agri-environmental measures.

The library at Scy Sanssouci.

■ **5)** Advising on, and implementing, sustainable management practices.

Agriland also helps to bring value to the grassland area by selling uncut forage each year to local farmers.

Part of the farmland is subject to agri-environmental schemes. These are:

■ **1)** Grass headlands around crops.
■ **2)** Wildflower strips between plots.
■ **3)** Natural grassland.
■ **4)** Wet areas.

The various farming operations are carried out by a local contractor, with whom the estate has worked for several years and thus benefit from his knowledge of the land.

Employment

The owners have always tried to make an indirect contribution to regional employment.

They have a general policy of subcontracting for farm work, gardening and forestry. This option allows effective control of wages and salary costs as the needs arise over the course of the year.

■ **Forestry:** a forestry engineer (establishing the annual felling plan and plantation work); a technician (marking the trees, monitoring the plantations and carrying out the felling). Labour and local companies for the planta-

tions and maintenance work (thinning, pruning, game protection, roads and tracks…).
■ **Agriculture:** a cropmaster and farm contract work (ground preparation, sowing and harvests).Property: two architects and a technician for small repairs and maintenance work.
■ **Park and gardens:** landscape architect and two companies for groundwork, plantations and maintenance.

Shooting

Up until 1960, by virtue of its biotope and its contours, the Condroz region used to offer superb shooting and was renowned for its pheasants, a situation which a handful of owners are courageously trying to maintain. The rabbit, once abundant, has entirely disappeared. Only the hare remains, but it is not hunted. Count Charles Cornet d'Elzius, as passionate about hunting in Europe as he was about hunting in Africa, concentrated his efforts on large game species, in particular wild boar, whose numbers have risen in Condroz since the 1980's. Stands of larch were planted in order that numbers of roe-deer could recover. From 2000, woodland stags have made their appearance, coming in from the large royal estate of Ciergnon, which is situated about 12 kilometres away. An estimated 20 red deer, including – since 2008 – some hinds, now roam the 4000 hectares principally made up by the private hunting estates of Jannée, Scy, Castelalne and Ramezée. In dialogue with the shoot owners and representatives of the Department of Nature & Forests, the Famenne-Condroz Shooting Council determines a legal plan for stag shooting, whose purpose is to increase the age of the stags and the quality of the trophies whilts maintaining a population of reasonable numbers. Each individual owner organises plans for shooting roe-deer and wild boar on their own land, in order to limit the damage to wood and crops. At Scy, the average number of animals shot each year is 1 to 2 stags, 20 roe-deer, 40 wild boars and 10 foxes, over an area of 1200 hectares including 600 ha of woods.

The estate is criss-crossed by many roads, and one major highway in particular records a continuously high number of accidents, some of them fatal, when large game crosses. A clear open margin no less than 25m wide is maintained or created along the public highways, which allows the ani-

Elisabeth Speeckaert and Etienne Streel, manager of Agriland and responsible for crops at Scy.

Scy Sanssouci Estate

mals to be seen more easily and at the same time diminishes the risk of trees falling across the public road in storms.

The many ponds, wetlands and artificial lakes offer a perfect habitat for wild ducks which are shot in September and October. Since 2007, the Walloon Region has authorised the shooting of Canada Geese *(Branta canadensis)* of which there is an excessive population.

Future

The future will depend on the choice made by the three children of the current owner. To continue, together or individually, a 240 year history of uninterrupted family transfer. Globalisation, professional mobility, social and family instabilities are some of the many inevitable risks that have been added to human pressures and to actions taken by the state on behalf of nature. Each generation has known wars, crises and conflicts that it has been able to surmount by the will to conserve a privileged place, charged with history, and by a concern to manage an economic heritage "as a good father should", adapting to the political, social and economic evolution of the world.

Winston Churchill said:

"A pessimist sees the difficulty in every opportunity; an optimist sees the opportunity in every difficulty".

Scy Sanssouci Estate

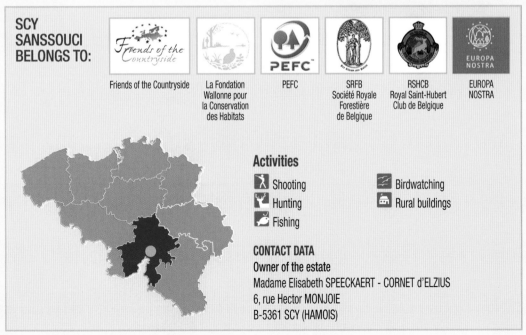

Widening the Gauderies valley and wetlands. This work, completed between 2006 and 2007, has allowed the Black Stork to return and nest.

SCY SANSSOUCI BELONGS TO:

Friends of the Countryside | La Fondation Wallonne pour la Conservation des Habitats | PEFC | SRFB Société Royale Forestière de Belgique | RSHCB Royal Saint-Hubert Club de Belgique | EUROPA NOSTRA

Activities

- Shooting
- Hunting
- Fishing
- Birdwatching
- Rural buildings

CONTACT DATA

Owner of the estate

Madame Elisabeth SPEECKAERT - CORNET d'ELZIUS

6, rue Hector MONJOIE

B-5361 SCY (HAMOIS)

Žďár Kinský

Continental

Location: Žďár nad Sázavou district, province of Highland region-Vysočina, Bohemian-Moravian Highlands region, Czech Republic.
Surface: 6,846 ha.

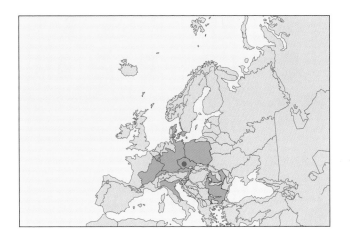

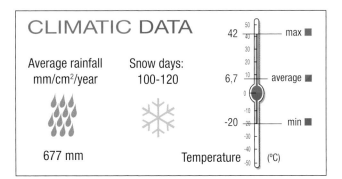

CLIMATIC DATA

Average rainfall
mm/cm²/year

Snow days:
100-120

677 mm

Temperature (°C)

42 — max
6,7 — average
-20 — min

SUMMARY

Žďár Kinský is situated on the borders of Bohemia and Moravia in a picturesque region of the Bohemian-Moravian Highlands, in the centre of the protected landscape area of Žďárske vrchy. The estate has a surface area of 6,846 ha.
Its history is closely associated with the development of the Cistercian monastery in Žďár and dates back to the second half of the 13th century.
The pilgrimage church of St. John of Nepomuk on Green Hill is the greatest achievement of the architect Jan Santini-Aichl and a unique architectural monument, which was included as a UNESCO Word Heritage site in December 1994. This family estate was nationalised in 1948 after the Prague Coup. At end 1992 it was restituted to its lawful owner, MVDr Radslav Kinský. On February 1st, 1993 the castle, forests, agricultural land, fish ponds, administrative and farm buildings were integrated back into a consistent estate which started its economic activities.

Žďár Estate

Žďár Kinský is situated on the borders of Bohemia and Moravia.

Ždár Kinský **(Czech Republic)**

Facade of the Abbot's Winter
Residence, by Santini-Aichl.

HISTORY

The tumultuous history of Ždár Abbey is closely linked to European history. The Abbey was a belated offshoot of the great monastery building wave which had been sweeping across Europe from Citeaux (France). The Cistercian monks who founded it in 1252 on territory donated by a local nobleman were, true to their calling, looking for a "wilderness" where they could bring Christian civilization through prayer and work ("Ora et Labora"). They certainly found it: primeval forests, swamps, peat bogs and a harsh climate almost defeated them, as related in the contemporary chronicle "cronica domus sarensis". It suffered grievously from the Religious Wars: it was burnt down by the Hussites in 1423. A few years later, it was restored and the estate enlarged under King George of Poděbrad, when the 200 ha Dářško lake was reclaimed from a swamp forest (one of the largest lakes in the country). During the devastating Thirty Years War (1618-1648), the monastery fell again on hard times. It is reputed to have been saved from the Swedish army by the monks first enticing the host into the bogs and then beating them down to their watery death with clubs, not a particularly Christian behaviour, but perhaps justified self defence. Meanwhile the nearby town of Ždár grew and was granted full city rights.

After passing through various hands, the monastery had the great fortune to elect a particularly able and energetic Abbot, Vaclav Vejmluva, in 1705, when the Counter-Reformation movement was in full swing. Vejmluva restored the economic status of the estate through enlightened management, rebuilt and enlarged the dilapidated church and buildings, founded an academy for young noblemen, kept off the plague by sanitary measures, so that the skull shaped cemetery he had specially built for plague victims remained unused. But his greatest claim to fame is to have entrusted all this rebuilding to Jan Blažej Santini-Aichl (1677-1723), a brilliant Prague born architect of Italian descent. Santini developed a Baroque style of his own, combining the spiritual inspirations of the Gothic and the Baroque ages. Moreover, Vejmluva commissioned him to build an entirely new church, on the hill dominating the monastery pond, dedicated to a Czech priest, John of Nepomuk, whose beatification was then being considered in Rome. His name reflected the Cistercian Abbey he had originally come from, the very same one from which, almost 200 years before his death, the Ždár founding fathers themselves had come, so that this choice of patron seemed particularly apt. The church, Santini's chef d'oeuvre, consecrated in 1722, has been on the UNESCO World Cultural Heritage Sites list since 1994 and is a main tourist attraction. Unfortunately, the

Typical baroque window design
in the Abbey, by Santini-Aichl.

378

Abbey suffered yet another devastating fire and Vejmluva died shortly afterwards, in 1738, maybe from despair at seeing his work destroyed.

The monastery never recovered and was finally closed down by Emperor Joseph II in 1784; it was at first run under the "religious fund" set up to manage former monastery estates so as to finance the social work that they had been supposed to carry out: schools, hospitals and charity. In 1826, the Ždár estate was auctioned. It was bought by Count Vratislav of Mtrovice, as a dowry for his granddaughter, who married a Prince Dietrichstein. In the meantime, the Napoleonic wars had also left their traces: the abbot's summer house drawing room, the "salon français", shows frescoes from a French professional decorator from Napoleon's army (a straggler or a prisoner?) – Bernadotte is even reputed to have spent a night here on his march down to Austerlitz. Throughout the 19th century, the estate was run as a commercial concern, a brewery and iron works set up in the monastery buildings; the Abbey church remained in use, but the St John church was shut down, and even used as a barn, until the parish priest obtained its rehabilitation on the condition that the space between the church itself and its cloister wall served as a cemetery – which is still in use and does not add to the beauty of the place... The estate was handed down to one of the Dietrichstein daughters Clothilde, who set up two institutions which are active to this day within the Abbey precincts: a primary school and a voluntary fire brigade, and finally came into the Kinský family, the present owners, through Eleonore Clam-Gallas, a great-niece of Clothilde's and Count Kinský's wife, in 1930. The estate had by then been greatly reduced by the 1919 land reform carried out by the first Czechoslovak Republic. The Kinský family restored the buildings and resided there two or three times a year, for the deer and stag shoots, and skiing in the winter.

The events leading to World War II also touched on Ždár: Count Kinský and his wife were openly opposed to the Nazi-sponsored so-called Sudeten movement. In 1938, Lord Runciman was sent by the British Government to "investigate" the true situation in Czechoslovakia and was entirely taken in hand by the German-inclined side of the nobility of the country. President Benès asked Count Kinský to invite Lord Runciman and get him to meet the Czech-inclined nobility, so he could hear the other side of the story. As witnessed by the Runciman and other signatures in the family guest book, which miraculously survived both the Nazi and the communist regimes, this was done in Ždár on August 5th to 7th, unfortunately to no avail: Lord Runciman had already chosen sides and the Munich Treaty followed on September 30th. Count Kinský instigated two "Declarations" of Czech noble families, to state their opposition to the partition of the country and their fidelity to the Czechoslovak Republic, the first one presented to President Bénès, and the second to President Hacha who succeeded him in November 1938. The signatories had to pay heavily for their action: two were shot, others were deported and all had their property directly put under Nazi management, the Kinský s being lucky to undergo only the last. They were forbidden access to their Ždár estates entirely and could only reside in the Bohemian family estate, in Chlumec nad Cidlinou, also run by German management. The end of the war saw fierce fighting in the Ždár district, the town suffered bombing and civil casualties. The local "partisan" groups, who had been hiding in the estate woods, seem to have mainly been active in "liberating" the local distillery and plundering it. The Red

Zelena Hora chapel.

Army ran a military hospital in the house, and although they did not remain there long, they rendered the premises impossible to live in. The family, who had regained possession upon the Nazi defeat, moved into the summer house by the pond. The whole place had been ransacked, pieces of antique furniture were floating on the lake and broken china littered the woods. Count Kinský was named Citizen of Honour by the Žďár town council on July 14th (his birthday) 1947 in recognition of his active opposition to the Nazi regime. This family come-back did not last long: the Communist coup of February 1948 put the property under state management and sent Count Kinský and his wife into exile. The estate was officially nationalized on April 9th 1953 and dismembered into various state administrations.

The estate was claimed by and handed back to Count Kinský's son Radslav in 1992, under the Czech restitution law passed by the Czech parliament after the Velvet Revolution of 1989. The re-unified estate has been run since as a whole, first by Count Radslav until his death in 2008 and now by his sons. President Vaclav Havel visited it on March 7th 1996, to celebrate the revitalization of one of the leading Czech private estates.

DESCRIPTION

The Žďár estate lies on the Bohemian and Moravian frontier, half-way from Prague to Vienna and truly in Central Europe: four rivers spring from the estate, two of which flow west towards the Elbe and two east towards the Danube. Most of the estate lies at an altitude of about 600 m, varying between 500 m (river beds) and 810 m (Žakova Hora National Natural Reserve), in continental climate conditions.

The estate covers approximately 6,800 ha, of which 5,775 ha are forest, 750 ha are fish ponds and 200 ha are farmland, together with a European virgin forest (39 ha) and other natural reserves (680 ha in total, of which the first two were created by the current owners' grandparents in 1929) as well as a unique complex of Gothic-Baroque monastic architecture by Santini-Aichl (1677-1723). The estate falls entirely under various protection regimes for forests, ponds and land (national natural reserves, Natura 2000, water reserves, soil protection) or real estate (National Monument, Unesco World Heritage Site).

The long-term sustainable forestry plan aims to promote natural re-growth in the Norway Spruce stands (83% of area) and re-introduce indigenous species (beech and fir mostly) to increase bio-diversity, improve soil quality and stabilize the stands. Special care is taken to protect water sources supplying both drinking water and numerous fish ponds.

Wildlife is relatively abundant with Red Deer *(Cervus elaphus),* Roe Deer *(Capreolus capreolus),* Wild Boar *(Sus scrofa),* Hare *(Lepus europaeus),* ducks and migratory birds including rarer species

Four rivers spring from the estate, two of which flow west towards the Elbe and two east towards the Danube.

Žďár Estate

such as the Black Stork *(Ciconia nigra)* (Natura 2000). The fish farm produces Carp *(Cyprinus carpio)*, Pike *(Esox lucius)*, Perch *(Perca fluviatus)*, Zander *(Sander lucioperca)*, American Trout *(Micropterus salmoides)* and Coregone *(Coregonus lavaretus)*. A special carp hybrid was developed from crossing the local carp with a Siberian species, presenting a high resistance to the rough local climate. The estate is in the national genetic database as a source of seeds for Norway spruce, beech and fir tree as well as for its local and hybrid carp, a testimony to the natural vitality of the region.

Geomorphologic situation

The estate lies mostly on the older disrupted fold mountains of the "Czech Massif", with the lower parts around the Velké Dářko pond (208 ha) on pre-Neocene sediments. The lay of the land is characterized by slightly undulating shapes with flat ridges, rock outcrops, extensive plateaux and deep, wide valleys.

Organisational structure of Kinský Žďár a.s

When Dr. Radslav Kinský (1928-2008) received back the family's scattered forests, arable land, fish ponds and the largely derelict monastery buildings, he reintegrated them into one entity and, on February 1st 1993 he re-launched activities. The company now is a joint stock family company with five business lines: forestry, agriculture and fish farming, retail department store, real estate management and support functions, with 85 permanent employees.

Forestry

Natural conditions are favourable to forestry, with good soil conditions, 677 mm of rain per year and annual growth rates in the 5-7% range for spruce. Following generations of spruce-based production of charcoal for the local steel mills and glass manufacture between the 17th and 19th centuries, forestry planning under family management progressed in the 1920s towards a delicate balance between the fragile health condition of the forest stands, uncertain economic conditions, the long term perspective of the forest owners as well as the requirements progressively imposed by forestry regulations.

A testimony to this is the establishment of the first two private Nature Reserves in the country by the current owners' grandparents in 1929.

The dominance of Norway Spruce *(Picea abies)*, a severely unbalanced age structure and the high damages due to years of red deer overpopulation are the three main challenges facing forestry management.

Species composition and forest stands yields

Softwood accounts for 91% of the area or 97% by volume, with Norway Spruce prevailing (83% of area), followed by European Beech *(Fagus sylvatica)* (5%), Scots Pine *(Pinus sylvestris)* (4%), Common Larch *(Larix decidua)* (3%), Silver Fir *(Abies alba)* (2%), Black Alder *(Alnus glutinosa)* (1%) and Sycamore Maple *(Acer pseudoplatanus)* (1%).

The absolute yield for spruce is 29.6 with annual growth yields regularly above 5%, providing high quality wood-when not damaged by red deer and associated rot. 70% of stands were damaged by an over-population of red deer between the 1950s and the 1980s. European Beech has an absolute yield of 26.4.

The target is to slowly increase beech and fir at the expense of spruce, where soil and stands permit.

The estate's countryside integrates forests, ponds and fields in a highly diversified mix.

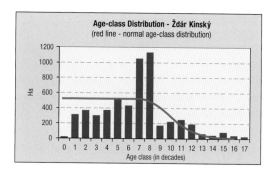

Age-class Distribution - Žďár Kinský
(red line - normal age-class distribution)

The most abundant species in the forest of Žďár is the norway spruce, followed by beech, scots pine, common larch, silver fir, black alder and sycamore maple.

Žďár Estate

Age class structure

In the winter of 1930, the region suffered extensive and severe snow damages, resulting in stands approaching maturity that are twice above normal levels.

Due to the age structure, wind and snow-breakage amount to 30% of average annual production, such as in 2006 (over 41,000 m³, almost one year of production), 2007 with the Kiril storm (22,000 m³), or in 2008 with the Emma and Ivan storms (22,000 m³).

Recent developments in forestry management

The focus is on regenerating age classes 5-7 in spruce and on reinforcing bio-diversity with the introduction of soil-improving and reinforcing species, mainly beech and fir. Cutting has been accelerated since 1993 in the weaker stands while the next plan (2010-2019) will slow down slightly, thus redressing the age structure progressively. With timber prices fluctuating wildly across central Europe since the 2006 storms, great attention is paid to forest care, with more interventions in young or poor stands and reduced cutting in the high quality stands. Each forester has an average of 800 ha under management, a reasonable ratio to ensure close monitoring of stands. A target of 1,000 ha maximum per forester will be progressively reached within the next ten years.

Apart from windfall clearings, only sheltered-clearing is used in plots of less than 1/2 ha. The rotation of old stands is lengthened to 110 years, opening the stands slowly to promote natural re-growth underneath, achieving 50 to 75% natural re-growth in spruce stands. Thus when the old stands are finally cleared, there is a 20-30 years old sub-stand already in place. This reduces the net rotation of the forest to 80 years, while promoting natural re-growth and future stand stability against windfalls. The average stand density is therefore high at 9.60, with two to four storeys in each stand.

With climatic change – less precipitation with higher fluctuations, more days with tropical temperatures – signs of stress are appearing, with increased yellowing and drying-out of spruce, most probably from the combination of climate change, acid-rain induced soil-poisoning from the 1950s to 1990s and the continuous threat of engraver beetles – a persistent and highly menacing local pest.

Bio-diversity target species

Target species – mostly spruce, beech and silver fir – are determined plot by plot in the forestry plan, sometimes by less than 1/2 ha sections. It is a delicate balance between the natural optimum based on detailed soil analysis, the production possibilities of particular species on different sites and the goals of reinforcing stand stability, preserving the genetic value of the stand and supporting the non-productive functions of the forest as required by the owners' management strategy and by environmental regulations.

Game management

Hunting is conducted in traditional fashion – mostly stalking – and is sold commercially. The excessive population of deer is the key reason why the estate manages hunting directly rather than renting hunting territories. This is a reflection of an overall over-population of deer in Czech forests, which makes attempts at reducing their numbers futile unless conducted in sufficient scale across regions.

A group of Roe deer in a feeding place.

Žďár Estate

Žďár Estate

Žďár forest has significantly gained in liveliness since 1993."Not a minute to lose!", as Maréchal Lyautey replied, when told that replanting olive trees in Northern Africa was futile since they took eons to produce olives...

Game management is severely loss making due to the numerous and costly enclosures against game damage to new stands. This is however an investment worth making in view of the speed and quality of spruce regeneration under the sheltered-clearing system and the robust growth of beech and fir in recently diversified stands.

The future of forestry management

In short, promoting a varied age structure via natural re-growth and supporting bio-diversity with indigenous species is not just a nice, if rather costly, dream come true. It is a critical weapon for the forest to fight for its adaptation and survival and for the family estate to restore long term value. Complete rebalancing in age structure and species mix is obviously well beyond the horizon of current generations and under continuous threat of wind and snowfall, climate change and pollution. But regular visitors can testify that the Žďár forest has significantly gained in liveliness since 1993.

"Not a minute to lose!", as Maréchal Lyautey replied, when told that replanting olive trees in Northern Africa was futile since they took eons to produce olives...

Fish farming and agriculture

The fish-farm manages 80 ponds (750 ha) at altitudes of 550 to 750 m in river spring areas, mainly for Carp (80%), American Trout, Coregone, Tench, Pike and Zander. The fish-farm has self-sufficient hatching and breeding units. Ponds are usually emptied and fished out every one to two years. The biggest pond, the Velké Dářko (208 ha) takes over two months to empty.

The company sells fish live, at differing stages of growth, from recently hatched to fish ready for consumption. Half to two thirds of the production is sold locally, the rest mostly in Germany and Slovakia.

80% of the ponds belong to a protected regional water basin reserve, with recently imposed and severe production limits, based on natural hatching and low-feed production, unfortunately without any

Žďár Estate

fair indemnification for owner-managers under current Czech laws on environmental protection. A complete restructuring of the business is under consideration, combining natural production in ponds and intensive production in artificial basins.

Out of the 200 ha of arable land, only half are manageable after extensive but still unfinished efforts to consolidate the scattered plots. Production consists of wheat, barley, oilseed rape (colza) and a small unit of pigs and slaughter cattle. Farming is currently sub-critical and efforts to restructure it should bear fruit by 2011.

All revenues have been reinvested since restitution to revitalize the forestry, fishery, agriculture and buildings and invest in new business lines such as a 4,000 m² DIY & Garden Centre. Still, a lot remains to be done after fifty years of almost continuous management under the Nazi and Communist regimes.

All revenues have been reinvested since restitution to revitalize the forestry, among others.

Žďár Estate

Žďár Estate

THE ART OF LETTING GO

The pale yellow solar disk is slowly sinking into the sea of green lying at my feet, as I sit on a high seat on the hill above the Radostín meadows, overlooking the forest of the Rašeliniště nature reserve. A few roe deer trot along on their way to supper in the fields behind. Busy thoughts race through my mind as the wind shapes long waves in the high grass below.

Our days are structured and, more often than not, dictated by wildly differing tempi. One of the main challenges of a manager is to handle those conflicting time horizons. As a partner in a leading European strategy consultancy firm – my other job in town – and as a former investment banker, my long term horizon is two to three years away; most of the managerial decisions I take are actually one week to one month decisions. As an estate manager, on the other hand, my short term horizon is ten years, if not fifty; most of my decisions are based on the work of my predecessors two generations before and, God permitting, will positively impact the lives of my grand-children.

A recent testimony to this is the small memorial monument we have just inaugurated in the forest in honour of my grand-parents, celebrating the two nature reserves that they created on our estate in 1929: the lessons learned from observing the evolution of those nature reserves over the last eighty years are fully reflected in our new ten-year forestry management plan, whose draft is waiting on my desk for final approval. Drawing heavily on the management plan approved by my late father after restitution of our estate in the nineties and on the management style of the family before the estate was seized by the Nazi and communist regimes, this new plan will hopefully help nature fend for itself against the pregnant dangers arising from acid rain and climate change, while enabling us to implement the managerial and economic adaptations required by new and challenging market conditions.

I need the humility to respect the work of many generations before me, the wisdom not to meddle with their achievements and the self-confidence to promote change where required, while knowing that it may take two generations to find out if I was

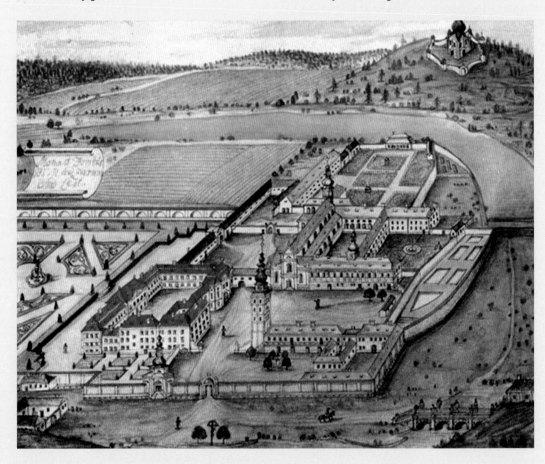

Mid XVIIIth century drawing of the Abbey as conceived by Santini-Aichl.

wise or maybe just lucky rather than found wanting, if not even foolish.

Managing conflicting time horizons is something that family businesses are somewhat better at than listed firms who suffer the high pressure of issuing quarterly results reports to anonymous shareholders. The flipside to this virtue are the risks associated with generational change and the difficulty of pursuing the three overlapping goals of family business: entrepreneurship, wealth management and family values.

On an estate such as ours, where conservation and restoration of our natural and historical assets are prime values, the complexity of managing a family business is compounded by the conflicting requirements of a heavy, clumsy, opaque, contradictory and often outright irresponsible regulatory framework. A dear aunt of mine, having fought a particularly epic battle against local bureaucrats to be able to repaint the façade of her own castle, concluded: "I always thought Kafka was a highly creative author but I now realise that he was a mere reporter".

As I ponder the complexities of managing overlapping time horizons and of steering the conflicting interests of numerous stakeholders, I slowly realize that while sitting on my high seat I have let my battered mind be overwhelmed by Kafkaesque worries and – how can this be? – just maybe by a touch of my own amplified sense of self-importance.

A tongue-in-cheek Haiku by the Japanese poet Hosaï springs to my mind from the slowly fading scenery surrounding me:

Under the wide sky,
No hat

Hosaï, Buddhist monk and unabashed drunkard, you stand among the greatest poets of the 20th century. I take my hunting-hat off in deference to your wise mind and let go of those busybody worries of mine, opening up to the wide sky above my now uncovered head: I still have a few things to learn from you about the art of letting go.

I settle back in wait. The long grass undulates with the silent wind, undisturbed as the forest fades under the darkening sky. The roe deer are long gone.

Constantin Kinsky, Žďár forest, June 2009

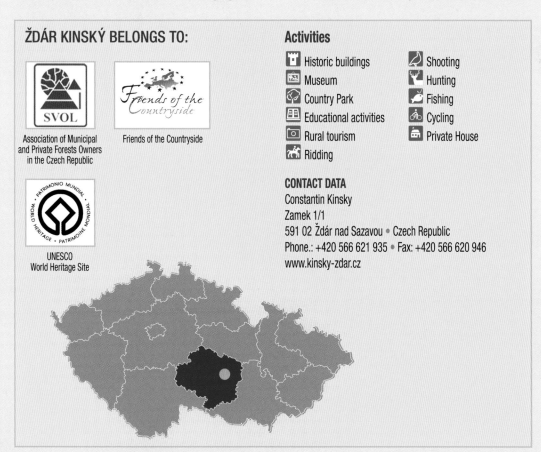

ŽĎÁR KINSKÝ BELONGS TO:

SVOL
Association of Municipal and Private Forests Owners in the Czech Republic

Friends of the Countryside
Friends of the Countryside

UNESCO
World Heritage Site

Activities

- Historic buildings
- Museum
- Country Park
- Educational activities
- Rural tourism
- Ridding
- Shooting
- Hunting
- Fishing
- Cycling
- Private House

CONTACT DATA
Constantin Kinsky
Zamek 1/1
591 02 Žďár nad Sazavou • Czech Republic
Phone.: +420 566 621 935 • Fax: +420 566 620 946
www.kinsky-zdar.cz

Theme 5

Climate change and new energies

New Holland,
energy independent farm

SUMMARY

From its origins, New Holland is characterized for making farming activity easier and more efficient, through innovative and affordable products, aimed to simplify people's life and to allow them to do more with less. This pioneering spirit had led us to look always further, anticipating the evolution of farming by designing effective and viable solutions for their customers, enabling them to stay productive even in an ever changing scenario.

The growing importance of environmental issues, their close connections to the agricultural business and the uncertainty linked to the price and availability of fossil fuels, were the basis to develop our Clean Energy Leader initiative: a project that made New Holland the brand with the deepest commitment to bio-fuels and the broadest range of products running on 100% biodiesel. They are moving ahead in-to the future: the future of farming.

New Holland

The New Holland NH2™ tractor is the first tractor in the world to be powered by hydrogen. This experimental tractor replaces the traditional combustion combustion engine with hydrogen fuel cells to generate electricity.

New Holland is characterized for making farming activity easier and more efficient, aimed to simplify people's life and to allow them to do more with less.

New Holland

AN EASIER, SAFER, CLEANER FUTURE, WITHIN REACH

The energy landscape has changed. The society is still dependent ton fossil fuels, but its raising costs, together with a growing environmental awareness, and government policies, has stimulated the research of alternative sources of energy. New Holland has some results, but major changes are expected in the near future.

Consequently, this changed the agricultural scenario. The first generation biodiesel industry has grown, and now rapeseed, corn and sugar cane are inputs in the energy generation. Conversely, the raising oil prices have impacted negatively on farmers operating costs.

Fuel and energy represent a large amount of the farmers input costs. Farmers are scattered and dispersed around the country. Therefore, the costs of bringing fuel and energy are also very high. Farmers need to minimize their risks and keep their operating costs low. They need stability and independence to better control their business operation.

Farmers normally have a large amount of available space. And a large amount of resources that can be used to produce energy. **The Energy Independent Farm** is a new approach, where farmers will be able to generate their own energy to run their farm and agricultural equipment.

And all of this will be done using Hydrogen, 100% generated from renewable resources, which farmers have plenty of.

A LONG HISTORY:

- 1895 - Abe Zimmerman began in an equipment repair shop in 1895 in New Holland, Pennsylvania, USA, which is where our name comes from. In the same year, Alexandre Braud introduced stationary threshers to farmers in western France.
- 1903 - Zimmerman started the New Holland Machine Company and was producing agricultural products, including a feed mill, to help the farming community around him. In the early 1900s, Henry Ford had just started his automobile company in Detroit. Ford, whose mass-production methods revolutionised the automobile industry, also saw an opportunity to mass-produce tractors.
- 1906 - Leon Claeys, a Belgian mechanic, started to build threshing machines, and built his factory in Zedelgem, Belgium, where New Holland's factory still stands to-

day. In 1907, Ford came out with the prototype for the world's first mass produced, gasoline powered tractor, named an "automobile plow".

- 1917 - This tractor went into actual production. It was renamed the Fordson Model F, and produced by a new business, Henry Ford & Son Company.
- 1918 - Fiat Model 702 tractor was launched and went into full production a year later at the car and truck plant in Turin, and won the International Ploughing Contest in Senlis (France). Model 702 was the very first Fiat agricultural tractor, as well as the first Italian tractor to be built on an industrial scale.
- 1930s - Fiat's founder, Senator Giovanni Agnelli, wanted his tractor to become an integral part of Italy's agriculture and so he began an association with the Italian agricultural co-operatives.
- 1939 - Ford introduced the 3-point hitch on the 'N' tractor Series: one of the most successful tractor families ever.
- 1947 - The Company changed its name into Sperry New Holland and the same year it made a major breakthrough in hay harvesting technology with the introduction of the haybine mower-conditioner.

In the late 1950s, production of two new Fiat models, Model 18 *"La Piccola"* and the 411 brought Fiat tractors true international success. By the 1960s, Claeys was one of the biggest combine manufacturers in Europe.

- 1964 - Sperry New Holland bought a major interest in Claeys.
- 1973 - Fiat 640, the most sold tractor of the famous Fiat "Nastro Oro" Series, was launched. An international success that still continues today.
- 1974 - Sperry New Holland introduced the world's first twin-rotor combine: a winning idea, still leading the industry today.
- 1975 - Braud launched his first grape harvester, model 1020. This was further improved with the famous Braud 1014, the best selling grape harvester in the history of the vineyard, with over 2000 units sold in less than four years.
- 1970s - By the end of the 1970s, Fiat Trattori was selling to 140 countries around the world.

New Holland

In the early 1900s, Henry Ford had just started his automobile company in Detroit. Ford, whose mass-production methods revolutionized the automobile industry, also saw an opportunity to mass-produce tractors.

- **1980s** - Ford was a major player and its tractor division had been responsible for a number of industry innovations, including the use of power hydraulics, rubber pneumatic tyres, diesel engines, and the 3-point hitch.
- **1986** - Ford bought Sperry New Holland and formed Ford New Holland Inc.
- **1991** - Fiat, who had acquired Braud, purchased an 80 per cent interest in Ford New Holland and the full integration process was completed at the official launch of New Holland at our worldwide convention in 1994. Under the ownership of Fiat, – through CNH, the sector born in 1999 from the merger between New Holland N.V. e Case Corporation – it gained access to unprecedented resources, which enabled the company to follow an aggressive plan of product renewal and take its customer service to a new level.

This is a story of ingenuity, constant improvement and all round experience. The story of New Holland Agriculture, the Fiat Group brand that's making technology even simpler, more accessible and more efficient, and setting new European and international benchmarks.

New Holland Agriculture has over a century of experience in producing agricultural equipment and continually strives to unearth new solutions capable of improving the quality of work of millions of farmers all around the world. It has sofar achieved this objective by offering increasingly innovative and efficient products that are alos easy to use.

Model 702 was the very first Fiat agricultural tractor, as well as the first Italian tractor to be built on an Industrial scale.

THE VISION: "THE SUSTAINABLE FARM CONCEPT"

New Holland is a forward looking company enabling their customers to be one day completely energy independent, meaning that they will be able to generate their own energy in a sustainable way with the resources that the farmers currently possess. The idea is to use this energy to power their agricultural and other equipments and buildings. This is what they call the self-sustainable farm concept.

ENERGY INDEPENDENT FARM CONCEPT

New Holland's Energy Independent Farm concept has far-reaching benefits for its customers, allowing them to create, store and use power in a convenient format. Central to the concept is the ability to produce electricity from natural, environmentally-friendly sources and then reuse that electricity in a convenient and practical way. The impressive hydrogen-powered NH^2™ tractor, which won a Gold Medal at the SIMA Innovation Awards 2009, is just one part of a greater vision to free farmers from the increasing cost of fuel.

Fuel costs form a significant proportion of farmers operating costs now and in the future. New Holland believes hydrogen technology will give farmers an independent supply of energy, which could be used in a wide variety of vehicles and applications, giving them greater control over the future of their business.

The traditional barriers to the use of hydrogen center on its distribution and availability. The wide roaming capability of cars and lorries means use of hydrogen in commercial and personal vehicles has been limited primarily by the lack of an extensive national distribution system, which would be very costly to implement.

The Energy Independent Farm concept envisages farmers producing their own compressed hydrogen from water and storing the hydrogen on the farm. Using a process called electrolysis, electricity produced by wind farms, solar panels or biomass and biogas processes situated on the farm would break water down into hydrogen and oxygen. While the hydrogen-powered NH^2™ tractor is

New Holland

the first practical step, it is wider implications of New Holland's Energy Independent Farm concept that could revolutionize the agricultural industry and allow it to leapfrog the energy concerns of other industries.

Farmers are in a unique position to benefit from hydrogen technology. Unlike many people, they have the space to install alternative electricity generation systems, such as solar, wind, biomass or waste, and then store that power as hydrogen. Apart from the environmental benefits, such a system would allow customers to become energy independent and improve their financial stability.

UNIQUE ADVANTAGES OF USING HYDROGEN

Many electrical production systems are currently in use by farms around the world, harnessing the power of the wind, sun and biomass. However, the electrical power that is not used at the time of production must be sold back to the national power system or lost. The Independent Farm

Concept extends this process by allowing the power to be stored in the form of compressed hydrogen, which could then be used directly in farm machinery or in generators to provide electrical power and heat for buildings and numerous applications.

Hydrogen-powered vehicles have been in development for many years, and in agriculture, offer benefits over battery-driven vehicles, which are efficient only in a stop-and-start cycle and take a long time to recharge.

Vehicles powered by hydrogen overcome these obstacles by using a hydrogen fuel tank feeding fuel cells to generate electricity within the vehicle, offering greater efficiency and improved flexibility. Fuel cells have a long working life and avoid the environmental issues of disposing of batteries.

Energy-dense hydrogen can be stored conveniently in a tank on the farm as a compressed gas and the vehicle can be refuelled quickly. The relatively short operating distance from a central working base would give vehicles easy access to a central hydrogen tank installed at the farm, or satellite tanks both fixed and mobile.

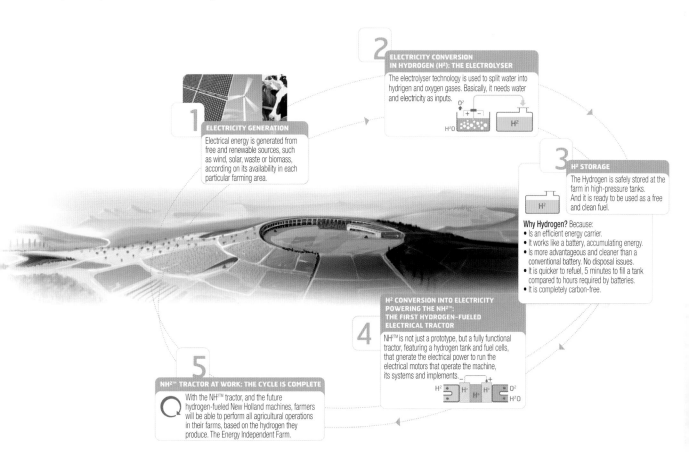

1 ELECTRICITY GENERATION
Electrical energy is generated from free and renewable sources, such as wind, solar, waste or biomass, according on its availability in each particular farming area.

2 ELECTRICITY CONVERSION IN HYDROGEN (H_2): THE ELECTROLYSER
The electrolyser technology is used to split water into hydrigen and oxygen gases. Basically, it needs water and electricity as inputs.

3 H_2 STORAGE
The Hydrogen is safely stored at the farm in high-pressure tanks. And it is ready to be used as a free and clean fuel.

Why Hydrogen? Because:
- Is an efficient energy carrier.
- It works like a battery, accumulating energy.
- Is more advantageous and cleaner than a conventional battery. No disposal issues.
- It is quicker to refuel, 5 minutes to fill a tank compared to hours required by batteries.
- It is completely carbon-free.

4 H_2 CONVERSION INTO ELECTRICITY POWERING THE NH$_2$: THE FIRST HYDROGEN-FUELED ELECTRICAL TRACTOR
NH$_2$ is not just a prototype, but a fully functional tractor, featuring a hydrogen tank and fuel cells, that gnerate the electrical power to run the electrical motors that operate the machine, its systems and implements.

5 NH$_2$ TRACTOR AT WORK: THE CYCLE IS COMPLETE
With the NH$_2$ tractor, and the future hydrogen-fueled New Holland machines, farmers will be able to perform all agricultural operations in their farms, based on the hydrogen they produce. The Energy Independent Farm.

NEW HOLLAND LOOKS FOR FURTHER ENERGY SAVING SOLUTIONS

Today many alternative sources of energy are being investigated. Wind, solar, biomass, geothermal...you name it. Many of them are still in its infancy. Others are more developed and are already being used. But even if they are not yet massively adopted, and still are not yet commercially viable, we are not far from this scenario. And we believe that it will be available shortly. As an example, many specialists point out solar energy is about to grow significantly in the following years. A recent study compares the costs of electricity with the costs of solar energy today and in 2020. The conclusion is that in 12 years, in most of the western countries, solar energy will be less expensive than electricity.

Another line of investigation is **Biomass**. This is a very promising alternating, and major companies are investing heavily. Biomass can be used to pro-duce biodiesel, the so-called cellulosic ethanol, or to produce a synthetic gas, often called 'syngas', which can be later distilled into biodiesel, if needed. The costs are still above the price of oil. But costs are decreasing fast and specialist forecast that this solution would commercially viable on the long term.

Basically, biomass is obtained from fast growing wood crops, which are harvested every 2 to 4 years. The harvested trees need to be processed to chips (coppice). Then, they are processed to generate gas, or be used in heating plants. One of the main bottlenecks today is an efficient harvest of this material.

And to cope this problem, New Holland step in and is also making a major contribution. In SIMA, New Holland is presenting the new Coppice Header, using the awarded FR9000 self-propelled forage harvester. The new header is able to cut trees with a trunk diameter of 15 cm dou-bling in this way the harvesting acreage so far

The FR9000, New Holland's flagship of the self-propelled forage harvesters.

New Holland

The T7000 Auto Command with the new Continuously Variable Transmission.

achieved by the current products. The header is made of a tension fork that extends above the header itself. It has the task of curbing the trunk prior to sectioning it.

New Holland has also developed new continuoously variable transmissions for small tractors as well as for tractors in the over 100 hp segment delivering excellent performance at the best fuel efficiency. Steering systems have also been improved by the Brand with innovative solutions like the ABS SuperSteer™ system, awarded recently at the Agritechnica show, which increase tractor manoeuvrability and reduce the fuel consumption and the pollutant emissions.

This innovation reinforces our commitment to provide innovative solutions that are cleaner to the environment, and improving also our product's versatility and efficiency.

CONCLUSIONS

New Holland Agriculture has always been engaged in an ongoing search for accessible, simple and environmentally friendly solutions. It has earned its role as a Clean Energy Leader, being the first brand in 2006 to fully support the potentials of biofuels in agriculture and now to present the world's first hydrogen-powered tractor. All our products and features bring today innovation and accessible technology to fields all over the world. We continue to look to the future, searching for ingenious ways to make technology simple and change farmers' lives. This philosophy is behind all our projects that aim to a future of eco-agricultural sustainability and we want to maximise land productivity, because this planet needs more food and farmers deserve more return on their investment and hard work. We want to offer environment-friendly alternatives to keep operating costs low, while increasing the level of independence of farmers.

In line with this philosophy New Holland Agriculture joined a business consortium of leading corporations which are participating to a high propfile, global research launched by McKinsey & Company institute and the International Finance Corporation (member of the World Bank Group). This research is focused on the future of water resources and as the use of water for agricultural activities is one of the key aspects we decided to support it because we will learn how to protect, to secure water resources and to ensure a future of profitability and independence to farmers. This study sheds a light on the use and abuse of water in agriculture, and the measures that can be implemented to increase productivity "per drop". Precision farming technologies for example could be tuned to optimize irrigation efficiency and to crop protection during harvesting to reduce losses. It shows also to both farmers and financial institutions that many agricultural measures both make good financial sense and also can save water. This water study is yet another important step our brand is taking toward sustainable and profitable farming.

Francesco Quaranta
Europe Marketing Director

THE CLIMATE CHALLENGE AND THE LAND MANAGER: A EUROPEAN PERSPECTIVE

Michael Sayer
Vice-President, Friends of the Countryside

In recent years, there has been growing concern about climate change and the influence of man on climate means and variability through the release of greenhouse gases, most importantly carbon dioxide (CO_2) but also methane (CH_4) and nitrous oxide (N_2O) and chlorofluorocarbons (CFCs). This led to the United Nations Framework Convention on Climate Change (1992) which aims to stabilise greenhouse gases in the atmosphere 'at a level that would prevent dangerous anthropogenic interference with the climate system'. Subsequently, the industrialised (Annex I) parties to the convention by the Kyoto Protocol (1997) committed themselves to a range of targets which would average a 5% cut on 1990 levels of emissions during the five-year period 2008-2012. In 2001, the Country Land and Business Association (CLA) published *Climate Change and the Rural Economy*, and subsequently the European Landowners' Organisation and CLA, together with the University of East Anglia, established the CLIO project to examine the potential effects of climate change on European estates using 21 case studies. This report was published as Viner, D. *et al., Climate Change and the European Countryside* (2006) and contained a description of the CALM (Carbon Accounting for Land Managers) methodology which enables estates to calculate their own greenhouse gas emissions and their carbon stocks and sequestration.

PHYSICAL SCIENCE

Past climate is known at global scale from the instrumental record since about 1850, although locally records sometimes go back further (enabling reconstruction back to 1659 in the case of the Central England Temperature Record). Otherwise palaeoclimate is reconstructed largely through the analysis of proxy sources such as tree rings, ice cores and ocean and geological sediments. The prehistoric climate has varied principally between long glacial and shorter inter-glacial periods, believed to be the consequence of changes in the Earth's eccentricity, axial tilt and precession as it orbits the sun (the Milankovitch effect). The last glacial period lasted some 60,000 years until 14,000 years ago and globally the temperature was some 5° Celsius cooler than now, whereas the previous (Eemian) interglacial, which lasted 10,000 years, was up to 2° C warmer than the present. The maximum rate of emergence from the last glacial was some 2° C per thousand years. Change since the industrial revolution has been on a greater and accelerating scale compared with the variations in the northern hemisphere known as the 'medieval warm period' of the 11th and 12th centuries (the low resolution data makes the scale difficult to evaluate) and the 'little ice age' of the 17th century (which was probably not experienced globally). Levels of atmospheric CO_2 have varied in the range of 180 to 300 parts per million (ppm) between glacial and interglacial periods respectively over the last 650,000 years.

Since 1750, there has been an increase in net global radiative forcing of + 1.6 Watts per square metre. Global temperature has risen by 0.74° degree Celsius over the last century with warming greatest at higher northern latitudes. 1998 (enhanced by El Niño) and 2005 were the warmest years in the instrumental record since 1850. Atmospheric CO_2 concentrations have risen from 280 ppm in pre-industrial times to 315 ppm in 1958 to 387 ppm in 2008 and the concentrations of other greenhouse gases, especially CH_4 and N_2O, have also risen. CO_2 is by far the most abundant greenhouse gas and when the atmospheric concentrations of all greenhouse gases are taken together, they are calculated as CO_2 equivalent. The science is exhaustively reviewed by the Intergovernmental

Panel on Climate Change (IPCC) in the first volume of its Fourth Assessment Report (AR4), *Climate Change 2007: The Physical Science Basis*.

For fourteen of the estates in *Climate Change and the European Countryside*, local records were adequate to compare climate before and after 1990, and thirteen of these showed decadal rates of increase in average annual temperature from 0.31°C to 0.73°C. The highest increases occurred in central Europe (Dobříš and Reitzenstein), south-eastern England (Holkham and Windsor) and Finland (Wehmaa). The fourteenth estate (Cappoquin), showing an increase of only 0.02°C, is on the south coast of Ireland. (See *Fig. 1*).In the context of IPCC projections for Europe, these rates are alarming, given that even if global mean temperature rise were contained to 2°C above pre-industrial levels, northern Europe could be expected to experience double that increase.

IMPACTS AND ADAPTATION

A wide range of impacts is already beginning to become apparent. Those expected for Europe are summarised in *Fig. 2*.

Crops

The ELO strongly endorses the view, recognised by the IPCC, that water balance and weather extremes will be of critical importance to land management, and that an increase in the frequency of extreme events is likely to reduce yields beyond the impacts of mean temperature change. The expected expansion of agriculture in Africa, Asia and Latin America will be particularly vulnerable. In Europe, spring droughts and wet autumn drilling periods are among the principal risks, but the late summer drought of 2003 reduced yields in France by 30% for maize and forage, 25% for fruit and 21% for winter wheat. Damage from late frosts after warmer winters will increase. There is increasing experimental evidence to support the intuitive position that early stabilisation of climate will reduce damage to crops. It is likely that the yield of rainfed wheat reaches its optimal capacity in relation to temperature increase at about 450 ppm CO_2 equivalent. Northward movement of cereal crops in Europe will usually be obstructed by physical barriers including soil type, forest cover and lakes.

Fig. 1. Observed decadal increases in average annual temperature since 1990 for estates participating in the CLIO project

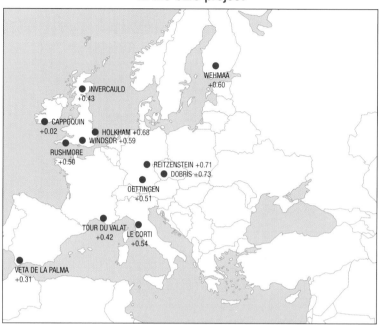

Fig. 2. Key vulnerabilities (Europe). (IPCC, AR4, II, Fig. 12.3.)

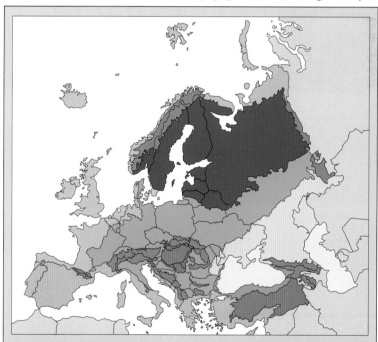

AT: Increased coastal erosion and flooding; stressing of marine bio-systems and habitat loss; increased tourism pressue on coasts; greater winter storm risk and vulnerability of transport to winds.

CE: Increased frequency and magnitude of winter floods; increased variability of crop yields; increased health effects oof heatwaves; severe fires in drained peatland.

BO: Waterlogging; eutrophication of lakes and wetlands; increased coastal flooding and erosion; increased winter storm risk; reduced ski season.

ME: Reduced water availability; increased drought; severe biodiversity losses; increased forest fires; reduced summer tourism; re-

duced suitable cropping areas, increased energy demand in summer, reduced hydropower; increased land loss in estuaries and deltas; increased salinity and eutrophication of coastal waters; increased health effects of heatwaves.

ST: Decreased crop yield; increased soil erosion; increased SLR with positive NAO; increased salinity of inland seas.

TU: Thawing of permafrost; decreased tundra area; increased coastal erosion and flooding.

MT: Glaciers disappearing; reduced snow cover period; upward shift of tree line; severe biodiversity losses; reduced ski season; increased rock fall.

Fig. 3a

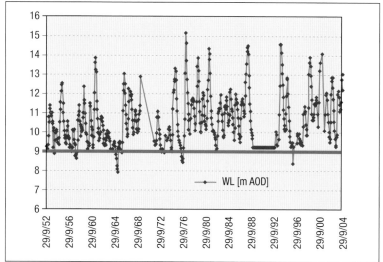

FIG. 3b

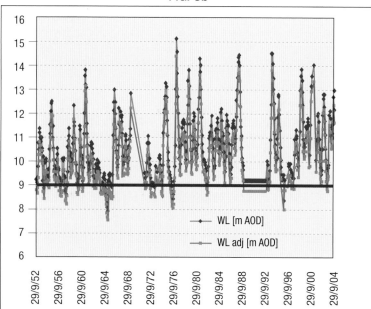

Fig. 3 Chalk groundwater hydrograph at Cuckoo Lodge, Holkham estate, Norfolk, UK: a) the record for 1952 – 2004, b) water level adjusted to 95% representing a climate in 2050 based on the UKCIP02 high scenario on a conservative view. Groundwater elevations (WL) in m above Ordnance Datum (sea level). Yellow bar represents drought threshold. (*Climate Change and the European Countryside*, 70.

Water resources

Changing rainfall patterns are likely to result in loss of run-off in Mediterranean Europe, but the expected increase in northern Europe, with heavier rainfall events, will not necessarily be accompanied by higher levels of groundwater recharge, in part because of the greater intensity of rainfall events and increased evapotranspiration. (See *Fig. 3*) There is urgent need for more research on indi-vidual aquifers. River flows are expected to reduce in summer (in the Alpine region exacerbated by glacier retreat and loss of snow melt), with associated eutrophication of some water bodies. Adaptation for cropping will require more water storage and more efficient use of water, but on-farm reservoirs are expensive, and the resource to fill them will normally be available only from winter rainfall. Much arable land is unsuited, by its profile, to irrigation and change of cropping and/or land use may be required to retain it in production.

Livestock

Livestock are likely to be affected by reduced grazing seasons in Mediterranean Europe, and more generally by an increase in the proportion of unpalatable forage grasses in swards. In addition, the more heat-resistant breeds of livestock tend to be less productive. An increase in disease from a range of vectors including Sheep Tick *(Ixodes ricinus)* is already being experienced. Additional vaccination programmes, which in some cases may need to be extended to wild populations, are likely to be required against disease.

Forestry

The correct balance of species in relation to the site and expected climate will be critical for the stability of forests, with special importance for plantation forestry. There is concern for the long-term future of beech *(Fagus sylvatica)* and Norway Spruce *(Picea abies)* due to increasing summer drought and insect pests such as Spruce-Bark Beetle *(Ips typographus)*, Nun Moth *(Lymantria monacha)* and Pine Sawfly *(Neodiprion sertifer)*. The potential time lag in adaptation is governed by the rate of climate change in relation to length of rotation or age at harvest. It is likely that uneven-aged mixed forestry will offer better stability against climate change, gale damage and pests but conversion from even-aged, clear-felling systems raises significant issues of management and cashflow. Fire risk is expected to increase, especially in the Mediterranean, where the fire season is expected to lengthen. An increase in the severity of wind storms is expected. Hurricane Lothar on 26 December 1999 affected Couvet (Switzerland), Hverringe (Denmark), Mivoisin (France) and Oettingen (Germany), where it brought down six years' harvest.

Coastal zones

A sustained rise in local temperature of 2.7°C would result in the gradual (but in practice irreversible) loss of the Greenland Ice Sheet except for remnant glaciers (most of the loss in terms of area occurring over the first thousand years), with a consequent rise in mean sea level of up to 7 m. Under the A1B socio-economic scenario this level of mean global warming would occur by 2100.The return period for surge events is expected to shorten. (See *Fig. 4.*) There is inadequate support for the development of pro-active, soft engineering techniques for coastal stabilization even in Europe, where costs may often have to be born by local communities and private individuals. Salinisation of groundwater, and coastal rivers during periods of low flow, already a localised problem in some parts of Europe, is expected to increase.

Ecosystems and biodiversity

Ecosystems and biodiversity are expected to become increasingly vulnerable if temperature warms by more than 2° to 3°C. Climate moves northwards by about 150/200 km, or uphill by about 100/150 metres, for each 1°C of temperature rise. Many habitats and species are unlikely to be able to migrate at this speed and there will often be physical barriers. Mediterranean, montane and wetland ecosystems are expected to be particularly affected with potential biodiversity loss of some 30% of species. Estates such as El Castañar and Veta de la Palma (Spain), Herdade do Pinheiro (Portugal), Tour du Valat (France), Mautern (Austria) and Invercauld (Scotland) are all likely to be significantly affected.) The establishment of migration corridors represents a possible response. Salmonids are likely to be adversely affected.

MITIGATION

Atmospheric CO_2 equivalent of 450 ppm would entail a temperature increase of about 2.1°C. Stabilisation of atmospheric greenhouse gases by 2100 to keep temperature increase below 2° would require emissions to peak by 2015 with cuts of 80% on 1990 levels by 2050.The likelihood of achieving this outcome is assessed by the IPCC in terms of socio-economic scenarios and stabilisation trajectories. (See *Fig. 5*) Because of

Fig. 4. Potential effects of a storm surge in 2080 under a UKCIP02 medium-high emissions scenario, Holkham, Norfolk. (Climate Change and the European Countryside, p.73, Fig. 9.)

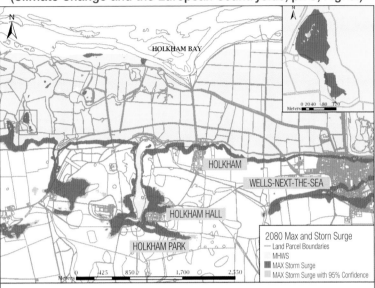

2080 Medium-High Emissions Scenario - Projected Relative Sea-Level Rise at Holkham for maximum RSLR and storm surge (MAX and Storm Surge) and maximum RSLR and storm surge with error (MAX and Storm Surge with 95% Confidence). Baseline is 1999 Mean High Water Spring tides (MHWS).

the length of the carbon cycle and the consequent compound effect, the later cuts in emissions are left, the deeper they have to be to achieve a given target. Land managers can offer mitigation by reducing their own emissions, by managing carbon stocks in trees and soils so as to induce additional carbon sequestration, and by producing renewable energy and construction materials. The global potential for mitigation by land management is assessed in *Fig. 6.*

Fig. 5. Stabilisation trajectories by category in relation to temperature increase. (IPCC, AR4, III, Fig. TS 11.)

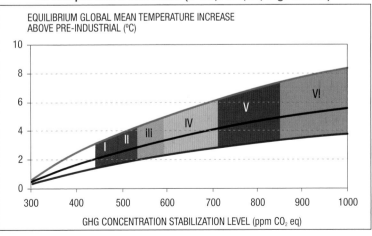

Fig. 6 Cumulative cost abatement strategies for agricultural CH_4 and N_2O, forestry and biomass under a range of 2100 stabilisation scenarios. (IPCC, AR4, III, Fig. 3.29.)

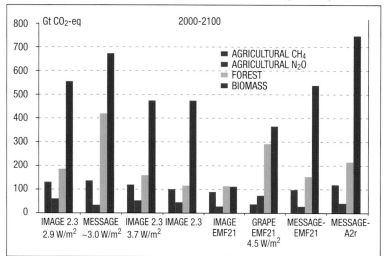

CALM

Land use is the fundamental basis for the integration of agriculture, forest sequestration and substitution (biofuels, biomass, construction). The CLIO project developed CALM (Carbon Accounting for Land Managers) as a simple integrated means of calculating emissions and sequestration for rural estates based on IPCC methodology as applied in the UK model, using records of inputs, yields and stock. Subsequently, a modified and updated version for UK conditions has been made available on-line at www.elo.org and at www.cla.org.uk/calm This has the potential for adaptation for record-keeping land management businesses worldwide.

Direct energy use

Energy use by agriculture and forestry is small and CO_2 emissions could best be reduced by conversion to locally produced biodiesel and biomass.

Carbon in woody biomass: the role of forests and woodland

Many central European and Scandinavian forests and some large French ones have been managed very efficiently for timber production since the nineteenth century and often earlier, but many smaller woodlands are under-managed with trees failing to reach their potential. This is more noticeable in primarily agricultural regions. The timber quality and the standing volume, and

hence the carbon stock, in under-managed woods can potentially be increased. Sylvicultural systems and rotation lengths may also be adapted in managed forest, but with implications for cash flow in relation to time of harvest. In many cases uneven-aged forestry may make it possible to grow bigger trees, as at Couvet (Switzerland). However, while a clear-fell system will often result in a fluctuating carbon stock compared with an uneven-aged system, this will be significantly mitigated where the clear-fell system is operated by compartments in a forest where there is a good balance of age classes.

Soil carbon

Despite the potential for zero-till agriculture in some regions of the world, in European conditions the need for periodic normal cultivations significantly reduces the scope for mitigation by tillage regime. Carbon release from soils is expected under higher temperatures, exacerbated by erosion, but soil carbon could be conserved or increased by land-use change where appropriate, for example by conversion of marginal arable land to permanent pasture or woodland in the Mediterranean, and by conservation of peat soils, which are vulnerable to degradation especially at lower altitudes.

Biomass and local generation of heat and power

There is significant scope for local power and heat generation from biomass, both from short-rotation coppice and forestry waste, including from conversion of roundwood to saw logs. There is a need for an integrated European system of feed-in tariffs, which should include estate-produced wind and hydro power (Mautern is an example of an estate selling hydro power to the Austrian national grid).

Biofuels

Despite the concern surrounding potential competition with food crops, there is a natural role for home-grown European biofuels within the normal arable rotation, both as a break crop and as a use for cereal surpluses (typically feed wheat). There is therefore, however, a structural limitation to the contribution of homegrown biofuels (savings for the United Kingdom have been variously, but informally, estimated from about 10% of fuel use to 1 megatonne of carbon annually of emissions in current conditions). This will not be achieved without the correct, harmonised tariff regime.

Construction

The use of timber in construction can substitute carbon-intensive materials such as brick and heavy concrete, for which emissions have been estimated at 4.000 kg and 2,900 kg CO_2 per cubic metre respectively. This might be encouraged by building standards and renewable obligations, potentially coupled with carbon intensity tariffs. The maturity of the paper market could release an unquantified volume of construction timber in current conditions. There is need for much better data on the existing use of timber in construction. However, the low price since the 1980s remains a major constraining factor in increasing production and rotation length. (See *Fig. 7*)

Methane and nitrous oxide

CH_4 arising largely from livestock digestive systems but also from irrigated rice fields, and N_2O from nitrogen-based fertilizers and livestock waste, are the biggest agricultural sources of greenhouse gases. Their global warming potentials are respectively 21 and 310 times that of CO_2 although CH_4 has a shorter atmospheric life. However, the scope for emissions reductions remains constrained by the complexity and relative intractability of the nitrogen cycle, once rates and timing of nitrogen fertiliser application have been optimised. Emissions within EU15 however are currently declining. The development of anaerobic digestion and biogas production (as in Denmark) and, potentially, ongoing research into the carbon/nitrogen balance in livestock feed would enable useful savings in CH_4 emissions from housed livestock. There is a need to avoid extensification policies which potentially transfer emissions to, and cause additional land-use change in, other countries.

Emissions Trading Schemes

In general terms, the effectiveness of the first trading period under the EU scheme was impaired by initial over-allocation of allowances. Net new afforestation since 1990 as understood by Article 3.3 of Kyoto should also now be included, based on five-yearly certificates with the obligation on

Fig. 7. Evolution of financial returns from timber in CHF per cubic metre (1966-2000), forest of Couvet, Switzerland. (Climate Change and the European Countryside, p.54, Fig. 4.)

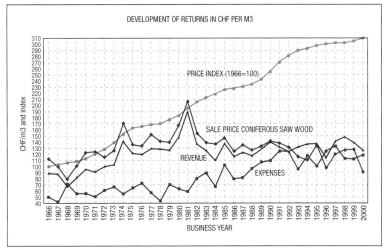

the buyer to renew. This however presupposes the widespread diffusion of forest inventory practice on a level comparable to central Europe and Scandinavia, where standing volumes are typically measured every ten years, and there is an urgent need to extend this.

Price of carbon

The price of carbon remains consistently too low to encourage mitigation. Although it has been calculated that a price of US$100/tonne for carbon could be enough to halt deforestation, a price in the US$73/165/tonne would be adequate only for stabilisation at over 550 ppm CO_2 equivalent, or +2.9°.

Reduction of Emissions from Deforestation/Degradation: the challenge to substitution policy

It has been estimated that tropical deforestation contributed emissions of 1.3 gigatonnes of carbon per year in the 1980s rising to 1.6 gigatonnes a year in the 1990s. Deforestation continues at a rate of 13 million ha/year due largely to agricultural expansion. There is substantial concern that imports of biofuels and timber by Annex I countries are also real or potential drivers of this process. Whilst it is clear that decarbonisation of the economy is essential, land-use change must be part of all equations, and it is unlikely that substitution policies will develop fully and land

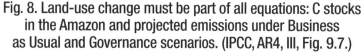

Fig. 8. Land-use change must be part of all equations: C stocks in the Amazon and projected emissions under Business as Usual and Governance scenarios. (IPCC, AR4, III, Fig. 9.7.)

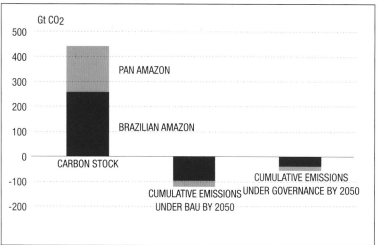

management thus be enabled to optimise its contribution to mitigation, even in Europe, without an effective agreement on land-use change and deforestation in developing countries. (See *Fig. 8*)

CONCLUSIONS FOR INTERNATIONAL CLIMATE POLICY

What, then, do land managers need from the Framework Convention on Climate Change and from the Conference of Parties whose fifteenth meeting will seek to agree a successor to the Kyoto Protocol at Copenhagen in December 2009? What can land management potentially contribute, given the right policies?

- Land managers face significant threats from climate change and need urgent policies for stabilisation of atmospheric CO_2 equivalent so as to keep an increase in pre-industrial temperatures below 2°C. This implies overall cuts in emissions in the order of 80% on 1990 levels by 2050 and cuts in the order of 40% for Annex I countries by the early 2020s. There needs to be agreement on a series of five-year commitment periods to achieve this, with the inclusion of the larger developing countries from at least 2018.

- The role of land management is central for successful adaptation in terms of food production, water resource protection, forest management, soil conservation, coastlines and biodiversity.

- The essential contribution to mitigation is through increasing the sequestration of carbon in forests and through providing fibre for energy and material substitution. In Europe, it remains unlikely that 80% cuts in CH_4 and N_2O emissions are feasible without major extensification of agriculture and the transfer of production and emissions elsewhere.

- There are significant constraints due to lack of investment in adaptation, the failure to develop mechanisms to include net afforestation since 1990 in trading schemes, the need for a robust agreement on deforestation and land-use change in the developing world, and the low prices prevalent both for carbon and renewables.

- CALM has been developed as an initial tool to raise the awareness of land managers and to enable them to estimate their own contributions to emissions, sequestration and mitigation. Any farm business in the world with records of inputs, outputs and stock could use this with appropriate adjustment of certain factors.

NEW ENERGIES: THE EUROPEAN ESTATEMANAGING LAND AS FOOD HUB, FUELING STATION AND/OR CARBON ORCHARD?

Corrado Pirzio-Biroli
CEO, RISE Foundation

Climate change puts business and society at cumulative, long-term risk. The failure to stop it would jeopardize food, energy and environmental security leading the world towards collapse. The failure of agriculture to match population explosion and preserve the environment would lead to widespread hunger in developing countries and mass migration of people (half a billion according to the UN), mostly to developed countries. The failure of energy security would cause energy black-outs, economic depression and mass unemployment with incalculable consequences. Environmental failure inhibits society's survival. There is a close interconnection between energy on the one hand and environment and food on the other. The European Estate plays a role in all three respects. Our focus here is on new energies, taking into account their repercussions on emissions as well as on food.

According to the International Energy Agency (IEA), our energy policies are non-sustainable within one generation: it is unlikely that the world can meet the expected increase in energy demand of 60% by 2050 while reducing Greenhouse Gas (GHG) emissions. But Governments and businesses are changing their ways to address the issue. GHG emissions are considered more and more as pollutants requiring regulation, and allowing for potential liability policies and damage claims affecting co-responsible businesses. Climate change has made renewable energies a star sector in our economies. New investments in renewables have reached $148bn in 2007.

And yet, fossil fuels (coal, gas and oil), and nuclear power remain our key energy sources. "The world faces a fossil energy future to 2030" (IEA). Its energy path is unsustainable. Business as usual would require oil production to rise from 87m b/d today to about 116m b/d by 2030. In its 2008 World Energy Outlook, IEA predicted a rate of production decline from the world's main 800 oil fields of 6.7%, with conventional oil peaking in 2020[1].

Oil prices will remain volatile, and rise substantially again over time. General Electric's CEO does not "see a disruptive new technology that changes the game in the next 20-30 years. It is not the nature of this industry. Everything that has been developed so far – wind, solar and so on – has taken decades to come to fruition. My expectation", he said, "is that it will remain that way".

What are then the most desirable renewable energy sources? There is no single, definite answer. It all depends on geography, technology, public opinion as well as politics, let alone events, repercussions, and of course cost. If one wants to avoid misjudgments, political blunders and misallocation of resources, no new and/or renewable energy sources should be promoted without first submitting each to a Life Cycle Analysis (LCA)[2].

Not all fossil fuels are strong polluters. Coal is the dirtiest. Gas is much cleaner than oil, and clean coal technologies exist: US coal-based electricity providers already emit 70% less pollutants per unit of energy than 30 years ago. Work is going on regarding a next-generation clean coal-fired source of power with smaller emissions. "Super-critical" boilers can increase coal's low energy efficiency by 45%. "Carbon-capture and storage" (CCS) power plants can cut emissions from fossil fuel power plants by 90% by liquefying the car-

---

[1] The world will need to invest $360bn a year (which is difficult when oil prices are low) to meet oil demand. Even if all current plans for renewables, energy efficiency, and savings were implemented the share of fossil fuels would go down only slightly from an expected 82% to 76 % in 2030. The new oil and gas field discoveries off-shore in Brazil, Ghana and Liberia do not change this picture much. To avoid global economic collapse, we would have needed to begin "a mitigation crash programme 20 years before peaking". Oil analyst Robert Hirsch concluded that "without timely mitigation, the economic, social and political costs of world oil supplies peaking "will be unprecedented". (Source: an interview by George Monbiot in the Guardian, 15 December 2008).
[2] LCA calculates all direct and indirect inputs and outputs (including waste), and costs on the basis of (ISO 14040-43) international standards. Admittedly, LCA analysis is nothing more than an instrument and can provide widely different conclusions regarding emission and energy consumption. Much depends on location, timing and technological change.

bon-dioxide and burying it underground, storing it in salt caverns or depleted oil and gas fields, but it will be expensive and full commercial viability may come only at half century.

After analyzing the amount of energy that each energy source can produce in terms of Watts of power output per square meter of land disturbed, Jesse Ausubel of the Rockefeller University, New York asserts that nuclear energy, followed by gas, are "the best options to minimize new structures and the rape of nature". Both are non renewable sources of energy. The full footprint of uranium mining involves relatively little land, and the dense heart of the atom has the smallest footprint of any energy source in nature. It has been calculated that if one wants to obtain the same amount of energy/electricity that a 1000 Megawatt nuclear power plant can produce, one would need: 2500 square kilometers of prime agricultural land producing biomass, 770 square kilometers with wind farms, and 150 square kilometers of photovoltaic solar cells plus land for storage and retrieval. In other words, a 1.5GW nuclear plant would need 10 hectares as against 18,700 hectares for an equivalent amount of wind energy. These figures must let us reflect in a world in which human habitats, agriculture, transportation and ecosystems compete for land. The limitations of alternative energy sources explain why we are experiencing an atomic revival. One can indeed expect nuclear energy demand to outrun supply for decades. This does not mean that there are no substantial problems also with nuclear power. Some of these are as yet unsolved: radioactive waste storage, safety and security. Others are possibly unknown, because much information in this sector is shrouded in secrecy. Nuclear power is a big bet on solving its waste problem one day. Nuclear waste (including cesium, plutonium and strontium) remains radioactive for at least 100,000 years (or 3,000 generations). It is currently stored in pools filled with water that are submitted to leakage and terrorist risks[3]. Moreover, operating nuclear plants also release continuing, poisonous emissions in small quantities into the atmosphere. Public opposition remains strong, new installations difficult to place, and "geological disposal" of waste encased in tough materials unresolved. Nor is there agreement on the real costs of nuclear energy. Nuclear power does not come cheap. New EPR plants

planned in France cost over €4bn each, and experts expect the cost to rise to €6bn. This does not include the decommissioning costs at the end of their 40 years of life. To keep costs down and provide economies of scale, nuclear reactors will have to be standardized.

Renewable energy sources may be renewable, but not all of them are green[4]. If one submits each of them to proper Life Cycle Analysis, all renewable energies are actually net producers of CO_2 via their production systems in that they emit more CO_2 than they save. The various forms of renewable energy involve vast infrastructure (concrete, steel, access roads etc.). Because renewables don't benefit much from economies of scale, more renewable kilowatts require more and more of the best land. Their net emission scores are much higher than advertising material and public perception would seem to indicate. Let us have a closer look.

Two currently very fashionable renewable energy sources are solar and wind energy. They have grown over the last quarter of century by 41% and 28% per year, respectively, but still represent no more than 0.1% of energy capacity. Solar and wind energy suffer from intermittence, functioning 25% of the time or less on average; and lack storage capacity. These are serious handicaps[5]. It has been estimated that the European electric blackout of 6 November 2006 was partly due to the network instability caused by Germany's vast wind energy farms. Unlike solar, wind has the additional disadvantage of generating most of its energy at

---

[3] Nuclear waste is normally "spent fuel", long rods of uranium burnt in nuclear reactors; after only 5% of the fuel rods are decomposed in the reactor, they are no longer capable of supplying the steady chain reaction a power station demands and (after recovering only 10% of spent uranium through processing) must be disposed of. They come out of the reactor at around 400°C, and take 30/40 years to become safe enough to handle and a century to cool completely. So far, as a temporary solution hundreds of thousands of tons of spent nuclear fuels sit in cooling ponds (over 450 in Europe alone) with no final destination. If one pool looses its water its stored nuclear waste would explode causing damage equivalent to the Hiroshima bomb. Scientists believe such waste can be stored safely hundreds of meters underground in secure repositories, but public opinion is distrustful. Only Finland, France and Sweden expect to open repositories by 2025. Attempts by other countries to designate geologically suitable sites or find communities ready to accept nuclear waste repositories have failed. Only some Governments have set deadlines for dealing with this matter, without knowing how. (See: "How the waste was won", Financial Times, September 19/20, 2009).

[4] For a good, recent report on the subject see: Le dossier noir des énergies vertes, Sciences et Vie, no.1086, March 2008, pages 54-74.

[5] The average load rate for on-shore wind-energy in Europe is actually 22%, but wind is so capricious that the electric grid needs to take over 78% of the time in less than ideal circumstances. According to Betz Law, a fall in wind speed of 10% translates into a fall in production of 30%.

night, when demand is lowest. As energy networks cannot accept more than one third of power from intermittent sources, solar or wind energy cannot produce much more than 8% of their power (1/4x1/3). Both may become more attractive if the electricity they produce could be stockpiled by more efficient and less polluting batteries. This would indeed be a major step, in particular as regards the transport industry, which causes 20% of world emissions[6].

Regarding wind energy in particular, supporters consider it the most economic and sustainable of all new energy sources, whereas critics consider it contrary to EU sustainable development policy. Wind energy is actually non polluting as long as it pumps water or grinds grains, but becomes a polluter as soon as it is connected to the electricity grid because of the thermal correction required to compensate for intermittence. Fault finders minimize the contribution of wind energy to lower emissions because of resort to gas or diesel plant back-up (increasing fossil fuel imports); wind farms require high-voltage power stations in order to compensate for intermittence of supply[7]. Wind energy is costly. It has been calculated that investment costs of off-shore wind farms in the UK is $4,000 per MW, comparable to those of 1MW of nuclear power, but twice the costs of state-of-the-art coal-fired power stations, and four times those of standard-combined-cycle gas turbine plants. Wind energy costs have been rising because of supply-chain shortages. There is growing controversy as to the environmental impact of wind turbines. 5MW masts are as high as 180 metres with a diameter of 150 metres with enormous stability problems. A wind farm of 1GW needs concrete (which emits CO_2), equivalent to 60% of what is needed for a nuclear installation; it also requires 125t of steel (a far greater emitter of CO_2), twice as much as for nuclear. An excessive number of windmills can even produce net GHG emissions[8]. Wind farms also cause noise, ruin the common natural landscape and cultural context, reduce the real estate value of adjacent private properties (without compensation), degrade the quality of life of way-side dwellers, let alone their health, and affect natural habitats and bird biodiversity. As environmental illnesses spread, the Académie Française de Médecine and the UK Noise Association recommend a minimum distance of windmills from dwellings of 1500m. Off-shore wind farms, albeit more expensive, have fewer draw backs and are much more acceptable to the public. The excesses of today's artificial wind energy market feed private riches to the benefit of subsidized investors and operators, financed by taxpayers, without true environmental benefits.

As to solar energy, solar panels still suffer from very high costs (five times those for fossil or nuclear energy) due to the high price and low efficiency (10%) of photovoltaic cells and to shortages of silicon. Silicon is produced from abundant sand through energy-thirsty heating at high temperature and currently represents half of the cost per solar Watt. Solar energy needs heavy metals in batteries and panels, and the low quality carbon used by the world's biggest producer of solar panels in China causes high CO_2 emissions. While more expensive than wind energy, its costs are coming down and may dwindle with new materials. The main advantage of photovoltaic energy is perhaps that as an electronic product it has an enormous innovation potential. One can expect silicon production to become less refined and cheaper. New technology will soon allow photovoltaic cells to be applied onto glass as paint, and even to replace silicon altogether with organic composite products, not to mention plastics. Experts expect solar energy costs eventually to match those of fossil fuels. New "solar thermal energy generation" companies make use of large mirrors to focus sun rays on power conversion units and produce concentrated solar power to drive turbines, either by heating water to steam, or by heating hydrogen to expand generating electricity. Solar power has great prospects for individual units in the developing countries and lacks the negative landscape impact of wind energy, which is running into increasing popular opposition.

Currently it is claimed that the cleanest renewable energy source, with the lowest emissions, is hydroelectricity, which accounts for barely 2.2% of

---

[6] Some 30 kgs of lead are needed to allow a battery to stock 1 KWh of energy. In order to have autonomy of 60km a vehicle would need 100-150 kgs of lead batteries.

[7] Germany's wind power operator E.ON revealed in 2004 that in 2003 the average wind in-feed was only 6.7% of installed capacity, and that this resulted in fluctuating power delivery necessitating back up by fossil fuel plants amounting to 80% of installed wind capacity (ABS Energy Research Report Ed2 2006).

[8] See: J. Soens (2005), *Impact of wind power in a future power grid*, KU Leuven thesis.

energy capacity. But dams cause destruction of habitats, deterioration of water quality, delta erosion; and dams in tropical areas can cause a number of water related illnesses and can produce so much methane that their emissions are comparable to those of natural gas power stations. Moreover, new dam sites are difficult to find. Other potential clean energy sources are wave and tidal power, and waste incineration. None of them is commercially feasible as yet. Big progress is being made with landfill gas, including gas plasma technology to convert "black bag" household waste to energy leaving less than 1% for the landfill. The biggest hope perhaps is Hydrogen. Scientists are trying to bring hydrogen and oxygen together releasing just energy and water. Hydrogen is one of the most abundant elements in the atmosphere. While it can be extracted from coal, natural gas and organic waste, scientists try to break apart the hydrogen and oxygen atoms and use fuel cells to bring them together again releasing energy in the process. Using renewable sources to split the water and initiate a "water to water" hydrogen fuel cycle would allow the production of energy with zero pollution. Cheap catalysts have now been found for the electrolysis process making hydrogen from water. MIT professor Nocera believes that it will be possible within a decade to use solar panels to simultaneously power homes and charge hydrogen fuel cells. But hydrogen development is a big challenge. It is not an independent energy source in itself. It requires energy, preferably renewable energy such as solar in order to supply initial power. It is a highly explosive gas that needs to be compressed to be stored and such compression would require one half of the energy hydrogen can produce. As other renewables, hydrogen would require bi-directional power systems in which energy consumers can also be energy producers, and "intelligrids" to ensure stable power systems with optimal management of many separate production and consumption units[9].

Another energy source that deserves special attention and is of particular interest to European Estates is agro-fuels. These are renewable fuels derived from biomass, generally in the form of liquid transportation fuels. There are two main categories: a) bioethanol (ethyl alcohol), which can be derived from sugarcane, sugar beet, maize, wheat, and starchy cereals (barley, sorghum, rye); and b) biodiesel (fatty-acid methyl ester), which is derived from oilseeds crops (soyabean, sunflower, rapeseed) and palm oil. There is also biomass from wood. It is mostly used for heating wood, which represents 10% of total energy consumption, but 80% in several African countries.

Agro-fuels are being promoted as the philosopher's stone for cutting emissions and energy independence. Governments are pushing their production via excise tax credits, renewable fuel standards and mandatory blending, farm and vehicle subsidies, R&D support, loans and grants, and import protection. According to the OECD, such public support is "irrational" and market distorting[10]. There are increasing warnings from scientists, academics and institutions such as EEA, EFSA, FAO, IFAD, OECD, JRC and the BRS[11], as well as (initially favourable) NGOs, that there are serious flaws with subsidizing agro-fuels. Current agro-fuel production has an insubstantial and shaky record in reducing greenhouse gas emissions as compared to conventional diesel or petrol (except Brazilian ethanol from local sugarcane). Gas emissions of biofuels are generally much higher than claimed, depending on the production process and the fuel, agricultural machinery and plant protection products used in crop growing, as well as on the alternative uses of land.

Although its market share remains small (currently 1% in EU and 3% in US road transportation), agro-fuel production has recently escalated, reducing food production and increasing food prices (according to FAO, by 30% in 2007) thus causing a major structural shift in commodity markets[12]. Mounting competition between food for people

---

[10] Public support is wasted unless a country is competitive (Brazilian ethanol), has the capacity to become a competitive, sustainable producer (Malaysian palm oil not based on rain forests), or has the potential to achieve the technological capacity and economies of scale required for efficient production. Removing budget support and mandates for biofuels would reduce biodiesel production in the EU and the US in 2013-2017 by over 80%, and reduce EU bioethanol production (if import tariffs are dropped as well) by 80%.

[11] European Energy Agency, European Food Safety Authority, Food and Agricultural Organization, Organization of Economic Development, EU Joint Research Center, International Fund for Agricultural Development, UK Royal Society, and World Food Program.

[12] Currently some 6% of cereal production and 8% of vegetable oil production are devoted to agro-fuel feeding 954 biofuel plants world wide (2007). Acreage under oilseeds (soya and colza/rape) declined to make place for maize; soybean-and-colza-based oil supplies contracted and their prices shot up, pulling palm oil prices along to the point that palm oil itself became less interesting for bio-diesel production.

---

[9] See the fascinating book *The Hydrogen Economy* by Jeremy Rifkin.

and fuel for cars has had serious implications for food prices and world hunger, worsening the food balance[13]. Grain price changes have knock-on effects on livestock, poultry and pork prices, because maize/corn, wheat and soya beans (soy meal) are used also as animal feed. Agro-fuels penalize the poor, who spend most of their income on food. They increase the food bill of the over seventy net-food-importing developing countries, aggravating their indebtedness, and nullifying budget restoration and development assistance efforts. Agro-fuels accelerate the drive towards economies of scale forcing the expulsion of small farmers from their land.

Agro-fuels require a lot of water, and mostly good irrigated agricultural land, both of which are finite, and cause environmental degradation (mainly in non-European countries). Greenpeace has called palm oil (the most energy efficient crop so far) a "climate bomb" in Indonesia. Agro-fuel targets have indeed knock-on effects on the destruction of natural habitats. They help drain tropical peat lands, which contain vast quantities of CO_2. They cause deforestation and hence additional CO_2 emissions. Carbon certification and sustainability criteria and supervision are currently weak instruments, difficult to apply. They are of little help in deciding which plants and production methods provide a sufficiently acceptable net contribution to greenhouse gas reduction to deserve to count towards target implementation. Some 10,000 square metres of agricultural land are needed to produce 1,500 liters of ethanol a year with only limited CO_2 savings compared to a liter of petrol[14]. Agro-fuels are of little help in reducing prices of heating oil and petrol at the pump. Unlike energy savings, their availability tends to increase overall energy demand, leaving oil demand unchanged.

The OECD concludes that biofuel support policies in OECD countries are costly, any savings of GHG emissions and fossil energy are limited, impact on commodity prices is substantial, and consequences for environmental sustainability and biodiversity negative. They actually have questionable effects on all of the world's three main challenges: food security, energy security and environmental security. Environmental NGOs have rightly called for a moratorium on agro-fuels. So did the independent Scientific Advisory Committee of the European Environment Agency, which asked for the suspension of the "overambitious" 10% biofuel target - "an experiment, whose unintended effects are difficult to predict and difficult to control"; it advocated a new, comprehensive scientific study on the environmental risks and benefits of biofuels. It has been estimated that meeting the 10% biofuel target may require shifting 10m hectares of land (40m ha with the more ambitious US bioethanol target) to biofuel production.

However, agro-fuel advocates respond to criticism by underlining that first-generation agro-fuels represent but a necessary phase towards the development of second-generation technology, which is said to be just around the corner without involving loss of food production. Potential second-generation agro-fuels are mostly based on cellulose that is present in many biomass sources such as trees (cellulosic ethanol), switchgrass, willows, jatropha, myscanthus, pongamia); they can also be obtained from food crop waste such as wheat stalks, maize straw (corn stover), husks, grass and from weed food refuse. Several potential crops for second-generation agro-fuels have the advantage of not being grown on farmland, or deforested land, and preserve the food component of plants, and may be grown with relatively little water and fertilizer on fallow land, without therefore displacing food production[15]. One can also use biotechnology to decrease the production costs of agro-fuel plants, increasing yields (up to three times those of wheat, or 20 tons/ha). Yield per hectare may be boosted with genetically engineered sugar (by 100%); rape seed (+60%) and sweet sorghum. It may become possible to plant crops in soils lost to salinisation, and to genetically produce plants that can grow in marginal or otherwise unusable farmland.

But second-generation agro-fuel skeptics recall that relevant research started a long time ago

---

[13] It has been calculated that every 1% price increase in commodities increases the number of undernourished by 16 million (Runge and Senauer). If the US mandated biofuel production targets are to be met, two-thirds of corn will have to be transformed into ethanol, making the US a net importer of corn. Filling an American 4X4 SUV with 80l ethanol would require some 220kg of corn, i.e. the amount of calories sufficient to feed a person for one year (Runge and Senauer).
[14] Incidentally, biomass from cultivated forests would compete with crop land or with wood for housing and furniture and produce CO_2 when transported. Its burning produces emissions of dioxin and fine particles. As to biomass from deforestation, it is not renewable: it actually emits more GHG than coal.

---

[15] There are other more interesting second-generation biofuels such as synthetic diesel produced from biomass inputs including wood pulp and waste (Sun Diesel), biomass-to liquid (BTL) plants, biodiesel from biogas. As these are basically not typical agro-fuels, they are not dealt with here.

(early seventies). They retort that most agricultural waste is organic material useful to maintain the soil structure, nutrients and its store-of-carbon function. According to a letter sent to Science Magazine, removing 75% of crop residues to transport them (at a CO_2 cost) to the biofuel refinery could increase the rate of soil erosion a hundredfold. Our addiction to cars would then lead to "peak soil as well as peak oil" (Monbiot). In order to compensate for the nutrient loss, more fertilizer (potash) would have to be used, causing additional CO_2 emissions. It is therefore unlikely that second-generation agro-fuels could avoid most of the pitfalls of the first generation. Moreover, it remains to be proven whether large-scale cultivation of non-food crops such as myscanthus, jatropha or pongamia are commercially feasible, and whether the benefits will trickle down to the small farmers instead of concentrating on big farmers and large corporations.

Current agro-fuel policy in Europe (and more in the US) is an illustration of "The March of Folly" described by the late American historian Barbara Tuchman, of pursuing government policies contrary to their own interests ("misgovernment"). Agro-fuel subsidies, together with tax-rebates and import protection, impact on all three major looming world scarcities: food, energy and the environment. On all three there has been not just market but also government failure. Actually, current agro-fuel policies do not help correct such failures, they aggravate them. They actually ignore fundamental political realities, economic and social aspects, power and income differentials among and within countries, let alone human rights. They are an ethical failure.

Scientists keep working to improve the efficiency of photosynthesis, carbon capture, nitrogen fixation and many other cellular processes that boost biomass yields. There are at least three ways to make second-generation agro-fuels: a) pushing the brewing process converting grain or sugar into ethanol, b) the thermal method heating waste products to produce synthetic gas, which is then recombined to form a liquid fuel, and c) making biofuels from algae using carbon dioxide as a feedstock. Enzymes can allow production of cellulosic ethanol from the inedible parts of crops such as straw stalks (or from wood or food waste). Biomass-eating bacteria can break down cellulose.

But there are huge problems to bring each method to fruition. For instance, using enzymes to ferment starch or sugar into alcohol is easy, but waste products contain much larger amounts of lignin, which is harder and more costly to break down[16]. Cellulosic molecules are difficult to transform into sugar to produce ethanol.

There are good prospects with genetically modified algae ponds yielding ten times more bio-diesel per hectare than jatropha and any other plant, and minimizing ecological damage (if grown in closed tanks). Algae can also help to capture carbon dioxide from burning fossil fuels. The most efficient may become biofuels derived directly from the photosynthesis of green micro-algae, which may prove able to convert into bio-diesel with a yield 30 times above that of oilseeds with a much lower need for fertilizers and pesticides. But I fear it may take up to mid century to produce biofuel from algae on a large enough scale to influence near-term policies.

A new technology that can help withdraw carbon dioxide from the atmosphere is *biochar* sequestration or "green carbon". When combined with bioenergy production, it is a clean energy technology that reduces emissions as well as sequesters carbon. It consists in heating plant biomass without oxygen (low-temperature pyrolysis process). Pyrolysis converts trees, grasses or crop residues into biochar with twofold higher carbon content than ordinary biomass. Biochar locks up rapidly decomposing carbon in plant biomass in a durable form. Locking carbon up in soil makes more sense than storing it in plants and trees that eventually decompose. It has been shown to improve the structure and fertility of soils, thereby improving biomass production. It can be mixed with manure, and enhance the retention and therefore efficiency of fertilizers. It may also decrease fertilizer run-off.

The best way to reduce energy demand is not to generate emissions in the first place. It is less costly to save energy than to produce it. US expert Amory Lovins has been talking of "negawatts" to define a megawatt of power avoided or saved from use on the grid. This can be obtained through energy saving technology and regulations, which

---

[16] See: "Hopes ride on the next generation" by Fiona Harvey, Financial Times 16/09/08).

are developing fast, as well as through energy-saving consumer behaviour, which still leaves much to be desired.

Technology can help enhance energy efficiency[17] and reduce energy use by appliances, develop micro-generation units such as roof solar panels and mini-wind turbines, upgrading current energy networks around such units (smart grids) and building smaller power stations close to energy users. Smart grids would enable full use of intermittent energy sources limiting stand-by, back-up energy supply, reducing power-line losses, and using waste heat to warm local buildings. Much here depends on increasing R&D on energy efficiency and storage, and on new energies.

Apart from establishing industrial energy-saving standards, regulations can and should also:

- update biofuel strategies suspending or abolishing the 10% biofuel target[18] by 2020,
- improve and generalize the European Emissions Trading Scheme, a mandatory cap and trade system for CO_2 emissions, giving carbon a meaningful price, setting limits to the emissions of the most energy-intensive companies, penalizing company emission increases and rewarding reductions; allowing companies to trade permit allocations to limit CO_2 amongst each other; such permits should be bought at auction and generalized; this is the best way to slow down fossil fuel extraction rates,
- establish punitive fees for energy consumption exceeding strict levels,
- upgrade electricity distribution systems to a "smart grid", or *electranet*, that would allow people to generate their own electricity from renewable sources and sell it back to the power grid[19].

Another effective, regulatory approach is Reducing Emissions from Deforestation and Degradation (REDD). So far forests have not been valued except for their wood, although they provide a lot of value in the storage and reprocessing of carbon. Deforestation accounts for up to 25% of all GHG emissions. If REDD is included in the Kyoto process, this will be a momentous event. In the Eliasch Report (linked to the Stern Review in 2008) it is estimated that it will cost up to $33bn a year to halve emissions from forests by 2030, but that long-term benefits would be $3,700bn. REDD proposed payments in the form of carbon credits to encourage forests to be saved. Forest and land use credits should be included in emission trading schemes[20]. This could help encourage and enhance the management of land for carbon as compared to managing it for beef, agro-fuels or the like.

As to behavioural changes, they can mean such things as turning down thermostats for heating and turning them up for air-conditioning, and turning off lights and appliances when not needed. Such changes can be encouraged via a number of GHG emission-reducing measures such as:

- using emission performance standards to provide incentives to the cleanest technologies; giving priority to energy efficiency and carbon saving on the demand side, whose potential is far larger than carbon savings on the supply side; strengthen regulations promoting moderate temperature targets in public buildings, both in summer and winter, and recommended targets in private homes,
- using the fiscal instrument to limit emissions[21], notably imposing a large surtax on gas-guzzling road transport vehicles, steeply increasing motorway fees, particularly on lorries, using the proceeds to subsidize rail and combined transport, making (privatized) train prices for piggy-backing motor-vehicles so cheap as to become irresistible.

Government policy is of paramount importance in all this and beyond. It should also be primarily a

---

[17] An example are modern wood-burning stoves that have a 90% energy efficiency, three times greater than old stoves and far greater than rural stoves in Africa, which need 20 times more wood for the same heat.

[18] At least 10% of final energy consumption in transportation must come from renewable energy sources by 2020, a part of which is to come from first generation biofuels.

[19] From «International star (Al Gore) plays coy on domestic plans», Financial Times, 13 November 2007.
Al Gore was reported joining Silicon Valley in setting up the fund management company Generation Investment Management in order to tap the public markets, where "more money is allocated in an hour than by all governments in the world in that space, and promote clean technologies".

[20] Like in New-South Wales, Australia. See:" Climate Change, The Redd Planet, Financial Times, 2/12/08

[21] Al Gore suggested "eliminating the payroll tax and replacing it with carbon dioxide tax". Over twenty years ago the Jacques Delors' Commission proposed a reduction in taxes on labour compensating the fiscal shortfall via a CO_2 tax (rejected by the UK on grounds of principle). Scandinavia and some other European Countries have done so. Moreover, one should offer full investment tax credits, subsidies, and price support for renewable energies like solar energy, wind energy (mostly off-shore), other bio-energies in the form of landfill and sewage treatment gas, biogas from organic wastes, sewage sludge and demolition food, renewable-energy-based hydrogen fuel cells, and low carbon technologies such as batteries, carbon capture and storage.

government task to consider ethical and political issues related to public policy. For instance, as regards biofuel subsidies, politicians should assess potential consequences on food security, food-fuel competition, and of a geopolitical nature such as potential adverse impacts on the developing world. All governments including the US and China, which together represent 45% of total world carbon emissions, should give clear policy signals taking into account the need for fairness[22].

CONCLUSION

Oil and gas will remain the main energy sources for the next generation. It will be tough to be able to substantially reduce world emissions with existing fossil and renewable energy technologies.

We actually face a "green paradox": green measures tend to push down future more than current prices of oil & gas, which leads resource owners to extract their stocks faster than otherwise. Measures to reduce CO_2 emissions may therefore accelerate carbon extraction. In addition to fuel demand, environmental policy will therefore have to tackle also fuel supply. In addition to efforts to reduce CO_2 emissions, notably by burying carbon, it has to try and limit carbon extraction. But carbon sequestration is far from easy because of its energy intensity and space requirements. Carbon capture from fossil fuels requires much more storage space than the underground space occupied by the relevant resource. According to the Panel on Climate Change, the world's depleted coal mines, oil and gas deposits and natural caves offer room for just one tenth of the CO_2 that would be generated by all recoverable carbon resources[23].

Nuclear energy is on the way up, because one cannot do without it to meet the Kyoto targets. Renewable energies have become the stars of the show. Climate change cries out for new sources of energy. There has been talk of a "Green New Deal"

to get us out of the economic crisis. Lord Stern has put its annual cost at 1-2% of global GDP by 2050, requiring some $45,000bn (or $1,200bn per annum) to be invested in clean energy. There are unprecedented opportunities for transforming the economy from high-carbon and environmentally unfriendly to low carbon and environmentally sustainable "green growth" (Sir Nicholas Stern). Early, shrewd investors can make huge profits. But, as the sour state of many bio-fuel refineries indicates, irrational investor exuberance for renewable energy businesses – launched on flawed economics with volatile commodity and raw material prices – faces growing risks, particularly if and when government support is withdrawn.

The development of new energies is confronted with policy contradictions. For instance, how far can one reasonably go in adopting energy security measures if they reduce food security, or in pursuing emission reductions to the extent they may jeopardize energy security? In this connection, it is worth recalling the warning of the English novelist and scientist C.P. Snow (1905-1980) who once said: "Technology is a queer thing. It brings you great gifts with one hand, and it stabs you in the back with the other". Renewable energies have more net emission foot-prints than most people are aware of. No new energy sources should be promoted without submitting them to Life Cycle Analysis. Such an analysis would notably slow down the current political band-wagon regarding on-shore wind farms, and even more so, agro-fuels, and promote developments with energy conservation, solar energy, biogas from waste and eventually, hopefully hydrogen energy. All things considered, the latter may well be the best hope of low emission renewable energy over the longer term.

None of the suggestions made in this note is easy to implement. The best way would be to apply most of them so as to distribute the pain and weaken opposing lobbies. As long as governments continue with "gesture politics" supporting new energy strategies that help politicians (with the best intentions) to acquire green credentials, and provides them with the illusion of an easy technological fix, they will divert their attention from getting on with more important, less popular measures for saving the planet.

There will be "no substantial progress without new kinds of energy systems, new kinds of auto-

---

[22] Emissions in China, India and Sub-Saharan Africa are 1/3, 1/5 and 1/10th lower than US emissions per capita. While industrialized countries' emissions must go down, developing countries' emissions must be allowed to catch up with them. The EU agreement on 15 December 2008 on climate change is too weak a signal to pull along countries such as the BRICS on Kyoto II.
[23] See: Hans Werner-Sinn, "How to resolve the green paradox", Financial Times, 27 August 2009.

mobiles and new buildings" (Jeffrey Sachs). Jeremy Rifkin's vision is to retool the motor industry, reconfigure the power grid, and covert buildings into power plants. He believes in the shift of our energy regime from national power grids and transmission lines and centralized control, to distributed, digitalized management capturing local, renewable technologies. He advocates an accelerated development of automotive technology from the internal combustion engine to electric and hydrogen fuel-cell plug-in vehicles. He also calls for new construction designs and materials. All these he sees as the entry points to a third industrial revolution and a post carbon economy.

This will take time. We might witness breakthroughs from outside the energy industry such as nanotechnology, bio-sciences or unsuspected other sources.

There is no single answer then as to the overall mission of the European Estates for both private and public benefit. Many an estate will continue to play a role in feeding the world. Others will be tempted to act also as a fuel station despite its pitfalls. Hopefully a growing number will play a constructive ReGreening role as carbon orchards. The context in which they are called to operate is that of a vast overhaul of rural livelihoods towards optimizing carbon and bio-diversity. Governments would have to, or should, recognize the relevance of such a public service activity. At a prospective value of, say, at least €30 or more per tonne in the long run, carbon could be a good crop!

Ciguiñuelas

Mediterranean

Location: Navas de Estena, Ciudad Real.
Navalucillos and Hontanar, Toledo. Spain.
Surface: 3,990 ha.

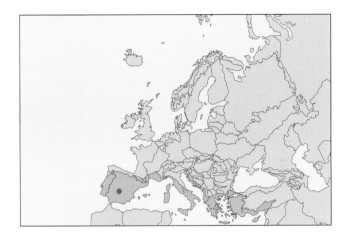

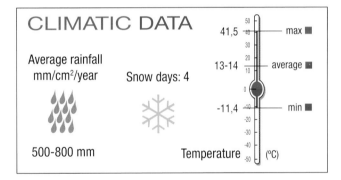

CLIMATIC DATA

Average rainfall
mm/cm²/year   Snow days: 4

500-800 mm   Temperature   (°C)

41,5 — max
13-14 — average
-11,4 — min

SUMMARY

Ciguiñuelas, with a surface area of 3,990 hectares, is located between the provinces of Toledo and Ciudad Real, right in the heart of the *Montes de Toledo* (Toledo Mountains) in central Spain.
The philosophy pursued by the proprietors for more than 30 years has been to conserve the landscape, restore the forest canopy and make a determined effort to preserve the fauna typical of the Montes de Toledo. As a result, Ciguiñuelas stands out as a clear model of the integrated management of agriculture, forestry, hunting and ecotourism, for which reason it has been proposed as a *Wildlife Estate* for the Mediterranean region in other words, as a model estate on which sustainable, efficient and practical management of the natural resources to be found there is guaranteed. A *Wildlife Estate* carries a label of good hunting management, endorsed by the Directorate-General of the Environment of the European Commission, among other institutions.

Ciguiñuelas Estate

View over Ciguiñuelas from the top of Rocigalgo.

HISTORY

The name of this property is a corruption of *cigüeñuela*, the Spanish name for the Black-Winged Stilt *(Himantopus himantopus)*, a wading bird of the Recurvirostridae family with long pink legs, black bill, coat and wings, and a conspicuous white neck and underparts. As its habitat is confined to lake and marshy areas, mentioning the name of this estate inevitably brings to mind the different watercourses which begin in the high peaks that border it to the north.

At first, the property was called "El Cerezo", and later took its definitive name from the area of land where the main building was constructed.

Its historical origins can be found amongst the ecclesiastical and municipal property which was disentailed at different moments in the 19th century. At that time, it was a range of hills lying far from civilization, almost uninhabited except for the goatherds whose goats fed on the bushy vegetation. However, in about 1900, a motor road was opened, starting in Risco de las Paradas, crossing the lower slopes of the mountain range to reach the waters of the River Guadiana in El Portillo de Cíjara. From that time on, Ciguiñuelas became accessible, better known and even exploitable.

Some time later, a French timber company planned the construction of a narrow-gauge railway to make use of the oak growing in the woodland which covered the steep slopes, and the cork of the cork oaks in the lower parts. The land was levelled out but the rails were not laid, and the level ground is still known by the name of "the French line".

In 1922, Jaime Díez de Rivera y Figueroa, Marquis of La Villa de Orellana, became the owner of the 12,000

The name of this property is a corruption of *cigüeñuela*, the Spanish name of the Black-winged stilt.

hectares lying on the southern slopes of these mountains. He began to work the estate, ploughing the flat areas, laying out roads, building a new farmhouse, constructing sheepfolds and introducing cattle. He also commissioned his relative, the architect Eduardo Figueroa, Count of Yebes and author of *Veinte años de caza mayor (Twenty years of big game hunting)*, whose prologue by Ortega y Gasset constitutes the best philosophical treatise on hunting, to make plans for a manor house. Construction began in 1934 and the house was used as a barracks during the Spanish Civil War (1936-1939).

The hardships of the postwar period affected this area perhaps more than others, as it became a setting for gangs of bandits, made up of deserters from the republican army and common criminals who ravaged the region during the 1940s.

Two gangs of bandits stood out in particular: those led by Chaqueta Larga and El Manco de Agudo. The latter, José Méndez Aguado, carried out his criminal acts from Navalucillos and Ventas con Peña Aguilera to the north, as far as Los Yébenes to the east and Abenójar to the south, over an extensive area of land that covered almost the whole of the Montes de Toledo. He began his villainous deeds in the summer of 1940 and, after carrying out a large number of robberies and kidnappings, facing up on several occasions to the regular forces of the Civil Guard, he finally died in an encounter with the same forces on the pastureland of Garbanzuelo (which almost borders on Ciguiñuelas) on 12 March, 1949.

Chaqueta Larga (Long Jacket) was the nickname of Joaquín Ventas Cintas, who operated principally in the mountain area which stretches from the banks of the Estena river to those of the Guadiana. As in the previous example, his crimes centred on the scattered population that resided in the mountain villages and farmhouses, committing all kinds of offences, including the raping of defenceless women who lived in isolated places. In 1948 he disappeared, crossing the French border.

This critical situation led Orellana, the owner, to sell the 12,000 hectares to José María Tradacete López, who acquired them with the idea of running a herd of 10,000 goats and carrying out intensive felling of the trees. In view of the profit obtained from this latter activity, Jaime Díez de Rivera tried to break the purchase agreement, giving rise to a lengthy lawsuit which ended with a judgement in favour of José María Tradacete.

But the latter did not enjoy possession for very long and, in 1950, he sold the estate to Pilar Colón de Carvajal, marchioness of Castiglione, who had just disposed of the pastureland of El Molinillo, also situated in the Montes de Toledo, to José Biosca Torres. The amount received in the latter purchase agreement was not sufficient to cover that of the new property and it was therefore supplemented by a fifty-year mortgage which would turn out to be very costly for the new owners. Moreover, it became necessary to make further investments to run Ciguiñuelas, restore the stately home and refurbish the rest of the buildings which had deteriorated as a result of the damage they had suffered; as a consequence, they first sold off the hectares comprising the hills of Muelas, where the Estena river has its source in the eastern part of the estate, and then the land of El Maíllo, made up of this stream and its valley of cork oaks. The purchaser, the industrialist Alfredo Mata Peón, thus brought together 3,000 hectares which he baptized with the name of Chorreras de Muelas.

The Castiglione family continued with the improvement work undertaken before the Civil War; they cleared the low hills that were suitable for farming, employing forty families of settlers from Portugal and Extremadura to do the work. They also paid great attention to hunting, understanding that it was a very valuable resource for the property, marking out the reserves and appointing keepers to look after them.

Nevertheless, Prado Colón de Carvajal family did not own the property of Ciguiñuelas for very long either and, in 1960, they sold it to a mercantile company called Dehesa El Cerezo S.A., constituted in equal parts by Eduardo Sainz de Vicuña, Castor Cañedo Pidal and Manuel Prado Colón de Carvajal. Five years later, the latter of these transferred his shareholding to the other two, who thereby became the only owners of the famous estate.

The Main House was built in 1922 by the Marquis of Orellana.

The two owners, relatives as well as great friends, and in full agreement as regards their dreams and projects, got down to improving the property, suspending the charcoal making, getting rid of the goats in order to safeguard the spontaneous regeneration of the trees and shrubs, appointing six keepers to watch over and maintain the hunting and the forestry, sowing the flattest parts to provide fodder and stubble for sheep, and opening up new tracks to gain access

The "El Capricho" oak, a catalogued individual tree.

to the different areas. The repopulation of the pine trees dates back to this period, imposed by, and in partnership with, the Administration and against the wishes of the owners.

In 1975, when Castor Cañedo passed away, the estate was divided up between Eduardo Sainz de Vicuña and the descendants of his partner and friend. The latter separated a portion of the estate to form an independent property, while Saínz de Vicuña kept the trading company and an area of 3,990 hectares, including the lands of Chorrancos, Los Campillos, Chaparroso, Cerro del Hombre, Río Frío and Guajaraz.

Activity did not cease: significant reafforestation work was begun, this time with native species, as a result of which holm oaks, gall oaks and cork oaks cover areas that charcoal making and indiscriminate tree felling had left bare. In regard to hunting, a great step was taken when, in 1979, 16 spanish ibex from the Sierra de Cazorla were reintroduced, so that the most emblematic hunting species in Spain could return to the peaks of El Rocigalgo range.

The extraordinary vegetation cover of Ciguiñuelas can be seen as a summary of the history of this exemplary estate, and represents a further example of how private property has protected and championed the native tree species of the Iberian peninsula. A trip over the plains of Castile illustrates this aspect better than whatever may be written about it: the towns are located in wide open regions of barren land, devastated by its inhabitants in their search for firewood for their kitchens, while the only remaining wooded areas are where there has been an owner to look after them.

Marquis of Laula

DESCRIPTION

We can basically divide the estate into two areas, in accordance with relief. To the north of the road which crosses the estate we find a sierra, steeply sloped and reaching considerable heights, among which the peak of El Rocigalgo (1,441 metres above sea level), the highest summit on the estate and in the whole of the Montes de Toledo, stands out. It is a rough area, with ravines, stony areas and rocks.

To the south of the road there is an area of more gentle relief, in which ravines with rivers and streams flowing through them alternate with hills with more even slopes. In this area we find the lowest elevation on the estate, on the riverbed of the *Río Frío*, on the boundary with the *El Avellanar* Estate (654 metres above sea level).

The two most important permanent watercourses on the estate are the *Río Frío* and the *Agua de Ciguiñuelas*. These watercourses, together with many others of a seasonal nature, have their sources on the estate itself.

Along the course of the *Río Frío* there is a reservoir, which guarantees a supply of water throughout the year. Moreover, there is a network of pools providing drinking areas for animals.

Vegetation
The characteristic vegetation is Mediterranean with a few pockets of an Atlantic and Eurosiberian nature. The most noteworthy types of vegetation are the following:

Mountainous areas with cork oaks
Spread more widely across the southern half of the estate, we find mature woodland made up of

Ciguiñuelas Estate, 1960. In the picture, Carmen Pérez Seoane, Countess of Berantevilla and Her Royal Highness the Princess Teresa de Borbón.

Marquis of Laula

Cork Oak *(Quercus suber)* with some specimens in full production, accompanied in some areas by Pyrenean Oak *(Quercus pyrenaica)* and Gall Oak *(Quercus faginea)*, with some specimens of Strawberry tree *(Arbutus unedo)*.

Pyrenean oaks

The Pyrenean Oak *(Quercus pyrenaica)* forest is represented on the estate by mature, generally monospecific stands, although on occasions it is accompanied by cork oaks and strawberry trees. It generally has an undergrowth of Gum Rockrose *(Cistus ladanifer)*, Tree Heath *(Erica arborea)* and Bracken *(Pteridium aquilinum)*.

Mediterranean mountain

This occupies a large part of the estate; in this type of vegetation we find the four species of oaks of the area: the Cork Oak *(Quercus suber)*, the Holm Oak *(Quercus ilex)*, the Pyrenean Oak *(Quercus pyrenaica)* and the Gall Oak *(Quercus faginea)*, accompanied as mentioned above by some specimens of Strawberry Trees *(Arbutus unedo)*.

The accompanying thicket is basically made up of Gum Rockrose *(Cistus ladanifer)*, with a scattering of species characteristic of Mediterranean woodland such as Tree Heath *(Erica arborea)* and Rosemary *(Rosmarinus officinalis)*, among others.

Riverbank vegetation

Chiefly found on the banks of the rivers and in shady areas at the sources of the streams, forming the upper forest level, there is a riverine forest made up of White Ash *(Fraxinus angustifolia)*, Willow *(Salix spp.)*, Maple *(Acer spp.)*, Yew *(Taxus baccata)*, Holly *(Ilex aquifolium)* and so on. The last two species form part of the Catalogue of Protected Species of Castilla-La Mancha.

These riverbank areas also offer protection to flora of Atlantic, Mediterranean-Atlantic and sub-tropical-Mediterranean nature which exist on the estate, such as yews and hollies, Laurustinus *(Viburnum tinus)*, Royal Fern *(Osmunda regalis)*.

Reforestation

In accordance with the objectives of improving the estate and its profitability, there have been a series of acts of reforestation with Cork Oaks

Ciguiñuelas is in the heart of the Montes de Toledo country.

(Quercus suber), Sweet Chestnut *(Castanea sativa)* and Stone Pine *(Pinus pinea)*.

Pine groves

In some areas of the estate there has been some replanting of *Pinus pinea* and *Pinus halepensis* in partnership with the State Forestry Services, which is now overmature and is principally for timber production. This dates back to the end of the 1970s.

Pastureland

The natural pasturelands are annual and rather poor, made up of the *Vulpia* species or *Agrostis pourretii*.

Crop areas

Forming a far-reaching mosaic over the whole surface area of Ciguiñuelas, and more concentrated in the southern half, we find dry agricultural land used for the growing of cereals and permanent meadows in the irrigated areas. Rye and oats are grown on the dry land, While Common Vetch *(Vicia sativa)*, and Sudan Grass *(Sorghum sudanense)* are grown in the irrigated areas.

Fauna

Amphibians & Reptiles

Among the group of amphibians we should highlight the presence of the Iberian Newt *(Triturus boscai)*, an endemic Iberian species of limited distribution in the western half of the peninsula.

The community of reptiles includes a large number of species, although they do not appear to be present in high densities. Among this group we must mention the presence of the Spanish Terrapin *(Mau-*

remys leprosa) and the Schreiber's Green Lizard (Lacerta schreiberi); the latter species is endemic to the Iberian peninsula and both of them are included in Annex II of the Habitats Directive.

Birds

Seventy-nine species of birds have been recorded, both on migration and breeding. The presence of the Golden Eagle (Aquila chrysaëtos) and the Peregrine Falcon (Falco peregrinus) are of particular note.

Mammals

The total number of species of mammals recorded on the estate is 30.

- **Insectivores:** from the biogeographical point of view, the most noteworthy of the four species present is the Iberian Mole (Talpa occidentalis), the only one endemic to the Iberian peninsula.
- **Chiroptera:** the seven species of bat detected are included in the National Catalogue of Endangered Species as being of

AMPHIBIANS & REPTILES

Family	Specie	Common name	Family	Specie	Common name
SALAMANDRIDAE	Triturus boscai	Iberian newt	GEKKONIDAE	Tarentola mauritanica	Moorish gecko
	Pleurodeles walt	Spanish ribbed newt	LACERTIDAE	Podarcis hispanica	Iberian wall lizard
	Salamandra salamandra	Fire salamander		Psammodrumus algirus	Algerian sand lizard
DISCOGLOSIDAE	Alytes cisternasii	Iberian midwife toad		Lacerta screiberi	Green lizard
BUFONIDAE	Bufo calamita	Natterjack toad	AMPHISBAENIDAE	Blanus cinereus	Iberian worm lizard
	Bufo bufo	Common toad	COLUBRIDAE	Macroprotodon cucullatus	False smooth snake
PELOBATIDAE	Pelobates cultripes	Spadefoot toad		Natrix maura	Viperine snake
RANIDAE	Rana perezi	Common frog		Malpolon mospessulanus	Montpellier snake
EMYDIDAE	Mauremys leprosa	Spanish terrapin		Elaphe scalaris	Ladder snake

BIRDS

Family	Specie	Common name	Family	Specie	Common name
ARDEIDAE	Ardea cinerea	Grey heron	CUCULIDAE	Clamator glandarius	Great spotted cuckoo
ANATIDAE	Anas platyrhynchos	Mallard		Cuculus canorus	Common cuckoo
FALCONIDAE	Falco peregrinus	Peregrine falcon	STRIGIDAE	Athene noctua	Little owl
	Falco naumanni	Lesser kestrel		Otus scops	Scops owl
	Falco tinnunculus	Common kestrel		Tyto alba	Barn owl
	Falco subbuteo	Eurasian hobby		Asio otus	Long-eared owl
	Falco columbarius	Merlin		Strix aluco	Tawny owl
ACCIPITRIDAE	Pernis apivorus	Honey buzzard		Bubo bubo	Eurasian eagle owl
	Circus pygargus	Montagu's harrier	CAPRIMULGIDAE	Caprimulgus ruficollis	Red-necked nightjar
	Circus cyaneus	Hen harrier	APODIDAE	Apus apus	Common swift
	Milvus milvus	Red kite	MEROPIDAE	Merops apiaster	European bee-eater
	Milvus migrans	Black kite	UPUPIDAE	Upupa epops	Hoopoe
	Elanus caeruleus	Black-winged kite	PICIDAE	Dendrocopos major	Great spotted woodpecker
	Buteo buteo	Common buzzard		Picus viridis	Green woodpecker
	Circaetus gallicus	Short-toed eagle	ALAUDIDAE	Lullula arborea	Woodlark
	Hieraaetus fasciatus	Bonelli's eagle		Galerida cristata	Crested lark
	Hieraaetus pennatus	Booted eagle		Galerida theklae	Thekla lark
	Aquila chrysaetos	Golden eagle	HIRUNDINIDAE	Delichon urbica	House martin
	Aquila adalberti	Iberian imperial eagle		Ptyonoprogne rupestris	Crag martin
	Accipiter nisus	Eurasian sparrowhawk		Hirundo rustica	Barn swallow
	Accipiter gentilis	Goshawk		Hirundo daurica	Red-rumped swallow
	Neophron percnopterus	Egyptian vulture	MOTACILLIDAE	Motacilla cinerea	Grey wagtail
	Gyps fulvus	Griffon vulture		Motacilla alba	White wagtail
	Aegypius monachus	Black vulture	TROGLODYTIDAE	Troglodytes troglodytes	Winter wren
PHASIANIDAE	Alectoris rufa	Red-legged partridge	MUSCICAPIDAE	Saxicola torquata	African stonechat
	Coturnix coturnix	Common quail		Monticola solitarius	Blue rock thrush
CHARADRIIDAE	Charadrius dubius	Little ringed plover		Erithacus rubecula	European robin
SCOLOPACIDAE	Scolopax rusticola	Eurasian woodcock		Turdus merula	Blackbird
			Turdus philomelos	Song thrush
COLUMBIDAE	Columba palumbus	Wood pigeon		Turdus viscivorus	Mistle thrush
	Columba oenas	Stock pigeon		Turdus iliacus	Redwing
	Columba livia	Rock pigeon		Phoenicurus ochruros	Black redstart
	Stretopelia turtur	Turtle dove		Phoenicurus phoenicurus	Common redstart
			Luscinia megarhynchos	Nightingale

BIRDS

Family	Specie	Common name
CISTICOLIDAE	Cisticola juncidis	Streaked fantail warbler
	Cettia cetti	Cetti's warbler
SYLVIIDAE	Sylvia atricapilla	Blackcap
	Sylvia cantillans	Subalpine warbler
	Sylvia undata	Dartford warbler
	Sylvia melanocephala	Sardinian warbler
	Phylloscopus collybita	Common chiffchaff
	Phylloscopus bonelli	Bonelli's warbler
	Hippolais polyglotta	Melodious warbler
PARIDAE	Parus major	Great tit
	Parus cristatus	Crested tit
	Parus caeruleus	Blue tit
AEGYTHALIDAE	Aegythalos caudatus	Long-tailed tit
SITTIDAE	Sitta europea	Eurasian nuthatch

Family	Specie	Common name
CERTHIIDAE	Certhia brachydactyla	Short-toed treecreeper
ORIOLIDAE	Oriolus oriolus	Golden oriole
LANIIDAE	Lanius senator	Woodchat shrike
CORVIDAE	Pica pica	Common magpie
	Corvus monedula	Jackdaw
	Corvus corax	Common raven
	Garrulus glandarius	Eurasian jay
STURNIDAE	Sturnus unicolor	Spotless starling
PASSERIDAE	Passer domesticus	House sparrow
	Passer montanus	Tree sparrow
FRINGILLIDAE	Fringilla coelebs	Chaffinch
	Carduelis cannabina	Linnet
EMBERIZIDAE	Emberiza cia	Rock bunting
	Miliaria calandra	Corn bunting

MAMMALS

Family	Specie	Common name
ERINACEIDAE	Erinaceous europaeus	Hedgehog
SORICIDAE	Crocidura russula	Greater white-toothed shrew
	Suncus etruscus	Etruscan shrew
TALPIDAE	Talpa occidentalis	Iberian mole
VESPERTILIONIDAE	Pipistrellus pipistrellus	Common pipistrelle
	Pipistrellus kuhlii	Kuhl's pipistrelle
	Myotis myotis	Greater mouse-eared bat
MOLOSSIDAE	Tadarida teniotis	European free-tailed bat
RHINOLOPHIDAE	Rhinolophus ferrum-equinum	Greater horseshoe bat
	Rhinolophus hipposideros	Lesser horseshoe bat
	Rhinolophus euryale	Mediterranean horseshoe bat
LEPORIDAE	Oryctolagus cuniculus	Rabbit
	Lepus granatensis	Iberian hare
GLIRIDAE	Eliomys quercinus	Garden dormouse

Family	Specie	Common name
MURIDAE	Rattus norvegicus	Common rat
	Rattus rattus	Black rat
ARVICOLIDAE	Microtus duodecimcostatus	Mediterranean pine vole
MURIDAE	Apodemus sylvaticus	Wood mouse
	Mus spretus	Algerian mouse
	Arvicola sapidus	Southern water vole
CANIDAE	Vulpes vulpes	Red fox
MUSTELIDAE	Mustela nivalis	Least weasel
	Martes foina	Beech marten
	Mustela putorius	European polecat
VIVERRIDAE	Genetta genetta	Common genet
FELIDAE	Felis silvestris	Wildcat
SUIDAE	Sus scrofa	Wild boar
CERVIDAE	Cervus elaphus	Red deer
	Capreolus capreolus	Roe deer
BOVIDAE	Capra pyrenaica hispanica	Spanish ibex

"special interest". None of them are endemic nor do they present serious conservation problems in the area.

- **Rodents:** the seven species present in the area form a community which is typical of the mediterranean environments in the southern half of the peninsula.
  From among the species of lagomorphs and rodents, only the Iberian hare, Iberian Hare *(Lepus granatensis)* the Algerian Mouse *(Mus spretus)* and the mediterranean Pine Vole *(Microtus duodecimcostatus)* can be regarded as exclusive representatives of the Mediterranean area.
- **Carnivores:** five species constitute the community of carnivores in the area.
- **Ungulates:** the ungulates on the estate are represented by four species, two of which constitute the basis for the hunting activity which takes place in the area: the Red Deer *(Cervus elaphus)* and the Wild Boar *(Sus scrofa)*, the other two species being the Roe Deer *(Capreolus capreolus)* and the Iberian Wild Goat *(Capra pyrenaica hispanica)*.

GOALS

The most noteworthy aspect of Ciguiñuelas is the magnificent management which has been implemented there[1] for more than six years, easily appreciable both in terms of the the estate's figures and its current condition. The goals of the management of Ciguiñuelas are:
- Conserving and improving the infrastructure of the estate.
- Promoting its use for big game hunting, in terms of both quality and quantity.
- Realigning agriculture. More economical and efficient crops for hunting. Adaptation to the new CAP.
- Promoting the forestry. Conserving and improving the existing stocks and increasing the forest area.
- Renewing and consolidating an efficient and stable human team.

FUTURE MEASURES TO ACHIEVE THE ESTABLISHED GOALS IN CIGUIÑUELAS
A.- AGROFORESTRY MEASURES
- Progressive realignment of cereals sown on dry meadows. Less cost and work - similar production.
- Reafforestation plan for less productive agricultural areas and areas with no tree cover. Investment: 100% recoverable and an annual income of € 180/ha.

A REDUCTION IN COSTS AND AN INCREASE IN INCOME

B.- HUNTING MEASURES
- INCREASE IN INCOME PER HUNTING PARTY:
  1. Sale of a greater number of hunting days
  2. Reduction in agency commission
  3. Improvement in results - progressive rise in prices
- REDUCTION IN COSTS PER HUNTING PARTY
- INCREASE IN INCOME FROM ROE DEER: Live sales and an increase in the number of animals shot.
- SALES OF LIVE DEER

A CONSIDERABLE INCREASE IN INCOME AND A REDUCTION IN COSTS

MANAGEMENT OF THE CIGUIÑUELAS ESTATE. ROLE OF THE PROTECTED AREAS

Ciguiñuelas Estate is made up of two clearly differentiated areas. One part, the northern half, is located on the sunnier slopes at the foot of the Sierra of El Rocigalgo. The other, the southern half, is made up of alternating hills and small valleys along the streams of *Valle del Pero, El Maíllo, Agua de Ciguiñuelas, Riofrío* and so on.

As for its vegetation, we can differentiate several kinds, among which we must highlight, owing to their presence across the entire area, the Pyrenean Oakwoods *(Quercus pyrenaica)*, the Cork Oakwoods *(Quercus suber)*, the Mediterranean woodland (with holm oaks, strawberry trees, cork oaks and associated thicket), the beds of the streams (with characteristic riverbank vegetation), some fertile irrigation plains and dry cropping areas.

The management of Ciguiñuelas Estate is directed basically at commercial hunting and forestry activities, in a way that is compatible with conserving the natural environment. As a result, maintaining the heritage and natural value of the estate takes precedence over any other aspects in the management model that is applied. The daily management and the planning of any activity are conducted by professionals comprising the Technical Management (made up of a team of Forestry Engineers) and the Administrative Management, with the proprietors playing an active part in the decision-making.

Commercial hunting is focussed on big game species which are naturally present on the estate, such as the Red Deer *(Cervus elaphus hispanicus)*, the Iberian Wild Goat *(Capra pyrenaica hispanica)*, the Wild Boar *(Sus scrofa)* and the Roe Deer *(Capreolus capreolus)*. The first two constitute the aim of the hunting parties – *monterías* – which are organized each year on the estate, in which special emphasis is placed on maintaining the ancestral hunting traditions of the Montes de Toledo. Of the seven hunting parties held by the reserve annually, only four actually take place, approximately 40% of the total surface area being set aside each year. This prevents the overexploitation of the resources,

Crops grown for wildlife resemble a mosaic.

maintaining a satisfactory level each year as regards the quantity of animals obtained and the quality of the trophies. Each year, recurrently, an average of 120 deer and 180 wild boar are hunted by the *monterias* in Ciguiñuelas. In addition to the hunting activities, roaring stags are stalked during the rut, together with roe deer during the barking period, and significant trophies are obtained.

Hunting activity on the estate is based on its Technical Hunting Plan and is rounded off with the selective elimination of specimens (defective males and females), fundamentally by means of live capture. This method permits a policy of true selection to be made without the excessive use of conventional methods of selective hunting, in which constant hunting activity disturbs the peace and quiet of the different species on the reserve.

The philosophy of the management model applied has led it to improvement in the food resources on the estate itself. Although these lands in the Montes de Toledo are not of very high quality from the agricultural point of view, traditionally the *querencias* (areas where the game animals prefer to lie) were sown with cereals to be eaten by the wildlife. One of the innovations introduced in the last few years has been to create permanent meadows by sowing annual herbaceous and leguminous crops in those cultivable areas with the worst soil. This provides grazing of abundance and quality for the animals. Over time this practice considerably improves the quality and structure of the soil and similarly prevents the erosive processes caused by continuous farming of these kinds of poor soils, generally on light slopes. Planting quality grazing has been chosen in preference to traditional cereal crops, mainly to conserve the soil and to increase the biodiversity of this kind of natural pasture.

Moreover, the best working land, covering about 150 hectares, has been conserved; it is still sown with cereals, to be eaten by the game or, in exceptional years, to be harvested.

Nevertheless, given that there are periods of real food shortages for game in these latitudes, supplementary food is supplied from time to time and at specific moments when the provision of natural food is scarce; this is based on mixtures of grain and forage.

The other definite commitment by the proprietors of Ciguiñuelas has been to conserve and improve its woodland heritage. As well as the

Ciguiñuelas Estate

forestry work undertaken to maintain its natural oak stocks, continuous reafforestation work has been carried out on the agricultural land for the last ten years. At present, 145 hectares of Cork Oak *(Quercus suber)* have been replanted, together with 20 hectares of Strawberry Tree *(Arbutus unedo)*, 3 hectares of Chestnut Tree *(Castanea sativa)* and 2 hectares of Walnut *(Juglans regia)*. In addition, using plants from the tree nursery on the estate, scattered areas of the land have been replanted with native species which are emblematic of the area, such as yews, maples, strawberry trees, holm oaks and cork oaks.

The current forestry activities on the estate include harvesting cork from the cork oaks. For this purpose the surface area of Ciguiñuelas is divided into three parts, with a total average production of 23,000 castilian quintals (1.058 tons kg) of cork every 10 years.

When determining the objectives and the management and use of the estate's natural resources, the protection schemes affecting it must always be taken into account. 30% of the total surface area is located within the Cabañeros National Park, which applies conditions to some significant aspects, such as the commercial hunting of species like the roe deer. Similarly, some maintenance and improvement work is restricted, among which we should mention the conservation of some roads and tracks and the period during which certain forestry work can be carried out. Similarly, no new infrastructure for hunting or new roads can be built on the surface area affected.

The population of Red deer *(Cervus elaphus* ssp. *hispanicus)* is perfectly adapted to the local climatic conditions.

Ciguiñuelas **(Spain)**

Ciguiñuelas Estate

Furthermore, Ciguiñuelas is situated in the Montes de Toledo SPA (Special Protection Areas for Birds) and the SCI, and its lands are included in protective orders for some listed species. The estate is regarded as a crucial area for the Iberian Imperial Eagle *(Aquila adalberti)*, the Black Stork *(Ciconia nigra)* and the Black Vulture *(Aegypius monachus)*, as well as an area of importance for the Iberian Lynx *(Lynx pardinus)*. Owing to the fact that the estate is included within these protection schemes of the Natura 2000 Network, not a single benefit or subsidy for the conservation of this natural heritage has been received but, in contrast, we find ourselves faced with an increasing number of legal impediments and administrative obstacles in order to manage this estate correctly. An obvious example of this has been the elimination of all the land included in the Natura 2000 Network from the new programme for the Afforestation of Agricultural Lands in Castile-La Mancha, a programme which has up to now produced excellent results for the estate, and thanks to which we were able to re-plant the 165 hectares of woodland that is currently in such good condition in Ciguiñuelas.

What is occurring in Spain on private land which is integrated into the Network of Protected Areas of the different Autonomous Communities is a paradox. By virtue of the fact that an estate has been conserved for several generations in laudable fashion, with great human and economic effort, the public administration "rewards" the owners, unilaterally, by including their property within a Protected Area. Implicit in this "honorary title" is, in most cases, a reduction in the rights to use it and a series of restrictions which apply when setting in motion the mechanisms for its management and sustainable use, practices which, over the years, have enabled these lands to be conserved in such an exemplary fashion.

Álvaro Sainz de Vicuña y Bemberg

Ciguiñuelas hosts some Yew trees over a thousand years old, hidden in the most remote spots of the peak of Rocigalgo.

C. Otero

PROCESS OF CORK EXTRACTION DURING MONTH OF JULY
LOS CHORRANCOS, CIGUIÑUELAS

C. Otero

The "pela" process of removing the cork bark is done in the head of July, in a cycle wich happens every ten years.

CIGUIÑUELAS BELONGS TO:

Friends of the Countryside

Rise Foundation

APROCA Castilla-La Mancha

WE initiative

Activities & attractions

- Rural Tourism
- Birdwatching
- Hunting
- Riding
- Walking Trails

CONTACT DATA
D. Álvaro Sainz de Vicuña y Bemberg
CIGUIÑUELAS
C/José Bardasano Baos, 9 - 1º • 28016 Madrid
Tel.: +34 91 344 18 52
alvaro.sdvb@cfg.es

La Cassinazza

Continental

Location: Cassinazza di Baselica, Lombardy, Italy.
Surface: 1,040 ha.

CLIMATIC DATA

Average rainfall
mm/cm²/year

Snow days: 8

784 mm

Temperature °C

38,3 — max ■
12 — average ■
-17,2 — min ■

SUMMARY

La Cassinazza is a vast private estate of 1,040 hectares located south of Milan in the countryside of Giussago (province of Pavia), where new methods of managing natural resources are being developed in line with the most recent EU agricultural policies.
The works performed by Engineer Giuseppe Natta at La Cassinazza between 1996 and 2006 enables us to better comprehend the concept of *Third Generation Agriculture*. This term implies two things: firstly, the use of agricultural techniques to produce non-material goods such as biodiversity and attractive landscapes, in order to improve the quality of the rural environment and promote its use for non-agricultural activities; secondly, ensuring that all non-agricultural activities which are transferred to rural areas, are compatible with the rural landscape itself. These "neo-rural" activities are essentially urban in origin, a factor which in turn introduces us to the concept of Ruralization, this being the opposite of Urbanization, a process which creates an urban environment in the countryside.
And as a result of the management carried out at La Cassinazza, we can now enjoy spectacular landscape, where the natural habitat, flora, fauna and wildlife are clearly in harmony with each other.
The project is a joint enterprise involving the support of other countries from ELO (European Landowners' Organization) and the EU Environment Commission.

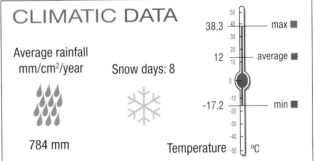

Since 1996, 20% of the area of La Cassinazza has been used for the production of environmental services. The picture summarises the landscape and biodiversity improvements which have taken place over ten years.

M. Marioli

HISTORY

The history of La Cassinazza is a report about the birth of the new estate dating back to the last two decades of the 20th century.

In the 1980s Giuseppe, the son of Professor Giulio Natta, winner of the Nobel prize for chemistry in 1964, decided to create a lasting institution in memory of this great scientist.

He thought nothing could be more eternal than a piece of prime land, nothing more fascinating than a landscape full of wildlife, and nothing more exclusive than locating it in a highly urbanized area where natural heritage is rare.

If it were feasible, the creation of a large area of land with pleasant landscape, rich in natural life and in a highly urbanized environment, would be the perfect monument in honour of the memory of Professor Natta, who was not only an industrial chemist but also a man of science, with a thirst for knowledge and a keen love of the natural world.

Taking many issues into consideration, mainly for symbolic reasons, he located an agricultural area between Milan and Pavia, near one of the earliest protected areas in Europe, the Visconti Park, created at the beginning of the 14th century and enclosed by a high wall, in order to protect the natural habitat, specifically for hunting, from the destructive effects of intensive agriculture.

This park does not exist any more; the bricks of the wall have been used through the centuries to construct religious, civil and rural buildings, and any residual natural life has been eliminated in the last fifty years by intensive cultivation.

It was in this area that he bought La Cassinazza, which had originally been a farm of 400 hectares but which has been enlarged over the years to its current size (in 2008) of 1,040 hectares.

It was originally considered inconceivable that such a project could succeed, as La Cassinazza is situated eighteen kilometres from the cathedral of Milan, which sits right in the centre of the city.

The project undertaken at La Cassinazza, namely to create a type of agriculture whose product is both product and environment and landscape, would not have been economically possible without the intuition of Mr. Ray McSharry, European Commissioner during the early nineties.

This enlightened Commissioner, having perceived the increasing demand from Europe's citizens for environmental quality, and anticipating European politics of the next century, established, under EU regulations 2078/92 and 2080/92, that the production of environment and woodland on arable land should benefit from the subsidies originally limited to the production of crops. As a

The creation of wood belts, wet areas and pastures has considerably increased landscape quality and biodiversity.

M. Marioli

consequence, both environment and landscape have acquired an economic value, payable in real terms.

Using the grants previously mentioned, which were, substantially, rewards given for the production of environmental services, a program was started in 1996 for the improvement of the environment and landscape of La Cassinazza, and whose results have exceeded all expectations.

Two aerial views of part of La Cassinazza, taken in 1996 and again in 2006, together with the report on changes in biodiversity and fertility, are enough to demonstrate the landscape and environmental improvements achieved.

The original target, to create a living monument in memory of Professor Giulio Natta whose beauty and interest can only increase over the course of time, has probably been achieved.

From agricultural desert to agri-environmental farm

La Cassinazza is private-owned property, situated on the alluvial plain of the Po river ecosystem and where work has been in progress since 1996 to restore the landscape to its natural conditions. The former rice-growing farm known as "La Cassinazza" has been converted into marshland – a rich mosaic of different habitats (wetland, meadow and grassland), producing a large increase in biodiversity.

The principal environmental features of La Cassinazza Estate, with figures, are:

Habitats
- Hedgerows.
  – Characteristics:
    - 75 km in length.
    - 60,000 plants utilized.
    - Shrubs and trees planted in double or triple rows.
  – Objective:
    - To minimize the effects of the movement of agricultural machinery.
    - To identify boundaries.
    - To enhance the landscape.
- Rows of trees.
  – Planting pattern: 8 metres.
  – Species: White Poplar *(Populus alba)*, Black Poplar *(Populus nigra)*, Lombardy Poplar *(Populus nigra italica)*, White Willow

M. Marioli

(Salix alba), Black Walnut *(Juglans nigra)*, and Mulberry *(Morus* spp.).
- Wooded areas.
  – Surface: 70 hectares.
- Marshlands with shallow water.
  – Surface: 20 hectares.
  – Areas of land have been converted into marshes with shallow water, where migratory birds breed and feed.
- Marshlands with deep water.
  – Surface: 30 hectares.
  – Large pond (11 ha) stores more than 200,000 m^3.
- Wet grassland.
  – Surface: 100 ha.
  – Most of the area is kept as meadow, along with strips of woodland on the edges, representing around 20% of the total surface area.
- Dry grassland.

Flora and Fauna
Landscape restoration has led to an increase in the number of fauna and flora species. As of the end of 2008, 193 bird species have been recorded at La Cassinazza, with an additional five species for which an origin in the wild can be ruled out. We can see the increase of birds in La Cassinazza in the graphic on the next page:

In the picture a Little Egrett *(Egretta garzeta)*.

La Cassinazza (Italy)

Fields for rice production near pastures for environmental use symbolize the Third Generation Agriculture of La Cassinazza.

Early observations show the importance of the environmental farm at La Cassinazza as a migratory stopover or wintering ground for many bird species: Teal *(Anas crecca)*, Mallard *(Anas platirrhynchos)*, Green Sandpiper *(Tringa ochropus)*, Black Winged Stilt *(Himantopus himantopus)*, Ruff *(Philomachus pugnax)*, etc.

The breakdown of species includes:

- "Over-summering" (ex. house martin, night heron, swift);
- "Summer breeders" (ex. cuckoo, marsh warbler, nightingale);
- "Migrants" (ex. dunlin, red kite, wood sandpiper);
- "Over-wintering" (ex. bittern, marsh harrier, skylark);
- "Non-breeding residents" (ex. black-headed gull, great white egret, teal); and
- "Residents" (ex. blue tit, great spotted woodpecker, kingfisher).

La Cassinazza has been a regular wintering site for the globally endangered Spotted Eagle *(Aquila clanga)* since 1999.

When you go for a walk, it is rare not to see butterflies and dragonflies flitting around hedgerows and shrubs.

Twenty-nine species of butterfly have been recorded. The presence of the Large Copper *(Lycaena dispar)* deserves special mention as it belongs to the Red List for butterflies (endangered) and features in Annexe II of the EU Habitat Directive.

Some new mammals which have come to La Cassinazza following habitat restoration:

- Habitat sensitive species: Polecat *(Mustel putorius)*, Water Vole *(Arvicola rupestris)*.
- Fragmentation sensitive species: Hazel Dormouse *(Muscardinus avellanarius)*.

Large Copper *(Lycaena dispar)*.

Pintail Duck *(Anas acuta)*, a winter visitor.

Black-winged stilt

Number of nests — Year (2000, 2001, 2002, 2003, 2004, 2005, 2006)

Black-winged stilt *(Himantopus himantopus)*.

The reintroduction of roe deer has been a great success.

THE NEST BOX PROJECT

During the course of the winter of 2000-2001 we began a project to install nest boxes at La Cassinazza. We started by installing over one hundred nest boxes for songbirds, which we then monitored over the course of the following breeding seasons.

Main goals of the project:
1. Identifying the species that use nest boxes in the project area.
2. Evaluating the importance of nest boxes in lowland agricultural habitats.
3. Comparing the evolution of the composition and number of species using nest boxes over time, especially with regard to the maturation of hedgerows.

Summary of results
The following table summarises the final results for the 2001, 2002, and 2003 breeding seasons. In all three years, the occupancy rate was very high, in all cases around 90%.

| | Number of nests | | | |
	2001	2002	2003	2004
Tree Sparrow	89	90	96	68
Great Tit	2	1	4	3
Blue Tit	2	3	2	0
Wryneck	0	2	0	2
Starling	0	0	3	4
Great Spotted Woodpecker	0	0	2	9
Common Dormouse	1	2	1	1
Unidentified	1	0	1	4
Empty nest box	7	2	1	0
Lost nest box	1	0	0	0
Wasps or hornets	0	7	9	3
Total	103	107	119	94
Total occupied	94	97	108	94
Occupation rate	91%	90%	91%	100%

The great majority of nest boxes were used by Tree Sparrows, while blue tits and great tits occupied only a few boxes each. The only pair of great tits to breed in 2002 used an old nest box located on the ground at the foot of a small tree next to a path, and they fledged three broods. On the other hand, all three nesting attempts on the part of Blue Tits failed. The nest boxes that were occupied by wrynecks are a particularly successful aspect of our project, since the species was previously absent as a breeder at La Cassinazza. Of the 9 nest boxes occupied by great spotted woodpeckers in 2004, probably only three were actually used for egg laying.

Present uses
- Livestock.
- Agriculture.
- Fishing.
  - This is a private activity, not commercial.
- Forestry.
  - At present some trees and bushes have been reintroduced but these are characteristic of the Ticino Valley.
- Hunting.
  - When: twice a year: on the last Saturday in October and the Saturday before Christmas.
  - Species: Pheasant *(Phasianus colchicus)* and Hare *(Lepus europaeus)*.
- Birdwatching Private activity.

The ongoing habitat restoration efforts at La Cassinazza are a precious opportunity for birdwatchers. As soon as the first efforts got underway, birds rapidly began to recolonise the area. In the midst of a huge expanse of intensive agriculture, and right at the edge of a large city, the presence of an area rich in food, water, and plants, and most importantly free from disturbance, has been a powerful magnet attracting birds from all around.

This activity began in August 2000, with regular surveys taking place at least once a week. The results have been spectacular: an unexpectedly high number of species have been observed, many of which are quite interesting, including several local and even national rarities. The birdwatchers' keen efforts have amassed an invaluable amount of data, which has made it possible to accurately define the phenology of the bird species occurring here. These records are also used to prepare an annual Bird Report.

The number of bird species recorded at La Cassinazza has risen by 138% in the last 12 years.

La Cassinazza **(Italy)**

M. Marioli

The threshold of stillness, guarantees higher concentrations of birds at the end of the summer.

LA CASSINAZZA AND CLIMATE CHANGE

This project created four hundred hectares of marshlands and hedgerows. It has had a dual impact on climate change. It decreases carbon emissions because less soil is in contact with oxygen in the atmosphere and because there is no ploughing. Compared to soil in classical farming, carbon sequestration has increased, as it would on any marshland. This has been enhanced through the planting of hedges. "La Cassinazza" is also an example of adaptation to climate change. In addition to the denitrification of the nearby river, it has created a buffer zone in the event of flooding. Sluices are opened and store excess water, thus protecting surrounding villages. As more extreme meteorological events such as heavy rain are caused by climate change, "La Cassinazza" is a perfect example of how to adapt.

Ronan Girard. (2005, february)
The impact of climate change rural areas and coastal tourism. *Country side. P. 10-11*

LA CASSINAZZA AND NAVIGLIO WATERFALLS

The Naviglio is a big canal whose construction began 500 years ago and ended in the 1700's. It was originally used for transportation and irrigation.

La Cassinazza borders the Naviglio for two kilometers, in which two small waterfalls are present. Their extractable energy is only 550 kW, but the investment is made worthwhile by a surcharge for the energy produced, thanks to 15-year Green Certificates.

La Cassinazza developed an innovative project in which the water intake, turbine, and generator are placed underneath the road that runs parallel to the canal, and are thus invisible, without any impact on the landscape. The energy obtained will feed the heat pumps serving a large number of neorural offices. In return, La Cassinazza guarantees the upkeep of the canal and its banks, in order to make it navigable for tourism purposes.

Use of water jumps of Naviglio for electricity production. All the plant is under the ground.

430

Current projects at La Cassinazza:
Third Generation Agriculture
and neorural activities

In order to monitor the natural increase in bio-diversity, a weekly survey is performed at La Cassinazza of the presence of birds, wild mammals, butterflies, dragonflies and plants, and soil fertility is measured yearly. The resulting data are recorded in a special database.

The weekly journals kept by Dr. Roberto Garavaglia, who deserves most of the credit for this impressive work and information, including the photographs, are collected and updated every week on the web site: www.belleuropa.net.

This information constitutes important historic documentation and verification of the experiment into the possibility of recreating good quality landscape and of restoring the biodiversity lost from intensively cultivated farmland (agricultural desert). It has encouraged the study of rural areas and their economic potential, from a point of view which differs from the conventional approach to agriculture.

The result is a new vision of the rural world, particularly valid for agricultural land adjacent to intensively populated areas, where environmental quality is a scarce asset. It will probably contribute to the future evolution of rural areas close to urban centres.

That this approach can produce tangible results is proved by the results obtained at La Cassinazza.

Before discussing the two groups of current projects at La Cassinazza, we will describe their economic general assumptions, using a new language if required. It is almost certainly the case that an understanding of these assumptions will enable other Estates to design and carry out different projects, suitable for their own specific territory but using the same principles.

The production of environment and landscape on rural land requires the same employees and

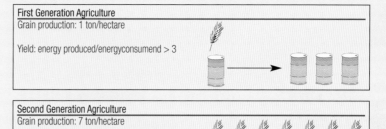

First Generation Agriculture
Grain production: 1 ton/hectare

Yield: energy produced/energyconsumend > 3

Second Generation Agriculture
Grain production: 7 ton/hectare

Yield: energy produced/energyconsumend < 1

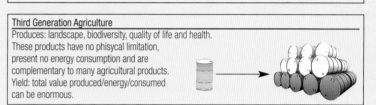

Third Generation Agriculture
Produces: landscape, biodiversity, quality of life and health. These products have no phisycal limitation, present no energy consumption and are complementary to many agricultural products. Yield: total value produced/energy/consumed can be enormous.

La Cassinazza	1996	2006	%
N° bird species	80	190	+138%
N° wild mammal species	16	26	+62%
N° butterfly species	21	35	+67%
N° dragonfly species	13	39	+200%
Soil fertility (C.E.C. meq/100g)	7	12	+71%

basically the same equipment as used for agricultural cultivation; for this reason it can be considered as a form of agricultural cultivation, which we call Third Generation Agriculture.

The fact that many products of Third Generation Agriculture are non-material is a consequence of the fact that, within the economy, growth comes increasingly from the non-material (or service) sector. Nowadays 75% of the population of Europe performs non-material (or service) works, whereas before the Second World War the percentage was the reverse.

Landscape and environment quality are public assets and resources which everybody can freely enjoy, but rural land property in Europe is usually private. The owner is therefore the only person who can surround himself from the inside, and ex-

A view of the neo-rural farm. From the outside and from ground level it is indistinguishable from a classical Lombardy *cascina*.

M. Marioli

Internal view of the neo-rural farm.

Landscape sculpture at La Cassinazza.

M. Marioli

clusively, with an environment of high quality and who can eliminate, through properly managed woodland and other natural screens, any contingent negative components of landscape visible from inside his property.

This is the reason why, in areas close to cities, where the concentration of wealth is high but where environmental quality is a scarce resource in high demand, the volumes originally occupied by agricultural buildings may assume a relevant value when placed inside rural areas kept as precious natural parks by Third Generation Agriculture.

An interesting and particularly suitable use for large buildings, the majority of which were originally designed for agricultural or cattle breeding purposes, is office accommodation for companies performing non-material work of high value but low environmental impact. Examples of these are in technical and financial engineering, remote systems and net management and similar professions, where the work is performed by high-earning staff who appreciate the quality of the working environment, itself known to have a positive effect on professional efficiency.

In addition to the quality and beauty of the working environment, a unique tool has to be guaranteed: internet communication speeds similar to those in town.

People who work in an attractive countryside environment at jobs that would generally be done in an urban setting can be referred to as the "neorural" population. Similarly, the transfer of urban work into areas of attractive countryside can be called Ruralization. This latter term is the opposite of Urbanization, where it is the urban environment which is transferred into the countryside, destroying its quality.

The first group of projects at La Cassinazza takes advantage of the situation just described.

The second group of projects deals with the use of natural resources rather than with agricultural production. These are resources which are available over, under and on the surface area of the estate. Generally speaking, if we exclude the extraction of raw materials, these resources are wind, sun, the fall of water in rivers and canals, and the water table. Because of the climatic conditions at La Cassinazza, energy from the wind and the sun cannot be harnessed economically, but there is limited possibility for the generation of hydroelectric power, and an important opportunity for heat exchange using the water table.

Two examples of projects at La Cassinazza which illustrate the first group (the concept of ruralization) are the use of the old historic stable for the last 20 years to accommodate a neorural population of 130 people, and a new building, specifically designed for a rural population of 300 people, which from the outside offers a view that is indistinguishable from a classical square-shaped farm of the area, the "Cascina Lombarda".

These two very different examples are particularly interesting, because they serve to contrast the common opinion that, in order to conserve a beautiful rural environment, some kind of agricultural work has to be performed. This is completely wrong. Industrial-scale agriculture (Second Generation Agriculture) uses machinery and materials that cannot be kept in old historic buildings without their substantial destruction, or requires new

buildings that contrast markedly with the historical rural landscape.

The situation in relation to the original buildings at La Cassinazza is a good example of the general average situation, because La Cassinazza was formed by the recent amalgamation of seven farms that all had land and buildings. They consist of residential accommodation for farm labourers, labourers that do not exist any longer (more than fifty families were once required to cultivate 1,000 hectares; nowadays there are only 4 workers); sheds which are too low or unusable without destroying their original shape; old historic stables; horrible recent industrial constructions built in the last 70 years, useless for rearing cattle under good health conditions; old and useless concrete silos. All these farm buildings form a large volume of decayed structures that cover, with their pertaining yards, 1,5% of the total surface area of the estate.

The use of the old stables at La Cassinazza for office accommodation has proven to be the best operation for the conservation of a rural building of this kind in the region; the old shed is used to house a collection of historic farm tools and implements, perfectly conserved as museum objects.

The new building for a neorural population of 300 people shows a completely different approach and occupies a surface area of about 5,000 m² and a volume of 35,000 m³. It was previously used as a horrible pig rearing facility, covering an area of two hectares. This new building, when observed from the outside and at ground level (uniquely possible in this flat area), is indistinguishable from a historic "Cascina Lombarda". The landscape quality is thus strongly increased and the area covered by the buildings reduced to one quarter.

This new building not only complies with the basic condition of compatibility with quality rural landscape, but its internal roof (invisible from the outside) is purposely designed and shaped for solar panels and complete insulation that meets the maximum low efficiency in energy consumption standards (5,1 kWh/m³/y). The energy supply is 100% renewable and locally produced, thanks to the combined use of heat pumps which transfer heat from the water table and the Naviglio cascades in order to produce electricity.

The Naviglio cascades are located in eighteenth century locks, no longer used but with historic value. A solution was found in which all the necessary plant and equipment is located underground or under the water, in order to avoid any tangible modification of the shape and beauty of the existing locks and landscape.

LA CASSINAZZA BELONGS TO:

Belleuropa

European Waterfowls Habitat Fund

Anders Wall Foundation

Friends of the Countryside-Meta

Agroitica Acqua & Sole SpA

Rise Foundation

CONTACT DATA
www.belleuropa.net

Mezzana Bigli

Continental

Location: Lombardy, Pavia, Italy.
Surface: 1,182.85 ha.

CLIMATIC DATA

Average rainfall
mm/cm²/year

Snow days: 7

555 mm

Temperature °C

36 — max
16,5 — average
-14 — min

SUMMARY

The estate of Mezzana Bigli is situated in the region of Lombardy, in the north of Italy. It extends to 1,182.85 ha, and includes a beautiful lake for sport fishing. Wetlands are abundant on the estate. Mezzana Bigli belongs to Count Federico Radice Fossati, and the success of its exploitation has been the multifunctional activities that have been developed on the estate.

Go for a walk around Mezzana Bigli, and you can find many agricultural activities, including crops of maize, wheat etc., forestry, fishing, pig-breeding, fish-farming, agri-tourism, hunting with dogs, tomato production, bio-energy production, etc...

Mezzana Bigli Estate

The estate is situated between the River Po and the Rivers Agogna and Scrivia.

Mezzana Bigli **(Italy)**

HISTORY

The name derives from the Latin Mediana *(medianus)*, a name which in the Middle Ages was attributed to those places in the territories of Pavia, Lodi, Piacenza and Parma, "where there are more frequent variations in the course of the Po (or) bends in the river forming islands or almost islands", as we read in the book "Mezzana Bigli Nella Storia", published by the Pro Loco Mezzanese in 2000. Indeed the natural location of the countryside between the rivers Po, Agogna and Scrivia supports the use of this name.

There are different views on the name of the settlement itself. For Francesco Forte, Mezzana was the ancient Mediana Laumellorum, while Monsignor Goggi points to its existence in 1463 as Mediana Isolaria, of which Giacomo Corti della Guazzora was the owner. From the 16th century, the term Biglia or Bigli was officially added, being the surname of the noble family that in 1525 were the feudal lords of the settlement. The oldest reference to Mezzana Bigli was in the Contado of Pavia in 1250; amongst the taxable towns of Lomellina appeared "Glarea Meçana", which is to say Gerola with Mezzana.

This would suggest that the territory of Mezzana Bigli was civically united with Gerola, in the county of Pavía. Both Pollini and Casalis agree that the first inhabitants of Mezzana Bigli came from Gerola and date the first nucleus of houses to a time no earlier than the 17th century. According to Forte, on the other hand, Mezzana already existed as a part of the commune of Gerola in the 15th century.

Mezzana Bigli is situated on the left bank of the River Po, although the course of the river has changed several times.

At that time there were only a few wooden houses, with thatched roofs and clad with bundles of brushwood. According to Casalis, these first inhabitants were of somewhat robust complexion and gentle nature. The position of the settlement, being so close to the water, was not ideal, and periodic flooding caused much damage. Between the 14th and 15th centuries feudal nobility alternate very regularly in the area, the first being the Corti and Sannazzaro families. The Beccaria family is recorded as being present in 1355.

By decree dated 17th May 1525, the new Duke of Milan, Francesco II Sforza, gave Gerola with Mezzana, Campalestro and Guazzora to Giovanni Antonio Biglia, a member of a Milanese family of great lineage.

The Biglia family died out at the end of the 17th century. The two heiresses Pia Anna and Fulvia married into two different families. Mezzana was given to Pia Anna, married to Eugenio Confalonieri from a noble Milanese family, while Fulvia, married to the Marchese Crivelli of Milan, inherited Balossa.

The most recent development in the family occurred in the twentieth century, when Carolina, the second daughter of Eugenio Confalonieri, married a member of the Radice Fossati family, who are the current owners of Mezzana Biglia.

DESCRIPTION

Challenges and issues

The flat and open countryside of the Po valley that we see today is the result of the huge hydrological and agricultural work which perfectly exemplifies a very significant chapter in the economic history of Italy.

From the Middle Ages through the Renaissance and the Age of Enlightenment, an innovative system of cultivation, agronomic doctrine, entrepreneurial capacity, the instruments of capitalism, advances in administrative and social structures, and long hard labour brought the plains of the River Po to a position of pre-eminence and leadership in the nation's progress.

Witness to this is the continual evolution of the Azienda Agricola Federico Radice Fossati, situated in the Lomellina Lombarda area of the province of Pavia, the ancient capital of the Lombards and wonderful city of the arts.

As we have seen, from being gifted to the Bigli family by Francesco II Sforza – the last Duke of Milan – in 1525, the estate passed through the female line to the Confalioneri family, of whom Federico Confalioneri played a role in the political unification of Italy, and then to the Radice Fossati family.

From that moment on, Federico Radice Fossati and his sister Maria Ludovica restored a strong attachment and scientific links to the rural world by reconciling respect for the environment with the needs of mankind.

The reorganization envisaged by this entrepreneur fits with the principle that the new millennium should guarantee an efficient primary system

Mezzana Bigli Estate

437

(agricultural production), through innovation and vertical integration, a multifunctional approach and renewable energies.

Since 1977 the management of the estate's agriculture has been undertaken by family decisions and its development has followed four main guidelines:

1. Land and water

Mezzana (literally "in the middle of the rivers") is at the centre of four branches of the the river: the Po, the Agogna, the Scrivia and the Curone. Water plays a fundamental role, both as a resource (irrigation) and as a risk (wetland marshes and flooding).

Over the years we have focused on restoring 76 hectares of wetland and marsh which had become dried out, and on developing irrigation using pivot systems in areas where it was needed (172 ha). The total workable area amounts to 1102 ha of which 733 can be irrigated.

In the dried out marsh areas, fish farming has been established in the adjacent canals, consisting of 30 ponds, 850 m^2 of trout farming, as well as catfish and native river crayfish.

Water also means that tourism can be developed along the river, which has led to the creation of the Western Po Navigation Company (CONPO) which operates tourism services between Mezzana Bigli and Pavia.

Hydro energy: a project for a hydro power station at Chiusa Cantona on the River Agogna is being built.

2. Innovation and integration

The development of traditional crops has been focused on rice (227 ha) and an integrated subsidiary company through the Verigrup co-operative, which handle 12,000 tonnes. Furthermore, macrobiotic rice, under the brand name of "Un Punto Macrobiotico" is on sale at 120 sales outlets throughout Italy and is supplied to 57 restaurants.

Innovations in cultivation have been:

- Tomatoes: 70 ha are cultivated by the estate and integrated through membership of a company called Solana S.p.A. which is the largest and most modern industrial operation in the sector in northern Italy, processing 200,000 tonnes of tomatoes annually.

- Production of onions and potatoes have been integrated into a modern plant by the name of UNICA s.r.l. which processes, packages and refrigerates 25,000 tonnes of potatoes and onions every year and supplies all the major distributors.

3. Multifunctional agriculture

On one of the estate farms, at Erbatici, there has been a tourist development comprising a brasserie (80 covers), an equestrian centre, the "Grané" multipurpose hall (seats 30), and direct sales of estate products such as Casa Confalonieri wine, sausages, Mulino della Colonna rice, honey, beef and pork.

In addition other cultural activities have been established, with exhibitions, conferences, musical evenings, an opera season, sporting activities such as a cycle track, canoeing, team building, the Usellona hunting reserve, an aerodrome, an hangar of 2000 m2 and capacity for 55 Ultra-Light (ULM) aircraft.

4. Renewable energies

The final sector of interest are renewable energies. This started with the introduction of a biogas system to produce the estate's own electricity for the pig-breeding unit at Bellaria in 1999, where 10,000 pigs are produced every year.

At the present time we are working on renewing the plant and integrating a more modern 1 megawatt system using cereals grown on the farm as well as all the by-products and waste which are treated in an anaerobic fermentation process in two large digesters. In 2009 we founded a company by the name of Oxem S.p.A., in association with the Oxon company – a well-known agrochemical company whose head office is at Mezzana Bigli – and we are currently producing 200,000 tonnes of biodiesel annually by the transesterification process using vegetable oil derived from farmed crops such as oilseed rape, soya and sunflowers. As sidelines, we have established two further companies: Agrodinamica s.r.l. – a agricultural service company specialising in agricultural production for energy – and EnergEtica Onlus whose activity focuses on promoting renewable energy activities within agriculture.

Mezzana is situated in the Lombardy region in the north of Italy. It lies in the valley of the Lomellina, in the province of Pavia. Its southern border is the River Scrivia, which marks the boundary of the region of Piemonte; to the north it is bordered by the River Agogna. Both these streams are arms of the great River Po.

Mezzana Bigli has a surface area of 1,182 ha, its ownership being divided as follows:

Ownership Regime	Surface
• Rented by Casa Confalonieri SRL	936.85
• Rented by Boschi Est Mezzana SRL	220.00
• From the Government	26.00
• Total	1,182.85

The estate lies in the districts of both Lomellina and Oltrepò Pavese and is characterized by the presence of the dominant River Po, the longest river in Italy, which flows 652 km eastward across the north of the country.

The first maps, made in the 18th and 19th centuries, show this authentic rural property to be characterized by irrigation ditches and channels. As mentioned earlier, the name 'Mezzana' indicates that the area is entirely and naturally surrounded by branches of the river Po. The Agogna, Scrivia and Curone are three main streams running directly through the estate before flowing into the river Po. Water is at the very forefront of life in this region.

The area of the Pavia plains covered by the Mezzana Bigli Estate is almost flat, with a uniform average height of 65 m above sea level. As mentioned earlier, the estate and its surrounding area is characterized by the alluvial floodplain which ensures a great abundance of irrigated water. Because of its geographical position, the territory has a humid continental climate, which frequently leads to the formation of fog.

The estate is a magnificent area of agricultural land where rice, maize and poplars are at the forefront of farming activity, and where the traditional irrigation system of flooding is still used.

The estate is a magnificent collection of agricultural fields where rice, maize and poplars are at the forefront of the farming activity.

AZ. AGR. DOTT FEDERICO RADICE FOSSATI. ANNATA AGRARIA 2006/2007

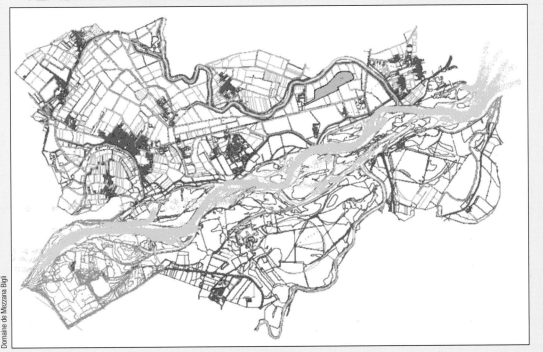

Domaine de Mezzana Bigli

The River Scrivia runs along the southern edge of the estate, with the River Agogna on the northern side. These two rivers are tributaries of the great River Po which divides the estate in half in a pronounced way.

The Lapwing *(Vanellus vanellus)* is a migratory bird of wetlands, common on the plains of the River Po in winter time.

- Little Bittern *(Ixobrychus minutus)*
- Goldcrest *(Regulus regulus)*
- Long-tailed Tit *(Aegithalos caudatus)*
- Wren *(Troglodytes troglodytes)*
- Great Bittern *(Botaurus stellaris)*
- Night Heron *(Nycticorax nycticorax)*
- Mallard *(Anas platyrhynchos)*
- Common Teal *(Anas crecca)*
- Robin *(Erithacus rubecula)*
- Grey Heron *(Ardea cinerea)*
- Great Cormorant *(Phalacrocorax carbo)*
- Great White Egret *(Egretta alba)*
- Little Egret *(Egretta garzetta)*
- Yellow-legged Gull *(Larus michahellis)*
- Black-headed Gull *(Larus ridibundus)*

Development of the land and landscape

Mezzana Bigli Estate is a labour-intensive business with 12 full-time employees including the manager.

Agriculture and forestry take full advantage of Lombardy's special climate and topography. These factors, together with excellent management, mean that the estate has been able to survive and be enhanced by a policy of diversification, to arrive at a point where it can proud of what has been achieved.

Farmland

Intensive agricultural farmland accounts for 58% of the estate's total land area.

The region is one of the largest and best-known areas for the production of rice in Italy and can be considered as the most important of the four areas through which the River Po flows, namely the provinces of Novara, Milan, Vercelli and Pavia.

A great variety of bird species linked to wetlands is found on the estate;

Amongst the many crops produced at Mezzana Bigli are some internationally recognised "prestige products", such as the Italian short grain Cannaroli rice called "Il Mulino della Colonna". 236 ha of the arable land is dedicated to growing rice. The rest of the land is farmed in a very traditionally Italian way. Some of the other crops produced are sugar beet, tomatoes (34 ha), maize (104 ha), soya, rape seed (59 ha) and durum wheat (90 ha).

The affiliated company of Solana S.p.A. produces 20,000 tonnes of tomatoes annually.

Mezzana Bigli Estate

Crops grown at Mezzana Bigli		Area (ha.)
CROPS	Rape seed	59
	Wheat	54
	Maize	104
	Tomatoes	34
	Rice	236
	SET-ASIDE	25.59
	Uncultivated	14.68
	Total	527.33

Trout, carp, sturgeon, salmon, tench and crayfish are all raised in the fish farm.

Mezzana Bigli Estate

At Montemerlo the following crops are grown:

Crops grown at Montemerlo (Mezzana Bigli)		Area (ha.)
CROPS	Maize	36
	Wheat	36

Forestry

Intensive forestry exploitation accounts for a further 28% of the land (301.57 ha(.

Of this, 200 ha are planted with Poplar (*Populus* spp.), and 83 ha with valuable hardwoods.

HARDWOODS

Area (ha)	Clone	Year of plantation
6.0	Ash, Maple, Walnut	2004
15.1	Walnut, Alder	2002
7.2	Walnut, Alder	1999
7.0	Walnut, Alder	1998
7.0	Oak, Alder	1998
17.5	Ash, Hornbeam	1998
23.5	White Poplar, Robinia	1998
83.3		

A further 20 ha are also devoted to producing bio-mass, the ultimate ecological combustible material for sustainable energy.

Animal breeding

Pigs are reared intensively at Mezzana Bigli for pork production. 12,200 animals, mainly of the Goland breed, are fed every day with a mix of crops produced on the farm.

The estate also has a commercial fish-farming enterprise for food production. This is in enclosed waters on an extensive basis. The fish involved in this commercial production are the Trout *(Salmo trutta)*, Carp *(Cyrpinus carpio)* Sturgeon *(Acipenser sturio)*, Salmon *(Salmo salar)*, Tench *(Tinca tinca)*, and River Crayfish *(Austropotamobius pallipes)*.

Bio-energy

The estate deserves particular mention in connection with the recent progress made in implementing bio-gas production deriving from the fermentation of animal waste. From this, it is possible to supply the energy requirements of the entire farming structure. The regional authorities of Lombardy contributed to this project.

The animal waste is conveyed to a big receiving tank enclosed by a hermetic rubber 'balloon' where fermentation is developed. When the process is finished, it is collected and used as fuel in a special generator that provides electrical energy.

Sturgeon *(Acipenser sturio)*.

441

Mezzana Bigli (Italy)

Numerous activities are possible on the estate: bio-fuel production, equestrian centre, fishing, fox hunting, shooting and many more.

On the other hand, Oxem has officially inaugurated a new bio-fuel factory using the **Desmet Ballestra** technology. This new bio-fuel factory has been designed to produce bio-fuel of very high quality, conforming to EU standard EN 2414, and based on a mixture of different raw materials – rape seed, soya, and palm oil. The factory has a production capacity of 200,000 tonnes per year.

Equine centre

Another important attraction present on the estate at Mezzana Bigli is the prestigious riding school. The estate has an equine business centre, large and well-organized, with paddocks, a horse carousel and circle, a covered and open-air riding school and a field of hurdles. The main activity of the equine centre is training, but 40 / 50 boxes are also available for horse livery.

Educational/Recreational activities and tourism

With the Province of Pavia, the estate is working on an eco-museum project called "l'Ecomuseo del Po Pavese", entirely dedicated to the cultural heritage and landscape. The purpose of the eco-museum is to develop a dynamic process within which the communities conserve, develop, improve and enhance the regional value of cultural heritage and reinforce local tradition. This work is being done in collaboration with University of Pavia.

From 2006, whilst retaining its traditional quality farming systems, the estate became active in agri-tourism, converting a farm-house into an interactive learning centre. The methodology used helps to create an experience that is recognised as being sensitive, emotive and recreational. Groups and individuals participate in an interactive programme in which they learn how to act and respect nature.

Alongside the River Po, a dock has been built where ships and boats of all kinds are welcome to disembark passengers willing to come and visit Mezzana Bigli Estate. Guided tours are organized from the bridge at Mezzana Bigli to the bridge at Becca.

The river offers many more recreational activities, such as fishing and cultural journeys in the company of professionals to observe the wildlife and to learn traditional fishing techniques.

Airfield

Mezzana Bigli Estate has a private airfield for Ultra-Light Motorized aviation with an advanced weather station. The runway is 800m long and 50m wide. A covered hangar of 2000 m² can hold a total of 55 ULM aircraft.

Business and Leisure Centre

The old barn, inaugurated in 2007 as "Il Spazio Granè di Erbatici" and immersed in an outstanding remote and natural setting, was re-organized and renovated with modern technologies. It offers an ideal framework for every kind of reception, meeting, team-building, congress and even theatre.

Federico Radice Fossati
President of the National Poplar Commission

Mezzana Bigli Estate

The many different sports activities offered on this estate include bathing areas, with a magnificent sand beach specially constructed for this purpose.

MEZZANA BIGLI BELONGS TO:

C.I.E. Centro
Ippico Erbatici

FISE
Federazione Italiana Sport Equestri

CONPO Compagina di Navigazione
del Po Occidentale

CLUB ASTRA
Scuola di volo

Fattorie Didattiche

Il Mulino della Colonia

Spazio Granè

Friends of the
Countryside-Meta

Activities & attractions

- Historic Building Site of Interest
- Birdwatching
- Country park
- Garden
- Country sports
- Cycling
- Fishing
- Flying
- Walking trails
- Restaurant
- Swimming
- Team building
- Horse riding
- Fox hunting
- Game shooting
- River boat tourism

CONTACT DATA

Azienda Agricola
Conte Dottore Federico Radice Fossati • Confalonieri
Via Teresa Casati, 3
27030 Mezzana Bigli-Pavia • ITALY
federico@federicoradicefossati.it • www.erbatici.it

Wanås Estate

Wanås

Boreal

Location: Skåne Län. Scania. Goinge, Knislinge, Sweden.
Surface: 4,090 ha.

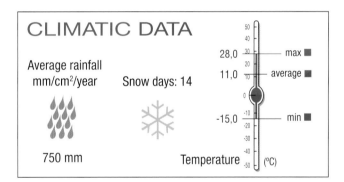

CLIMATIC DATA

Average rainfall
mm/cm²/year

Snow days: 14

750 mm

Temperature (°C)

28,0 — max ■
11,0 — average ■
-15,0 — min ■

SUMMARY

Situated in the south of Sweden, Wanås Estate consists of 4,090 hectares with mainly commercial forestry, a variety of agricultural soils from peat to clay and good grazing land between the two. Over the years Wanås Estate has become a model for organic farming and since 1987 international artists have been invited to exhibit their works of art in the park surrounding the castle.

Our vision
"We believe that an efficiently managed estate can be combined with the good care of its natural resources";
"We believe that the responsibility for nature, culture and historic sites can best be carried out by an active and modern family farm organization";
"We believe that agriculture has an important role in the development and future of rural areas"; and
"We believe in respect for relevant legislation and in open and clear communication with society".

Following the Swedish-Danish Wars, a new Manor House was built in 1566. It can still be seen today.

Wanås Estate

HISTORY

Between 1767 and 1817 a renovation of the whole estate was completed.

The old cow-sheds and stables in stone were built by Betty Jennings between 1756 and 1760.

Wanås Estate

Wanås Manor, originally a fortress, was first owned by Squire Eskild Aagesen (around 1440) and has one of the most fascinating histories of all the stately homes in Skåne (Scania). Its geographical location left Wanås vulnerable during the Swedish-Danish wars, and the original fortress was burned in the Nordic Seven Years War (1563-1570). A new building erected in 1566 incorporated what remained of the old one. Drawings from 1680 show the manor house more or less as it appears today.

During the Snapphane wars (1675-1679), the manor at Wanås was a centre for the Danish resistence and enemies were hung from the 500-year-old oak that still stands in the park. Alter the turbulent years of war, extensive repairs were undertaken by Baroness Lena Sofia von Putbus, whose initials can be seen on the eastern gable of the main building. The old cow-sheds and stables in stone were built by Betty Jennings between 1756 and 1760.

Between 1767 and 1817, a renovation of the whole estate was completed: the lake was enlarged, the two wings and the big barns built, and avenues of trees planted in all directions leading to Wanås. In 1901, the low structure to the west was built and half of the moat surrounding the castle was filled in.

Since the early 1800s Wanås Castle and Estate has been privately owned by the Wachtmeister family.

DESCRIPTION

Property land-use

The total area of 4,090 ha is distributed as follows:

- 3,072 ha Forestry
- 530 ha   Arable land
- 265 ha   Grassland
- 73 ha   Water surface
- 90 ha   Roads/power lines
- 60 ha   Remaining land

There are currently 530 ha of arable land and 265 ha of pasture. Organic farming prohibits the use of chemical pesticides and artificial fertilisers. Instead the cornerstones of production are the restrictive use of nutrients, the rotation of legume cultivation with pasture and grazing, and efforts to minimise the loss of plant nutrients. All the crops produced are used internally. A small portion of feed is contracted from neighbouring farmers. Due to the harsh climate, there is a shortage of protein feed to be harvested.

The farm

Milk has been produced at Wanås since the 1700s but some 20 years ago an important economic driving force, namely lack of profitability in the dairy farm, gave birth to a new way of farming. The estate converted the traditional farm into organic in 1989 and decided to build a new cowshed for 400 cows producing an average of 3 million litres a year, today one of the biggest organic dairy farms in Europe.

Due to the constantly growing demand for organic milk in Sweden and other countries, production escalated from an initial 60 cows to 250, and nowadays stands at 450.

In 2000 the Wanås Estate became certified for organic production. It is a member of KRAV, a key player in the organic market in Sweden which develops organic standards and promotes the KRAV label. It is an incorporated association representing farmers, processors, trade and also consumer, environmental and animal welfare interests.

With an annual production of more than 3 million litres, the Estate is the biggest dairy farm regionally and the third largest milk producer in Sweden. Of the total production, 700,000 litres is used to produce blue cheese that can be purchased internationally. The remaining 2,300,000 litres are mainly supplied throughout the region.

The farm employs 7 full time workers, responsible for managing the 450 milking cows and the 450 heifers, which are divided into four main buildings. Cows are milked twice a day for 12 months of the year. The cows feed outside for half of the day between May and August.

Modernization

The buildings and barns next to the castle had fallen into poor condition, and were converted into space for art exhibitions and a place in which to welcome visitors in the summer.

The old barn, constructed during the time of Carl Axel Wachtmeister (1734-1865), was used to store the increasingly bountiful grain harvest before it was taken to the mills along the Alma river. Most of the grain was ground during the spring flood. Carl Axel Wachtmeister was an energetic agriculturalist and highly interested in architecture. Today, entirely rebuilt, the barn has three complete floors and two attic floors used for art exhibitions.

Wanås Estate is one of the biggest organic dairy farms in Europe. A 500 metre raised line by Maya Lin winds through the landscape.

Wanås Estate

Wanås **(Sweden)**

Milk production is more than 3 million litres per year.

There are five big game species in Wanås: elk, red deer, fallow deer, wild boar and roe deer, with some magnificent specimens like this one.

In 2004, the current monarch of Sweden, King Carl XVI Gustav, inaugurated the modern equipment and new facilities to convert the traditional dairy farm into organic. These facilities made it possible to produce milk in both quality and quantity. Today, an average of 120 cows are milked per hour.

To maintain quality, the milk must be cooled from about 38°C (cow body temperature) to 3°C for safe storage. Before entering the two existing tanks, milk is cooled by a refrigeration unit acting as a heat pump, moving heat from milk to water. This energy gives enough heat for the entire Faro building.

For the future, the landowner and management team is planning to produce Bio-gas from cow dung, as this is something that fits very well with organic farming. When that is achieved, Wanås will be very close to 100% self sufficient in energy. Electricity is produced in hydro turbines in the Alma river and heating is produced from wood chips.

Forestry

Wanås Estate's location provides great conditions for both animal breeding and forestry.

The 3,070 ha of forest are mainly within the natural range of spruce:

	Volume m³	%	Growth/ha m³	%
Pine	55.488	12	2.477	13
Spruce	240.219	52	12.573	64
Beech	39.036	8	344	2
Oak	47.826	10	548	3
Alder	53.814	12	2.686	14
Larch	17.369	4	629	3
Other	8.394	2	-	-
TOTAL	462.218	100	19.525	100

The productive capacity is excellent.
- Volume/ha: 150 m³
- Growth/year: 6.4 m³/ha
- Max.Growth/year: 9.6 m³/ha

Unfortunately the forests were hit by the big hurricane in 2005. The volume of spruce was reduced by 30% (120,000 m³) in the older age classes (30-60 years). Planting and cleaning up after this catastrophy has taken a long time. The forests are FSC (Forestry Stewarship Council) certified, promoting responsible management which offers customers the ability to choose products from socially and environmentally responsible forestry, and around 50 ha of forest are under the Natura 2000 EU scheme as a method to secure favourable conservation status for habitat types and species on the site.

The forester works closely with the gamekeeper to improve land, landscape and natural habitats for wildlife. The forest is managed by a forest ranger, who works at Wanås for 30% of his time. The silvicultural and logging operations are all done by contractors. This means using the most modern equipment in management, such as digi-tilized forest maps, GPS, and highly efficient machinery. Wanås works closely with local sawmills and pulpmills.

Conservation and hunting

The estate maintains the property in great condition for the various fauna which live here. The area is home to Elk (Moose) *(Alces alces)*, Roe Deer *(Capreolus capreolus)*, Red Deer *(Cervus elaphus)*, Fallow Deer *(Dama dama)* and Wild Boar *(Sus scrofa)* and a dozen or so artificial ponds and extensive wetlands have contributed to improved breeding successes among wild duck and pheasants.

Ecological sustainability is a core value of hunting tourism at Wanås Estate. The biological resources set the framework of the activity. Hunting tourism at Wanås Estate is considered as an increasingly important economic return. Sören Hansen, a former South African gamekeeper has been responsible for game conservation and hunting services at Wanås Estate for 25 years. Knowing every great spot and wildlife corridor within the estate, he shows a full understanding of wildlife conservation. He organises hunting-days for guest parties and looks after the ecological sustainability in order that it can continue to operate in the long term.

The many changes in the natural habitats have increased the population of the large game species of red deer, roe deer, fallow deer, elk and wild boar. Forestry and game conservation makes Wanås Estate an appealing and attractive game

Wanås Estate

Spruce, pine, alder, oak, beech, and larch make up the estate's forestry.

Wanås (Sweden)

Wanås Estate

spot not only for large game but also small game species such as wild ducks and pheasants, Hare *(Lepus europaeus)*, Grey Partridge *(Perdix perdix)* and Wood Pigeon *(Columba palumbus).*

Art exhibition

Swedish and international contemporary art has been shown at Wanås since 1987. From the paths that meander through the park, visitors can see everything from monumental sculptures to conceptual installations. Wanås is the venue for a growing permanent collection with the focus on unique site-specific sculptures by European and American artists.

Wanås Estate is a place where the past meets the present, and where art enjoys a special relationship with the natural setting and historical environment.

The foundation is aimed at making it possible for the artists to realize large and ambitious projects, to have a chance to experiment and try out new ideas. The motto "the artist is always right" means that at Wanås artists can make the impossible possible and let dreams come true.

Since 1995 responsibility for the artistic activities has lain with the Wanås Foundation, with new exhibitions each year. This year, the programme of the Wanås Foundation revolves around the environment. The art exhibition addresses man's relationship to nature. The Foundation applies environmentally sustainable habits to its daily practice. Two ecological university projects are being conducted in collaboration with the Foundation. In addition the Foundation arranges an interdisciplinary international seminar on ecologically sustainable development.

> *"This is not a new theme in art; nature has played an important role throughout art history and been given political, religious or scientific importance, depending on the time. Many of today's artists show interest in man's impact on the environment. They visualize art's ability to interpret urgent issues and show possibilities of change. Art has a voice beyond that of politics and science, and can therefore add new perspectives to the environmental debate."*
>
> (Curators: Elna Svenle & Marika Wachtmeister)

The Wanås educational programme extends to children, young people and adults. In collaboration with Wanås, schools, workplaces, colleges and universities throughout the region continually use this forum as a resource for their own teaching and tuition.

The park with its numerous permanent works of art is open all year round. Exhibitions in the barn and the stables are open from May to October.

Collection

At present 37 permanent works by such artists as Dan Graham, Jenny Holzer and Robert Wilson are displayed in the park. All the Nordic countries are represented by such arstists as Per Kirkeby (Denmark), Charlotte Gyllenhammer and Ann-Sofi Sidén (Sweden), Ruri (Iceland) and Sissel Tolaas (Norway). The indoor installation "Lignum" by Ann Hamilton ocupies the entire barn and attracts big audiences.

A permanent exhibition by the artist Maya Lin was inaugurated in 2004. It is situated in a field close to the cow-shed. A 500 metre raised line by Maya Lin wins throught a field in wich cows grace.

Educational programme

The extensive educational programme offers dialogue-based guided tours or workshops that revolve around the artworks in the park, the barn and the stables, as well as the historical exhibition.

The permanent educational programme at Wanås began in 1997. From those first informal "art walks" through the park, today's programme has expanded to include a variety of guided tours.

The Wanås educational programme caters for small children, university students and adults alike. There are projects for schools, and continuing education is arranged for teachers and other profesional groups, who seek inspiration through the art on display at Wanås.

In co-operation with Wanås Gods AB, Scania's largest producer of organic milk, the educational centre arranges visits to the farm. School children are allowed to visit the cow-sheds where they can see calves and cows and follow the eco-stamped production of milk. Also, school children may make their suggestions as to the themes for workshops.

The Wanås Youth Projects are conceived as an artistic activity for high school students in close liaison with an artist/tutor, school and artistic institutions. The project form has been progressively refined since 1997 with the aim of stimulating a deeper involvement in art among the students.

Wanås' commitment to art education is an effort to help children and teenagers better understand contemporary art and give them a chance to increase their enjoyment of art, and satisfy their desire to create.

The permanent educational programme at Wanås began in 1997, and caters for small children, university students and adults alike.

Estate

Today life on a farm must also include activities apart from the production of food and timber, and these activities will become more importat in the future.

POINTS OF VIEW

Our forefathers were regarded as people who did something important with their agricultural land: they cultivated it and they produced a product which was tactile and needed. Their lifestyle was clear and accepted. Nowadays the urban citizen cannot identify with the 1% of the population which is still farming.

Today life on a farm must also include activities other than the production of food and timber. Depending on a variety of possibilities these activities will become more important in the future. Farming includes many assets, and the modern farmer must also be an inventive entrepreneur.

From my experience, I can give an example of how two such unrelated operations as farming and art have profited from each other in a most unexpected way and to the benefit of the estate.

- We encourage public access to the farm and our agricultural operations give valuable experience to the public visiting the estate;
- The art project has become a political factor locally and regionally. So far we have received unusually positive reactions, even from traditionally anti- landowner bodies;
- Organic farming and environmental questions are easily understood on the site by the media, and can thereby vitalise broader discussions;
- Artists work with uncertainty; they are used to visions and problem-solving, which is a help for entrepreneurship in business;
- Farming has historically provided subjects for artists. Our wide field of work touches many of the important subjects of today's political discussion.

C-G Wachtmeister

452

Wanås Estate

WANÅS BELONGS TO:

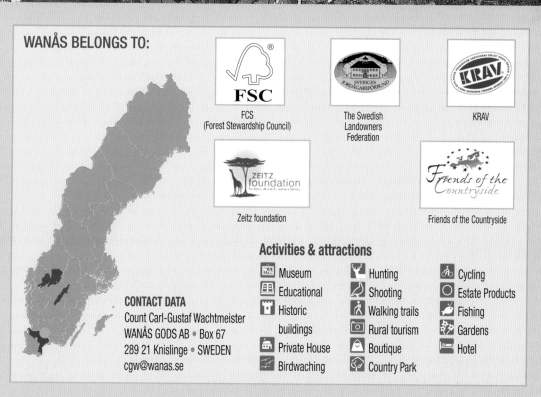

FCS
(Forest Stewardship Council)

The Swedish
Landowners
Federation

KRAV

Zeitz foundation

Friends of the Countryside

Activities & attractions

- Museum
- Educational
- Historic buildings
- Private House
- Birdwaching
- Hunting
- Shooting
- Walking trails
- Rural tourism
- Boutique
- Country Park
- Cycling
- Estate Products
- Fishing
- Gardens
- Hotel

CONTACT DATA
Count Carl-Gustaf Wachtmeister
WANÅS GODS AB • Box 67
289 21 Knislinge • SWEDEN
cgw@wanas.se

Wrams Gunnarstorp

Boreal

Location: Gunnarstorp locality, region of Skane, Sweden.
Surface: 3,300 ha.

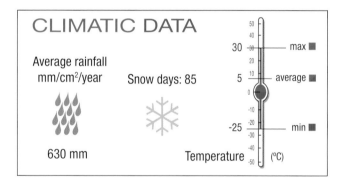

CLIMATIC DATA

Average rainfall
mm/cm²/year

Snow days: 85

630 mm

Temperature (°C)

max ■ 30

average ■ 5

min ■ -25

SUMMARY

In the heart of beautiful Skåne, Wrams Gunnarstorp Estate has become one of the most innovative private estates in Europe with its modern bio-gas plant treating agricultural waste. Some traditional activities are still practised, such as forestry, exceptional wildlife management and enhancement of the landscape and nature of this historic and emblematic Swedish countryside.

G. Janssens

Wrams Gunnarstorp has a tradition dating back to the 15th century.

The Manor House is built of bricks similar to the Royal Palace in Stockholm.

HISTORY

The Wrams Gunnarstorp Estate has a tradition dating back to the 15th century. At that time it was called Vramsgård. It belonged to the archbishop of Lund and was in Danish hands, since the southern part of Sweden, Skåne, was then occupied by Denmark.

The history of the building at Wrams Gunnarstorp can be divided into three main time periods, when the appearance and location of the building were more or less the same: 1400-1640, 1640-1850, and 1850 to the present day.

In the first period, the main building was in another location situated closer to the church. At the start of the 16th century, when the church was short of money, the then archbishop of Lund, Birger Gunnersen, gave it to a knight, Hans Skovgaard, in 1517.

However, a new archbishop, Aage Sparre, took over soon after Birger Gunnersen and did not like the idea of Hans Skovgaard controlling such a large proportion of the church in the northwest of Skåne. He therefore soon took the place back from Hans Skovgaard. But Hans Skovgaard was a powerful man, and took his case to the king, and after a long and slow process was finally able to retrieve Gundestrup i Vrams, which was the estate's new

name, in 1528. Since there already was a castle with that name it was decided to put a Wram in front of Gunnarstorp, after the village Norra Wram where the castle is located.

In about 1550, Hans Skovgaard built a new main building further away from the church, which is the location today. This new building is today the north wing and is the first building which can be associated with the actual castle. The estate was then passed down through several generations of the Skovgaard family, until Ingeborg Holgersdatter Ulfstand inherited the estate in 1620. Her husband was a Danish admiral called Jorgen Vind. He had the current palace built in 1633-1644. His son Holger sold it in 1665 to his sister's husband Christoffer Giedde because he did not like the new forces in power and did not want to become a citizen of Sweden. Giedde had a second marriage, to Anna Sofia von Essen from Estonia.

A letter is extant from that time. In 1696 Hensius, the private teacher in the palace, wrote to Otto Magnus von Essen in Estonia:

"The palace is built of bricks, square just like the palace in Stockholm. This princely palace lies in the middle of a big garden in which one can not only find all the fruit in Livland but also many grapes, walnut trees, peaches, and all the fruit

trees one can only see in Germany. Even the barns are built of bricks and inside is also endowed with bricks so it looks even cleaner than the streets in Reval (today's Tallinn). On both sides there are animal yards where not only small but also many big deer and roe deer are kept. Around the estate there are 32 ponds with the finest fish like carps and Crucian carps, so I with my own eyes saw three barrels of these and other fish being moved to other ponds. Of the beautiful fields, delightful meadows and pleasant groves there is an abundance. The vast forest that lies behind the estate and consists of oak and beech brings to the landlord a large income from acorns since the peasants around bring their pigs there and pay one tenth for every pig. So many times from those 3000 that go there he gets duties of 300".

In 1705, their daughter Hedvig Elisabet Sofia Giedde inherited the estate. When she married Casper Johan Berch from Estonia, the castle accrued to him. Their son Otto Christopher then inherited the castle in 1761. Since he had no children he chose his cousin's son George Philip Berch to be his successor. George Philip Berch was a major in the Russian army, but he chose to leave the army in order to live in Sweden. In 1797 he arrived at Wrams Gunnarstorp in a troika, a sleigh draw by three horses, in which he had travelled all the way from Russia. The old sleigh is still at Wrams Gunnarstorp and can be seen in the museum.

The many changes in national allegiance in Sweden's history meant that the farmers in the villages came to say that the castle was in "foreign Russian hands", and George Philip Berch was not particularly popular amongst the villagers. Since Sweden and Russia been at war during the reign of King Karl XII, they looked upon the Russians as bitter enemies. The villages were even ready to go as far as to buy the castle from George Philip Berch and give it to Hedvig Gädde's sister's son, the Baron von Liewn, but he declined their offer. After the death of George Philip Berch, his wife Ulrika Juliana Berch inherited Wrams Gunnarstorp.

In 1839 she, however, exchanged Wrams Gunnarstorp for a smaller estate at Össjö and seventeen barrels of gold, a result perhaps of the poor economy and possibly the hatred of the villagers.

When the Tornerhjelm family became the new owners, the first Swedish family to live there, a big restoration of the castle began in 1839 and was not completed until 1850. The old barns were taken down and moved. The new barns, designed by the famous Swedish architect Carl Georg Brunius, were rebuilt north of the castle.

In a letter to Carl Georg Brunius, written on 14th January 1844, Rudolf Tornerhjelm told him that he now wanted to renovate the castle and at the same time add a second floor. He did not like Brunius' proposal however, and instead asked the English architect Charles James Richardson.

But Rudolf also turned down Richardson's proposal as well. The renovation of the castle was finally done by the Danish architect Gottlieb Bindsböll in the style of Christian IV. After Gottlieb's death, the restoration was completed by another Danish architect Christian Ferdinand Zwingmann, who added a more Dutch renaissance style to the façade.

DESCRIPTION

The surrounding area

Wrams Gunnarstorp Estate, in the municipality of Bjuv, is situated on the south-western side of Söderåsen, 3 km from Åstorp. Under the 1971 local government reform in Sweden, "old" Bjuv (a market town (or Köping) since 1946) was amalgamated with Billesholm and Ekeby in 1974.

The municipal arms depict a miner's torch lighting up a dark area. The reason is that Bjuv Municipality has had a coal mining industry since the 18th century. At the end of the 19th century there was a flourishing clay industry, based on the coal.

There are a large amount of ancient remains and landmarks from the Stone Age and through the Bronze Age scattered all over Skåne. The province belonged to Denmark until 1658, when it became a part of Sweden as a result of the Swedish invasion of parts of Denmark.

Becaused Skåne is a frontier province, there are a large amount of castles and forts in the region. Skåne presents a rich variety of astonishing natural scenes. It is said to be a flat province, which is totally wrong. You can experience almost everything you possibly could ask for in this extremely varied province.

Among the decorations can be found escutcheons of the noble families whose members have owned the estate – Skovgaard, Ulfstand, Vind, Giedde, Berch and Tornerhjelm.

The barn complex where horses were bred in the 1800s has been restored in traditional style.

Preserving the cultural heritage

The construction of **the manor house** started in 1633 but its current appearance dates from the mid-1800s. The building consists of four connected brick houses; the northern one has two floors and the three others have one floor. Originally the castle was not one complete building; two of the houses were completely detached. Part of the eastern wing dates from the end of the 1400s, and the northern wing was built in the 1550s.

The architecture is Dutch Renaissance or so-called Christian IV in style. This style flourished in Skåne in the early 1600s and has the Dutch pattern of red brick walls, light sandstone decorative work, and gables. These characteristics were highlighted in the extensive restoration work carried out in the 1850s, according to drawings of the Danish architect C. F. Zwingmann. Among the decorations can be found escutcheons of the noble families whose members have owned the estate – Skovgaard, Ulfstand, Vind, Giedde, Berch and Tornerhjelm.

The manor house has many well maintained interiors. For example, the two halls in the southern wing have painted beam ceilings from the time they were built. One of them is dated 1636, and the "White Lounge" contains furniture which has largely remained intact since the end of the 1700s. The barn complex of the 1800s also has multi-stage gables.

On the eastern side there is a big garden known for its hedges of Hornbeam *(Carpinus betulus)* and Boxwood *(Buxus sempervirens)*. A fountain built in the 1600s still can be found in the garden. In 1749 Carl von Linné stayed at Wrams Gunnarstorp during his travels around Skåne and was impressed by the beauty of the park. A Swedish botanist, physician and zoologist, Carl von Linné is known as the father of modern taxonomy and is also considered one of the fathers of modern ecology. At the time of his visit, the hornbeams had just begun to form the arch that today covers the charming alley.

The park is 300 years old, some parts originating from the 17th century. The park is mostly famous for its Hornbeam and Common Boxwood hedges, and it also has its own flower named after it, the Wrams Gunnarstorp Rose. The park has had several changes of shape and appearance through the centuries.

In his book about the journey he undertook through Skåne in 1749, and his visit to Wrams Gunnarstorp, Carl von Linné described the medicine which was produced from the grapes of a special bush. The medicine was used to mitigate and in some cases even cure sick animals. Linné was also impressed by the common boxwood hedges and the peaches, apricots and other exotic fruit which was grown in the garden. Linné was so impressed by the park that returned a second time.

The hornbeam path has a stunning layout, with three gravel paths leading up to its three entrances, one at each end and one through the centre. The path is 63 metres long and about 4 metres high. The trunks are between 0.2 and 1.0 cm in diameter.

The common boxwood hedges have considerable historical value mostly due to their great age

G. Janssens

(300 years). They have been described by many people, of whom Carl von Linné is the most famous. The hedges grow in two parallel lines and there is a small footpath in between, about 2 metres wide. The hedge is 50.7 metres long, 6.4 metres wide and about 3 metres high. At the end of the path the hedges emerge into two semicircles, which reach up to the English park. Between the semicircles there are 12 globe shaped bushes.

Since both the hornbeam and the common boxwood hedges are very old, support pillars have been put up in order to maintain the shape and structure of the hedges.

The park has several ponds. One of the greatest features of the park is that it has a rich supply of water. When Carl von Linné visited Wrams Gunnarstorp, he was very impressed by the water system. He wrote in his book that there were a total of 30 ponds in which fish were bred. The water came from a lake in the forest and was then transported down to the park through two small streams.

One of these streams emerges into a cascade of water which goes through the park and consists of six levels. The present cascade dates from 1993-94, but was built long before that.

Today the water system still exists, but several smaller ponds have now been merged into bigger ones. The ponds are all connected so that the water can alternate between them. Bridges have been built over some of the ponds. The park also has two fountains, one on each side of the west entrance.

The English park is located at the top of the hill and has a beautiful view overlooking the rest of the estate and the castle. The English park consists mainly of trees and bushes. There used to be a pavilion, which has now been taken down. The English park was constructed in the 19th century, after Rudolf Tornerhjelm became the new owner, during a major reconstruction. Many new and quite unusual trees were planted.

The park has two avenues leading up to each entrance. Leading up to the west entrance is an avenue of Chestnuts (*Castanea* sp.), while the south entrance has a very unusual double avenue with trees in double rows at each side.

The deer park, or also known as Djurgården (Animal Park) is an enclosed pasture surrounded by a stone wall, which originates from the 16th century. Initially, the manor house was a hunting lodge and the herd of Fallow Deer *(Dama dama)*

introduced in the 17th century remains on the estate. It is one of the oldest herds in Sweden. South-east of the manor house, there is a stone wall 2 metres wide and 3 kilometres long.

This stone wall surrounds the historic 80 hectares deer area and has been preserved. The actual size of the deer herd, both inside and outside the walled area, varies from 500 to 600 animals, many of which are superb breeding specimens.

Preserve and enhance the landscape

Over the years, the Wrams Gunnarstorp Estate has made considerable efforts to preserve and enhance the landscape – and also to make it more attractive and available for those residing in the three neighbouring municipalities of Bjuv, Åstorp and Klippan.

A 300 hectares area of mixed deciduous forest (Beech *(Fagus* spp.*)*, Larch *(Larix* spp.*)* and Oak

Wrams Gunnarstorp has about 2,000 hectares of forestry, of which 67% is spruce and the remainder mixed deciduous trees, primarily oak and beech.

G. Janssens

G. Ja

(*Quercus* spp.)) has been specially set aside for equine sports and orienteering. The same area includes a lit fitness path.

Three wetland areas, totalling more than 8 hectares, have been constructed on the estate. These wetlands capture the nutrient-rich surface water from the hillsides and thus curtail the supply of nutrients to the nearby Vege River.

Winner of the Anders Wall Award

In 2009 Wrams Gunnarstorp Estate won the award promoted by the Anders Wall Foundation (Sweden), Friends of the Countryside, DG Environment and the Royal Agricultural Academy of Stockholm.

The Anders Wall Award was created to encourage and promote efforts made by creative entrepreneurs who have contributed to the creation of a "positive rural environment". This includes landscape preservation, biodiversity enhancement, cultural heritage conservation and contribution to the rural economy within the European Union.

Distribution of land-use

Before the Tornerhjelm family became owners of the estate, operations were focused on forestry and dairy production. Today, the estate has become profitable as a result of reconsidering these activities and by exceptional management in forestry, agriculture and wildlife.

Forestry

A large amount of continental Spruce (*Picea* spp.) was introduced into the estate's woodland at the end of the 19th century. Today, the estate has about 2,000 hectares of forestry, of which 67% is spruce and the remainder mixed deciduous trees, primarily oak and beech.

As one of the few large forest areas in a relatively well-populated catchment area, the estate's forestry activities attract the attention of many interested parties.

In conjunction with the new planting of deciduous trees, the estate has largely elected to plant hybrid Aspen (*Populus* sect. *Populus*), which sharply reduces the time that the plantations need to be fenced off to protect them from grazing game animals.

A company (Skogsutveckling Syd AB) is responsible for the total forest area. The forest is administered and marketed by this contract-based company.

FOREST

• Pine	1372 ha
• Beech	386 ha
• Oak	140 ha
• Deciduous	237 ha
• Forest road	35 ha
• Total	2135 ha
• Growth/year	21,000 m³

Agriculture

At Wrams Gunnarstorp today the agricultural area comprises 800 hectares, of which 750 hectares is used for growing crops. The crops produced are Winter Wheat *(Triticum aestivum)*, winter rape *(colza)*, winter barley, sugar beet and spring barley, and grass. Wheat is the biggest crop production, followed by rape and barley. A small part of the estate is used as pasture land. The soil is very heavy, resulting in most of the sowing being done in the autumn, as it is safer.

At Wrams Gunnarstorp the agriculture is operated in a very conventional way. It is not very ecological but we are very careful with what we use and what we do, and we are careful not to drive on the land when it is wet. For example, we do not plough any more, partly because it helps reduce the costs and also for the well-being of the soil. The plough reduces the humus content in the soil, which in 2005 was very low; we therefore decided to stop the plough in order to preserve the humus content.

Only organic fertilizers are used, mainly generated from the bio-gas plant. Before the bio-gas plant all the organic fertilizers came from the pigs, which are raised for slaughter. However, the bio-gas produces a lot more organic fertilizers which in the long run produces a higher quantitative and qualitative crop production.

G. Janssens

Apart from agricultural land and crop production, the estate raises 8000 pigs for slaughter each year and the manure produced is very well suited to the bio-gas process.

Dairy farming ceased in 1966 and was replaced by meat production, but in 1980 Wrams Gunnarstorp switched exclusively to growing crops. Because of the area's heavy soil and very low humus content, the need for commercial fertilizers was considerable.

Wildlife and biodiversity

Apart from Fallow Deer, the estate also has Wild Boar *(Sus scrofa)*, Badgers *(Meles meles)*, Rabbits *(Oryctolagus cuniculus)* and Hares *(Lepus europaeus)*, as well as Golden Eagles *(Aquila chrysaetos)* and Sea Eagles *(Haliaeetus albicilla)*, although these birds do not nest in the area. For a

In 2009 Wrams Gunnarstorp Estate won the award promoted by the Anders Wall Foundation.

CROP PRODUCTION

• Winter wheat	bread	326 ha
• Winter barley	feed	50 ha
• Winter wheat	feed	26 ha
• Spring wheat	bread	82 ha
• Spring barley	bread	98 ha
• Oats	bread	75 ha
• Sugar beet		10 ha
• One year fallow		77 ha
• Game-crop & pasture		63 ha
• Hay		38 ha
• TOTAL		845 ha

FARMING TODAY
(MD RUDOLF TORNERHJELM)

"In an effort to reduce and eventually completely phase out the use of commercial fertilizers, pork production commenced in 1995, which was followed in 2006 by a bio-gas venture, which generates substantial amounts of high-quality bio-fertilizer for farming operations. One of the major advantages of bio-fertilizer is that it has a high concentration of ammonium nitrogen, which is quickly absorbed by plants, as opposed to nitrate nitrogen, which is a dominant component of commercial fertilizer.

Another advantage of bio-fertilizer is that it is applied to the fields in liquid form, as opposed to commercial fertilizer which is applied in solid form and requires rain for it to be absorbed by plants".

number of years, the Wrams Gunnarstorp Estate has been applying a game conservation plan, which includes the creation of a game grazing area in the form of a 60-70 metre wide zone between the forest fringe and the tilled areas.

In addition, three small wetlands have been created during the past decade, which have improved conditions for plant and animal life considerably. The wetlands are deemed to be particularly favourable for Pike *(Esox lucius)*.

The wetlands were constructed in 2001-2, the reason being that we have large water areas which drain from Söderåsen (the Southern Ridge) straight into a brook which then transports the water to the Vege River which flows into the ocean. The problem was that a lot of nutrients were carried with the water. A lot of the nutrients came from the forest, since the estate is often struck by storms which create large clear areas up on the Ridge, resulting in a lot of the nutrients running into the water. There are also large areas of arable land from which large quantities of water drain straight into the brook. For a very reasonable cost it was possible to dam the river in three different places, which provided the estate with excellent wetlands.

These new wetlands came to prove very beneficial for bird life on the estate, such as the quantity of ducks, which in turn improved the game conservation. The wetlands also provided waterside habitat for many of the wild animals out in the field, supplying them with good protection where they could come both for shelter and water.

The wetlands help us to prevent large quantities of both nitrogen and phosphorus from flowing into the watercourses, and they have also generated a nice environment for all the surrounding animal life. When the wetlands were first created we received financial support from the EU. Every year we receive financial support from the EU as well as from the Swedish government, in exchange for maintaining a certain water level and making sure the surrounding area is well kept.

NEW ENERGIES

The biomass plant

A sophisticated heating system based on straw was acquired by the estate in 2000 to heat the entire castle and 8 farm buildings, 8 houses and the drying plant. Approximately 1400 straw bales each weighing 450 kg are now replacing 100-110 m³ heating oil per year. This figure of 3 kg of straw replacing 1 litre of oil is both positive and favourable.

Cranes that breed in Scandinavia migrate at the end of the summer looking for milder weather throught the winter on the distant grasslands

The bio-gas plant

The present owner had the idea of building a bio-gas plant in the early 2000s, prompted by a study trip to Denmark where he saw the advantages of the technology. About six years later, the bio-gas plant was constructed and can be seen today as a model for the fast-growing bio-gas industry.

The plant was built without subsidies and is a result of close cooperation between the Wrams Gunnarstorp Estate, a leading food-industry company (Findus, owned by Unilever) and E.on Gas Sverige AB. In 2005 the company Sôderasen Bioenergy was founded to run the project. After the environmental assessment and planning process the construction of the plant started in 2005 and was ready for production in November 2006.

The bio-gas plant at Wrams Gunnarstorp Estate was built accordingly to proven technology and is considered an important part of the estate's work with environmental issues, not least because of the high-quality of the bio-manure. It is practically odour-free and meets the nutrient requirements for all the arable land on the estate.

The bio-gas plant and substrate

Apart from pig manure, the substrate includes slaughterhouse waste and waste products from the Findus food processing factory in Bjuv, 2 km from the estate. A combination of these waste products make highly suitable substrates for bio-gas production. The bio-gas plant can treat up to 65,000 tons of organic material per year which in turn produces 21,000-24,000 MWh of upgraded bio-gas per year, which is sufficient to supply fuel to 1200-1500 gas vehicles.

After digestion, the bio-manure is stored in five tanks, each with a volume of 5000m³. From there it is pumped in above-ground hose spreaders which apply the bio-manure to the land. Approximately 45,000 tons of bio-manure is produced annually, which is spread on the 780 hectares of arable land and other farmland in the neighbourhood.

From 2007, the plant has produced at full capacity and the bio-gas is of high quality (70% methane). To date, the experience with the plant has been positive, and no serious problems have been encountered.

Contribution to sustainable, local economic development

Bio-gas production on the Wrams Gunnarstorp Estate is the heart of a cooperation project between local farming, the regional food industry and an energy company, with a focus on eco-cycle thinking. The basic concept is to raise yields and improve the soil and thus increase the value of the property by utilizing the supply of bio-fertilizer. But in a wider perspective, the venture and related cooperation entail capitalizing on a golden opportunity for farming and forestry to become major energy suppliers in a natural eco-cycle.

Apart from using its own pig manure, bio-gas production at Wrams Gunnarstorp also uses pig manure from nearby farms, sludge from vegetable washing at the Findus food processing plant in Bjuv, and slaughterhouse waste. High-quality bio-fertilizer is returned to the neighbouring farms and at a future stage the tractors on the estate will be powered with proprietary bio-gas.

Part of the sludge from Findus is piped to the bio-gas plant on the estate, where the dry substance is separated and left to decay. The nitrogen-rich water is kept in a pool and is subsequently spread on grassland or used to water new vegetable areas. The plants absorb the nitrogen, which results in a natural treatment process.

One future aim is to be able to manage a substantially larger share of the processing water from Findus through a system of dams and thus reduce dependence on chemicals and open up the potential for other farms in the vicinity to be part of the water-recovery system.

Water collection is of key significance from the recycling perspective. The effects of climate change include increased rainfall, but that is not synchronized with the growing periods. By retaining water in dams, it is possible to avoid having to extract water from natural watercourses during the summer.

Wind-power is another piece of the jigsaw in efforts to attain sustainable economic development. The plan is to place wind farms up on the uninhabited parts of the ridge. The gains are twofold: Local companies can be offered renewable and climate-neutral energy at the same time as wind-power generates income for landowners – primarily forest owners – over the period of at

Wrams Gunnarstorp **(Sweden)**

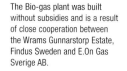

The Bio-gas plant was built without subsidies and is a result of close cooperation between the Wrams Gunnarstorp Estate, Findus Sweden and E.On Gas Sverige AB.

least 20 years that it takes before newly planted woodland provides a return.

Cooperation between local players in such widely different industries as farming and forestry, energy and food processing has created considerable understanding among the parties. The shared approach, the awareness that everybody plays a role in the cycle and the mutual trust generate ideas for new environmental ventures.

Benefits for the environment and society

The bio-gas plant at Wrams Gunnarstorp is profitable both for the company that runs it and for the environment. The amount of purified bio-

gas produced at the plant is equivalent to a reduction in fossil carbon dioxide emissions of a little more than 4,000 tonnes per year, which has reduced the total carbon dioxide emissions in the municipality of Bjuv by 3.4%. The estate's advantageous location close to the gas grid means that there is a market for all the bio-gas produced.

Wrams Gunnarstorp Estate

The bio-manure produced by digestion is a valuable source of nutrients, so there is less need to buy in mineral fertilizer. Apart from the nutrient content, the bio-manure increases the humus content of the soil, which is particularly valuable for the heavy clay soils that are found across large areas of the estate. The hose spreading technique has reduced the transport of manure by heavy vehicles. Furthermore, complaints are no longer received about the smell of manure following spreading.

"We need to limit our dioxide emissions. For many years this has been the most important issue, in order to put a stop to climate change. We're also aware that fossil fuels are a limited resource. The solution is renewable energy options.

We need energy that is carbon dioxide neutral and compatible with the environment. If it's locally produced, that's a major bonus. The final item on our wish list is that it should be flexible. Imagine a form of energy that can be used for heating, as a fuel for vehicles and in industrial processes. In this sense bio-gas is a perfect solution. But to achieve our obstacles for bio-gas we need to cooperate with others. The plant in Bjuv is a perfect example of all this. And therefore a perfect a role model for an energy plant".

Hans Kreisel, CEO of E.On Gas Sverige

"Bigadan's role in the bio-gas project at Wrams Gunnarstorp has been to design and build the bio-gas plant as a turnkey project and to take full responsibility for the daily operation of the plant for a period of 5 years. Moreover, Bigadan is 24.5% co-owner of the plant.

On the Wrams Gunnarstorp Estate, the joint venture between an experienced bio-gas technology provider (Bigadan), a big landowner (Wrams Gunnarstorp) and a major utility supplier (E.On Gas) has proven to be a good match in order to obtain a profitable bio-gas project.

The bio-gas plant is a large and significant project for Bigadan and one of the most successful and far-sighted projects we have helped to implement during our 25 years in the bio-gas business. Therefore Bigadan expects to be able to implement the construction and management concept from Wrams in many similar projects thoughout Europe in the years to come".

Karsten Buchhave, CEO of Bigadan A/S

Wrams Gunnarstorp **(Sweden)**

PRIVATE OPINION

The property as it is today has changed and evolved greatly over the last couple of years. Before, the estate was to a great extent reliable on forestry and agriculture, but especially on the forestry. However, due to some rather serious storms in the late 1900s and the early 2000s, along with possible future climate changes with might cause even more powerful storms in the next decade, all this added up to the conclusion that we had to spread the risks between different areas within the estate. Hence a large project was begun to try and change the role and shape of the forest. One aim of the project was to turn the forest into more of a coniferous forest, but also to add to the deciduous part of the forest and plant more hybrid Aspen, Poplar, European Larch *(Larix decidua)* and also Sitka Spruce *(Picea sitchensis)*. This was partly the result of a considerable increase in the annual amount of rainfall on Söderåsen (the Southern Ridge), which in turn leads to faster growth of plants, which increases the interest for a larger energy assortment in the forest. The changes made to the forest also mean that the agriculture now had a greater responsibility as far as the income of the estate was concerned. This in turn means that the demands on agricultural output will be greater.

One way of spreading the risks within the agriculture was to start a venture to produce pigs for slaughter, which also provided us with more organic fertilizer for the soil, but this was still not enough to fertilize 740 hectares each year. It was therefore important to find something to help increase the nutritional value of the land, and this was what raised the interest for bio-gas production. The bio-gas plant enables us to fertilize the entire area with organic matter every year which presents us with whole new possibilities of increasing the average harvest yield. The bio-gas makes it possible for us to handle greater amounts of fertilizer which means that we can increase the production of pigs raised for slaughter. We also have less of a problem with neighbours due to the reduction of smell.

At the same time it is important to keep in mind that all the minor revenues generated from things such as leaseholds, hunting, the Christmas fair etc., still provide a valuable contribution to income which does not weigh on the forestry or agriculture. All these smaller incomes supply money that can later be invested in agriculture and forestry.

The next step will be looking at permission to build a wind-power plant. This would further increase our energy production and give us yet another important pillar to lean on. With all these measures lined up from forestry and agriculture, pigs for slaughter, bio-gas plant and possible future wind-power plant, we have many sources of income which makes us less vulnerable to things such as storms and other catastrophes.

To conclude it can be said that is undeniably very interesting and a unique opportunity to form alliances with the major energy companies. It enables us to cover more secure contracts than forestry and agriculture, along with the fact that we don't have to take the entire risk on our own. We should be facing a very bright future.

Rudolf Tornerhjelm

Wrams Gunnarstorp Estate

WRAMS GUNNARSTORP BELONGS TO:

Friends of the Countryside

Swedish Landowners Association

Apart from pig manure, the substrate includes slaughterhouse waste and waste products from the Findus food processing factory in Bjuv, 2 km from the estate.

Activities

🏰	Historic building	📷	Rural tourism
〰	Birdwatching	🚶	Walking trails
🦆	Shooting	🦌	Hunting
🌿	Gardens	🐟	Fishing

CONTACT DATA

Mr Rudolf Tornerhjelm
Wrams Gunnarstorp Gods
260 50 Billesholm • Sweden

Theme 6

Agrotourism and historical heritage

NATURAL AND HISTORICAL HERITAGE

Guillaume Janssens
IIMA

Ghislain d'Ursel
UEHHA

While natural and cultural heritage sites represent key resources for the tourism industry, the two sectors are largely dependent on state action, with financial balance and economic development being sensitive issues.

In its most narrow definition, the European tourism industry creates more than 4% of the Community's GDP, with about 2 million enterprises employing about 4% of the total labour force (representing approximately 8 million jobs.)

Through the re-launch of the Lisbon strategy, the European Union's objective is to "deliver stronger, lasting growth and more and better jobs". Hence tourism is recognised as an important factor in growth and job creation for Union member countries.

The richness and variety of our heritage is indeed an invaluable asset. But with the current growth and development of the tourism sector it faces many challenges such as competition, the management of tourist flows and adjusting to the demands for new forms of tourism.

Some adapted forms of tourism such as 'agritourism' or 'heritage tourism' are considered to be a niche or emerging market, offering additional options for diversification and adding stability to incomes.

Natural and cultural heritage tourism is important for various reasons: it has a positive economic and social impact; it establishes and reinforces identity; it helps preserve the cultural heritage, with culture as an instrument; it facilitates harmony and understanding among people; it supports culture and helps renew tourism.

But if left uncontrolled it can also cause a great deal of harm. Excessive numbers of tourists can threaten sites and contribute to their deterioration. Too many visitors in a home or park not designed for that purpose can lead to wear and tear, breakages, theft and even excessive carbon emissions.

Too much publicity can turn sites into clichés, standardizing them and even causing the gradual loss of their cultural identity. If there are too many people crowding onto a site, this can spoil the anticipation of discovering it. The infrastructure built to cope with these numbers may also be inadequate. Stalls and local folklore can commercialize a site and reduce its authenticity.

Cultural heritage tourism has a number of objectives that must be met within the context of sustainable development such as: the conservation of cultural resources, accurate interpretation of resources, authentic visitor experience, and stimulation of the earned revenues of cultural resources. We can see, therefore, that cultural heritage tourism is not only concerned with identification, management and protection of the heritage values but it must also be involved in understanding the impact of tourism on communities and regions, achieving economic and social benefits, providing financial resources for protection, as well as marketing and promotion.

The conservation of historic monuments is not an easy task. It is not only expensive, but it also requires a lot of skills and a feeling for the intrinsic value of the monument.

Ecotourism appeals to ecologically and socially conscious individuals. Generally speaking, it focuses on volunteering, personal growth and learning new ways to live on the planet. It typically involves travel to destinations where fauna, flora and cultural heritage are the primary attractions. Ecotourism is a conceptual experience, enriching those who delve into researching and understanding the environment around them. It gives us insight into our impacts as human beings and also a greater appreciation of our own natural habitats.

Public authorities should be aware of the role of private owners as important stakeholders in maintaining and running historic monuments. Private owners have the credit of having maintained their houses in good condition for centuries, while participating actively in the cultural and social life in their country, sometimes with an international reputation.

The Union of European Historic Houses Association (UEHHA) is dedicated to the conservation of Europe's great artistic and architectural heritage, namely its private historic houses, their contents, gardens, parklands and estates which represent about 35% of Europe's listed heritage. Historic houses, numbering about 50,000 major proper-

ties across Europe, form an essential part of its cultural heritage. Successive governments in all countries have recognised that these properties and their environments are best and more economically preserved in private ownership for the benefit of the society and future generations. This heritage may be threatened by changes to the legal, fiscal, regulatory and environmental framework, and UEHHA closely monitors and responds to developments in these areas whenever proposed by the EU and its agencies.

EUROPEAN LANDOWNERSHIP - HISTORICAL AND LEGAL PERSPECTIVES[1]

Michael Sayer
Vice-President, Friends of the Countryside

CLASSICAL LANDOWNERSHIP AND ROMAN LAW

Many readers of this book may have heard as children the story of the Roman patrician Lucius Quinctius Cincinnatus, who was found ploughing his land when summoned to the dictatorship. He became the exemplar of the idealised agricultural virtue later promoted by Cato, Cicero, Virgil and Ovid. The poetic perspective of Virgil's *Georgics* has its practical counterpart in Columella's agricultural manual *De re rustica*, and Pliny the younger, consul in AD 100, with his villas at Comum, Tifernum and Laurentum, took, like his uncle, the same close interest in estate management, the price of land and the yields of crops. A deep fusion of the interests of countryside and town bound the classical world together, underpinning its moment of optimal internal stability in the Antonine age.

Roman law gave the owner of private property *(patrimonium)* considerable freedom of disposal

whether by sale or by will. The Twelve Tables, dating from eight years after Cincinnatus was dictator, had reserved an eventual place for the rights of the *gentiles*, the members of the clan, on intestate succession. This perhaps indicates that lands had originally been clan lands and subsequently divided; but even the memory was obsolete by the time of the praetorian scheme in classical law. Intestacy was regarded as a misfortune, and the heir was normally designated by will. Those unjustly omitted might claim up to a quarter of the estate, the *pars legitima* or quarta *Falcidia*, by extension of the principles of the lex Falcidia of 40 BC which had protected the heirs by cutting down excessive legacies to save them a quarter of the inheritance. The testamentary fideicommissum is known from the time of Augustus and could be coupled with directions not to sell specified properties, and in 326 there was a general prohibition

[1] This is a slightly revised version of the article published in 2003 in Europe's Natural and Cultural Heritage.

on the sale of the family house where the ancestral imagines were kept during the son's minority. The final disappearance of a distinction between agnates and cognates on intestacy, however, dates only from Justinian's novels.

In late Antiquity, the greatest Roman senatorial families had enormous properties, usually described as praedia or fundi. Olympiodorus states that many had annual incomes of about 4,000 pounds gold besides corn, wine and other goods in kind worth a third as much again. Others had incomes of 1,000 or 1,200 pounds gold. The orator Symmacchus, consul in 391, was considered to be in the middling category, but we know that he had three houses in Rome and one in Capua, fifteen villas mostly on the edge of the city or in the Campagna, and praedia in Samnium, Apulia, Sicily and Mauretania. Saint Melanie the younger, who with her husband decided to sell her property and give everything to the poor and endow churches in 404, had according to her *Vita* an income equivalent to over 1,600 pounds gold. Her lands lay not only in Italy and Africa but also in Spain and Britain. She had an estate near Rome with sixty farms and 400 slaves, and she gave the church at Tagaste an estate bigger than the town itself, with a villa, craftsmen, goldsmiths, silversmiths, coppersmiths, and complete with two bishops (one for the Donatists). This degree of diversification is matched by the impressive estate management of the Apion family in Egypt a century later, who provided irrigation equipment for their tenants, planted vineyards, built cisterns and farm buildings, and provided the bricks.

Other senators, however, might own a single farm. These were closer to the economic level of the *coloni*, the peasant and tenant farmers whose legal tie to the land was reinforced from the fourth century. The legislation underlines the concern of large landowners to keep people in the countryside, and the big estates may have been the consequence, as much as cause, of a decrease in the number of small owner-occupiers. There is a parallel in laws affecting workers in other essential industries, and the apparent shortage of manpower may reflect a demographic decline in the late empire. If so, it would in turn help to explain the increasing reliance on federate barbarian troops in the army, which had such disastrous results when in the fifth century the Empire could no longer effectively assimilate them, and the speed with which so many small southern Italian cities disappeared under the Lombards.

FEUDALISM AND CONTRACT IN A EUROPE OF THE REGIONS

The fall of the Roman Empire in the west produced a changed world, even if the degree of discontinuity has often been exaggerated. The virtual collapse of the state's ability to tax and therefore to pay salaries led to the allocation of fiscal land to the support of offices, especially that of the local count with its administrative, judicial and military functions, which would become hereditary under the later Carolingians. It also necessitated a direct link between landownership and liability to personal military service. As the Carolingian polity disintegrated, castles were built across Europe from the tenth century and defence became almost entirely a local function. The evolution of private lordship, based on fidelity and often vassalage, was part of the process whereby local private jurisdictions of the manorial type arose. Combined with the development of new forms of subordinate tenures, themselves with dues and services attached, these factors crystallised eventually into a feudal system, not only in terms of tenure but military and therefore political structure.

Customary law superseded Roman law in varying degrees according to region, and with a virtual disappearance of written instruments and testaments, the local inheritance laws became standardised on the basis of what Roman lawyers would have understood as default provisions for intestacy. Apart from the last revisions of the Lombard and Germanic codes and the Carolingian capitularies, legislation as such largely ceased from the seventh century until the revival of academic law and the strengthened monarchies of the twelfth. The role of free landowners as jurors, the Frankish scabini or the twelve thegns of the wapentake in Anglo-Saxon England, was central to the community's participation in justice. The church in particular offered continuity and Benedictine stability, and its early cartularies (records) would lead the way in normalising expectations of written documentation and a good legal title, although the jurisdictional immunities which it obtained for so many of its holdings as it struggled to preserve them were themselves typical of the new medieval age.

The fief appears as a grant of the means of subsistence first in the ninth century, and rapidly came to indicate a subordinate holding of church or fiscal land in the south of France and Catalonia, where its development soon encompassed the lands attached to castles for the support of their garrisons, and can be studied through numerous written contracts *(convenientiae)*. It was not to be confused with the outright ownership still indicated by *patrimonium*, *praedium* or *allodium*, although it had something in common with another form of conditional tenure, the *praestarium* or *precarium*. (The local use of feudum to translate the Anglo-Saxon bocland (literally bookland, because granted by royal charter), was in this sense inexact.) Because it initially came into existence essentially at estate management level, it was not until the later eleventh century that the rights and property attached to office, originally held either at pleasure or for life, and which had typically been described as a *beneficium*, started also to be seen as a fief. At this point, and with increasing frequency from the twelfth century, as lesser lords sought the protection, or came to accept the authority, of more powerful ones, lands often underwent a process of feudalisation while remaining in their owners' hands. What is usually specific in the south of France and Catalonia, and is often understood where not explicit in the charters of Frederick Barbarossa, was elsewhere often achieved tacitly by homage.

The English *Domesday Book* of 1086 was compiled just as a feudal hierarchy was developing. Although it is a tax record, and not a register of feudal obligations, it carefully deduced legal title back to the holder of the land in the time of King Edward the Confessor. However, it was arranged within each county under the names of those who were directly responsible to the crown, tenants in chief in all but name. Nearly all the great lay landowners had received their lands from William the Conqueror following the dispossession of Anglo-Saxon predecessors in the years 1066 to 1076 and the same individuals, like the bishoprics and abbeys, had recently had their military service quotas

fixed. As these landowners apportioned the duty of knight service to the lands of their own dependants, whom they had often endowed following the conquest, so the knight's fee or fief was created, a process largely complete by 1166. Security of tenure after the wars of Stephen's reign was guaranteed by Henry II's new assizes. A feudal pyramid had evolved in which all freehold land, and finally all land, was understood to be held on feudal terms with the crown as ultimate feudal lord. This complete feudalisation of tenure was unusual in European terms, but it also spread to Scotland (except for the former Norse *odal* lands), even though Scotland never had a Norman conquest.

Across France, Italy, Germany, Britain, Ireland, the Low Countries and Spain north of the Ebro, feudalism integrated with land law a series of rights and obligations which were often of pre-feudal origin. Their standardisation was one of the objects of contemporary legislation, such as the English Magna Carta of 1215. This famously guaranteed the right of free men, and typically therefore, outside towns, free landowners, to be tried by their equals: a right which thegns at least enjoyed by King Alfred's time. The classic unit was the manor, where the lord, either a knight or a member of a family eligible for knighthood, had the duty to fight in time of war and exercised usually minor rights of jurisdiction over the free and "unfree" peasants who occupied their own lands under him and owed various dues, renders in kind or cash, and labour services. Feudal property was typically subject to certain obligations such as homage and payment of a relief on succession (and escheat in the absence of heirs) to the superior lord, who had rights of wardship over heirs who were minors. There might also be restraints on alienation, which in some contexts arose from the fief's origins in estate management, and was an issue which came to require a conceptual distinction between sale and subinfeudation.

In Italy, Lothar III and Frederick Barbarossa were concerned to avoid fragmentation, or at least to obtain the lord's consent, whilst in England the Magna Carta sought to preserve the feudal services. From the time of Henry III until the1640s, tenants in chief needed a license first, while from 1279 gifts to monasteries required a license in Mortmain. Elsewhere there might be restrictions on acquisition, as in parts of Italy and most of Germany, where non-noble buyers needed formal qualification. In France, they had to pay the *franc-fief*. The origins lay sometimes in estate management, sometimes in fiscal opportunity, since the lord's right to services (unless the alienation was to the church), could actually be preserved by substitution, as the English statute *Quia Emptores* (1290) demonstrated. Social theory added its own rationalisation as knighthood evolved into an order.

In western Europe, the dues and services of the peasants tended to become fixed by custom and gradually eroded in real terms, a process probably accelerated by the Black Death of 1347-51 and by periodic rebellions such as the Jacquerie of 1358 and the English Peasants' Revolt of 1381. By this period, serfdom and "unfreedom" were rapidly disappearing. In England, bond land (manorial copyhold) survived until 1925, but there had been no bondmen for over half a millennium. The annual quitrents were fixed, and eventually nominal, and since the late medieval period copyhold could be sold or left by will just like other land. It had an analogy in the emphyteutic tenures of Galicia, which were also finally enfranchised in the 1920s. In England, the manorial system was transformed by the fifteenth century as wage labour replaced labour services, just as paid armies replaced the feudal levy, and leases replaced and obviated the creation of copyhold tenures. The manor court survived to formalise successions and transfers affecting the copyholds, and to control acts of waste or the exercise of rights of common. Often the lord of one manor would acquire copyhold of another manor to round out his estate, and sometimes buy in the copyholds of his own.

It remains the fact that there was a renewed interest in feudal forms in some places in the sixteenth and seventeenth centuries. This is expressed in Piedmontese legislation, and in the grants of rights of jurisdiction, however residual in practice *merum et mixtum imperium* might be, in the Milanese or in Medicean Tuscany. The formula remained in use in 1799 when Admiral Nelson was granted Bronte in Sicily, where feudo is still the term for a country estate. Gaelic families in Ireland were re-granted their lands under the Tudors and early Stuarts on nominally feudal terms. Even though there had been no feudalism in Scandinavia, the supporting estates given to Swedish counts from 1561 were technically granted as fiefs, as were those of Danish counts and barons ninety years later, although in Denmark they were constituted from the family's own lands.

Although feudalism was absent from the rest of Europe, where the term fief or *Lehn*, where it occurs, does so late or in a limited or specialised context, many of the features which were part of feudalism were more widely found. The revolution in royal government in the twelfth century led to the same need for constitutional charters as in the west. In Hungary, in 1222, the duty to fight remained attached to the land in the early modern period, and what was quantified in terms of service units in Hungary from 1397 was being reassessed on similar principles in Sweden, Denmark and Lithuania in the 1520s. Rights of jurisdiction and labour services existed across Europe. In Spain, where private jurisdiction in the form of the señorío had existed along with services but without feudal tenure from medieval times, the Habsburgs made widespread grants of jurisdiction over hitherto self-governing smaller towns of the *realengo*. In eastern Europe and Denmark, the labour services intensified from the later fifteenth century. This provides the contrast between *Grundherrschaft* and *Gutsherrschaft* in Germany, and was the basis for the demesne agriculture of the Polish *folwark* and the great estates of the German east. Here land was typically allodial (not subject to a feudal superior), but in Muscovy from the fifteenth Century the conditional *pomestye* began to replace the allodial *votchina* under Ivan III and a distinction between the two tenures remained until 1731.

DEVELOPMENT AND DIVERSITY IN SUCCESSION LAW

Under the Salic and Ribuarian codes, ancestral land (the famous *terra Salica* or *haereditas aviatica*), could pass only to sons: as the Edict of Chilperic made clear later in the sixth century, the daughters could only take if they had no brothers (a qualification which escaped the fourteenth century's revival of interest in this principle). The position was similar under Lombard law. However, much of Roman law survived in the Visigothic kingdom and in southern France, not least under the influence of the great Gallo-Roman families who provided much of the Merovingian episcopate. Marculf in the late seventh century provided models for fathers wishing to give land to daughters in their lifetime or by will. Visigothic law allowed parents to give one child an advantage of up to a third of their property, the *mejora del tercio* of medieval Spanish law, and to give up to a fifth to the church or otherwise as they chose. Carolingian Europe indeed faced a quandary over gifts to the church. A distinction could often be made between acquired and inherited property, but it might be necessary first to buy out the more immediate relatives, or at least obtain their consent, widely embodied from the tenth to the twelfth in the *laudatio parentum*. The subsequent heirs might also expect to confirm the gift. In France, this was gradually resolved as the reserve of the heirs became fixed in custom, and as the nearest heir came to have a right of pre-emption at the agreed price in the event of sale, the *droit de retrait lignager*.

Primogeniture began to develop in western France during the eleventh century, often with a transitional phase in which brother succeeded brother (the potential tensions are illustrated in the classic early example of Ile-Bouchard in Touraine), although where there were two or more properties there might be a division. In the Angevin-Norman nexus it was adopted in the twelfth century in Normandy and England, where it was already effectively in place under Henry II: although the rights of grandchildren whose fathers had predeceased their own parents remained unsettled somewhat longer. In England, as in Normandy, the eldest son came to take everything, although in Normandy this did not apply below the level of the *fief de haubert*, and if there was only one fief, the cadets held shares from him in parage. Primogeniture applied too in Scotland and in Neapolitan and Sicilian fiefs following Norman ('Frankish') rather than Lombard law. In the absence of sons, the eldest daughter took, although in England from the later thirteenth century daughters took as coheirs. Across northern and western France, the *droit d'aînesse* was defined in the local customs, whose codification began in the thirteenth century

(Philippe de Beaumanoir being the best-known jurist involved). The eldest son (or daughter) took two-thirds in Brittany, or half if there were more than two in the region of Paris, where daughters took equally: the eldest also taking the manor house with the *vol du chapon* (the distance a cockerel would fly), but always subject to a series of local variations from *pays* to *pays*, sometimes restricting its exercise to nobles, or to fiefs. Younger sons might have shares, which eventually came to be held of the eldest, while daughters simply had marriage portions. Further south, there was greater testamentary freedom, although the results might be similar.

In Italy under Lombard law, as in Germany, equal division among sons remained the rule. Although feudal law, stemming from an academic attempt in the twelfth century *Libri Feudorum* to rationalise Conrad II's *De Beneficiis* of 1037, often assumed an exclusion of women, and also those not descended from the first holder of a fief, unless mentioned in the act of investiture. In practice, the daughters normally succeeded in the absence of sons, the position accepted by Barbarossa's investitures and a possibility that the *Sachsenspiegel* later had to admit. In parts of Germany, such as Hesse, where most *Rittergüter* were restricted to males, it was customary to invest the sister's son in default. In Naples and Sicily, Frederick II made female succession the norm in the absence of sons.

What began to change things was the development of family settlements after the general law had evolved. In England, from the time of Edward I, this was done by fine and recovery, or later by feoffments to uses, before the form of the strict settlement was perfected by Sir Orlando Bridgeman in the seventeenth century. Royal grants from the early fourteenth century, typically by Capetian and Plantagenet kings, began to restrict lands and titles to the male line in order to preserve the possibility of escheat, just as families were themselves beginning to exclude female heirs in favour of remoter agnates. In Hungary and Poland, there was an increasing tendency to pay out daughters and keep the land in the male line: in Hungary they had a quarter between them, but a daughter might be authorised to succeed as the *filia praefecta* by the crown from the 1330s. The revival of the *fideicommis* in Italy from the fourteenth century onwards could lead to similar results. In Spain, however, as the mayorazgo (in Portugal *morgado*), it served usually not to exclude daughters in the absence of sons but to impose a complete primogeniture, by extension of the earlier mejora, and to render the property inalienable. As derogation from existing law, it technically required a royal license, which however was mere formality, and as heir married heiress, many of the great Spanish accumulations of estates and titles were formed. In Scotland, the crown was willing simply to re-grant estates and title on the terms desired *(novodamus)*. The *fideicommis* spread to Germany slowly from the sixteenth century, introduced among the high nobility sometimes by will but often by elaborate *pacta gentilitia* or Hausgesetze which sometimes also received, if they did not always need, imperial sanction. (The example in the erection of the duchy of Württemberg in 1495 is unusually early.) It spread rapidly to Bohemia. In Poland, as the *ordynacja*, it initially required the approval of the *sejm*. In Scandinavia it was used from the seventeenth century and in Russia only from the eighteenth.

INSTITUTIONAL PROPERTY

The crown lands, although not always distinguished from the ruler's own assets, retained a clear identity, and bishoprics and monasteries, together with the Military Orders in Spain and Portugal, made up an extensive institutional sector. Many towns had their own lands, the baldios whose income could often discharge the communal tax assessment in Spain, or the municipal forests of Germany. Indeed, much European forest owes its survival to institutional ownership, such as the great ducal forests of Normandy, Maine or the Bourbonnais, now the backbone of the forêt domaniale in France, with their long rotations. Or the huge forest of Bialowieża, hunting preserve of the Lithuanian grand dukes and Polish kings. Each manor too had its own common lands, but in England these were only for the use of the tenants, whose rights of common were usually for grazing or fuel, while the lord retained the right of the soil. There were, however, pressures on some of these sectors. Crown lands could be extensively alienated in difficult times,

as in Hungary at the end of the fourteenth century. At the Reformation, monastic property was widely secularised, as at the dissolution of the English monasteries in 1536-9. Under the Catholic Kings, the grand masterships of the Military Orders were united in the crown, and periodic sales of their lands followed under the Habsburg and Bourbon kings, notably the great *dehesa* of La Serena in 1744.

ESTATE MANAGEMENT

Estate and household management can be followed as recognised disciplines from the thirteenth century. Church estates were often at this date a model, and the Cistercian involvement in agriculture is only one of the better-known examples. Specialisation came in the early modern period. Sheep were prominent in Tudor England (the Spencer family were a classic example of a family whose wealth was founded on sheep). The long-distance trade in wine and wheat was already well established. Sicily was long the granary of the Mediterranean, and the economics of water transport made it cheaper in Venice than the grain grown twenty miles away on the *terraferma*. Many Polish landowners produced for the grain trade of the Vistula, often shipping it themselves to the port of Danzig. In northern Italy, wheat was often replaced by rice, and the great *risaie* of, for example, the Veronese and Vercellese (the latter still important), were one of the reasons for the great farm buildings of the *Padana*.

There was a revival in agricultural textbooks, such as Gervase Markham's husbandry books of the 1620s. The 4th Earl of Bedford introduced the Dutch engineer Vermuyden to set about the drainage of the Cambridgeshire Fens in the 1630s. England indeed underwent a continuing agricultural revolution in the eighteenth century, which deliberately integrated livestock and cereals, promoted by Charles, 2nd Viscount Townshend ('Turnip Townshend') at Raynham on his retirement from politics, and above all by Thomas William Coke ('Coke of Norfolk'), at Holkham. Apart from creating a home farm, Coke let farms on leases of from 7 to 21 years to his tenants, setting out the crop rotations to be followed, the famous Norfolk four-course rotation of turnips, barley, grass, and wheat first being specified in 1815. The annual sheep-shearings, held at Holkham from the 1770s to 1821 (with some friendly competition from the 6th Duke of Bedford at Woburn), were an essential part of this, as were the gracious farmhouses and solid cottages of the Holkham estate. The English tenant farmer provided his own working capital, in contrast to the system of *métayage* or *mezzadria*, which survived in parts of Europe into the mid-twentieth Century, whereby the landlord provided part of the seed and shared the crop.

The greater landowners were able to diversify their interests. Minerals were an obvious example, especially coal mines which fuelled the industrial revolution, but also lead mines, foundries, forges and metallurgy (in 1771, 36 out of 43 factories in the *généralités* of Caen and Alençon were owned by noblemen and in 1788, 10 out of 12 in Brittany). The 3rd Duke of Bridgewater developed canals, the Marchese Carlo Ginori the porcelain factory at Doccia. Others went in for urban development: the great London estates, Grosvenor, Cadogan, Howard de Walden, Bedford or Portman, remain classic examples with counterparts elsewhere in England, such as Folkestone (Radnor) or Eastbourne (Devonshire). Ironworks were often established by Swedish landowners.

Model estate villages were built in many places, and not only in England, where the tradition lived on through Queen Victoria's reign and long into the twentieth century. In Sicily, over a hundred new rural villages and small towns were founded in the interior from the sixteenth to the eighteenth century, especially in the first half of the seventeenth, usually with the authority of a *carta populandi*, complete with church, convent and the landlord's palazzo, much as described by Lampedusa in *Il Gattopardo*. One can see similar examples in Poland, where Zamość was founded in 1584 by Jan Zamoyski, five years before the *sejm* approved his family ordynacja, or at Rydzyna. Sometimes this could be matched by a real paternalism, exemplified in the Liechtenstein estate rules of 1601-2. It produced, too, a flowering of rural architecture.

The villas of Palladio in the Veneto form the perfect, and much emulated, example of classical elegance with accompanying farm buildings on a human scale. There were other models too, the small manor houses of Tudor and Jacobean England, the great house with angle towers going back to the medieval castle, the moated manorhouse or *wasserschloss* found from East Anglia across the Netherlands, Belgium, and the Rhineland, Denmark and Scania, or the *säteri* of Sweden, so often with a Mansard-style roof. The flanking offices and farm buildings, which Palladio had incorporated with colonnades, formed a continuing theme in the *communs* of French châteaux but were also typical of the houses of Schleswig-Holstein. Country estates also sustained the parish churches so important to rural Europe, many of them originally founded by landowners, as mentioned in England by Bede and the laws of Edgar. In the country houses were collections and libraries, and around them grew landscape parks and gardens. Hunting, and later shooting, were always important sports, but carefully managed. Much of the managed and natural habitat of the countryside was preserved with this in mind, from Coto Doñana to the English shires. Game laws across Europe were concerned to impose close seasons, and examples for hares and partridges are known in Aragonese laws from 1349.

POLITICAL RIGHTS AND RESPONSIBILITIES

Landownership was central to the nexus of political responsibilities and rights. On the continent in early modern Europe, it was typically as nobles that landowners enjoyed full civil rights and took part in the surviving regional diets and *états*. They might also be personally exempt from certain taxes and customs dues, for example on land up to one Swedish mile from the manor house, although in southern France exemption from the *taille réelle* depended on the feudal nature of the land itself. In northern Spain, Hungary and Poland, the nobility included a class of numerous small freeholders, their economic position not so different from the forty-shilling freeholders who elected the knights of the shire for the English parliament, and who in turn voted a land tax assessed under parliamentary control. Such a context enabled Edmund Burke in 1792 to describe the Whigs as 'a party connected with the solid, long possessed property of the Country, … attached to the ancient tried usages of the Kingdom, a party therefore constructed upon a ground plot of stability and independence'.

REVOLUTION AND CHANGE

The French Revolution led quickly to the abolition of feudalism (1789), although the feudal dues were abolished against redemption payments, which survived until 1793. For many landowners, they were relatively unimportant, significant only where the demesne lands were tiny. More radical was the confiscation of ecclesiastical property, and in 1793 the sales of the property of *émigrés* as *biens nationaux*. This had the effect that where only one member of the family had emigrated, properties were often physically divided, and occasionally it might be possible to buy back the property sold at the auction. Confiscated forests were retained by the state and added to the public domain: after 1815 they were restored to the owners who otherwise had to rely for compensation on Villèle's *milliard des émigrés* (1825). Meanwhile in 1792 the *droit d'aînesse* was abolished, being replaced in the civil code of 1804 by the system of a légitime where there was essentially an equal share for each child with one share over for free disposal. It later becoming a model across much of Europe. Napoleon however permitted from 1808 the creation, on special authorisation in each case, of a *majorat*, an entailed estate in land or investments designed to support the titles which he began to confer in the same year both in France and Italy *(maggiorasco)*.

Ecclesiastical property proved vulnerable elsewhere on the continent. In Austria Joseph II had begun to secularise monasteries in 1781, and in 1803 the lands of bishoprics and abbeys were used across southern and western Germany to compensate the secular princes who had lost their lands with the yielding up of the left bank of the Rhine to France at the Treaty of Lunéville in 1801. In Spain, monastic property along with the lands of the Military Orders and many of the *baldios* and commons were sold from the time of Mendizabal's disentailing laws of 1836 and the monastic lands became *bienes nacionales*. This,

like much of what had happened in France, could be seen as liberal capitalism ousting outmoded forms, and many Spanish estates actually go back to this period. It had its English counterpart in the numerous private enclosure acts which in the late eighteenth and early nineteenth centuries divided up many of the manorial commons, compensating the commoners with freehold allotments. So too could the abolition of feudal tenure, the tidying away of patrimonial jurisdiction and labour services, normally in 1848-9 in central Europe, but finally completed in Prussia by Bismarck, changes which seldom had the profile of the long-pondered abolition of serfdom in Russia in 1861.

FROM STABILITY TO THE BREAK-UP OF THE BIG ESTATES

After 1660, landowning in Britain had two uniquely favourable centuries. After the Napoleonic wars, agricultural prosperity was protected from 1815 to 1846 by the Corn Laws. The so-called 'New Domesday' survey of 1873 was made at the high noon of the great estates. For example, in Norfolk, a county of 526,000 hectares, about 280,000 hectares belonged to some 233 estates varying from about 400 hectares to, in the case of Holkham, 16,800 hectares. The agricultural revolution, based on such a foundation, still marks the structure of British agriculture today, but it was not achieved without social problems. An enlarged class of agricultural labourers was created and their often difficult plight was illustrated by Cobbett's *Rural Rides* (1830) and the 'Tolpuddle Martyrs' (1833); and the Highland clearances, which illustrated all too well the intractable problems of subsistence farming in marginal areas. In Ireland, there was less investment by landlords, and the Wyndham Land Act of 1903 provided for the tenant farmers to buy their farms under a government scheme, leaving most Irish estates with just the parkland and moorland. The farming depressions of the 1870s and 1890s both took their toll in Britain, and the estate break-ups that began in 1917 under the pressures of war and taxation were compounded by another depression in the 1930s. In Norfolk this halved the number of estates over thirty years, reducing their area by two-thirds. The introduction of agricultural relief from Estate Duty and then deficiency payments for farming were essential measures assisting recovery.

The gradual loss of the *fideicommis* sometimes involved changes in the way estates were owned. This came in France in principle in 1792, then for the *majorats* in 1835. In Spain the original disentailing law of 1820 was reintroduced in 1836, with Portugal abolishing the *morgadios* by stages in 1832 and 1863. There were already in the eighteenth century restrictions in Lombardy, Tuscany, and Piedmont on the numbers of lives a *fideicommis* could last and although widely revived after 1814, they were forbidden by the Italian civil code of 1865. In northern Europe the context of abolition was later and different, in Germany and Denmark from 1919, Finland in 1931, Sweden only in 1963. In Britain, the issues were seen as purely technical. The powers of management and sale exercised by tenants for life of settled land were strengthened and reformed by legislation in 1882 and 1925, and the rule against perpetuities modernised in 1964.

The first half of the twentieth century increased pressure for land reform, which found an echo in the occupations in the Alemtejo as late as the 1970s. In the Mediterranean this centred on the anti-latifundists, the insecure position of the day labourers *(jornaleros)*, the deep poverty of parts of the south, and the owners' absenteeism, although this last point can be misunderstood, since the Mediterranean settlement pattern lacks the scatter of small nuclear villages typical of more northern Europe, consisting instead essentially of small towns where owners and workers both live. The would-be reformers made fundamental but questionable assumptions about intensification and the availability of water, especially given that the biggest estates were often on the poorest land. In the north, the Danish *Lehnsafløsningen* of 1919 required a payment of 25 per cent of the estate's value to the state, and the sale of a third of the area for reallocation. After 1945, a land reform with actual expropriation was imposed both in West Germany and Italy, breaking up many of the estates in southern Italy, but leaving German forest estates unaffected. In eastern Europe, there was wholesale confiscation followed by collectivisation. By contrast, French legislation of the 1960s and 1980s sought to limit the size of farming units, creating a special organisation (SAFER) to give the smallest farmers the first right to tenancies of additional land in preference to larger farmers or the landowner, a policy which perpetuated structural non-viability. British intervention concentrated on regulating the legal framework of tenancies, especially with the Agricultural Holdings Act of 1948 and later legislation. More recently, the new parliament in Scotland in 2003 introduced a 'community right to buy' giving pre-emption rights to 'community bodies'. This is exercisable at market value on the sale of land in which a community interest has been registered and after a community vote and with ministerial consent.

RESTITUTION AND COMPENSATION IN CENTRAL AND EASTERN EUROPE

It is now necessary to accept the long-term failure of European land reform, even as supported by the Common Agricultural Policy, let alone under the Communist collective-farm system, to provide adequate investment and to stop the drift from the land, whether of small farmers or farm workers. In the west, many farms remain at the margins of viability. In the east, where farms with outdated methods and equipment have struggled to survive in the post-1989 world, a land law has had to be recreated as a fundamental of constitutional, democratic, civil society, raising issues that have proved hard to face in the context of a legacy of inertia, suspicion, envy and, often, corruption.

In the Czech Republic, a full restitution was decided by the federal assembly, largely composed of former dissidents marginalised or imprisoned by a former régime whose legitimacy they did not acknowledge. Whatever had been confiscated since the Communist putsch of 1948 was restored if still in the hands of the state or compensated in bonds at then values if it had passed to a third party. It was a requirement that the applicant could show a legal title and Czech citizenship (a further condition of residence was later overruled) and claims had to be made by the end of 1992.

The restitution extended to moveable property and was without limit, a proposed ceiling of 250 hectares having been dropped when the impossibility of maintaining large castles without supporting assets was recognised. However, castles designated as 'national cultural property' were excluded, and the restitution did not extend to property (typically owned by those with German nationality) which had been confiscated by the post-war democratic government. The result was the return of some 600,000 hectares of forest and 400,000 hectares of farmland, although the major claim by the Roman Catholic church remains unresolved. Some 40 estates of the old Czech nobility were returned, usually consisting principally of a castle and forest with fishponds or lakes but relatively small amounts of farmland, most of which had been distributed to peasant farmers in 1948 and was only taken from them and collectivised in 1952.

In Hungary, however, there was no restitution but compensation up to 300 hectares paid in vouchers which then had to be used to buy land at auction, a procedure that effectively discounted the value of compensation by over 50 per cent and made recovery of the family's original land difficult. In Poland, legislation passed the parliament only for the president to block it. The matter remains deadlocked but there would be significant scope for the restitution of houses and forests in state hands. Much agricultural land, however, underwent a process of redistribution after 1945 and subsequently survived attempted collectivisation: in 1990, some 77 per cent remained in private ownership while 19 per cent belonged to state farms, mostly in the former German territories, which pose a special problem analogous to that of the Sudetenland. In Lithuania, restitution was capped at 150 hectares. In Romania, restitution has been hampered by legislative inconsistency, incoherence and obstruction. In Transylvania, the Austro-Hungarian land register has provided a basis for validation but elsewhere there has been difficulty in verifying claims, some of which have been unfounded, and the European Union assisted in the creation of a register.

In eastern Germany, where above all it might have been expected that the need to face the Communist (as well as the Nazi) past would have been well understood, a combination of political *léger-de-main* with a legal fiction was used to refuse the principle where confiscation had taken place between 1945 and the establishment of the 'German Democratic Republic' (DDR) in 1949. Thus those expropriated by the Nazis were restored: otherwise, the state retained ownership and abetted the confiscation. Remarkably, the pull of place has nevertheless been strong enough to bring back a significant number of former landowners to reacquire or rent their family property and play their part in the post-Communist reconstruction. Here, just as in the Czech Republic, this is always a courageous choice and typically requires the agreement and active commitment of two generations of the family, not only those dispossessed but also their children and their spouses, often with lives and careers elsewhere.

REFLECTIONS FOR THE FUTURE

Article 17 of the Charter of Fundamental Rights of the European Union (2000) guarantees the right to own, use, dispose of and bequeath property, guaranteeing fair compensation if property is expropriated in the public interest. It remains the case that a number of countries in the former Communist bloc are still having trouble living up to this. It nevertheless provides an acknowledgement of rights which go back to the dawn of written history and offers some security for the future.

Europe, and European agriculture, faces globalisation from within a fragile ring fence. Across the third world, economic disadvantage, social aspirations, bad government (in many cases) and climate change have the power to unleash a movement of people with the potential to buckle existing boundaries. Global pressures for a level playing field in legal and property rights and in the terms of trade, for the internalisation wherever possible of social and environmental costs, and for effective safety nets can only be resisted at the cost of further distortions. Paradoxically, the demands of environmental policy, sustainability and traceability all stress the urgent need, at the same time, for the validation of locality in the twenty-first century.

We can still respond to the prophetic ideal of Isaiah and Micah that every man should sit under his vine and under his fig-tree, and believe that *laborare est orare*, to plough is to pray, but our conservatism must be dynamic to be effective. European landowners from those of near-millennial ownership, expressed over time through a variety of legal forms, to those newly recruited by their love for the countryside can provide the essential basis not only for the production of food and timber in stable communities, but for rural diversification linked to the fundamental role of agriculture and forestry, for continuity of stewardship of water and soil resources, of coastlines, of biodiversity and huge areas of habitat, and a major contribution to the stabilisation of climate, truly that Benedictine *stabilitas* loci needed in a globalised world.

Blarney Castle

Atlantic

Location: Blarney, Co. Cork, Ireland.
Surface: 455 ha.

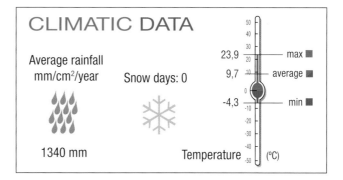

CLIMATIC DATA

Average rainfall
mm/cm²/year

Snow days: 0

1340 mm

Temperature (ºC)

23,9 — max
9,7 — average
-4,3 — min

SUMMARY

Blarney Castle and Demesne is an important and complex historic place accommodating a number of separate yet complimentary uses.
In addition to being one of the most popular tourist attractions in the country, it is a working farm, a family home and a venue for occasional equestrian events.
All these uses sit comfortably within an important historic landscape. The town of Blarney is an estate town associated with the demesne and there are a number of special and functional links between the two.

Blarney Castle Estate

Blarney Castle is one of the most popular tourist attractions in Ireland.

Ink and wash drawing
by R. Gibbs, c. 1810.

Blarney Castle Estate

HISTORY

Blarney represents a good example of direct landlord intervention during the later eighteenth century since, it was consciously planned and formally laid out as a small manufacturing centre.

Due to its abundant water supply, Blarney possessed the facilities to permit its development as an important industrial centre. This advantage attracted a wide diversity of industries set up in the town, including a bleach mill, an oat mill, a woollen mill, a leather mill, a stamping mill, a tape factory, a stocking factory and a paper factory.

The development of Blarney in the 1760s represented a new initiative in manufacture-driven urban growth which was to become commonplace in the county in the early decades of the nineteenth century. Initially probably not conceived as a major industrial complex, it later developed as one of the country's most industrially diverse but surprisingly integrated centres.

Origins of place name

There has been some debate regarding the origins of the placename "Blarney" (Moore 1912) and it has been interpreted as both Blárna, signifying little field, from blar, field or as Blar-airne, meaning sloe blossom (Blar, a blossom, and airne, the Sloe *(Prunus spinosa)*.

DESCRIPTION

The Vision

The vision for Blarney Castle and demesne involves ensuring the protection, long-term survival and enhancement of the estate, while benefiting from opportunities that exist to enhance the visitor experience and the range of facilities and services available on site.

Statement of significance

Blarney Castle and demesne is of exceptional significance because of:

- 1.- The status of Blarney Castle and bawn wall* as one of the largest and most important tower houses in Ireland.
- 2.- The fact that it retains many of its architectural features, and the bawn wall with three surviving towers.
- 3.- The way the surviving fabric on site is representative of key events in Irish history from the fifteenth century through to the twentieth century.
- 4.- The presence of the Blarney stone which makes the castle one of the most popular tourist attractions in Ireland, with a tourism tradition dating back to the eighteenth century.
- 5.- The exceptional example of the unique architectural continuum which is clearly legible with the presence of the two tower houses, the Queen Anne house and the nineteenth century Scottish Baronial house. In particular, the architectural fusion tradition which is evident at Blarney with the Castle and the Queen Anne house acknowledges both architectural and political transition.
- 6.- The presence of the Queen Anne house which appears to have been a comparatively early and extensive manifestation of the "Gothick" taste emerging in the eighteenth century in Britain and Ireland.
- 7.- The high degree of intactness and legibility of the eighteenth century demesne landscape which has retained most of its historic features, including the principal buildings, the demesne boundaries, the Rock Close,

---

* A bawn is the defensive wall surrounding an Irish tower house.

ornamental tower, the farmyard and stable yard, two bridges, many of the parkland trees, five lodges, three lime kilns, the ice house, the avenue, the line of the Old Cork Road through the demesne, the estate village and Turret Farm.

- 8.- The setting of the demesne within the broad fertile lowland river valley in which the land rises to the north and south of the demesne providing natural protection.
- 9.- The associations of the castle and demesne with the MacCarthys, the Jefferyes and the Colthursts, and the associations of the Mahony's with the woollen industry in the town.
- 10.- The architectural quality of Blarney Castle House, which is a rare example of the Scottish Baronial style in this region and an important example of Cork's Victorian architecture designed by one of the leading architectural practices of the nineteenth century in Ireland.
- 11.- The architectural quality of gate lodge 2 which is a very fine example of a late nineteenth century Gothic Revival lodge.
- 12.- The ecological value of the demesne which contains two habitats of national importance, Blarney Lake and the semi-natural *Oak-ash-hazel woodland*.
- 13.- The potential of the site to provide further important insights into life in medieval Ireland through the sub-surface archaeological remains within the castle and bawn.
- 14.- The development of Blarney in the 1760s which represented a new initiative in manufacture driven urban growth which was to become commonplace in the county in the early decades of the nineteenth century.
- 15.- The legacy of the woollen industry in Blarney town, which is a monument to the vision of John Jefferyes at the end of the eighteenth century and the Mahony's during the nineteenth and twentieth centuries, and which made an important contribution to the industrial development of Ireland over a period of 200 years, from 1775 to 1975.
- 16.- The presence of *Oak-ash-hazel woodland* which is of potential national importance. This includes sections of the Blarney

Blarney Castle Estate

Rock close.

Castle Woods pNHA, as well as other woodland areas outside the pNHA.

- 17.- The value of the site as an important educational resource as a document of Irish history from the medieval period through to the industrial period and beyond.
- 18.- The value of the site as an important archaeological site that can yield further information about the nature of large medieval castles of which Blarney is one of the most important examples.

Development of the land and landscape setting

The land surrounding Blarney Castle contains relics of almost 600 years of estate management

View from the castle looking north-east over the Blarney River with its islands (formerly the River Whey) at the tower of the Queen Anne house and at the ornamental tower.

Blarney Castle Estate

Blarney Castle (Ireland)

Entrance front (north façade)
of Blarney Castle House.

West façade
of Blarney Castle House.

and as such represents several major phases of landscape modification. During the fifteenth century when Blarney Castle was built little attention was paid to aesthetics when choosing a site for construction.

Defence was a priority and fertile land was critical. Other factors influencing choice were social and economic elements. Proximity to land-routes, fording points of rivers, etc. was also an economic necessity.

Large forest trees were probably felled and undergrowth cleared in proximity to castles and tower-houses to remove any cover that would allow enemies to approach the building un-noticed.

There is no doubt that even in the troubled times of the fifteenth and sixteenth centuries woods were maintained for timber. Vegetables, herbs, fruit trees and bushes were maintained in an appropriate place, possibly within the enclosure of a bawn or other walled area adjacent to the castle.

Some landscape features dating from the eighteenth century, such as the Queen Anne house, added to the tower house, shows that fashion in gardening had changed radically. While vegetables, flowers and fruits were still grown, the areas surrounding the houses and castle were treated as landscape design.

"Beauty with utility" was the maxim of the eighteenth century landscape philosophy. The value of agricultural improvements was not lost for the sake of any aesthetic gain. Essentially the ideal Arcadian landscape was a subtle combination of beauty with agricultural utility. The ideal involved the setting of a classical mansion or castle in a seemingly natural setting in which deciduous trees framed the building, and cattle and sheep could graze almost up to the doorstep. Views from the house over open "parkland" in which free-standing trees were dotted here and there were essential. A lake or river was desirable and craggy rocks a bonus. A belt of woodland generally surrounded the demesne.

The Rock Close is one of the most enigmatic features of Blarney Castle Estate. It was probably laid out in the late eighteenth century following the fashion for wilderness gardens. It is characterised by many ancient Yew trees *(Taxus baccata)*. Howley (1993) states that a notable feature in the developing practice of using buildings as focal points in the landscape is concerned with what has been described as "The Cult of the Ruin". This refers to the practice of using a ruin in a landscape for its picturesque effect with the intention of stimulating a sense of history through conjecture and contemplation of the ruin's past.

The Rock Close, as well as the area to the east of the castle, is characterised by many ancient Yew trees, several of which may pre-date the addition of the stone "antiquities". Yew trees also grow in the area of the lawn to the west of the castle close to the ruins of the eighteenth mansion and on the islands in the Blarney River .

Apart from the five lodges located on the estate, the farm enclosure and stable yard is situated to the south of the Castle, at some distance from the Blarney Castle House and is within what would have been the area enclosed by the bawn wall. The enclosure consists of two rectangular yards formed by ranges of farm buildings and masonry walls. The enclosing wall to the south is battered at the bottom and one of the towers of the bawn is incorporated into the wall on the western side. The enclosure is a regularly laid out late nineteenth century farm yard and stables. The buildings are simple well-built agricultural buildings with masonry walls and the interiors are plain, generally with plastered walls and ceilings.

Agriculture, Livestock and Horse-breeding

Blarney Castle Estate has about 120 hectares of grassland with one single objective: feeding a suckler herd of 115 Limousin cattle. The estate benefits from the Single Farm Payment and also a scheme called the Rural Environment Protection Scheme (REPS).

All the livestock are wintered indoors. All males are finished as Bulls after 18 months, and 10% of the herd is replaced with the best heifers. The remaining heifers are also finished before the second winter. Two silage pits and several hundred bales of silage are made, and tend to comply with the Nitrates Directive and Waste Management guidelines.

The estate intends to breed a few horses for National Hunt racing. There will also be examples of the Irish Draught, one of Ireland's best-known breeds, which was the backbone of Irish agriculture and of the British military and which, when crossed with a Thoroughbred, gives excellent agility and speed. The estate also plans to breed the true Connemara pony, traditionally used throughout Ireland for trekking.

Forestry

Forestry at Blarney Castle Estate is the main source of income. Of the 300 hectares of managed woodlands, two-thirds is commercial Sitka Spruce *(Picea sitchensis)*, Douglas Fir *(Pseudotsuga menziesii)* and Larch *(Larix* sp.) and one-third is composed of mixed Broadleaves: old Oak *(Quercus robur)*, Beech *(Fagus sylvatica)*, Ash *(Fraxinus excelsior)*, Sycamore *(Acer pseudoplatanus)*, etc.

This is mainly high amenity woodland adjacent to roads. There are two main blocks of forestry of about 40 hectares each. The rest is scattered as a

There are 5 lodges located on the estate.
Gate lodge on the western perimeter of the demesne.

result of the Land Acts of the early 20th century when the farmland was handed back to the tenants and the remainder retained by the landlords. The commercial woodland is subject to a plan and the woods are professionally managed.

Around the castle and lake there is a further 40 hectares of mixed woodland open to visitors, including woodland walks, a Fern Garden and a Bog Garden.

A Challenging Future

In 2009 Ireland faces a challenging future for its tourism. Being an island, there are problems of access. However, Blarney Castle is an iconic world brand and should survive, despite fewer numbers. Leisure is here to stay, and Ireland has many attractions of heritage and landscape. Tourism should recover after the current economic downturn. Timber prices will also recover, and agriculture will be leaner at the end of CAP. The future of a place such as Blarney will depend on dedicated management and dedicated owners, sufficient recognition by Government of the problems of estates in private ownership, and the ability to survive. Tax relief and assistance in Inheritance Tax are also important issues.

Visitor centre and shop.

Post office from the south east. Blarney Town.

threatened", and is only included because, previously, it had been considered to be possibly threatened, before its status was properly known.

Rigid Hornwort *(Ceratophyllum demursum)* is nationally scarce and its population in Blarney Lake would, therefore, be of county importance if it still occurs here. The absence of recent records should not necessarily be taken as an indication that it no longer occurs, but may just reflect the difficultly of surveying the aquatic vegetation in the lake. Bearded Couch *(Elymus caninus)* is very rare in Co. Cork so the population in the Blarney Castle Estate may, therefore, be of county importance if it still occurs here. Whorl-grass *(Catabrosa aquatica)* has a very scattered distribution in Co. Cork, while Goldilocks Buttercup *(Ranunculus auricomus)* mainly occurs in north Cork, so populations in the Blarney Castle Estate may, therefore, also be of county importance in that they contribute towards maintaining the overall range of these species in the county. However, whorl-grass is known to occur elsewhere along the Blarney River.

Ecologic appraisal of the estate

Flora - notable species

None of the species recorded from the Blarney Castle Estate are protected under the Flora Protection Order, 1999. One species recorded from the Blarney Castle Estate, Ivy Broomrape *(Orobanche hederae)*, is listed in the *Red Data Book* (Curtis and McGough, 1988); however, it is listed as "not

Fauna

Dead wood invertebrates

Trees with good senescent habitat are quite frequent in the in the parkland around Blarney House, and in some of the *Mature broad-leaved plantations with poorly-developed understorey,* including some very large trees with a good range of dead wood microhabitats. Long-established areas of parkland in Britain can support important dead wood invertebrate assemblages associated with ancient trees. It is possible therefore that some of the mature parkland and field boundary trees with senescent features could be of value for dead wood invertebrates.

Fisheries

While the River Martin is known to be important for Salmon *(Salmo salar)* and Trout *(S. trutta)*, the Brook Lamprey *(Lampetra planeri)* has been recorded from the river.

The Kingfisher is a quality ecosystem indicator.

Birds

None of the wintering waterfowl species regularly occur in nationally important numbers, and, in most cases, their numbers generally do not reach more than 20% of the threshold level for national importance. However, wintering Gadwall *(Anas strepera)* and Shoveler *(A. clypeata)* are of quite local occurrence in Co. Cork, so Blarney Lake may be of high local importance for these species.

Detailed information on the status of other bird species in the Blarney Castle Estate is not available, but the breeding population of Kingfisher *(Alcedo atthis)* would be of high local importance if it occurs. Kingfisher is listed on Annex 1 of the Birds Directive (92/43/EEC).

Red Squirrel

Red Squirrels *(Sciurus vulgaris)* occur on the estate, and there seems likely to be a good population present, given the availability of suitable habitat. Red Squirrels are protected under the Wildlife Act 1976, and are classified as near-threatened in a global context in the 2000 IUCN Red List of Threatened Species, but are widespread in suitable habitat in Ireland. There is a large amount of mature woodland habitat outside the estate, so Red Squirrels are also likely to be widespread and common in the local area. Therefore, the Red Squirrel population in the estate is not likely to be of more than local importance.

Otters

Badgers *(Meles meles)* and Otters *(Lutra lutra)* occur on the estate and the available information suggests that there might be quite a high level of activity.

Other fauna

A number of bird species that are amber or red-listed by Birdwatch Ireland (Newton *et al.*, 1999) as being of conservation concern are known to occur such as Woodcock *(Scolopax rusticola)*, Snipe *(Gallinago gallinago)*, Swallow *(Hirundo rustica)*, Yellowhammer *(Emberiza citrinella)*, or could potentially occur e.g. Stock Dove *(Columba oenas)*, Skylark *(Alauda arvensis)*, Spotted Flycatcher *(Muscicapa striata)*, Stonechat *(Saxicola rubicola)*, and Redpoll *(Carduelis cabaret)*. While snipe and woodcock have been recorded on the estate in winter, they are listed because of their declines as breeding species. Snipe could breed on the estate, but the adjoining Blarney Fen pNHA is likely to be much more important for this species in a local context. Suitable habitats for breeding woodcock does exist on the estate, but breeding woodcock are very rare in Co. Cork (Gibbons *et al.*, 1993), and are, therefore, presumably absent from many areas with suitable habitat. The remainder are species which are still widespread and numerous in Ireland, but are listed because they have suffered substantial declines. Their conservation requires wider countryside measures, not conser-

Blarney Lake.

Blarney Castle Estate

489

vation at the individual site scale. The population of Swallows may, however, be of some local significance, as this species does not frequently nest in colonies.

In addition to dead wood invertebrates, other invertebrate fauna of nature conservation significance can be associated with semi-natural woodlands. However, as there are generally not any obvious habitat features that can be used to assess the potential occurrence of these fauna, it is not possible to assess the potential nature conservation significance of the non-dead wood invertebrate fauna in the Blarney Castle Estate.

Habitats

Lake

Blarney Lake may resemble semi-natural lake habitat: probably either a *Mesotrophic lake (FL4)* or a *Eutrophic Lake (FL5)*. The latter can correspond to the habitat type *Natural eutrophic lakes with Magnopotamion or Hydrocharition-type vegetation* listed on Annex 1 of the Habitats Directive (92/43/EEC). Information about the trophic status and aquatic vegetation of the lake would be required to properly classify and evaluate the lake habitat. Lakes of natural origin are rare in the mid and east Cork, but there are large areas of semi-natural lake habitat that have developed in artificial lakes in the Lee Valley close to Blarney.

Eroding river

The section of the River Martin within the estate corresponds to the habitat type *Watercourses of plain to montane levels with the Ranunculion fluitantis and Callitricho-Batarachion vegetation* listed on Annex 1 of the Habitats Directive (92/43/EEC). As such, good examples of this habitat type are of international importance. However, this habitat type is very widespread in south-west Ireland.

The section of the River Martin within the estate is approximately 1.5 km long. This is a short channel length given that relatively unmodified eroding river habitat is widespread in the Lee catchment.

The river shows a typical sequence of erosion and deposition features indicating that the geomorphological processes are functioning well. However, there has been some bank modification which may constrain movement of the river channel, and the water quality appears to be slightly degraded.

Excluding the River Lee (a depositing river), there is approximately 20 km of main river channel in a 10 km square centred on Blarney Castle, most of which is likely to be eroding river. Therefore, the habitat is not rare in a local context, and given the degraded floodplain, it is probably unlikely to be one of the best examples of this habitat. Therefore, this habitat is provisionally rated as being of local importance.

Blarney Castle was built during the 15th century, then the defence was a priority.

Blarney Castle Estate

Oak-ash-hazel woodland

Most of the *Mixed broadleaved woodland* and *Mixed broadleaved/conifer woodland* on old woodland sites shows affinities with the semi-natural *Oak-ash-hazel woodland* habitat type. As some of these woodlands have been identified as proposed NHAs, I have evaluated the habitat quality of these woodlands in terms of their correspondence to semi-natural *Oak-ash-hazel woodland*. The areas included in this evaluation are the woodlands with well-developed understorey and/or ground flora. The Oak-ash-hazel woodland habitat type does not correspond to any habitat type listed on Annex 1 of the Habitats Directive (92/43/EEC). However, this habitat type is of "very limited extent" in Ireland (Fossit, 2000). Therefore, good examples of this habitat type are of national importance.

Most of this woodland is at least 200 years old. However, this degree of antiquity is typical of estate woodlands in Ireland and evidence of significantly greater antiquity would be required to make this wood notable in terms of its historical continuity.

The total area of this type of habitat in the estate is around 19 ha.

The *Oak-ash-hazel* woodland is a large, but fragmented and degraded example of this habitat type. While similar degraded examples of this habitat type are probably quite frequent in south Cork given the relative frequency of old estate woodlands, the occurrence of this woodland in association with limestone outcrops is probably quite rare in Co. Cork, and there is an unusual associated ground flora. The identification of some of this woodland as a pNHA suggests that the habitat is considered to be of national importance. This rating would appear to be difficult to justify, given the very degraded nature of the habitat in relation to semi-natural *Oak-ash-hazel woodland*. However, it is possible that most other examples of this habitat in Co. Cork are also degraded, given their association with estate woodlands. This possibility is further supported by the identification of the pNHA being based upon a survey that covered a lot of woodlands in Co. Cork (Goodwillie, 1986). If this is the case, then the woodlands in the Blarney Castle Estate may be one of the best examples of this habitat in Co. Cork, given their size and the presence of limestone outcrops and associated flora. In that context, this site may, therefore, contribute towards the conservation of the regional distribution of this habitat type in Ireland, justifying a rating of national importance. Establishing a history of woodland continuity dating significantly further back than the 200 years (established by the evidence reviewed in the report) would be another factor justifying a higher nature conservation rating for these woodlands.

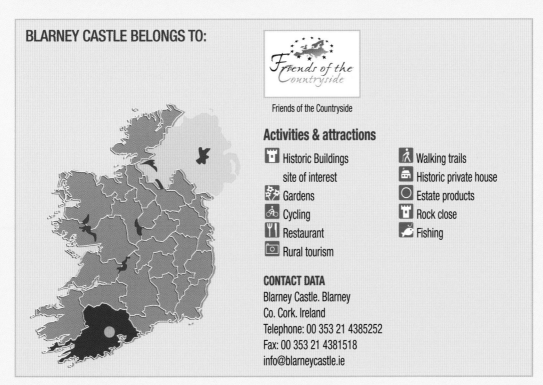

BLARNEY CASTLE BELONGS TO:

Friends of the Countryside

Activities & attractions

- Historic Buildings site of interest
- Gardens
- Cycling
- Restaurant
- Rural tourism
- Walking trails
- Historic private house
- Estate products
- Rock close
- Fishing

CONTACT DATA

Blarney Castle. Blarney
Co. Cork. Ireland
Telephone: 00 353 21 4385252
Fax: 00 353 21 4381518
info@blarneycastle.ie

Burg Gudenau

Continental

Location: Rhineland/ Drachenfelserländchen, Germany.
Surface: 246 ha.

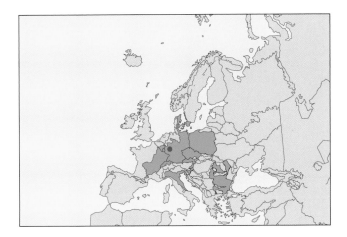

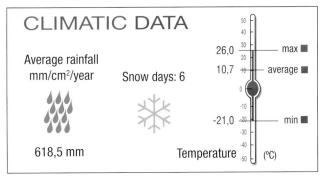

CLIMATIC DATA

Average rainfall
mm/cm²/year

Snow days: 6

618,5 mm

Temperature (°C)

26,0 — max
10,7 — average
-21,0 — min

SUMMARY

Burg Gudenau is a "Wasserburg" or moated castle, situated in the borough of Wachtberg-Villip near Bonn, in Germany. The first part was built around 1220 as a defensive tower, located at the end of a little valley and bordered by a small river called the "Aue".

In 1873 the castle was bought by Franz Carl von Guilleaume, member of an industrial family. The family was active in the cable industry and was directly involved in laying the first intercontinental telephone cable from Ireland to US.

The transfer of an historic estate from one generation to the other is a very intricate process and requires planning ahead in many respects. In that sense, it is an art-form in itself, and goes far beyond the idea that it is simply a matter of legal preparation.

Burg Gudenau is a classical example of how changing motives for ownership and changing economic, social and political circumstances impose new and often difficult tasks on the next generation.

E. Scholma

Aerial view of the buildings at Burg Gudenau an the Baroque park.

Burg Gudenau **(Germany)**

Franz Carl Guilleaume.

HISTORY

Burg Gudenau has been in the hands of the same family for over 125 years.

In 1882 the estate was purchased as a summer residence by the German industrialist Franz Carl Guilleaume. It was the time of the great industrial revolution in Europe and Franz Carl Guilleaume had been one of the German success stories. From a small family owned business producing ropes mainly for the shipping and agricultural sectors he created a world leader in reinforced steel cables for the construction, building and electricity industries, called "Felten Gui-

The factory of
Franz Carl Guilleaume.

lleaume Carlswerk AG". In 1899, under the management of his successor and son Theodor, the family showed its entrepreneurial strength and courage by laying – at its own risk – the first telegraph cable from Germany, via the Azores to the USA. This highly risky project, which included the need to build a special cable production facility near the coast as well as the purchase of its own fleet of ships to lay the cable, was achieved against the political pressures of England that refused a concession for the cable to land first in the UK. Thanks to the co-operation of Portugal, a concession was obtained for an intermediary landing in the Azores.

The venture turned out to be a huge success and the financial rewards were equally large. They formed the basis for the enormous and prosperous expansion of the family enterprise in the years to come, above all in telephone cables.

The German Emperor rewarded Theodor by conferring an ennoblement on him.

Upon the death of Theodor in 1933, Burg Gudenau went to his wife Hortense von Mallinckrodt and upon her death (1950) to their daughter Erna who had married Count Leopold von Strasoldo Graffemberg.

In 1965, her son Nikolaus Count Strasoldo, a successful banker and partner in the Bank Sal. Oppenheim Jr in Cologne, inherited the estate and in 1987 transferred it to his wife Maria Countess Alberti-Enno.

She left the estate to her daughter Henriette Strasoldo who married Enno Scholma, a Dutch banker.

Count Joseph Strassoldowith with his family. 17th century painting.

The Strasoldo family (originally also written "Strassoldo") originates from Italy and has historic roots in the Fruili region between Venice and Trieste. The original family estate in the village of Strassoldo is located between Palmanova and Aquillea and is, after a period of over 1000 years, still inhabited by the Counts of Strassoldo today.

For hundreds of years the Strasoldo's constituted a powerful influence in the region and accumulated vast areas of land.

The family became longtime loyal supporters of the Austrian Empire and earned great fame in the military for their heroic contributions to the defence of the Austrian Empire against the Turks and other invaders. Marshall Radetzky was married to a Strassoldo, Michael Count Strasoldo became Governor of Milan and the region of Steyermark, and Raimondo Strasoldo became bishop of Eichstadt.

Leopold Count Strasoldo who married Erna von Guilleaume was accredited at the Royal Bavarian Court in Münich on behalf of the Austrian Empire.

DESCRIPTION

Burg Gudenau is a "Wasserburg" or moated castle, situated in the borough of Wachtberg-Villip near Bonn, in Germany. The first part was build around 1220 as a defensive tower, located at the end of a little valley and bordered by a small river called the "Aue". Little is known about the exact changes that occurred to the house over the centuries thereafter. Around 1560 the four wings of the main castle were constructed with a gothic oriole and slated roofs, four towers and a park at the back. One of the four corner towers has a pointed top, the others are baroque.

In front of the main castle a so-called "Vorburg" or outer castle was built, containing mainly the farm buildings of the time, with defensive towers on both sides and in the middle, the latter also constituting the main entrance to the estate.

The current form of the park was created in the start of the 1700s as a baroque park arranged in

The Baroque garden.

Castello Strasoldo.

Burg Gudenau (Germany)

View of the Gingko or
Maidenhair tree
(Gingko biloba) in the garden.

E. Scholma

three terraces and influenced by the French garden architecture of the famous garden architect
Le Notre who created the park of Vaux le Vicomte
and Versailles. It is the only private baroque garden still existing in the Rhineland.

In the 18th century a half timbered house
(known as a "Fachwerkhaus") was built for the
people working on the estate, on the other side of
the water to the main estate property. It is up for
restoration and rental for commercial purposes,
creating an additional source of income to the estate owners.

The so called "Schwestern Haus" was built in
1910, also for the workers on the estate, and consists of three separate living units. Upon the clo-

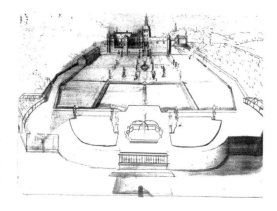

Plans of the Baroque park
arranged in three terraces and
influenced by the famous
French landscape architect Le
Notre who created the parks of
Vaux le Vicomte and Versailles.

sure of the pig enterprises in 1989, it was completely restorated and subsequently the building
was rented out in two parts on a commercial basis.

In 1967, three pig units and the forest manager's house were built, followed in 1992 by the
construction of a fattening unit for 1000 pigs. In
1994 the farm manager's house next to the
forester's house was built. In 2007 the big project
was the demolition of all the old pig units and re-
cultivating the land for agricultural purposes.

Evolution of Burg Gudenau

In 1873 the castle was bought by Franz Carl
von Guilleaume, member of an industrial family.
The family was active in the cable industry and
was directly involved in laying the first intercontinental telephone cable from Ireland to US. In those
days, Burg Gudenau was used as a summer residence. The family's main house was in Cologne.
Farming activity on the estate comprised both
dairy cows and the cultivation of potatoes, sugar
beet and wheat.

The year 1910 saw the renovation of the castle
to the most modern standards of the time, with
steam heating, a modern kitchen which is still in
use, and bathrooms, also still in use. Farming activities were diversified: breeding cattle, breeding

496

and fattening pigs, wheat, corn, sugar beet, apple trees (ca 1 ha). There was a team of 45 workers.

In 1945 the castle was burnt out whilst in use as a headquarters by the allied American army. The number of employees declined to 10.

The years 1955 to 1957 marked the restoration of the castle by Dr. Nikolaus Count Strasoldo, great grandson of Franz Carl von Guilleaume.

In 1967 a new farm was built, away from the main estate. The pig units were built to the latest standards and part of the old stables continued to be used. This year also marked the end of cattle breeding and of the dairy cows, as a result of the government subsidy scheme. At this time too, apple cultivation was also brought to an end and the land converted to agricultural use, again due to government subsidies. Part of the forest was also converted to agricultural land. Large agricultural machinery (combine harvester and large sowing drills) was bought outright, 100% owned. The number of employees was further reduced to 6.

During the period from 1967 to 1989, the number of employees was again reduced, to 3. A state of the art unit was built, for fattening 1000 pigs and for breeding pigs of a Rhineland hybrid breed. In 1992, swine fever caused a big problem for the estate's farming activities. This led in 1994-1996 to the complete closure of the pig enterprises. The estate now concentrated on cultivating grain and sugar beet only, divided approximately into shares of 1/3 sugar beet, 1/3 barley, 1/3 wheat. In order to cut capital costs, the main machinery requirements (for sowing, harvesting and ploughing) were purchased in combination with the neighbouring estate belonging to v. Wülfing.

During the years 1995-1997 the complete restructuring/restoration of the estate was launched. The conversion of the old farm buildings into luxury houses for long-term rent was another step towards the diversified management of the estate. The buildings on the estate comprised a total of 7 units, of between 230 and 400 sq.m. The principal cash flow came from renting out this real estate, rather than from agricultural activities. At the time, only 2 employees remained, one farm manager in charge of the daily agricultural work, one forest manager responsible for all forestry and hunting duties, and a part-time bookkeeper.

In 2006, reorganisation was again necessary; the discharge of the farm manager reduced the

E. Scholma

The castle was burnt out in 1945 whilst in use as a headquarters by the American army.

team one more time. The farm management tasks were contracted out to a neighbour, Mr. v. Wülfing; the contract is renegotiable at certain intervals; the overall economic risk and management duties remain with the estate owner. In order to cut wage and capital costs down further, the entire machinery was sold to the contract partner. The farm manager's house was rented out at a commercial price, resulting in additional income to the estate owner.

In 2008, the forestry manager was also discharged. The task of the forest manager was contracted out to another estate: there is a measure of advantage to both parties through costs cut on both sides. The forest manager's house was also rented out at a commercial price, resulting in additional income to the estate owner.

Old farm converted into luxury houses.

E. Scholma

E. Scholma

Burg Gudenau **(Germany)**

CHALLENGES OF BURG GUDENAU

Challenges regarding generational transfer for owners of historic estates

1. Generational transfer / an art form in itself

The transfer of an historic estate from one generation to the other is a very intricate process and requires planning ahead in many respects. In that sense, it is an art form in itself, and goes far beyond the idea that it is simply a matter of legal preparation.

Tax planning and legal planning are only two of many factors.

Most attention is paid to taxation and legal aspects, but despite this the end result is often a disaster.

The challenges confronting the two generations between whom the transfer has to take place lie rather in the ability and willingness of the transferring generation to communicate at the right moment and transparently with the new generation, and the willingness and the ability of the new generation to combine respect for and understanding of the tradition and the spirit of an historic estate with a cold look at the economies of the estate itself and the social, political and economic environment at large in which it has to survive.

Romantic feelings about becoming the inhabitant and master of an historic estate can be dangerous just on their own, as they often block a view of harsh economic reality.

Another important factor is the willingness of the old generation to transfer completely and at the right moment thus leaving space for necessary changes and new directions and motivating the following generation to take charge of their future.

2. Challenges regarding Burg Gudenau Estate over time

Burg Gudenau is a classic example of how changing motives of ownership and changing economic, social and political circumstances impose new and often difficult tasks on the next generation.

1872 - 1910

The original owner, Franz Carl Guilleaume, needed a summer residence to retire from the daily pressures of running an industrial conglomerate, and the same applied to his son Theodor. The wealth they acquired meant that there was not necessary to consider the financial sustainability of the estate. Respect for the historic spirit of the place however was less "in vogue" in those days, as they introduced highly modern facilities such as running hot and warm water, modern bathrooms, central heating and a large kitchen built to the latest technical standards. Also, the layout and division of the rooms was changed to accommodate modern taste. All of this was to the detriment of the historic fabric. The farming and forestry activities connected were run and managed in-hand but were not essential for the maintenance of the estate. In brief, it was a luxury hobby.

1910 - 1960

The two generations thereafter had to face the consequences of two world wars, the (partial) loss of the family fortune and the destructive influence of this on the estate.

At the end of WWII, the allied forces chose the estate as a local headquarters and, through an act of negligence, started a fire that destroyed the inner part of the house.

The greater part of the interior was shipped by

the allies to North America before the family had returned after fleeing the war.

The challenge became "mere survival" in a ruined and almost emptied house, a situation which continued until 1955 when Nikolaus Strasoldo took the first steps towards restoration, a process that would go on until well after 1960. Not only was money scarce, but so too were building materials and skilled craftsmen. It took a lot of patience and willpower to live through this process and to bring it to a conclusion.

The motive for maintaining the Burg Gudenau changed from being the "summer residence" to the main family residence.

1960 - 1995

This longer period of a constantly growing economy and a constantly changing political climate brought new challenges.

Thanks to a successful banking career, Nikolaus Strasoldo was able to put Burg Gudenau Estate onto a sound financial footing.

During this period, modern ways of economic thinking replace the idea of safeguarding a family

General overview of the estate.

home at all costs. The estate is an economic activity per se and must become profitable. It is no longer a luxury hobby.

Even at an early stage, careful thought and consideration was given to the impact of agricultural policies originating from Brussels, and the estate's farming operations were directed towards profitability and sustainability.

In 1976 a whole new farm operation was built. Cattle breeding and the dairy cows disappeared, the cultivation of fruit was brought to an end, and the resulting freed land and part of the woodland turned into agricultural land. This all under the influence of the ever changing subsidy rules from Brussels. As part of the new direction, a large modern pig breeding operation was built and the number of personnel (which before WWII amounted to 45) was reduced to 6 people. In order to reduce capital costs, large capital-intensive machinery was purchased in co-operation with the neighbours.

In hindsight the real question remains unanswered: was it really wise to do everything that Brussels said it was best to do? Has it brought the owner financial reward?

E. Scholma

3. The challenges for the current generation

1995 - now

3.1. Portfolio management instead of farm management

Around 1995 Nikolaus asks his daughter Henriette and her husband Enno Scholma, both bankers by profession, to take over the day-to-day management of the estate. The challenges facing them are again entirely different.

The social, economic and political climates have changed fast and will continue to change rapidly. "Learning by doing" is the main anthem, as both have no experience whatever in managing an estate or a farm.

It is time to take a long hard look at the economies of the estate and the economic, political and social environment at large.

The presumed disadvantage of having no experience of estate or farm management turns out to be an advantage.

Looking dispassionately through their sharply focused glasses, these two investment bankers decided that the operation had to be seen as a portfolio of different economic activities, generating a cash flow. Each activity must be(come) profitable.

A judgement had to be made about which operations had a chance for the future and which had to be abandoned.

In addition, ideas have now had be developed for other cash-generating operations, because the new generation takes the view that in order to be able to hand it on to the next generation, the estate must, by that time, be able to be self-financing and provide the owner with a certain income for himself (self reliance).

The motive for maintaining Burg Gudenau has thereby changed to a "commercial operation", from which a family must be able to live.

3.2. The decisions made

This has turned out to be an ongoing process of more than 10 years, evaluating, deciding, executing and learning from past failures. However, the most important aspect has been the implicit decision to manage the estate not as "farmers and foresters" but as portfolio managers, thus saying goodbye to the idea of the "romantic landowner".

The first thing that became clear was that the days of labour-intensive and risky pig breeding were over. The size of the operation was too small to achieve a level of economic sustainability. The pig breeding was shut down, and the staff (4) dismissed.

No economic use was ever found for the old pig buildings. The houses on the estate where the employees lived were emptied. It also became clear that in the long run the agricultural and forestry operations were too small to financially support the main house. After many ideas/experiments (biogas, mini-cultures, solar park, windmills, contracting work for other farms), it was decided that the model had to be one of moving away from fixed labour and other costs, towards a more flexible model of purchasing services as and when needed and at competitive prices. The farm manager and the forester were asked to leave. Their houses were emptied.

The end result is that the estate is still fully managed by the owners - completely at their own risk - but without staff (except for the garden). All the agricultural machinery was sold, and the financial information systems transferred to the accountant, thus making the relevant information more transparent and more easily and quickly available.

All other services are bought on a contract basis at competitive prices from neigbours or third parties. All contracts are short term, giving considerable flexibility to adjust quickly to changing market circumstances.

3.3. The opportunity

The area around Bonn, the former capital of Germany, is increasingly densely populated, and a place where the pressures of the modern world have become more and more evident.

The decision of the German government to move the capital to Berlin was accompanied by a clear cut and very effective plan to bring new business to the Bonn/Cologne region.

House building programmes, the creation of so-called business parks and tourism projects, all the result of ambitious town councils, start to threaten the estate.

But in the threat also lies the opportunity.

With more and more people coming to the Bonn/Cologne area for work, the need for proper housing and the desire for recreation and a natural environment is increasing year by year.

With this in view, by 1996 parts of the old stables had already been turned into luxury houses (average 250-300 m^2), rented out on an average basis of three years.

With more former employees' houses becoming available because their relevant functions are eliminated, more opportunities have arisen to turn these houses into rented properties.

The result, today, is an attractive portfolio of 8 romantically situated houses in perfect condition.

The income stream from rentals is now making a major contribution towards the cash flow.

3.4. Positive impact on whole estate

One thing leads to another. Investing in houses to rent meant that there was a need to increase the green space around them and, as a result, the overall look of the estate improved drastically. This gave rise to the decision to completely repaint the outside of the castle, an enormous task carried out well by the Simon family, a team of father and two sons, painters from the village. The splendid end result shows how much they put their heart and soul into the work.

Inside the castle, major restoration has been carried out to reclaim parts of the house still in disrepair after WWII. The original baroque dining room has been recreated, the 1910 kitchen restored to its original form out of a heap of rubble left untouched for decades, and closed windows, corridors and staircases have been re-opened and restored.

As a result of this renewal process, there has been a realisation that the estate should be considered a living organism, which grows better and faster the more care it gets.

From that point of view, the original baroque park has been reclaimed over a period of several years.

The plans have been based on a drawing by a Dutch artist, Roidkin, who sketched the park not long after its creation in 1710.

The original fountains, visible on the drawing, have all been put to work again, some for the first time in hundreds of years.

Baroque statutes (12 in total) have been purchased and placed back in the positions visible in the drawing and much of the vegetation planted at the time of its redesign as a landscape park in the 19th century has been cut back or removed by the forces of nature and not replaced.

It was also decided to give the area of the former pig buildings back to nature. Over a period of 4 months several million kilos of concrete and steel were carried away, and nowadays nobody would ever guess it had been there.

Further plans are now being put into effect to let more land go back to a natural state and to re-introduce small game, such as hares, rabbits and pheasants.

3.5. The local community as essential factor

In addition, the passage of time also established the fact that the estate cannot survive if it does not enjoy the sympathy and support of the local community.

There is historically a high degree of identification of the village with the estate and the family which owns it.

Traditionally, the Villiper Männer Gesangsverein, the male voice choir of the village, comes on the 1st of May every year to sing an "aubade".

Every year in the summer an open air Mass is conducted, after which traditional songs are sung ("Offenes singen").

These and other traditional ties are valuable and must be treated accordingly.

This requires an ongoing dialogue with the local community, including allowing the community to make use of the house from time to time.

As part of the restoration of the old stables, a huge hay barn became redundant. After first having been earmarked only as a garage for the tenants, it has, thanks to the insight of the conductor of the youth orchestra in the village, become the concert hall for the orchestra's annual concert, and easily accommodates 500-600 people.

The concert is given in honour of Anton Raaff, the most famous opera singer at the time of Mozart (they were friends) who was born in the village and worked in his early days as an administrator at Burg Gudenau.

Finally, the challenge for any new generation of owner is to understand and respect the estate's own spirit and character. Failure to do so will result in serious mistakes in handling the historic fabric, often leading to irreparable loss of character.

It is not too difficult. One only has to follow the "language" of the estate itself. This means using the materials that are already there when undertaking repairs, using the same paints as in the past rather than destructive modern chemical products, respecting the historic forms and functions of the building, and not using colours that did not exist when the house was created.

In brief, the combination of cold (economic) eyes and a warm (cultural) heart can make an estate prosper.

Burg Gudenau

BURG GUDENAU BELONGS TO:

Rise Foundation

Friends of the Countryside

Activities & attractions

- 🏰 Historic building & sites of interest
- Country Park
- Equestrian
- Local products
- Rural Trails
- Country Sport
- Rural tourism

CONTACT DATA
Enno & Henriette Scholma
Burg Gudenau
53343 Wachtberg - Villip • Germany
Tel: 0228-9323010 • Fax: 0228 932 30 12
burg-gudeneau@gmx.de

Dennenlohe

Continental

Location: Municipality of Unterschwaningen, Frankonia province, Germany.
Surface: 218 ha.

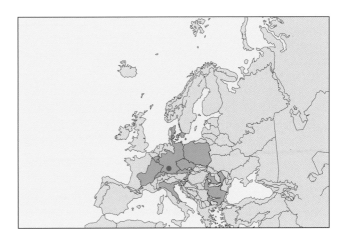

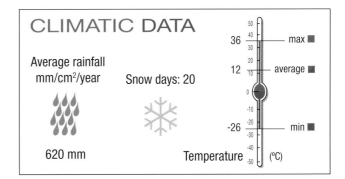

CLIMATIC DATA

Average rainfall
mm/cm²/year

Snow days: 20

620 mm

Temperature (°C)

36 — max ■
12 — average ■
-26 — min ■

SUMMARY

Schloss Dennenlohe is an exquisite 18th century house in the heart of the rolling Bavarian countryside. It offers audience members, guests and artists exceptional accommodation and the opportunity to perform, learn about or hear music in a unique and charming setting. Its beautifully cultivated gardens and parkland set beside a magnificent lake offer wonderful opportunities for relaxation and are a haven for wildlife. Ranking among the top twenty of Germany's most beautiful parks, the estate has been in the possession of the Süsskind family for 8 generations. Today, the manor house hosts a vintage car museum, a tavern, an antique shop and an art gallery in the historic hippodrome.

Baron von Süsskind has achieved his vision and, in doing so, has developed a completely new style of gardening in Schloss Dennenlohe Park. A patchwork of traditional cultured and wild landscapes is currently being developed on 26 hectares of land directly north of the Rhododendron Park.

"Creating a garden demands hands, head and heart."

Dennenlohe Estate

Dennenlohe Estate has been in the possession of the Süsskind family for 8 generations.

HISTORY

In 1711 Paul Martin Baron Eichler von Auritz bought the country estate of Dennenlohe with its derelict 12th century castle and adjoining lakeland. In 1734-50 he commissioned Leopold Retti to design and rebuild the castle.

In 1773, his successor sold the castle to Johann Graf von Fries from Vienna. The Baroque parterre in the pleasure garden was transformed into an English garden. By 1802 the castle had been sold again and had become the property of the Count of Pappenheim. The orangery was rebuilt.

In 1825 Gottlieb Baron von Süsskind, a merchant banker from the southern German town of Augsburg, bought Dennenlohe and in 1868 his son Albert built in the Neo-Gothic chapel in Dennenlohe.

In 1980, Robert Baron von Süsskind, the present Baron, took over the castle estate and in 1990 the Rhododendron Park was laid out. Between 1994 and 2000, all the castle buildings were renovated and the chapel was rebuilt. In 1998-99 the Persian Garden was laid out. In 2000 the amphitheatre was built and in the following years the islands in the Rhododendron Park were progressively planted.

In 2004 the Baroque farm buildings were renovated in the record time of just four months and in 2006, after three years of waiting, permission to build the landscape garden was finally granted. The project can now get underway!

DESCRIPTION

The castle and castle grounds are physically one entity, although the overall complex can be clearly divided into distinctive areas, each with a different theme.

From 1734 to 1750, the architect Leopold Retti designed not only the castle but a complete ensemble including the farm buildings and the private garden.

It was the present-day Baron von Süsskind who added two further attractions to the ancestral family castle: the Rododendron Park in 1990 and the landscape garden in 2006.

These additions have helped to promote Schloss Dennenlohe's popularity beyond national boundaries.

As a result of his father's death Baron von Süsskind was forced to end his years of travel as a consultant in St. Gallen, Munich and Brussels. In 1989 he returned home to the family castle in southern Germany. As the farm had been leased out on a long-term basis there was very little for an energetic thirty-five year old to do. However, once he had re-established his roots, he decided that he would like to plant some...

He transformed the orchard into a magnificent garden (the Private Garden), before embarking on a completely new venture – the Rhododendron Park. Baron von Süsskind had discovered a passion for the rhododendron, a passion that continues to devel-

The Rhododendron Park is a personal project of Baron von Süsskind .

Dennenlohe Estate

op and mature, and is perhaps unique in modern-day Germany. Whilst not uncommon for the 18th century nobility to invest a huge amount of money, time and effort into their gardens, today projects of this scale are only undertaken by national trusts and public institutions. But Baron von Süsskind has created a new park with its own inimitable style, as opposed to public garden administrators, who restore historical gardens according to original blueprints. No fancy PR campaigns, simple word of mouth advertising has made the Castle Park a popular tourist attraction. What you see in Dennenlohe today is the result of almost 20 years work. Every single item has been planted by the Süsskinds personally. The achievements of Baron and Baroness von Süsskind, by virtue of their personal dedication and boundless creativity – and a passion that sometimes borders on obsession – are unrivalled in Germany.

Since 2004 the Rhododendron Park has been open daily to visitors from April until the end of October. It is mentioned regularly in international gardening publications and has been the setting for several German television series. Since 2007 the Schlosspark has been an official Botanic Garden and Member of the BGCI and the Horticultural Society. Volunteer Programmes are possible during the spring and summer months.

As mentioned before, the foundations for the original historical castle garden design were part of the plans drafted in 1734 by Leopold Retti for the entire complex. He was influenced by the French art of gardening, in keeping with the Baroque fashion of that time.

Formal gardens were popular in the 18th century, with geometrical straight paths and vistas. The idea was to covey power over nature. These principles were employed for the castle gardens in Versailles and symbolised the absolute power of the prince.

It was not only the pleasure garden that conformed to the laws of geometry. In the vegetable garden, the asparagus and cabbage beds were laid out between precisely trimmed hedges and paths that looked as if they had been measured with a ruler.

However, formal gardens became outdated shortly after the castle was finished. The fashion during the Enlightenment demanded landscape gardens, which first appeared in England in the 1730s and within a few decades had replaced almost all the Baroque gardens throughout Europe.

Dennenlohe Estate

The pleasure garden, which had been laid out as a symmetrical Baroque garden, was transformed 23 years later into an English landscape garden.

Unlike the pleasure garden, the vegetable garden retained its formal character until it was transformed into spacious lawns in 1950. Baron von Süskind managed to create a breathtaking vista here. From the vase walk, a symbol of ancient Greece, one's gaze wanders past the Persian garden, through the round moon gate in the castle walls, then onwards through the Chinese section of the Rhododendron Park to the red bridge before continuing towards the Japanese section with its picturesque stone lanterns.

The Castle

Castle Dennenlohe is a luxurious Baroque castle, located right in the middle of the "Fränkischen Seenland", the lake-land of Franconia. Schloss Dennenlohe can be reached from Nürnberg within 40 minutes and from Munich within 95 minutes. Stuttgart, Dinkelsbühl and Rothenburg are nearby.

The rooms, which have excellent catering facilities, can be rented for business events and family celebrations, such as weddings or birthday parties. In the last 5 years Schloss Dennenlohe has been a sidescreen for various entertaining series on German television. The 11 individually designed rooms and 4 suites have all separate and completely restored bathrooms. Schloss Dennenlohe has stylish, elegant rooms for conferences, meetings, banquets and other festivities, different parlours, a billiard-room, a library and a romantic room with a fireplace.

Since 2004, the Rhododendron Park has been opened daily from April until the end of October.

Dennenlohe (Germany)

When the electric gates buzz open, the Baroque façade of Schloss Dennenlohe, which has remained unchanged since 1734, greets its visitors. The stables, gardens and the adjacent farm buildings date from the same period. High walls surround the castle and grounds, and create an atmosphere of peace and tranquillity. The architect, not just for the castle but for the entire complex, was the Italian Leopold Retti, master builder at the court of the Markgraf of Ansbach and a master of German Baroque architecture. Famous castles in Ludwigsburg and Ansbach as well as the Neues Schloss in Stuttgart were also drafted on his drawing board. He designed until generations.

Baroque Farm Buildings

Schloss Dennenlohe also boasts an impressive Baroque farm, consiting of an 80 metre long yard with stalls and barns on all four sides. It has always 〜nainstay of the castle and its ｒ〜ｓｉｄｅｎｔｓ.

Besides forestry, arable and lake-land farming, there was also a brewery, a sawmill and weaving mill. Up until 1823 courts were held in the administrator's office. The gallows were just 500 metres west of the farm.

In 1965 the **farming facilities** were leased out. At the end of 2003 Baron von Süsskind decided to restore totally the Baroque farm buildings, in light of the fact that the castle gardens and special events had become such popular tourist attractions. The baroque farm became a sight-seeing attraction in itself and the old farm buildings were put to new use.

In the historical **riding hall** horses were once trained for the cavalry. Today, it is used as an Art Gallery and Concert hall. The stables now function as a restaurant and café with a beer garden at the front, shaded by chestnut and apple trees.

The **Vintage Car Museum** is located in the historical cow shed and barn, which dates back to 1700. In the old days linen would be hung out to dry on the first floor, and hops would be left to ferment on the second floor. Forty cars and just as many motorbikes are on display in the museum, including the grandfather of all cars – an original model of the motor car for which Carl Benz and Gottlieb Daimler were awarded a patent in 1886. The motorized age was now ready to start.

Most of the cars date from the 1930s to the 1950s and are all roadworthy. The museum is sponsored by a private club of vintage car lovers. One of the highlights is the state limousine in which Conrad Adenauer, Willy Brandt and John F. Kennedy were driven around Berlin in 1963.

In **the castle shop** – originally stalls where the calves were housed – gift ítems, local products and garden books are available.

The family **Castle Chapel** is today used only to celebrate weddings and christenings. The original chapel dates back to the 14th century, but in 1868 it was rebuilt by Albert Baron von Süsskind in the Neo-Gothic style. His body was buried in the family vault in the southern German town of Augsburg, although his heart still rests in the Castle Chapel.

The Private Garden

The Baron's family uses the old castle garden privately. It is surrounded by a high wall along with the farm buildings and coutyard. This area is only open to the public during the "Gardens Day", on "Musical Sundays" and for classical concerts.

A particular feature of the private garden – "private refuge" for the baronial family – is that it is laid out on four different ground levels. Baron von Süsskind's passion for creating landscapes began here in the Private Garden. His first step was to plant the shrubbery. Then he transformed the boggy duck pond into a delightful Persian garden with a cascading waterfall, additional water features and shrub terraces.

Plans have also been drafted for future developments that include the construction of a shell grotto, with a brook connecting it to the Persian Garden.

The Rhododendron Park

The overall picture is of an impressionist still-life landscape in 3-D format. The Park, which boasts an abundance of rhododendrons, is a delightful com-

The architect Leopold Retti designed the castle at the beginning of 18th century.

Dennenlohe Estate

position of islands and bridges, light and colour. Asian temples and gates add an oriental touch.

Baron von Süsskind has spent almost every day since 1990 in his garden. A dozen islands have gradually emerged around the edge of the six and a half hectare lake, each representing a different theme.

The islands are connected by eleven bridges. Hints of oriental mythology are placed discretely among a wilderness of plants. The park has now grown to twelve hectares in size and offers exciting new impressions every month from April to October.

In the Rhododendron Park at Dennenlohe one can sense the spontaneity and creativity Baron von Süsskind puts into his work. He follows the principles of "lush planting". This refers to a system of planting that occurs naturally in the jungle. The shrubs and bushes are planted in close proximity, yet they are still able to develop their full natural growth potential. The concept of a wild landscape garden offered the best opportunity to put this into practice. The idea was to create an unstructured display that was by no means unplanned. Baron von Süsskind discovered his love for rhododendrons early in life. Originally native to the Himalayas, they were first shipped to Britain in the 18th century. Frequently only one plant out of a million would survive the long sea journey to reach its English port of destination intact. Despite this fact, rhododendrons are very easy to look after, making them ideal park plants.

The location beside the castle pond is ideally suited to rhododendrons as they thrive in a warm damp climate in humus-rich loam soil.

The Lake generates a favourable micro-climate for the rhododendrons. The water, ice-cold in February and March, lowers the air temperature and has a slowing effect on the plants. This means that the buds come out later in the year, avoiding damage from late frost.

In April and May the water exudes warmth into the atmosphere and causes a slight rise in temperature. It can happen that during the mornings the Private Garden is covered in hoar frost, whereas the thermometer stays above zero in the Rhododendron Park.

From the Heart, Dragon and Moor islands a stone bridge leads to Birch Island. Over the next bridge you get to the Theatre Island (where the amphitheatre is located) and a floating pontoon bridge then leads to the Wild Island (completely natural).

Dennenlohe Estate

The old boggy duck pond was transformed into a delightful Persian garden by Baron von Süsskind.

Via the hanging bridge with its two Shoji gates you reach the Bamboo Island before crossing some stepping stones to arrive at the Temple Island. Finally you leave Temple Island over the Chinese bridge which leads into the Landscape Garden.

The Landscape Garden Project

This concept will be continually developed until the year 2015 and combines the principles of landscape gardening along with ecological considerations of the 21st century.

Instead of a neat picture-postcard landscape, a biotope of beautifully modelled wild landscapes has been created providing a natural protected environment for threatened species of plants and animals.

The combination of eight completely different types of landscape in one area makes this project quite unique. No matter how long the winter, spring is sure to follow. Despite initial setbacks the potential for a first-class botanic attraction was clear from the very beginning of the project.

Heather. Planted on a range of parallel hills. The dales slope down towards the southwest, allowing

"You can tell a garden by its gardener"

The Rhododendron Park which boasts an abundance of rhododendrons, is a delightful composition of islands and bridges, light and colour.

G. Rogers

the cold air to flow away freely. Heather landscapes, formerly a common feature in southern Germany, have almost disappeared from the region.

Moor. In a joint project with the Botanic Institute of the University of Erlangen, ferns and flowering shrubs from the "Red List" of endangered species have been planted in this area. Grey Herons (*Ardea cinerea*) and Kingfishers (*Alcedo atthis*) come from a nearby lake to nest there.

Wave Garden. Here the ground has be modelled to form waves and dunes, creating a structured landscape in the smallest spaces, where the interaction between light and warmth alternates and affects the climatic conditions in the area accordingly.

Sunken Garden. A deliberate combination of the formal Baroque garden and a landscape garden. Whilst the shapes and forms are typically Baroque, the wild flowers planted in this part are indicative of a landscape garden.

Orchard. Traditional apple and pear trees have been planted in cooperation with a regional horticultural society. The "Most" – fermented fruit juice reminiscent of "Cider" – can be sampled and purchased on the estate.

Meadow Biotope. There are over twenty areas of different meadow biotopes ranging from dry through wet to bog meadows. At one time these were all native to the region.

Rose Hill. Planted with over 3000 species of roses to document the history of the cultivated rose, starting with the damask rose from Arabia. Native varieties of wild roses bloom on the west side of the hill.

The lake generates an excelent micro-climate for the rhododendrons.

Dennenlohe Estate

HOW DOES THE LANDOWNER FACE THE FUTURE?

The question for the seventh generation was – How could we make a profit from forestry? The livestock and arable parts of the estate were already tenanted.

In previous centuries, the farm made its profit from sheep, through spinning and weaving of the wool. There was also a stud and stables; training horses for the cavalry and of course the saw-mill, which processed timber.

However, after the Second World War, the erosion of all profitability on goods produced in general meant that it was only livestock farming (pigs and cows) as well as wood for (re)construction which made sense.

In 1989 the decision was made to sell the forest in order to secure the castle and the farm, because of this lack of specialisation.

Now, after 20 years of restoration, the Baroque ensemble of farm buildings and castle, with the Neo-Gothic chapel, and the different gardens have established a new source of income.

Now, after 20 years of restoration, the Baroque ensemble of farm buildings and castle, with the Neo-Gothic chapel, the development of the 3 hectares of walled garden and the newly planted 12 hectares of landscaped gardens have established a new source of income for the estate.

The season for the garden is from April to October, with the highlight of the rhododendron blossom in May and June as the main attraction. Nearly 50,000 visitors come to Dennenlohe annually.

The current aim is to prolong the season by planting different varieties of species as well as creating a new Arboretum. As time passes we are permanently enlarging the collections of plants as well as the overall size of the park.

We are increasing our visitor base through annual garden fairs, seminars, weddings, concerts and operas. With the restored farm buildings and their courtyard, we are able to offer our visitors a variety of things to do and see; a gift and plant shop, a self-service restaurant, an Orangerie café, an art gallery and a vintage car museum.

It is in this way that the Dennenlohe Estate has managed the critical and necessary structural change from agriculture to tourism.

In addition, Baroness von Süsskind has founded the "German Garden Book Prize". Every year an international jury looks for the best garden books in different categories.

She has also created the "Bavarian Garden Network" with over 40 excellent private and public parcs and gardens. For more informations see www.gartentour-bayern.de

Mit freundlichen Grüßen aus Dennenlohe

DENNENLOHE ESTATE BELONGS TO:

Friends of the Countryside

Gipfeltreffen-Bayern

German Gardenbook Prize

Activities

- Country Park
- Garden
- Historic building
- Historic private house
- Estate product
- Rural tourism
- Walking trails
- Cycling
- Fishing

CONTACT DATA
Freiherrliche von Süsskind'sche
Schloss- und Gartenverwaltung
Schloss Dennenlohe
91743 Unterschwaningen • Germany
Tel.: 0049 - 9836 - 96888 • Fax: 0049 - 9836 - 96889
schloss@dennenlohe.de

Dobříš-Zbiroh

Continental

Location: Přibram (Dobříš) and Rokycany/Beroun (Zbiroh) locality, Region of Central Bohemia, Czech Republic.
Surface: 17,000 ha (Dobříš: 4,500 ha and Zbiroh: 12,500 ha).

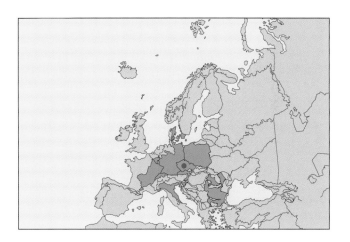

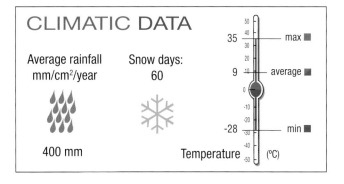

CLIMATIC DATA

Average rainfall
mm/cm²/year

400 mm

Snow days:
60

Temperature (°C)

35 — max ■
9 — average ■
-28 — min ■

SUMMARY

Large properties such as the Dobříš-Zbiroh Estate have passed through many economic, social and political difficulties and show important cultural heritage and unchanged family traditions. The castle and park attract many visitors and countryside lovers.
Well-known for its open, rolling landscape, the estate is alternately covered with woods, arable land, meadows and ponds. Forestry, fish farming, hunting and shooting are economic and traditional activities offered by the property and of great importance.

Dobříš & Zbiroh Estate

The origins of Dobříš Castle dated from the 14th century, although the present building, designed by the French architec J.R. de Cotte and the Italian G.N. Servandoni, dates from 1765.

Dobříš-Zbiroh **(Czech Republic)**

HISTORY

According to legend the founder of the town was a nobleman by the name of Dobrich, after whom the town was named Dobříš. Dobrich is associated with the construction of a wooden fortress on the so-called Golden Route, which was an important link between Prague and Italy at the time of the Přemysls.

The first written records, which mention Dobříš, date back to 1245, at which time a royal residence had been built there, where even the Czech King Vaclav I (Wenceslas I) had stayed at one time.

In the first half of the 14th century, John of Luxemburg commissioned the construction of Varkac, a Gothic stone castle, which stands on the cliffs above the present day castle. Originally it was intended to be the residence of the office of the Royal Hunt Master, but during the 18th century it was converted into a granary.

In 1422, Zikmund of Luxemburg pledged the Dobříš Estate to the brothers from Kolowrat. At the time the Hussites destroyed Dobříš because its inhabitants had supported Zikmund. Later the estate was given in pledge several more times, for example to the Lobkowiczs or Svihovskys from Ryzmburk. At the end of the 16th century, the first Dobříš castle was erected in the Renaissance style,

Since the Castle was returned to the family in 1992, reconstruction and restoration work has been incessant, mainly after Jerome Colloredo Mannsfeld inherited the estate in 1998.

but unfortunately no records about it have survived. In 1630 the Royal Hunt Master, Bruno Mansfeld, bought the castle, together with the whole estate, for 40,000 gold pieces from Emperor Ferdinand II. After his death, the estate was taken over by his son František Maximilian Mansfeld (1644-1692), who rebuilt the Renaissance castle into a Baroque residence with a large garden.

However, Dobříš castle was destroyed by the fire in 1720, and Heinrich Paul Mansfeld, the son of Bruno, prepared a plan for a new castle and a park designed by the French architect J.R. de Cotte and the Italian one G.N. Servandoni. The work was finished in 1765, and remains today.

At about the same time, Rudolf Colloredo, of Italian descent, started his career in the Imperial Army, and saw action in the Thirty Years War. As a reward for his valour he was awarded the castle and estate in Opočno in northern Bohemia, which was expropriated from the Trčka family.

In 1771 Maria Isabella Mansfeld married Prince Franz Colloredo of Opočno. This marriage resulted in the formal union of the two estates, Mansfeld's Dobříš and Colloredo's Opočno. In 1879, the Colloredo-Mansfelds extended the estate by buying the neighbouring land of Zbiroh from Baron Strousberg, famous as the former European "railroad king".

The estate was confiscated in 1942 by the Nazis and was returned, or was on the way to being returned, after the end of World War II, but very soon was once again expropriated in 1948 after the seizure of power by the Communists. The family emigrated to Canada, the U.S, Switzerland and Austria. The estate at Dobříš was taken over by the communist writers' organisation until the Velvet Revolution in 1989.

From 1992/93 onwards, Jeroným Colloredo-Mannsfeld (1912-1998) was able to recover considerable parts of the family's confiscated property in the Czech Republic, mainly his own estate in Zbiroh. There were complications on the rights of possession for his brothers' properties, they had died before the completion of the decrees of restitution.

Dobříš Castle came into the ownership of Jeroným Colloredo-Mannsfeld after the death of his childless uncle Jeronˇm in 1998, but the Dobříš Estate only came back to the family in 2005 and was divided into two parts.

DESCRIPTION

Development of the land and landscape setting

Land and Landscape

The small city and the castle of Dobříš, with part of the estate, is situated about 35 kilometres south of Prague between the woods of Brdy and the high land above the main river of Bohemia, the Vltava. The larger part of the estate, with the forests of Zbiroh, lays 40 km to the west between Prague and Pilsen, on the edge of the Křivoklat woodlands and the National Park.

The landscape is one of open, rolling countryside ranging between 400 and 650 metres above sea level. The land is alternately covered with woods, arable land and meadows, ponds and streams. There are also large forests, with only very few settlements outside the villages.

The estate's soils are not very fertile and they tend to solifluction. As a consequence of the widespread arable monocultures and forestry, the topsoil is relatively low grade.

Present land use

Livestock

At Dobříš, as indeed in the entire country, the original tradition of livestock farming ended with the transformation of private agriculture into the Soviet system of huge specialised units ("kolchoz"). Even now, following the privatisation of estates and farms, livestock production has been little revived. This is due to the lack of animal housing (which was ruined over the period of collective agriculture), specialised staff, and economic and technical knowledge.

Arable farming

There is no in-hand arable farming undertaken by the estate. The arable land is currently let out.

The farmed areas are mostly part of common cultivated units. The tenants are new private agricultural companies, which followed the former socialist co-operatives. There will be probably some major changes in the future and it seems possible that some companies will reduce their activities and more farmer-like entrepreneurs will replace them. There is considerable potential for more intensive production.

Fish farming

Pisciculture has a long tradition in Bohemia. In the 19th century, and probably earlier, artificial ponds were created ranging from a few square metres to several hectares and are typical elements of the rural landscape.

The estate now has approximately 400 hectares of fish-ponds. Carp (*Cyprinus carpio*) is the most important product, for both the local market and export. But other fish like Pike-perch (*Sandrus lucioperca*), Trout (*Salmo trutta*) and Catfish (*Silurus glanis*) are also cultivated. Pisciculture contributes 5-7% of the estate's income.

The wetlands on the estate provide attractive shelter for insects, fish, and aquatic birds. They also offer wonderful landscape.

Harvesting is the most important parts of fish farm work.

The caption on the right-hand side of the image reads vertically: *Dobříš & Zbiroh Estate*

Approximately 30% of the raw material and 50% of the manufactured products are exported.

Harvest plans

The type and the size of the forests are guided by the forest structure and the forest management plan respectively. The plan is reviewed every ten years and displays a very strict fixed regime. The idea goes back to the first forest laws at the time of the monarchy in the 19th century, when the use of wood increased as a result of the industrial revolution and arrangements were needed to safeguard a sustainable supply of the raw material.

The provisions of the current Czech forest law are quite strict, especially as regards volume and variety of trees. They are also aimed at advancing the conversion of the Spruce monocultures to mixed forests.

Norway Spruce (*Picea abies*) is the most important forest tree in Dobříš & Zbiroh Estate.

Forestry

Forestry is the economic base of the estate. More than 90% of the estate's productive area is woodland.

At Dobříš approximately two thirds of the forests are coniferous. Spruce (*Picea abies*) is the most important and numerous trees, Pine (*Pinus silvestris*) grows in the more arid areas, and Larch (*Larix decidua*) occurs in mixed crops. Beech (*Fagus silvatica*) and Oak (*Quercus robur*) are dominant in the deciduous one third.

Natural conditions for tree growth are no more than average, but modern methods of harvesting are very good. Some 30% of harvested timber is processed further to produce miscellaneous special products, for instance for horticulture or construction. The remainder is sold to the industry for sawn timber, pulp and paper.

Forest harvest

The choice of harvesting techniques in the working forest is extensive, and is governed by the open market situation and the availability of contractors and machines.

The estate does not have its own harvester, because nowadays it is no better nor more effective than human manpower, and there is no benefit in quality or costs. But as machines become cheaper and better, other considerations will apply. About one third of the coniferous wood is felled in this way.

The annual increment is around 5m^3 per hectare per year on the estate. In the past decade only 80-90% of the increment has been harvested. Two thirds of production is accounted for by coniferous wood, of which the same proportion is saw logs and

The estate does not have its own harvester, because nowadays it is no better nor more effective than human manpower, and there is no benefit in quality or costs.

one third divided between industry and firewood. In the first years of the free market economy, there were many small and medium-sized sawmills in operation, and the estate still had its own sawmill until three years ago. But even here, market concentration and rationalisation can be seen. Most home-grown timber is supplied to farms, but a significant proportion of softwood is still exported, especially to the large Austrian sawmills.

Bio-mass

After a delay of several years, the Czech Republic has firmly established its aspiration to strengthen production of alternative biogenic energy. Where transport distances are reasonable, the estate is increasingly selling waste wood and surplus timber as energy. But we need timber for major renovation work in the castle, which, together with the forester's house and the shooting lodges, is heated by gas, charcoal or electricity. So far this is the cheapest and most rational method, especially as the gas pipeline passes the doorstep. In the future, however, there will be great potential in this sector.

The economic benefits of extracting biomass from the forest must be seriously reviewed against the ecological compatibility of removing feed resources. Under no circumstances do we want to risk degrading any of our already weakened soils.

Pests

Around 80 years ago a huge area of coniferous forest in central Bohemia was the victim of a proliferation of the Nun Moth (*Lymantria monacha*). This disaster has thankfully not been repeated, since the imminent spread of the moth is monitored intensively and can be identified early, and controlling it chemically from the air is no problem.

The situation with Bark Beetles (principally *Ips typographus, Ips cembrae* and *Pityogenes chalcographus*) is different. Aerial control is not possible and they pose a latent threat. They can cause catastrophic dieback in the forest and even lead to the extermination of spruce forest, particularly after windstorms and as a consequence of global warming. The only protection is forest hygiene of the highest order – the immediate removal of afflicted trees and the barking of fallen trunks – and this requires intensive monitoring of the forests.

So far the operations have been successful in averting this threat, but storms and damage in the forests of Central Europe in recent years have raised the fear that things may get out of control.

Tree spacing

The country's specific and traditional intensive forestry is expressed by very dense planting levels. In Austria and Germany forests are planted at a density of 2,000 trees per hectare or less, whilst comparable places in the Czech Republic are planted at 4,000 trees per hectare or more. These stands are not usually thinned, but the trees are looked after until they reach the so-called First Forest or pole stage.

However, it should not be forgotten that thinning is a measure which does not usually cover its costs. In the Czech Republic even the classical First Forest pole stage thinning can cover costs.

Forest related...

As in other central European forests, the problems affecting wild game in the forests are important ones for the estate: settlement pressure on the one hand and hunting interests on the other hand may have a considerably adverse effect on game.

In particular, the traditional and positive values of having a wide diversity of game species – Red Deer (*Cervus elaphus*), Roe Deer (*Capreolus capreolus*), Wild Boar (*Sus scrofa*), Sika Deer (*Cervus nipon*), White-tailed Deer (*Odocoileus virginianus*) and Mouflon (*Ovis musimon*) – causes potential conflict.

Mixed forests only regenerate successfully when fenced. Peeling and damage to the bark requires the protection of individual trees. Otherwise, we strive to maintain a healthy and interesting wildlife stock that brings economic benefit.

The white-tailed deer is one of four deer species living on the estate. In forest eco-systems, determining the appropiate carrying capacity is relevant for sustainable deer management.

Dobříš & Zbiroh Estate

Forest certification

The forests on the estate are certified under the Pan-European Forest Certification system (PEFC). In a country, which has one of the most stringent forestry laws in Europe, this has no impact on the forestry, whose traditional high standards have ensured ecological and economic sustainability.

The European Natura 2000 network, in which around 3000 hectares of the estate are included, can trigger restrictions, which must been compensated. These can be based on a financial problem or a conflict of legal ownership.

Hunting

Game and hunting are of great economic and traditional importance in the Czech Republic, and certainly so on the estate. Hunting law, usage and practice all have similar historical roots and the problems caused by game are also comparable.

To hunt on one's own land in the Czech Republic one must have a minimum of 500 hectares. At Dobříš the estate is divided into hunting districts, some of them leased out and others managed directly by the estate for paying guests. There is stalking and hunting for red deer, sika deer, mouflon, roe deer and wild boar.

Tourism

Dobříš Castle offers very comfortable hotel accommodation and is available for concerts and social events such as weddings, banquets and receptions. Located on its premises are a municipal museum, the castle museum, an art gallery and a restaurant with coffee-shop.

Flora and wildlife

At the end of the 19th century the owner of the Dobříš Estate, Prince Josef Colloredo-Mannsfeld, returned from his travels through North America with several pairs of animals. Amongst them were Muskrats (*Ondatra zibethica*), the American Bullfrog (*Rana catesbeiana* or *Lithobates catesbeianus*) and some American game. These were settled in the park of Dobříš Castle, in the small estate zoo, or in the wider estate. Some of them died out, but some of their descendants have survived to the present. The Muskrats looked for wider freedom, multiplied, and within a few decades overcame the entire European continent. A small memorial in the French park is a reminder of the incident.

Protected areas

- The "Narodní přirodní rezerváce Kohoutov" (National Nature Reserve of Kohoutov) which contains 30ha virgin Beech forest. It was first declared as voluntary reserve by Jeronym Colloredo-Mannsfeld in 1933 and became official in 1966; forestry and extraction is forbidden.
- The "Přirodní rezerváce Lipa" (Nature Reserve of Lipa) is a local area of primordial deciduous forest and undergrowth, highly protected.
- The estate has 4,600 hectares of the total 68,000 hectares of a huge area called "Ochraněma krajína oblast Křivoklátsko" (Protected Landscape of Křivoklátsko). It was created in 1978 to protect the landscape and nature reserve and is part of UNESCO's "Man and Biosphere" programme. It involves many land-use restrictions.
- Approximately 3,000 hectares of the estate's forests are part of the Natura 2000 network, mainly in the Křivoklat Nature Reserve.

General infrastructure at Dobříš

The castle of Dobříš

This Rococo castle was constructed to the designs of the French architect Jules R. de Cotte and his Italian colleague G.N. Servandoni in 1745-65, after a fire destroyed the Renaissance castle.

The highly effective building design represents one of the most interesting examples of 18th century architecture in Bohemia, and is referred to as the "small Bohemian Versailles". It includes two parks, the public English one, and the French Park, which is part of the castle's museum area. A large amount of restoration has taken place over the last few years.

The forests of Dobříš and Zbiroh are a perfect places for shelter and food for deer.

Dobříš & Zbiroh Estate

The highly effective building design represents one of the most interesting examples of 18th century architecture in Bohemia.

The estate's Parks

The French Park is spread over five terraces. A majestic sculpture and fountain forms the imaginary centre of the landscape architecture, which ends on the opposite site of the Orangery which is currently still in bad condition. The cascading fountain is an exceptionally valuable work by Frantisek Ignac Platzer (1717-1787), who came from a family of sculptors in western Bohemia. Platzer's sculptures at Dobříš are considered to be the best example of his work.

The original concept for the French Park was based on a symmetrical design, along a central path, which joined the axis of the southern wing of the castle. At the beginning of the 20th century, this composition underwent a major change and part of the central path was replaced with ornamental box hedging.

Despite this change, however, the Dobříš castle garden remains a rare example of Rococo landscape architecture, whose floral ornaments and clipped hedges conjure up the atmosphere of Vienna's Schönbrunn on a smaller scale.

The natural landscape English Park was established in around 1800 by converting the former pheasantry and was completed no later then 1815. The layout of the English Park is diverse, copses of trees alternating with fields. Trees are primarily broadleaf native species, old specimens of Oak and Beech. Exotic species were introduced later. This natural landscape park was expanded onto the eastern terraces, where in 1879 agricultural buildings were demolished, including the former brewery.

One of the buildings that still stands in the English Park today is the former castle theatre. After the Second World War, this state-owned building was converted into apartments.

Overall the English Park has a very romantic feel and in today's modern world offers visitors a chance to take a pleasant stroll through a relaxed natural landscape.

The estate includes a number of other buildings

Some of the houses at Dobříš:

- Hunting guest house of "Křivovatka" (Zbiroh forests). The ruin of this typical little old Bohemian-style house was reconstructed in 2000, and has become a favourite lodging for fee-paying hunters.
- Forest house of "Vlastec" (Zbiroh forests). This fine house is well situated in one of the most beautiful parts of the estate's forest. It is now the home of the local forest supervisor but in the old days it was used often by the owner's family and guests.

Access to the estates

The entire estate is well served with access roads; approximately 20 metres per hectare. Some of them are asphalted; this is a heritage of the communist era, when many of roads were constructed for military use. Some roads were built for public traffic and have remained thus.

The network is further developed by forest roads, but it is not a dense one as the open terrain makes off-road travel possible. Forest roads in the Czech Republic are available to the public as cycle paths.

A secret of the estate

Each estate has its own little secret, which is not intended for publication. However, some of them have already found their way into the outside world; as for example the story of Isabella. On some nights, with a full moon, she haunts the halls and rooms of Dobříš. If you are convinced that her soul is already in paradise, you probably believe that you hear only the groan and creaks of the old parquet floors.

Dobříš-Zbiroh **(Czech Republic)**

REPRIVATISATION

As part of its efforts to privatize the economy and to effect reparation to citizens who had suffered injustice under the Communists, the democratic government enacted the first restitution laws in 1990/1991. However, at the start, the ownership of land would be limited to a maximum area of 250 hectares.

At the beginning of the 20th century, my family had owned 60,000 hectares. In the land reform of the first Czechoslovak Republic about a half of this had been transferred. The rule of law was respected and for this period, albeit short, compensation was paid.

For the theft by the Communists of 30,000 hectares, the reparation of just 250 hectares appeared to be only a symbolic act. But I remember my uncle Jeroným, who was already in the 80th year of his life and the last survivor of four brothers who had shared the ownership. He took great joy from the fact that he could have a piece of land from his old home, to call his own again.

We could select which areas of the large landed estate we wanted to have, and my uncle opted for an area predominantly designated as a nature reserve (Kfiivokláter Wälder), because it was the "paradise" of his and his brothers' childhood.

The legislators soon realised that limiting the area of land would mean that only a very few of the former owners, who mostly lived in exile, would return, particularly because the size of the land was not enough to encourage them to resume serious economic activity. Not to mention the fact that the old estates were connected to castles and a variety of other buildings, whose gradual reinstatement after 40 years of neglect would put too much strain on the earning power of a small area of land.

The laws were therefore changed and the restitution claims were expanded to all pre- Communist vested rights. In Europe, the Czech Republic has operated a basic policy of reparation that is exemplary.

Landholding and society

Nevertheless, it was evident from the deep social divisions that people who had lived for 40 years with the theories of "class enemies" and "exploiters" had become indoctrinated by them, and even today the national and ideological upheavals of the 20th century have not yet been overcome. Although property enjoys good legal protection and other frameworks permit an economic-friendly climate, nevertheless for over 17 years some legal proceedings of restitution cases have been in a judicial "infinite loop" (from lower courts up to higher courts and back again, and so on...), and private landownership is not yet popular nor really accepted in a large part of society.

The French Park is the favourite place for wedding ceremonies.

Although he was not compelled to do so, my uncle employed all those who had formerly worked on the estate when it was in public administration. I was always amazed how quickly the managers got along in the new private system, or learned the principles that to had to be mastered, so that a "multi-functional" forestry company – incorporating forestry, fisheries, game management, wood processing and tourism – can exist and survive economically.

Land use and capitalism

Our forestry management is highly intensive: by comparison with the rest of Europe the level of personnel is "much too high". It has added to our traditional high level of forestry culture and intensive forest protection measures. One must not underestimate the efforts required under the different national and international support programmes (e.g. to eliminate ecologically contaminated sites or to deal with Natura 2000). Even to this day the continuing process of integrating the different types of land use in the course of reprivatisation requires intensive effort.

A private forestry and agricultural enterprise should, more than the anonymous administrative apparatus of a state or a corporation, provide stability to its employees. By the term "capitalism" the people of the former socialist countries expected above all that their personal physical circumstances would improve. They are worried by the degeneration of neo-liberalism and their experience of the illusive work of capital markets.

The conservative capitalism of the landowner, however, differs fundamentally from such a view: the "ground rent" is not viable; it is tied to the sustainable earning power of the land.

Forestry and arable land is, in practice, not marketable, so there are no "take-over battles" between landowners. Instead, land owners have to wait for decades for economic growth to develop, not least from the primary products of the soil, and while climate change caused by humans is increasingly endangering the ecological balance of their manufacturing base.

The coming challenges seem enormous. But the relative position of agriculture and forestry could become strong once again. This allows me a cautious optimism, which is needed to achieve the protection of social peace.

Jerome Colloredo-Mannsfeld

DOBŘÍŠ-ZBIROH BELONGS TO:

Friends of the Countryside

Programme for the Endorsement of Forest Certification

Czech-heritage.com

Alfa Promotion Agency of Czech Republic

Activities

- Historic buildings
- Rural tourism
- Fishing
- Hunting
- Shooting
- Museum
- Educational activities
- Hotel
- Restaurant
- Country Park

CONTACT DATA
Dipl. Ing. Jerome Colloredo-Mansfeld
Zamek c.p. 1 263 01 Dobris
Tel: +42 (0) 318521240
info@zamekdobris.cz
www.zamekdobris.cz/

Domain of Pappenheim

Continental

Location: Pappenheim, Bavaria province, Weissenburg region, Germany.
Surface: 1,800 ha.

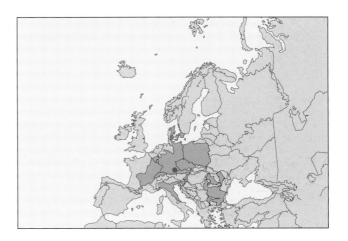

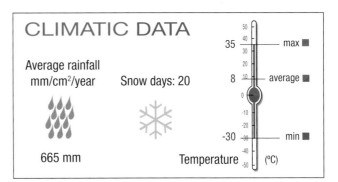

CLIMATIC DATA

Average rainfall
mm/cm²/year

Snow days: 20

665 mm

Temperature (ºC)

35 — max
8 — average
-30 — min

SUMMARY

The town of Pappenheim is situated on a picturesque bend of the Altmühl River, approximately 15 km south of Weissenburg. The estate is located within the Altmühltal Natural Park. Any activity which modifies the character of the nature, or which may damage its natural resources, landscape, the enjoyment of the nature or free access to it, is prohibited. All the building complexes are protected by the Bavarian Law for the Protection of Monuments, and the estate has a very active conservation programme for maintenance and enhancement. The most important sectors of economic activity are forestry, quarries and tourism. The estate's far-reaching economic and conservation activities have contributed to new initiatives and investments, which have in turn contributed to the development of the region.

Pappenheim Estate

A beautiful view of Pappenheim town: medieval streets, charming houses and unique historical monuments.

Domain of Pappenheim (Germany)

HISTORY

As discoveries from the castle hill and the county forest show, there were already settlements in this area in Roman and even pre-Roman times. The place was mentioned for the first time in 802, when the area was given to the monastery of St. Gallen. Therefore there must have been a village or a settlement existing there at that time.

The history of Pappenheim began in the 11th century, when the main village came under the control of the hereditary marshal of the Holy Roman Empire of the German Nation of the Lords, later Counts of Pappenheim. During their rule, which lasted unbroken from the 12th to the 19th century, they were closely connected with the emperors of the Holy Roman Empire, whom they served from the very beginning until the very end of its existence. In 1288 the village received the rights of a town and consequently became a walled town, with at least fifteen towers and three gates.

The castle, situated on high ground overlooking the town and in a U-bend of the river Altmühl, was built in the 12th century, and by the time of the Hohenstaufen dynasty of Emperors it was already an important fortress with all kinds of services. It constituted the centre of the scattered estate (county) of Pappenheim, which stretched throughout Swabia, Franconia and Bavaria and reached its greatest glory in the Middle Ages. It is worth mentioning all the ploughing work on the mountain plains and forests, as a result of which the so-called "county villages" appeared, by order of the marshals in the 13th century.

The castle was destroyed and rebuilt several times and continued to grow until the 16th century. At that time, the family decided to build residences in the city for each branch of the family. After 1593, the oldest marshal who was in power came to reside in what is today known as the Old Palace, in the old Herrengasse Lane. This building, which dates back to the 15th century, was the residential seat and offices of the government until 1806, when the autonomous government of the Counts of Pappenheim came to an end. The town constituted the centre of a small domain, which was solely dependent on the Empire.

The castle of Pappenheim sits high on a hill above a loop of Altmühl. It was the master castle of the Marshals and Counts of Pappenheim. It played an important role throughout the Middle Ages in the "Holy Roman Empire of the German nation".

Pappenheim Estate

The family ordered the building of the town and the palaces, and homes for each branch of the family. Shops and stalls were constructed inside the town, as well as other buildings necessary for government and the management of property, such as administrative buildings, houses for servants and craftsmen supply of the court of the counts, hunting lodges, orangeries, summer houses, farms, mills, and forestry buildings throughout the county. Likewise, churches, the monastery and the towers and gates of the town were also built.

Later the family founded the Latin school and several institutions. The dominant role of the family could be seen across the entire domains of the county, particularly in the construction of churches and public works.

The family was also able to exert strong influence over the shaping of the landscape. Gardens were built both inside and outside the town and around the castle, and avenues were created. Much of the land was ploughed, and the landscape of the valley developed its character as a result of farming, forestry and grazing.

When their sovereignty ended in 1806, many of the buildings lost their function, although many of them remained the property of the family. However, after the revolution of 1848 and the subsequent changes in land use, again many of the buildings lost their original purpose entirely and became superfluous.

A very considerable proportion of the family possessions were lost in the late 19th and early 20th centuries, as a result of many factors, which were not favourable to agriculture and forestry. These included changes in the economic climate, the political decision by Caprivi – Bismarck's successor as chancellor – the consequences of world wars, land reform and hereditary transfers partly ordered by the occupying powers after 1945.

The estate has been owned since the 11th century by branches of the family of the Counts and Lords of Pappenheim, and it was in 1989 that the family of the Counts of Egloffstein succeeded to the estate. Among the owners in past centuries were many important marshals in the service of the Kaiser. Marshal Heinrich died in 1214 after serving five Kaisers. The best known was Field Marshal Gottfried Heinrich Pappenheim, in the Thirty Year's War 1618-48. His troops achieved a literary and proverbial importance that has

reached beyond German borders, thanks to the German poet Friedrich von Schiller who, in his play "Wallenstein", included the assertion "daran erkenn' ich meine Pappenheimer" *("I know my fellow Pappenheims")*. In some countries this is a common expression, even in the original German form. In the 18th century, the baroque Count Friedrich Ferdinand was the last to run an expensive residence with the household of a souverain court, whose dispute in the crowning of the Kaiser in Frankfurt is mentioned by Johann Wolfgang von Goethe in his biography "Poetry and Truth". Among more recent owners we should particularly mention the last count in power, Carl Theodor, General Assistant of the first Bavarian king and his brother Albert, General Assistant of the second Bavarian king.

MAIN RESIDENCE AND OTHER PRIVATELY OWNED BUILDINGS

Main residences

The two main residences of the family, which are still used and lived in, are the Old and New Palaces. The former was built at the time of the Renaissance in the 17th century, incorporating previous buildings of the 15th and 16th centuries. It was concluded by adding two further wings in the

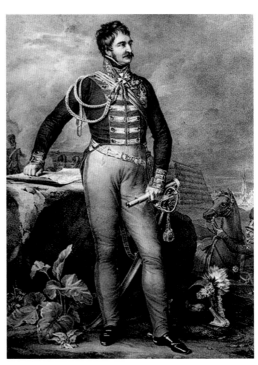

Carl Theodor Graf zu Pappenheim in a picture by Stieler.

I.L. Industrie-Luftbild B.R. Jahn

The castle today houses a lot of touristic attractions and activities.

Other buildings

The former Augustinian monastery with its church and five wings grouped around two small interior patios has been restored externally, and the church has been completely restored internally, although for the moment no purpose has been established. The church contains the family tombs and is used for ecclesiastical celebrations and for concerts in which only church music is played. Peculiarly, it was consecrated by the bishops of the two great religious faiths, and so it can be used by both of them. The castle is used for tourist purposes, both for ordinary visitors and also for special events such as services, historical exhibitions, a torture chamber, a museum of natural history and hunting, a chapel, a registry office for weddings, two halls for ceremonies and functions, a bar, a museum shop, a botanical garden, a herb garden, a dedicated open air area. Eight different buildings in and around the castle for additional purposes of exhibitions, events, festivities and service are under planning or construction. Next to this a 15 years programme of restoration for 1.5 km of walls sourronding and forming the castle is under work.

The town wall is completelly restored. Eighty per cent of its original length can still be traced, and completes the historical framework of the town.

The three farms are used to store equipment and machinery etc., or are partially leased out to farmers or other users. The housing on the farms is also rented out. The two orange groves in the garden of the New Palace are empty at the moment but will be restored, partly to their original purpose.

The estate owns a total of about 60 buildings, among which are the different wings comprising nine complexes. Together, these buildings constitute some 140,000 cubic metres of total constructed volume.

18th century, with additional interior work. The Baroque wing with its marvellous stucco ceilings collapsed in 1943 and was replaced by a wing demolished in the mid 1990s. The complex conserves the characteristics of different styles, from late Gothic to Pre-Classicism.

The most important building is undoubtedly the New Palace, built in the early 19th century. It was the first work of the Bavarian royal court architect Leo von Klenze, before he created the residential buildings in Munich for the king of Bavaria. Because much of the classical architecture in large cities was destroyed in World War II, the New Palace is among the few important remaining original works of German Classicism.

The family inhabits the two buildings. The administration has also been brought to the New Palace and the two houses are partly rented as housing and offices. Concerts and receptions are occasionally held in the ballroom of the New Palace.

The Nature History and Hunting Museum was planned and created by the three daughters of the owner: Countess Julie Rohan-Chabot, Princess Isabelle Leiningen and Countess Désirée Egloffstein.

Pappenheim Estate

Some of the historic protected buildings were restored for to rent or to rent then togheter with hunting licences. In 2007 several historic buildings were acquired to start a hotel business. The first part with 14 guest-rooms was opened in 2008.

C. Otero

DESCRIPTION

Land and landscape

The domains of the counts are situated in the town of Pappenheim and the sourrounding county villages as Langenaltheim, Übermatzhofen, Osterdorf, Göhren, Geislohe, Neudorf, Rothenstein and Bieswang. The town of Pappenheim is situated in a picturesque U-bend of the river Altmühl, approximately 7 km to the east of Treuchtlingen and 15 km from Weissenburg.

The topographical characteristics are defined by the castle on the hill in the centre of the town, the pasture land on the fertile plains of the Altmühl valley, the slopes covered with sheep pasture land, romantic rock groups and forest with leaf, mainly beech trees, and the vast plain of the Franconian Alb with its numerous villages.

The height fluctuates between 406 m above sea level, in the Altmühl valley, and 574 m on the plain.

Geomorphology

Geomorphologically, the whole of our area belongs to the vast calcareous mountain range of the southern Franconian Alb, which emerged from accumulated calcareous sediments in the flat basin of the Jura Sea, about 150 million years ago.

The area is characterized by the confined and often deep valleys of the Jurassic plain (Altmühl Valley), wooded slopes, and by the vast plain of the Alb itself. These are variously densely and sparsely populated and structured into small areas, the main resources being agriculture and forestry, trade commerce, commercial and industrial business, the latter mainly in more modest dimensions.

Hydrology

The river Altmühl dominates the estate. The estate owns about nine kilometres of the river. It runs through the town of Pappenheim where it makes a sharp U-turn, and gives its name to the Natural Park of Altmühltal in which all the estate lands lie. The fishing rights in the river are leased out.

Further to the north, between Suffersheim and Treuchtlingen, is the small Schambach stream in the romantic valley of the same name, the fishing rights of which also belongs to the estate.

While the fertile valley plains are well irrigated by underground water, the remainder of the Jura Mountains are classified as one of the driest areas, owing to their deep soils, their carstification and their relative lack of rainfall.

In this context, it is worth mentioning the slopes of the Altmühl valley, and the sweeping bend of the river, which surrounds the hill on which the castle stands. The small town of Pappenheim nestles along the two banks of the river, where the Palace parks, both old and new and the pasture land constitute an important green belt between the town's old and new quarters.

Pappenheim 's lovely town center is mostly medieval but as examples of all buildings styles up to the early 19th century classical Neus Schloss (New Palace), wich still houses the offices and residence of the descendants of the counts of Pappenheim.

Part of the botanical gardens in and around the castle.

Pappenheim Estate

Flora and fauna

The combination of a relatively mild climate and the highly calcareous nature of the existing soils have produced a situation in which many types of vegetation and a variety of associations of very different plants are able to develop naturally.

The natural variety of plants and wildlife that exists in Pappenheim today is a result of efficient forestry methods, the protection of mixed blocks of beech and spruce over many generations, and extensification of open areas for sheep grazing and fruit production. Furthermore, reintroducing an under-storey, forest rides and fallow land have also been instrumental in conserving this natural variety, and to speak of a Mecca for lovers of flora and fauna would not be going too far.

Of the 1,600 native varieties registered in the area, over 1,300 can be seen in the garden in Pappenheim Castle, which was created in 1997. Also in the castle is a historical garden dedicated to all types of herbs. It completes this collection of plants, whose theme is man's use of plants, both past and present. Curative herbs, colouring herbs, herbs for garnishing, cereals, magic herbs, oleaginous and textile plants, mixed herbs, greens and vegetables together account for more than 750. So at least more than 2,000 plants and herbs, mainly native but also including some non-native species, are represented and can be admired in these gardens.

Land use

The current commercial basis of the estate has developed from the economic transformation of enterprises, some of which were partly very old, by the abandonment of others, and other ventures, which were short, lived. The most important economic bases were always forestry, agriculture and, from the 19th century, the exploitation of quarries.

Some special ventures were tried, like the creation of a silver fox fur farm after the First World War, which did not survive long, while other older enterprises such as horse breeding, which was very important in the age of the marshals, were abandoned in the interwar period. The 1960s saw the end of sheep breeding, typical of this region.

It is true that agriculture was successfully modernized between 1960 and 1990, thanks to considerable investment. An important herd of Angus cattle was started, but in the end it could not be maintained because of the scattered nature of the estate lands, the excessive burden on old buildings, poor soils and the general economic situation.

Because of the disastrous economic development of the estate's agriculture, the decision was made at the beginning of the 1990s to continue reforesting the areas formerly dedicated to agricultural crops, and to abandon traditional farming.

The farm land which surrounds the town has been transformed, so that the old town is separated from any new buildings. The aim of this is to extend the notion of the gardens of the Palaces and the Castle whilst at the same time maintaining the sense of farming, in such a way that the town will be surrounded on all sides by a landscape similar to that of a park.

Enterprises, which had no economic future, have been abandoned. These were principally within the farming sector, and included suckler cows, crops, poultry farms and horticulture. A new tourism enterprise has been created, and property rentals have been intensified, particularly in the accommodation sector.

Agriculture

Agricultural production over the original area of 250 ha (mostly crops and grazing for suckler cows) was abandoned in 1993. Of this area, 150 ha were reforested between 1993 and 1996, and 50 ha were transformed into a green area partly with extensive pasture land and production of fruits for the purposes of hunting. Another 50 ha are let out on lease to farmers.

Forestry

As a result of unforeseen problems in farming, the emphasis was set on forestry, and a reafforestation programme has been implemented, the largest private programme of its type in Germany. An area of over 200 ha has been planned, as an exemplar of excellence in silviculture, ecology and landscape management. This has included the drafting of a landscape programme, in which several kilometres of avenues and rides have been planned as an architectural feature of the landscape.

The owners have commissioned the creation of a biotope and have selected a rich variety of trees, the majority being broadleaves. The newly forested areas are an exemplar of good practice and are visited by many groups from Europe and from further afield.

Rural Tourism

In order to increase and improve the attractiveness and economic power of the area, the estate entrusted the German Institute of Tourism from the University of Munich with the task of drawing up a scientific report on the possibilities of promoting tourism amongst ordinary citizens. This institute has undertaken many other initiatives, such as the promotion of communities and of tourist-based organisations, which have led to the subsequent revitalization of the region. The town was the centre of national attention on the occasion of the spectacular series of special events, which took place on the 400th anniversary of the Field Marshal Pappenheim, a marshal famous for the already mentioned proverb in German. The countless measures taken to re-

The belfry and a part of the sourrounding herb gardens.

C. Otero

store the buildings and gardens in the castle, to adapt them for tourism by adding many facilities and additional lighting, have increased the attractiveness and with it the number of visitors to the castle. The result has been that the town, the symbol of the region, presents itself in full harmony with its splendour. The restoration of so many buildings has brought considerable economic upturn in the region. Nowadays, the castle is a popular tourist destination for both the public and the well-informed expert. The number of visitors has grown sevenfold when compared to the situation 14 years ago. The visitors come to see the numerous attractions, such as the historical exhibitions, the torture chamber, the botanical garden, the gardens dedicated to all kinds of herbs, the museum of natural history and hunting, the videos in the museums, ceremonial halls, the chapel, several wedding rooms, a complete service for weddings and other festivities in the castle, a bar and the museum shop. The jousting tournaments, oldtimer rallies and other events of nostalgia, the garden exhibition, Christmas Market and other exhibitions attract more visitors to the region. Methods of advertising such as the Internet, brochures, radio and television are being used. There are guides to the area in German, English, French, Dutch, Italian, Spanish and Czech.

VARIETIES OF COMMERCIAL TREES PRESENT:

Broadleaved trees	38%
Acer platanoides	Norway Maple
Acer pseudoplatanus	Sycamore Maple
Aesculus hippocastaneum	Horse Chestnut
Alnus glutinosa	Black Alder
Betula pendula	Silver Birch
Carpinus betulus	Hornbeam
Fagus sylvatica	Beech
Fraxinus excelsior	Ash
Juglans regia	Walnut
Populus tremula	Aspen
Prunus avium	Cherry
Quercus robur	English Oak
Quercus petraea	Sessile Oak
Sorbus aria	Whitebeam
Sorbus torminalis	Service
Tilia cordata	Small-leaved Lime
Tilia platyphyllos	Large-leaved Lime
Ulmus glabra	Wych Elm
Ulmus laevis	European White Elm
Ulmus minor	Common Elm
Conifers	62%
Abies alba	Silver Fir
Abies grandis	Balsam Fir
Larix decidua	European Larch
Larix kaempferi	Japanese White Larch
Picea abies	Spruce
Pinus nigra	Austrian Pine
Pinus silvestris	Scots Pine
Pinus strobus	Eastern White Pine
Pseudotsuga sp.	Douglas Fir

The Ancestors "Hall" (in the castle) restored for visitors and festivities.

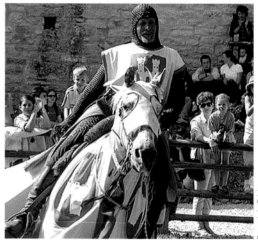

The Medieval Tournament.

Schule + Pappenheim

In addition to the entrance to the Castle, there is the chapel. The medieval roof is painted sky blue with 365 stars. Lit by antique lamps, weddings, christening and other religous ceremonies are held here.

A project called Schule + Pappenheim was developed for gymnasiums together with the Bavarian ministery of school and education. Outdoor classes are being organised in the medieval town of Pappenheim to give a realistic overview of the history, arts, economy and literature as well as fauna and flora. The project gives opportunity to schools to teach various subjects and topics in a related surrounded environment. Classrooms are being transformed for some days into streets, houses, the castle, palaces, museums , churches, etc. to which students are enable to interact with.

ANIMALS REPRESENTED IN THE NATURE AND HUNTING MUSEUM

Crayfishes
- Potamobius. astacus L.

Fishes
- Abramis brama L.
- Alburnoides bipunctatus
- Alburnus lucidus Heck.
- Anguilla anguilla.
- Aspius aspius
- Barbus fluviatilis Ag.
- Carassius carassius
- Cottus gobio L.
- Cyprinus carpio L.
- Esox lucius L.
- Gobio fluviatilis
- Lota lota L.
- Lucioperca sandra Cuv.
- Perca fluviatilis L.
- Phoxinus phoxinus L.
- Rhodens amarus Bl.
- Rutilus rutilus
- Salmo trutta fario
- Scardinius erythrophthalmus L.
- Squalius cephalus Heck
- Salmo (Trutta) irideus Gibb.
- Silurus glanis L.
- Tinca vulgaris Cuv.

Amphibians
- Rana dalmatina
- Rana esculenta
- Rana lesonnae
- Rana ridibunda
- Rana temporaria
- Salamandra salamandra
- Triturus alpestris
- Triturus vulgaris

Reptils
- Anguis fragilis
- Bombinia variegata
- Bufo bufo
- Coronella austriaca
- Hyla arborea
- Lacerta agilis
- Lacerta vivipara
- Natrix natrix

Birds
- Accipiter gentilis
- Acepiter nisus
- Acrocepahalus scirpaceus
- Actitis hypoleucos
- Aegolius caudatus
- Aegolius funereus
- Alauda arvensis
- Alcedo atthis
- Anas platyrhynchos
- Anthus trivialis
- Apus apus
- Ardea cinerea

- Asio otus
- Athene noctua
- Aythya fuligula
- Bonasa bonasia
- Bubo bubo
- Buteo buteo
- Carduelis cannabina
- Carduelis carduelis
- Carduelis chloris
- Carduelis spinus
- Certhia brachydactyla
- Certia familiaris
- Charadrius dubius
- Cinclus cinclus
- Coccothraustes coccothraustes
- Columba palumbus
- Columba oenas
- Corvus corax
- Corvus corone corone
- Corvus monedula
- Coturnix coturnix
- Cuculus canorus
- Cygnus olor
- Dendrocopos medius
- Dendrocopos minor
- Dendrocopus martius
- Emberiza schoeniclus
- Enberiza citrinella
- Erithacus rubecula
- Falco peregrinus
- Falco subbuteo
- Falco tinnunculus
- Ficedula hypoleuca
- Fringilla coelebs
- Fulica atra
- Gallinago gallinago
- Gallinula chloropus
- Garrulus glandarius
- Glacidium passerinum
- Hippolais sp.
- Hirundo rustica
- Jynx torquilla
- Lanius collurio
- Locustella naevia
- Loxia curvirostra
- Lullula arborea
- Luscinia megarhynchos
- Lyrurus tetrix
- Milvus milvus
- Motacilla alba
- Motacilla cinerea
- Nucifraga caryocatactes
- Oriolus oriolus
- Parus ater
- Parus caeruleus
- Parus cristatus
- Parus major
- Parus montanus
- Parus palustris
- Passer domesticus
- Perdix perdix

- Pernis apivorus
- Phasianus colchicus
- Phoenicurus ochruros
- Phoenicurus phoenicurus
- Phylloscopus collybita
- Phylloscopus sibilatrix
- Pica pica
- Picus canus
- Picus viridis
- Podiceps ruficollis
- Prunella modularis
- Pyrrhula pyrrhula
- Regulus ignicapillus
- Regulus regulus
- Riparia riparia
- Scolopax rusticola
- Serinus serinus
- Sitta europaea
- Sterna hirundo
- Streptopelia decaocto
- Strix aluco
- Sturnus vulgaris
- Sylvia atricapilla
- Sylvia borin
- Sylvia communis
- Sylvia curruca
- Tetrao urogallus
- Tringa totanus
- Troglodytes troglodytes
- Turdus ericetorium
- Turdus merula
- Turdus pilaris
- Turdus viscivorus
- Tyto alba
- Vanellus vanellus

Mammals
- Apodemus flavicollis
- Apodemus sylvaticus
- Arvicola terrestris
- Capreolus capreolus
- Castor fiber
- Cervus elaphus
- Clethreonomys glareolus
- Crocidura russula
- Crocidura suaveolens
- Eliomys qercinus
- Erinaceus europaeus
- Felis silvestris
- Glis glis
- Lepus europaeus
- Martes foina
- Martes martes
- Meles meles
- Microtus arvalis
- Mus musculus
- Mustela erminea
- Mustela nivalis
- Myocastor coypus
- Nyctalus leisleri
- Ondatra zibethicus
- Plecotus auritus
- Procyon lotor
- Putorius putorius
- Rattus norvegicus
- Rattus rattus
- Sciurus vulgaris
- Sorex minutus
- Sus scrofa
- Vulpes vulpes

The Hazel Grouse
(Bonasa bonasia)

Pappenheim, a designated Protected Area

All the estate property is part of the Altmühltal Natural Park; the whole of the forestry lies inside the designated protected areas of the Park, which were included in the Natural Parks regulation passed on 15-09-1995.

Within these areas any action which modifies the character of the park or which, by its characteristics, may damage the performance capacity of the natural resources, the landscape, the enjoyment of nature or free access to it, is prohibited. However, the organised exploitation of agriculture and forestry is fortunately excluded from these restrictions wich unfortunately are increasing directly and indirectly from year to year. This regulation is kept up to date and followed by means of a programme of care and development.

Profound and severe restrictions and prohibitions (others, depending on the area, are less severe) are applied to the designated and concisely described '5d' areas, under the Bavarian Law for the Protection of Nature, for which prohibited modifications have been published. These apply, for example, to the river Altmühl and to specific structures such as hedges and small woods, all of them in the estate's possession.

All the building complexes which are owned by the estate are protected by the Bavarian Law for the Protection of Monuments.

Anders Wall Award

Taking into account criteria such as preserving and enhancing the landscape, providing biodiversity, preserving the countryside's cultural heritage and contributing to sustainable economic local development, the Anders Wall Foundation (Sweden), Friends of the Countryside, DG Environment and the Royal Agricultural Academy of Stockholm gave an Award to Pappenheim Estate to encourage and promote efforts made by creative entrepreneurs who have contributed to a positive rural environment.

NEW CONCERNS AND INTERESTS OF THE LANDOWNER

The generation, which has held the property since 1989, has proposed various measures in order to achieve the following three fundamental objectives:
- Maintain the property for subsequent generations,
- Implement the necessary increases and improvements, as well as the necessary modernizations, including the abandonment of old enterprises and the introduction of new ones;
- Taking into account the family's responsibility over the region through its history and environment, to exploit the available space in order to promote or introduce necessary developments and measures, whose effects go beyond business and which benefit the community.

The restoration of the buildings and gardens has stimulated more measures in the town and in the surrounding area. The same can be said of the creation of the park and other green areas. These, together with the erection of a statue the first trees and flower containers planted in the main streets, have provided a stimulus for local and other administrative authorities, as have the placement of trees in other avenues. This program is going further with the creating of avenues leading from all sides to the town by planting trees. The improvements to the town partly undertaken by the estate, including the tidying up of the castle slopes and creating a park like landscape in other parts of the valley will be continued during the next years.

In 2002, as a result of the countless improvements made, the estate was awarded the most important prize in Germany for the protection of historic monuments. The prize money was assigned to the creation of a foundation aimed at promoting culture, the environment and the social aspects of the town and the region of the old 'county' of Pappenheim.

The owners make every effort to bring together the most diverse events in the area, in order to revive its development and thereby to make the town better known as an attraction, even beyond German borders. A series of publications has been created on the art, culture and history of the town, family and old county of Pappenheim. Nine studies have been published so far. In addition, other publications covering the area and its history have been promoted and published. A project for a large book on the history of the culture of the old county of Pappenheim is being prepared, as well as other exhibitions.

Dr. Albrecht Graf von und zu Egloffstein

MEMBERSHIP IN ASSOCIATIONS, ORGANIZATIONS AND COMMITTEES CONCERNING PLANNING, DEVELOPING, FORESTRY, AGRICULTURE, ENVIRONMENT, TOURISM, TRADE AND CULTURE MAINLY WITH PERSONAL FUNCTIONS.

Forestry association with other neigbour forest

PEFC Programme for the Endorsement of Forest Certification Schemes

Tourist organization for the Altmühl Valley

Tourist organization of the Franconian lake district

Friends of the Countryside-Meta

Bavarian farmers association

Bavarian forestry owners association

Bavarian landowners association

ARBEITGEBERVERBAND
FÜR DIE LAND- UND FORSTWIRTSCHAFT IN BAYERN E.V.
Association of farming and forestry entrepreneurs

Bavarian hunting association

German castle association

German society for art of gardening and culture of landscape committee for historic gardens

German national committee for protection of monuments

Bavarian committee for protection of monuments

- In addition membership in local committees for planning, developing, tourism, trade, culture and environment.
- Also membership in a great many of cultural associations but without personal functions.

Activities
- Boating
- Cycling
- Educational activities
- Events
- Fishing
- Gardens
- Historic buildings
- Hotel
- Hunting
- Kids
- Museum
- Renting of historic buildings
- Restaurant
- Rural tourism
- Walking trails
- Weddings / Festivities

CONTACT DATA
Gräflich Pappenheim'sche Verwaltung
Marktplatz 5, D-91788
Pappenheim • Germany
Phone: +49 / 9143 83 890
Fax: +49 / 9143 64 45
info@grafschaft-pappenheim.de
www.burg-pappenheim.de

El Guijoso Estate

El Guijoso

Mediterranean

Location: El Bonillo municipality, Albacete, Castilla-La Mancha, Spain.
Surface: 2,570 ha.

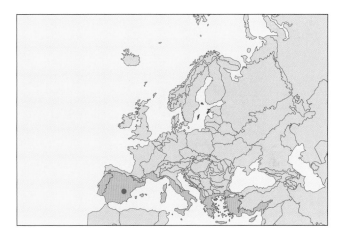

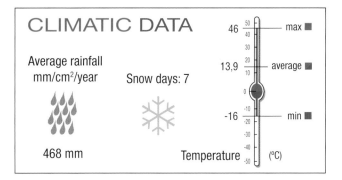

CLIMATIC DATA

Average rainfall
mm/cm²/year

Snow days: 7

468 mm

Temperature (ºC)

46 — max
13,9 — average
-16 — min

SUMMARY

El Guijoso is located in the heart of La Mancha, between the villages of El Bonillo and Ossa de Montiel, both of Roman origin, in the province of Albacete. Thanks to appropriate management of the hunting resource, El Guijoso is considered a special place for driven and walked-up shooting, as well as decoying. It has a surface area of 2,570 ha divided into cropping areas, vineyards and low and medium scrubland, with forest clearings of holm oaks and Spanish juniper.
It is the birthplace of the Pinilla River, which forms the lakes known as the Lagunas de Ruidera. Across the estate runs the Ruta de Quijote (Don Quixote Route), alongside the cave of Montesinos and other famous spots mentioned in Cervantes' novel.
There are facilities for livestock, olives, vineyards and winery in the estate, as well as rural houses for accommodation purposes.

El Guijoso Estate is situated in the heart of La Mancha, the country of D. Quijote.
Livestock, olives, vineyards, partridge shooting, new energies,
and conservation of landscape and wildlife are the principal features.

El Guijoso **(Spain)**

El Guijoso Estate

HISTORY

The land which makes up the estate has had different owners through its history. *El Guijoso* or *Casas de El Guijoso* already appears on maps that are as much as two centuries old. At different stages, divisions and name changes occurred as a result of inheritance and division, until late in the 20th century when the family Sánchez Muliterno, the current owners, managed to reunite all the property once again, reviving its historic and still remembered name of *El Guijoso*, by which, and in spite of all the changes, this natural space of La Mancha has been known.

DESCRIPTION

The name of El Guijoso, also called Pago Guijoso when referring to the denomination given to its wines, comes from the abundance of gravels (in Spanish: *guijos* – a name by which the people of La Mancha have referred to pebbles since very early times) which cover the ground in some parts of the estate.

The estate, with a surface area of nearly 2,600 ha, is located in the foothills of the Sierra de Alcaraz range, in the high plateau of the famous Campo de Montiel, mentioned by Cervantes in his famous book "Don Quijote de La Mancha".

The estate's natural environment, of enormous richness, is located very close to the Natural Park of the Lagunas de Ruidera and near numerous places featured in "Don Quijote de la Mancha", such as the cave at Montesinos or the castle at Rochafrida. The second stretch of the *Ruta del Quijote* passes through these areas.

The town of El Bonillo, granted the title of *villazgo* by King Charles I of Spain and V of Germany in 1538, has a population of 3,000 inhabitants and is located 17 kilometres from the estate. It includes the interesting 15th century Church of Santa Catalina, a golf course, large renewable energy plants – both photovoltaic and wind – and a 16th century pillory post. It is basically an agricultural and livestock area, with significant hunting activity.

Buildings
The main building is the complex called Las Casas de El Guijoso Viejo (Houses of Old Guijoso)

and comprises the principal house, seven houses for the estate workers and their families and some others for rural tourism, a tavern or inn and a hunting pavilion used for celebrations of up to 50 guests, plus the winery producing and aging its wines.

The principal house is a building of typical La Mancha style with a certain stately influence, a very individual construction scarce in La Mancha architecture, designed by a famous architect from the last century. It has a surface area of 1,400 m², divided into two floors and a basement area used for pantries, private cellar, etc. At the rear of the house there is a private garden of 30,000 m², with tennis and paddle courts, swimming pool, games for children, a pergola, natural lake and Spanish juniper trees, some of them a thousand years old, which makes it a garden of special attraction.

The winery is large enough to produce and age – to optimum condition – up to 250,000 bottles a year, plus 800 French oak allier barrels and stainless steel equipment for wine production, laboratory use, etc.

Another interesting building is the Casa Grande, located in the area called El Guijoso Nuevo (New Guijoso). It is 700 m² built and was

built by the current owner in 1995. It is used for guests. There are also another 7 houses in this area where workers and their families live; other houses are used for rural tourism, around the cobbled square known as La Era and a garden area.

Other noteworthy features are livestock sheds built to house 3,000 sheep, sheds to store machinery and cereals, a reservoir with a capacity of 2,000,000 litres of water, a cylindrical pigeon-loft built over a century ago for thousands of pairs of doves, offices, buildings for domestic services and

The Iberian Hare *(Lepus granatensis)* is smaller than the European Hare *(Lepus europaeus)*. It is perfectly adapted to the rigours of the Medierranean summer and the hard winters. It is associated with the red-legged partridge and rabbit who share its habitat. It lives in large numbers at El Guijoso.

Grazing land covered by holm oak and Spanish juniper, are remote and well conserved place.

oso Estate

El Guijoso (Spain)

The vineyards of El Guijoso have a guarantee of origin called PAGO, exclusive for a unique vineyard or winery. It is the highest level of guarantee of origin in Europe.

Natural environment

Edaphic factors

The granulometric composition or texture of the soil is sandy loam and clay loam. Combined together as a group it would be a sandy-clay loam texture, which is the most appropriate composition, especially for the cultivation of vines to make wine of excellent quality, combining fineness, bouquet and delicacy.

The estate is relatively flat, although with some areas of broken ground and gullies, all of it at an altitude of between 900 and 1,000 metres.

Hydrography

The estate is part of the 24th aquifer of the Hydrographic Confederation of the Guadiana River. In addition to the small streams and water courses that flow through the property, the most important feature is the Pinilla River, which rises on the estate in natural springs in the subsoil, from waters that come from the Sierra de Alcaraz. The Pinilla is the origin of the Guadiana River. Its waters flow into the first of the Ruidera lakes, the Laguna Blanca (White Lake), from which it descends from lake to lake in waterfalls until it gets to the last one, called El Rey (The King). From here on it is called the Guadiana River.

Among the works that are being implemented in this sector, the highlights are the steps taken to pre-

canteen for workers, storage warehouses, workshop, weighbridge, loading decks, henhouses, dog kennels and horse stables.

We should also emphasize the Casa del Pastor (Shepherd's House), an austere and spartan 19th century building, now restored, where you can appreciate the precarious life style of the working class in rural environments that existed until recent times.

Tempranillo, Cabernet Sauvignon, Merlot, Syrah, Petit Verdot, Sauvignon Blanc, Chardonnay and Nero D'Avola are cultivated.

serve wetlands, using a sustainable programme of hydrological resources and a concession of 4 million litres of water a year extracted from 20 large-capacity wells equipped with powerful water pumps, most of them connected, which creates an important hydrological infrastructure.

Dynamic water levels are located less than 50 metres deep, which permits high availability of water especially during the critical months of July and August.

Fauna and flora

El Guijoso constitutes a natural reserve for two protected species in the area: the Great Bustard *(Otis tarda)*, a very characteristic bird of the plains, and the Spanish Juniper *(Juniperus thurifera)*, a prodigious species in these lands which has seen its presence considerably reduced because of tree felling. As well as the spectacular Spanish juniper, the high and medium scrublands contain notable Oak forests *(Quercus ilex* and *Q. rotundifolia)*, while in the lower areas the representative species are Portuguese Oaks *(Q. faginea)*, Kermes Oaks *(Q. coccifera)*, Rosemary *(Rosmarinus officinalis)*, Esparto *(Stipa sp.)* and Thyme *(Thymus vulgaris)*.

Main uses and activities on the property

The 2,570 ha that form El Guijoso are divided as follows: 1,530 ha are dedicated to agriculture (1,030 ha irrigated – 960 ha of which are irrigated with 15 pivots, and a further 70 under cover – and 500 ha are dry land cultivation), 100 ha to vineyards and 25 ha to olive trees, and the remaining

905 ha of woodland are used as a hunting resource and pasture. About another 10 ha are buildings, paths, unproductive areas, etc.

Agriculture

The typical crop plan of El Guijoso is wheat, barley, oats, rye or maize, but also onions, peas and sunflowers. For this, 15 irrigation pivots are needed, one of them irrigating 131 ha, one of the biggest in Spain.

An average of 4,000 tonnes of agricultural products are produced every year (excluding grapes and olives).

Vineyard

The Pago Guijoso vineyard is considered one of the best in Spain, both because of the technology employed and because of the wine obtained from its grapes. It has the recognition of Guarantee of Origin PAGO, which is a G.O exclusive to just one vineyard, winery and space and the highest level that can legally be achieved in Europe. Because of that, it is part of the most exclusive wine club in the world. Tempranillo, Cabernet Sauvignon, Merlot, Syrah, Petit Verdot, Sauvignon Blanc and Chardonnay are cultivated. Experimental varieties are also cultivated in order to determinate their adaptation to the soil and climatological characteristics of this PAGO. All the vines are grown in espalier form with drip irrigation. The soil is one of the most important characteristics, because it is formed by gravels (guijos), from which the estate's name comes. This, together with the favourable microclimate of the

Bosque solar® in El Guijoso. The solar park is integrated into the landscape.

El Guijoso Estate

Ruidera Lakes and Pinilla River, is one of the reasons for the high quality of the grape obtained. Sixty-four of the 100 ha are managed under the Australian "Smart Dyson" system, which improves the concentation of substances to create wines of greater structure. The first vines were planted in 1984. Nowadays, it is one of the few vineyards in the world that has been awarded the Certifications of Quality ISO 9001 and Environment ISO 14001.

Winery

The prestigious wines of the Bodegas Sánchez Muliterno are crafted using the exclusive grapes grown on their own vines. The installation of the winery began in 1993, inside the architectural complex of the principal house. At the present time the winery can produce and age 250,000 bottles a year. Alongside the vineyard, it has the most exclusive recognition of Guarantee of Origin Pago Guijoso. Although endowed with the most modern facilities, the wine is made in the natural way respecting traditional processes. Aging is done in Allier barrels of French oak, of which there is a stock of 800 which are on average two years old. Must fermentation is carried out with selected indigenous yeasts, this being an important difference that determines the high quality of the wines produced in this winery, which have received numerous prizes in the most prestigious international competitions. The tanks are made of stainless steel with temperature control.

The winery is one of the area's main attractions, being visited by numerous tourists, since it

Juan Sánchez-Muliterno, managing director and a great connoisseur of wine production techniques.

El Guijoso Estate

is integrated in Castilla-La Mancha's Enological Tourism Association. Apart from visits, wine tasting courses and other activities related to the wine world are offered.

Wines from the Bodegas Sánchez Muliterno are found in the most exclusive and high level restaurant wine lists in Spain.

Alongside the vineyard, the winery has been awarded the Certifications of Quality ISO 9001 and Environment ISO 14001.

Olive groves

Twenty-five hectares are dedicated to organic olive production, where the varieties of Picual and Arbequina are grown. The plan is to install a mill in order to bottle high quality oil.

Shooting activity

El Guijoso estate is one of the best reserves for small game in Spain. The main quarry species are Rabbit (Oryctolagus cuniculus), Red-legged Partridge (Alectoris rufa) and Hare (Lepus granatensis), but there is also splendid Turtledove (Streptopelia turtur) and Woodpigeon (Columba palumbus) shooting, and some Mallard (Anas plathyrhynchos). Wild Boar (Sus scrofa) have increased in the last few years, and some specimens of singular trophy value have been shot. Rabbits are usually shot in walked-up form or with nets and ferrets in the almost 300 warrens that exist; Partridges are driven, Hares are hunted with greyhounds and Wild Boar in drives or from high seats, especially in land sown with maize. Deer are also frequently seen. It must be stressed that non-quarry species find El Guijoso an extra-ordinary habitat to live in, and it is not unusual to see steppe bird populations such as the Great Bustard (Otis tarda), or Wild Cats (Felis sylvestris), Foxes (Vulpes vulpes), Eagle Owls (Bubo bubo) or Short-toed Eagles (Circaetus gallicus).

Enological and rural tourism

The estate owns a few houses for rural tourism, built in the typical style of the area, very pleasant and fully equipped. To this traditional rural tourism we have to add that of wine and hunting. There is a tavern or hunting pavilion for meetings and lunches, especially used for wine tasting. The winery is a founder partner of the Enological Tourism Association of Castilla La Mancha, and is part of the most exceptional wine routes in the area.

Photovoltaic energy

In 2008 a photovoltaic energy park with 14,256 solar panels which produce up to 2,500,000 watts (2.5 MW) was installed on a plot of 15 ha. This enables a decrease of 3,000 tonnes of CO_2 emission, and can produce electricity for the whole village of El Bonillo, or of Ossa de Montiel, contributing to the environmental commitment.

Sylviculture

The main species in the estate woodland of El Guijoso are Holm Oak *(Quercus ilex)* and Spanish Juniper *(Juniperus thurifera)*, the latter forming part of the more extensive juniper areas left in Spain, comprising some examples that are one thousand or even two thousand years old. Some Common Juniper *(Juniperus communis)* and Scots Pine *(Pinus silvestris)* are also features of the landscape. The bush scrub mainly consists of Thyme *(Thymus vulgaris)* and Rosemary *(Rosmarinus officinalis)*, with a proliferation of Lavender *(Lavandula angustifolia)* and some other aromatic plants. The sight of fields of red poppies is impressive. The main use of the woodland is for firewood, and it is managed under conservation criteria.

Livestock

Three thousand sheep in modern sheds utilise the estate's pastures. They live alongside other domestic and farm animals such as dogs, hens, pigs, etc.

Eduardo Sánchez-Muliterno, the key figure in this Project and a successful businessman with a great vision of the future.

El Guijoso Estate

Agreements with bee-keepers are normally made, to place beehives and produce the coveted rosemary honey.

Apart from agricultural products (cereal, vegetables, oleaginous plants, etc) and those derived from the sheep, the estate produces the prestigious wines of the Bodegas Sánchez Muliterno, commercialized under the following brands:

- DIVINUS: Chardonnay fermented in barrel.
- VEGA GUIJOSO: Merlot with a year of aging in barrel.
- VIÑA CONSOLACIÓN: Cabernet Sauvignon with two years of aging in barrel.
- MAGNIFICUS: Syrah with a year of aging in barrel.
- FINCA LA SABINA: aging of Tempranillo.

STAFF. THE KEY JOB POSITIONS ON THE ESTATE ARE:

Name	Position	Years of Service
Eduardo Sánchez Muliterno	Owner and president	–
Juan Sánchez Muliterno	Managing director	–
Pedro Rodríguez y Doroteo Cañas	Foremen	15
Emilio Vargas	Management	15
Rocío Juncos	Enologist	3
Ramón Serrano y Simón Royo	Cellarmen	10

El Guijoso (Spain)

OBJECTIVES OF THE ESTATE

For the next few years the spotlights at El Guijoso will focus on:

1. Continuing to introduce wines into the international trade and increasing the profitability of the agricultural side by researching crop production.
2. Maintaining production through environmentally friendly criteria.
3. Increasing the production of renewable energy, for which a R+D project on biomass is in progress in order to use energy from agricultural waste.
4. Conserving the natural environment by encouraging native flora and developing the mammal species that are typical of this habitat.
5. Generating and utilising the resources of hunting, agriculture and conservation which generate jobs and social enrichment.

The winery is a founder partner of the Enological Tourism Association of Castilla-La Mancha.

THE CURRENT CHALLENGES

The challenges that the estate is confronting are the following:

- Reduction of CAP subsidies and other support.
- Considerably increase in the exodus of rural populations to the city.
- Consequences of climatic change on the natural environment.
- Lack of investment and public infrastructure in rural areas such as ICT or proper asphalted access roads.
- Excessive intervention by different administrations.

The strategy is to adapt management to these new scenarios, raising the profile of the commercial brand images, and moving into new sectors such as cheese production and bottling high quality oil.

Juan Sánchez Muliterno

El Guijoso Estate

The landscape has a lot of biodiversity and shelters an extensive catalogue of vertebrates with more than 170 species.

El Guijoso Estate

EL GUIJOSO BELONGS TO:

Enoturismo de Castilla-La Mancha

Enoturismo de Castilla-La Mancha

Activities & attractions

Shooting

Wine

Historic buildings

Rural Tourism

Birdwaching

Estate Product

CONTACT DATA
Finca El Guijoso
Tel: +34 967 193 222
Fax: +34 967 193 292
Manager: +34 608 078 023
Fax Manager: +34 967 370 755
Shooting Manager: +34 606 428 487
Reserves and accomodation:
administracion@sanchez-muliterno.com
www.sanchez-muliterno.com
www.pagoguijoso.es

Ford & Etal

Atlantic

Location: District of Berwick-Upon-Tweed, county of Northumberland, England, United Kingdom.
Surface: 6,000 ha.

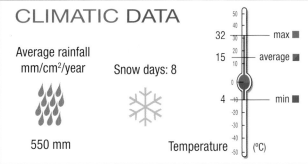

CLIMATIC DATA

Average rainfall
mm/cm²/year

Snow days: 8

550 mm

Temperature (°C)

32 — max
15 — average
4 — min

SUMMARY

Ford & Etal Estates are a traditional British agricultural estates of 6,000 hectares, located on the border between England and Scotland. Although administratively in England, the northern part of the county of Northumberland is very closely connected to the cultural and heritage traditions of the Scottish Borders. Great Britain is a crowded and increasingly urbanised island, but there are still areas that are remote and sparsely populated. With the cities of Edinburgh and Newcastle both about 100 km distant, the eastern Scottish Borders and North Northumberland, whose focus is the valley of the famous River Tweed, are difficult to access. Nevertheless the countryside and natural resources in this area are of great importance, and have played a major role in shaping the history of the United Kingdom.

Ford & Etal form an estate where the traditional activities of farming and food production now lie alongside an increasing number of small-scale micro-enterprises, many of these sited in former agricultural buildings or houses no longer required for farming purposes. Access to countryside activities and to the heritage is encouraged. The estate is a living and vibrant community, and is the richer for having had to face up the many challenges of modern rural life. There will be plenty more challenges in the years ahead.

Ford & Etal Estates

Ford & Etal is located on the border between England and Scotland.

Meet of the foxhounds
at Ford Castle 1922.

Lord Joicey

HISTORY

Since the Industrial Revolution of the nineteenth century, success in industry in Great Britain, as in other countries, has traditionally been followed by investment in land, often accompanied by improvement or change in the main residence and/or farms and country sports activities.

The 1st Baron Joicey, a highly successful coal owner from Newcastle, and Member of Parliament, purchased the historic castle and estate at Ford in 1907 and the adjacent estate of Etal in 1908. In the case of Ford, it was the first time in the estate's long history (records go back to the 13th century) that it had been purchased; all previous owners had acquired it through inheritance or marriage.

Lord Joicey's original plan was to allow his two sons to run the two estates separately from each other, and on each estate he made significant improvements to buildings, woodland, farms, etc. He died at Ford in 1936. His title and the estate at Ford passed to his eldest son James Arthur. Only four years later, however, in 1940, James Arthur died, with no male heir. The title, and the Ford estate, therefore passed to his brother Hugh, the second son of the 1st Lord Joicey, who was already installed at Etal.

During the Second World War, large houses such as the castle at Ford were requisitioned as hospitals and convalescent homes, and, on returning home to Etal in 1945, Hugh resolved to unite the management of the two estates into one. He chose to remain at the Manor House at Etal, rather than move to Ford Castle, and within a few years had arranged for the castle to be used as a residential centre for outdoor study, for the benefit of children from urban areas. In 1956 this use was formalised in a lease to Northumberland County Council, and the arrangement is still in place today. Almost a quarter of a million children have passed through its doors. For the vast majority of them, their week's stay at Ford is their first experience of living away from home; the benefits of the centre are therefore not only strong educationally but also contribute greatly to the social development of the young people of Northumberland and elsewhere. The Joicey family, now in its fourth generation, continue to be strong supporters of this arrangement, and take a close interest in the centre's affairs.

We hope and believe that the 1st Lord Joicey, and indeed all former owners and stewards of the estate, would approve of seeing so many young people, and adults, coming into closer contact with their historical and natural heritage. Their courses explore aspects of the environment, history, natural sciences, and culture. The majority of the children come from urban backgrounds, and many have never visited the countryside. At the other end of the scale, visitors in their "third age" appreciate the holistic way in which generations of land managers have cared for the countryside.

Joicey family, 1936.

Joicey family

BRIEF DESCRIPTION OF BIOPHYSICAL NATURAL CONDITIONS

The estate covers 6,000 hectares of productive agricultural land and is situated in the valley of the River Till, in the north of the county of Northumberland (north-east of England). The Till is a principal tributary of the River Tweed, famous for its salmon fishing, and is a major feature of the estate. Significant conservation work has enhanced its environment for migratory fish, otters and other river life.

Ford & Etal is surrounded by several farms and smaller estates, including Pallinsburn and Duddo. The Northumberland National Park, the largest National Park in England, and the Cheviot Hills lie to the southwest (highest point: The Cheviot, 815 metres). The valley of the River Tweed (the border with Scotland) is to the west, and to the east is the Northumberland coast, designated as an Area of Outstanding Natural Beauty.

The estate lies at an altitude of 40-120 metres above sea level, rising to 250 metres at the south-western corner where it touches on the northern edge of the Cheviot Hills

Its open fertile farmland ranges from heavy clay to lighter sand. Some of the lighter land has been extensively planted with trees. The following graph shows the principal landscape features of Ford & Etal Estates:

Cultivated lands

There are 36 farms on the estate, all of which are occupied by tenant farmers whose businesses focus on growing traditional crops, principally barley (for the brewing and distilling industries), wheat (for animal feed and flour), oilseed rape (for animal feed oils and for industrial uses), and livestock, principally sheep and cattle for meat production. There are also considerable areas of potatoes and carrots, grown for supermarkets. Annual rainfall is only about 600mm, so that irrigation for potatoes and carrots is sometimes necessary.

Pasture

Lowland meadows and pastures are species rich grasslands with a near neutral pH. Grassland in this area of the UK is characterised by low nutrient inputs and is traditionally managed for grazing, silage or hay. Its proximity to the river means that issues such as effluent and the application of nitrogen must be carefully controlled.

Forest

The woodland area is made up of small plantations, originally planted either for amenity or for country sports purposes. They comprise 70% conifer such as Scots Pine *(Pinus pinea)*, Larch *(Larix* sp.), Sitka Spruce *(Picea sitchensis)* and Norway Spruce *(Picea abies)*, and 30% broadleaf species such as Oak *(Quercus* sp.), Ash *(Fraxinus* sp.) and Beech *(Fagus* sp.). The majority of the woodland was replanted in the 1950s following the Second World War, a factor which has led to occasional imbalance in forest management programmes.

The majority of timber harvested on the estate is converted and processed in the estate's own

Landscape with a beautiful mosaic of crops.

FORD & ETAL LANDSCAPE (Surface - ha)

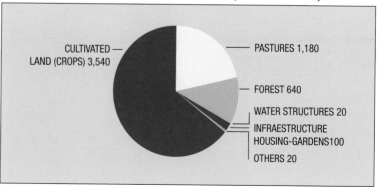

CULTIVATED LAND (CROPS) 3,540

PASTURES 1,180

FOREST 640

WATER STRUCTURES 20

INFRAESTRUCTURE HOUSING-GARDENS100

OTHERS 20

Etal Castle built in the mid-14th century.

sawmill. The forestry department is today the largest single employer on the Ford & Etal Estate, responsible for planting, thinning and felling the trees as well as maintaining the fences, gates and stiles around the estate.

Infrastructure - housing & gardens

Ford & Etal Estates is responsible for the up-keep of some 250 houses, cottages and other buildings, over the entire estate lands.

The more emblematic properties are:

Ford Castle

The castle's history dates back to the 14th century. King James IV of Scotland spent his last night at the castle before his fatal battle on Flodden Field in 1513, the last British monarch to be killed

in battle. Owned previously by the Heron, Blake, Kerr and Delaval families, all of whom had left their mark on the architecture of the original four-towered castle, the estate passed to the Marquis of Waterford in the early 19th century. The family had its own estate at Curraghmore in Ireland, so it was not until 1859 that Louisa Anne, Marchioness of Waterford, the widow of the 3rd Marquis, came to reside at Ford. She undertook further significant work to the castle, but her principal legacy is in the neighbouring village where she built a school for the children. A talented artist, she spent a total of 22 years painting watercolour murals in the school, each of which depicts a scene from the Bible in which the faces of the village residents are recorded.

Ford Castle is a Grade I Listed Building under the UK's designation scheme. The mosaic of history contained within it, which is as much the result of personal whim as of social and technical change, can not be altered by this or future generations of owners. No further tiles may therefore be added to the mosaic.

Etal Castle

Etal was built in the mid-14th century as a defence against Scots raiders, in a strategic position by the River Till. It fell to the Scottish King James IV's invading army in 1513, immediately before their catastrophic defeat at nearby Flodden. An exhibition tells the story of Flodden and the Anglo-Scottish border wars which ended with the accession of King James VI of Scotland to the throne of

Plant nursery enterprise in Etal village.

England (as King James I of England) in 1603, an event which marked the start of the "United Kingdom".

The castle fell into disrepair in the early 17th century. A new Manor House was built at the other end of the village in the mid-18th century, by which time peace between England and Scotland had been firmly assured, meaning that it was therefore no longer necessary to live in a defensive castle.

Today, the ruins of Etal Castle are in the care of English Heritage, but the adjacent building, in which the exhibition is housed, belongs to the estate. The arrangement was established in the early 1990s, and was the first joint-venture project between English Heritage and a private estate.

Other important places are:

Lady Waterford Gallery

Lady Waterford's "new" village school continued to serve its purpose until 1957. It is now the Village Hall, but also a registered museum. Local residents use it for many different community purposes, all watched over by the faces of their 19th century predecessors.

Castle Nursery

The 19th century walled garden of Ford Castle is just under a hectare in size, and today provides a magnificent setting for a specialist plant nursery.

Heatherslaw Cornmill

It is more than 700 years since the first record of a watermill on the banks of the River Till. The mill was restored in the 1970s, and the internal machinery from the 19th century still produces high quality stone-ground wholemeal flour from locally grown wheat.

PROTECTED AREAS

The estate includes three areas of land that have been given statutory protection to conserve species of flora or fauna which are of national and international importance:
- Ford Moss SAC.
- Holburn Moss SPA and RAMSAR site.
- River Tweed SAC.

Heatherslaw mill and river.

Ford Moss

Ford Moss is a Special Area of Conservation (SAC) under the European Natura 2000 directive. It is an active raised bog, occupying a shallow basin in undulating country, underlain by Carboniferous Limestone and with a depth of 12 m of peat.

The flora is typical of bog communities. Large areas are dominated by Heather *(Calluna vulgaris)*, Hare's-tail Cottongrass *(Eriophorum vaginatum)* and Cross-leaved Heath *(Erica tetralix)*. Carpets of Bog-Moss *(Sphagnum* sp.) occur, where the insectivorous Round-leaved Sundew *(Drosera rotundifolia)*, Cranberry *(Vaccinium oxycoccus)* and White Sedge *(Carex curta)* grow. Bog Myrtle *(Myrica gale)* grows around the periphery of the bog.

Woodland around the margins of the site contains stands of mature Oak *(Quercus robur)* and Scots Pine *(Pinus sylvestris)*, Birch *(Betula* spp.) and Willow Carr *(Salix atrocinerea, S. fragilis)*. Chickweed Wintergreen *(Trientalis europaea)* grows within the pinewood.

The moss is also of interest for its insect populations, notably two species of butterfly, the Small Copper *(Lycaena phlaeas)* and the Orange Tip *(Anthocharis cardamines)*.

Ford Moss is managed as a nature reserve by the Northumberland Wildlife Trust in cooperation with Natural England (the statutory agency in England) and the estate. There are substantial archaeological remains of former colliery workings, dating from the 17th century. The last mine closed in 1918. Many of the miners were depicted by Lady Waterford in her paintings in Ford school, and a major project to safeguard the archaeological and cultural heritage associated with local coal-mining was initiated in 2008 by a placement student from Newcastle University.

Holburn Moss

Holburn Moss is both a declared Special Protection Area and a RAMSAR site. It is a peat bog of 130 hectares, in which an artificial lake was constructed in 1934. It is an important roosting point for overwintering Greylag Goose *(Anser anser)* from Iceland. Other birds such as Wigeon *(Anas penelope)* and Teal *(Anas crecca)* also roost, and a few pairs of Shelduck *(Tadorna tadorna)*, Shoveler *(Anas clypeata)* and Tufted Duck *(Aythya fuligula)* regularly breed. In addition, Snipe *(Gallinago gallinago)*, Green Plover *(Vanellus vanellus)*, Oystercatcher *(Haematopus ostralegus)* and Scottish Grouse *(Lagopus lagopus scoticus)* can be seen.

Holburn Moss itself supports a variety of bog mosses together with other bog plants including Heather *(Calluna vulgaris)*, Cotton Grass *(Eriophorum angustifolium)*, Cranberry *(Vaccinium oxycoccus)* and Round-leaved Sundew *(Drosera rotundifolia)*.

As in the case of Ford Moss, Holburn Moss is also managed as a nature reserve by the Northumberland Wildlife Trust in cooperation with Natural England and the estate, and management meetings are held every six months.

River Tweed

The River Till is the only English tributary of the River Tweed. It rises in the Cheviot Hills, a granite massif that forms the borderland between England and Scotland; the Till runs south to north, and joins the River Tweed some 15 km before it flows into the North Sea at Berwick-upon-Tweed.

The whole of the River Tweed catchment area (5000 km^2) is a designated Special Area of Conservation (SAC) under the European Natura 2000 Habitats directive, principally for Water-Crowfoot *(Ranunculus* spp.*)*, Atlantic Salmon *(Salmo salar)* and Otter *(Lutra lutra)*. The three species of lamprey (Sea Lamprey *(Petromyzon marina)*, River Lamprey *(Lampetra fluviatilis)* and Brook Lamprey *(Lampetra planeri)*) are also present.

The River Tweed supports a very large population of Atlantic Salmon. It is the best example in Britain of a large river showing a strong nutrient gradient along its length, with oligotrophic conditions in its headwaters, and nutrient-rich lowland conditions just before it enters the sea at Berwick. The high proportion of the River Tweed catchment area accessible to salmon, and the variety of habitat conditions, has resulted in the river supporting the full range of salmon life-history types, with subpopulations of spring, summer salmon and grilse all being present. It supports a significant proportion of the Scottish salmon resource. In recent years, the salmon catch in the River Tweed has been the highest in Scotland, with up to 15% of all salmon caught. Considerable work has been done by the Scottish Environment Protection Agency and the River Tweed Foundation in tackling pollution and easing the passage of salmon past artificial barriers in the river. This has reversed many of the river's historical problems with water quality and access for salmon. Within this, the River Till is further known for its significant population of Sea Trout *(Salmo trutta trutta)*.

Because the River Tweed Catchment Area lies in both England and Scotland, a legal anomaly exists. The UK "Tweed Fisheries Act" was first introduced in 1857 but, after the devolution of Scotland in 1998, the Catchment Area was placed under the jurisdiction of the Scottish Parliament in 2006. Ford & Etal Estates is therefore obliged to

Atlantic Salmon *(Salmo salar)* of the River Tweed.

Fly fishing for Sea Trout *(Salmo trutta trutta)* in the River Till.

Joicey family

Joicey family

follow legislation implemented by the Scottish Parliament in Edinburgh although the English Environment Agency, based in Bedford in southern England, has responsibility for the 570 hectares of the SAC occupied by the River Till.

To counteract the effects of erosion and help stabilise the riverbank where it is sandy, willow saplings are planted on more vulnerable areas and stone "croys" are constructed in strategic places to establish a better environment for river life. These help to create deeper pools and faster flowing waters which flush silt from the riverbed, making a better breeding area for the minute creatures that the fish feed on.

Matters of irrigation have been addressed recently under the EU Water Framework Directive, and a plan to establish sustainable storage of excessive winter water supplies is being elaborated.

PRIMARY ECONOMIC ACTIVITIES - LAND

Ford & Etal comprises 36 registered farm holdings, currently let to 22 tenants. A traditional mix of cereal-growing and livestock husbandry predominate. Up until the 1970s, the estate's main work lay in its relationships with its farm tenants, its own in-hand farming operation, and forestry. Nowadays, the tenants of Ford & Etal Estates cover a much wider spectrum of activity and business, from traditional farming to modern micro-enterprises unconnected with agriculture. It is the combined economic activity of all of these businesses which is important, and by which the estate evaluates success.

The land is also used for recreation and country sports. Pheasant and partridge shooting on the estate are let to a specialist sporting agent. Roe deer stalking is handled by the estate itself. Sport fishing is plentiful and exciting, as the River Till is particularly noted for its large spring Sea-Trout *(Salmo trutta trutta)*. Salmon *(Salmo salar)*, Brown Trout *(Salmo trutta fario)* and Grayling *(Thymallus thymallus)* are also present. As well as the Protected Areas mentioned, Ford & Etal has a wide range of habitats that offer excellent opportunities for birdwatching. The local Bird Club holds an annual visit to the estate in May, to listen to the "Dawn Chorus" and record the number of species present. Work on enhancing smaller habitat areas is done in conjunction with the various farm environment improvement schemes that arise.

Demand for access to the countryside within the UK as a whole has risen rapidly, and, as on many estates, a network of cycle routes and walking trails has been developed around Ford & Etal. The National Cycle Route from Derby to Berwick-upon-Tweed (535 km in length) passes through the estate and along the River Till.

Cycle path created beside the River Till.

STAFF

Administration & management:	6	
Building maintenance:	4	
Private staff:	4	(Full-time equivalent: 3)
Estate Grounds:	2	
Forestry (harvesting)	4	(Full-time equivalent: 3.5)
Forestry (sawmill/production)	5	
Estate maintenance	2	
Sporting management	2	(Full-time equivalent: 1.25)
Tourism & Leisure	5	(Full-time equivalent: 2.75)
Total:	34	(Full-time equivalent: 29.5)

OPPORTUNITIES, THREATS AND CHALLENGES FOR FORD & ETAL IN THE RECENT PAST

Ford & Etal Estates is in many ways a traditional British agricultural estate. Agriculture still forms the backbone of the economy in the sparsely populated county of Northumberland and in the Scottish Borders. Until the mid 1970s income from farming and farm rents was almost the only source of revenue to the estate.

Over the last 50 years, advances in technology and husbandry have been remarkable. Combined with changes in the overarching agricultural support measures introduced by changes to the Common Agricultural Policy, and the normal external market forces of supply and demand, these advances have resulted in an exponential increase in productivity. On the other hand, job opportunities have reduced at an alarming rate, and the socio-economic health of rural areas has suffered greatly. Wildlife, too, has suffered.

The viability of farm economics has resulted in amalgamations of the smaller individual farms into joint tenancies. The 36 farms at Ford & Etal are now farmed by 22 tenants, giving an average size of 181 hectares. At the same time, older buildings used for agricultural purposes became redundant.

Using these redundant buildings as opportunities, the estate has implemented a policy of encouraging and facilitating new commercial enterprises in the countryside. Often, these commercial tenants rent residential property from the Estate as well. The policy began in the mid 1970s, with the restoration of the old water mill on the river Till. It had stopped working in 1958, and was in a bad state. It was the decision of the 4th Lord Joicey to undertake a thorough restoration programme, completed in 1975. The success of this, coupled with the fact that the Lady Waterford Gallery had always attracted a steady number of visitors, and, furthermore, the effect of a falling agricultural population on the viability of local services such as the village school, shop and pub, encouraged the family to adopt a policy of encouraging new businesses to develop in the countryside, loosely based on rural tourism.

The estate is now host to more non-agricultural businesses (32) than traditional farming tenants (22). With the exception of forestry, the estate only engages with the activities of these businesses in

John Marrin Books.

family

Heatherslaw Light Railway.

its capacity as landlord. The emphasis has changed; the estate makes available landed assets (buildings, land, etc.) and encourages commercial enterprise which will underpin a successful and sustainable socio-economic activity within the community.

These new businesses are all Small/Micro Enterprises (SMEs), built on visions and models of sustainability rather than aspirations of dynamic growth. This fits with the difficulties of accessing markets from such a rural location (being 100 kilometres distant from the nearest cities: Edinburgh and Newcastle).

In one case, however, the tenant has grown and developed his enterprise so much that he has had to transfer a part of the enterprise to the nearest industrial estate 15 kilometres away. His vision to produce handmade biscuits and cakes from the flour produced in the restored water mill has been very successful, and he now supplies his products across the entire UK. He wishes the core business to remain *in situ*, however, in order to preserve the important link between the product and its provenance.

Over the last ten years, employment opportunities have risen, inward migration has boosted local economic turnover, and the community is now vibrant and healthy. Although the origins of this policy were to encourage growth in rural tourism, the estate has refined this into an active policy of recruiting business tenants who do not totally depend on rural tourism, in order to counteract the seasonality of this sector.

The crucial criterion is that the businesses which rent premises on the estate should ideally show year-round sustainability. Local services and resources (school, pub, village shop, community hall, church, etc.) have been underpinned by this. Nevertheless, tourism and marketing are important considerations within the local economic context, and the estate has developed a model of marketing cooperative on behalf of its business tenants. It is prominent in sub-regional efforts to extend the traditional summer season into the spring and autumn shoulder seasons.

The profile of visitors and residents of the sub-region shows that outdoor activities, such as walking, cycling, country sports, natural history

575

Old sheds converted into a bakery at Heatherslaw Mill.

observation, horse riding, etc. are in strong demand. Infrastructural improvements are important in this context, in order to ensure and enhance the visitor's enjoyment of the countryside (especially in the United Kingdom where private property rights have stifled such access in the past). Improvements to car parking, signage, riverside walks, wildlife observation points, etc. have been introduced, using public funding opportunities where available, although not exclusively so. The estate, in cooperation with its farm tenants, has created a number of interesting circular walks and cycle routes, opportunities for canoeists, anglers, rock-climbers, shooting parties and horse riders.

Economic downturns, or changes in lifestyle, may have an effect on the leisure market, but the sustainability of the estate's business tenants, and the opportunities provided for free access and enjoyment of the estate's natural resources, should ensure that the community remains a successful model in terms of socio-economics.

Climate change has already presented Ford & Etal with challenges. Short-term issues such as the planning of annual crops – whether for food or energy – are separate from the need to take deci-

sions for the longer-term. The former are largely the responsibility of the tenant farmers, whilst the estate must focus on the latter. In this area of Britain, the trend seems to be towards generally wetter weather, with more risk of very strong winds. Wet ground prevents farmers from accessing the land, prevents foresters from accessing the forest, and makes it difficult for walkers and visitors to enjoy the countryside and wildlife or to participate in other activities. When the ground is dry enough, all three groups want to have access at the same time, and the window of opportunity is very restricted. To respond to this, the estate is now focusing on improving the condition of its network of tracks and roads.

We must also, however, remember the duty of care and foresight which landowners have constantly exercised for the long-term good of their estate and community. If predictions for global warming come into effect, then decisions about the planting of trees must, if possible, pre-empt them. Ford & Etal Estates were fortunate to predict the increased use of the countryside for recreational and business purposes; it is less easy to predict the species of tree that one should be planting, knowing that it will be at least 60 years before the tree is harvested. Already we have seen that the climate no longer favours the growing of Norway Spruce.

These challenges have been those of the late twentieth century. There will be more, for certain. Looking back at all the many challenges that have been faced over the years by private estates, would the European countryside be as rich, diverse, healthy, vibrant and attractive as it is today if land owners and land managers had not responded in they way that they did?

The main objectives and challenges for the estate are therefore:

- 1. To encourage, facilitate and sustain vibrant economic and socio-economic activity in this very rural area, reflected in full properties and associated rental income. Included in this are, for example, to help maintain a village school and as many local services as possible for the benefit of the community, and to encourage inward migration and affordable houses.

- 2. To strive for a satisfactory balance between the many factors facing the countryside over the next twenty years: pressures of social demand, food supplies, environment, energy supplies, financially healthy tenants, the recognition of normal laws of supply and demand, corporate social responsibility, and cross-compliance (which in turn is a balance of land stewardship, production, and environment).

Joicey family

Shop and Post Office in Ford Village.

FORD & ETAL BELONGS TO:

THE wildlife TRUSTS
Northumberland Wildlife Trust

NATURAL ENGLAND
Natural England

Friends of the Countryside
Friends of the Countryside

Activities & attractions

- Birdwatching
- Accommodation
- Rural tourism
- Historical buildings and monuments
- Education
- Outdoor sports
- Fishing
- Horse-riding
- Shooting

CONTACT DATA

Contact Person: Lord Joicey
Address: Ford & Etal Estates, Ford, Berwick-upon-Tweed, TD15 2QA
Telephone: 01890 820224 • Fax: 01890 820384
office@ford-and-etal.co.uk
www.ford-and-etal.co.uk

B. van Musscher

Heerlijkheid Mariënwaerdt

Atlantic

Location: Betuwe locality, region of Gederland, The Netherlands.
Surface: 965 ha.

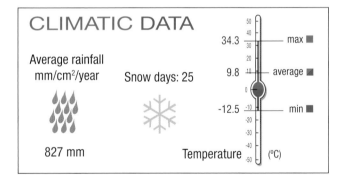

CLIMATIC DATA

Average rainfall
mm/cm²/year

Snow days: 25

827 mm

Temperature (ºC)

34.3 — max ■

9.8 — average ■

-12.5 — min ■

SUMMARY

Located in the central part of the Netherlands, Heerlijkheid Mariënwaerdt is a privately owned estate of 965 hectares in the Betuwe, an area in the province of Gelderland famous for its fruit production. The estate has been owned by the same family for eight generations. It is for that reason that it carries a unique character, not only in terms of nature, culture or history, but also with regard to the style of management and development. Thanks to the landowner's personal touch that can be found in everything, the estate has developed a unique identity.

Heerlijkheid Mariënwaerdt, a private estate of 965 hectares, is located in the Betuwe in Gelderland, famous for its fruit production.

HISTORY

A short history of Mariënwaerdt

Even though the original boundaries of Mariën-waerdt – established in 1129 – remained unchanged, the history of the estate can be characterised as one of notable changes in both form and ownership.

An abbey was established on the land in its earliest times. The land – called the Herigerwaard in Gelderland – was given to the church by the widow of Hendrik I van Cuijk. This enabled the church to establish a monastery which was named after Maria and which was more precisely named the Island ('waard') of Maria: Mariën-waerdt. It was heavily influenced by the order of Saint Norbert. The abbey was built like a small town, with amongst other things a church, a brewery, a smith, a shoe-maker, a bakery, a library and a kitchen garden. Its habitants played an exemplary role as they introduced new agricultural techniques, were active in medicine and provided food to the poor on a weekly basis.

The monastery of Mariënwaerdt was financially strong and religiously very influential. The dimensions of the abbey – not only in land but also in buildings – expanded, thanks to good management and gifts. Unfortunately, due to the abbey having been sited badly, the constant threat of flooding rivers and bad governance, Mariënwaerdt also experienced some very difficult times. In the centuries following its establishment, the abbey underwent several ups and downs.

After the last years of glory (1545-1563) under the leadership of Petrus van Zuyren, Mariënwaerdt began to decline. It started to loose its religious importance and had to suffer several financial backlashes. On the 22nd of March 1567 Mariën-

waerdt was attacked by a group of plunderers, an event that put a definite end to the monastery. In 1592 the ownership of the former abbey was taken over by the local government, who decided to sell it. After almost 150 years, Count van Bylandt bought the property in 1734. The family built the current estate of Mariënwaerdt on the remaining ruins.

The van Bylandt family

Albrecht Otto van Bylandt, married to Constantia, had 18 children, of which 12 were still alive when Albrecht Otto died in 1768. In his will he left one-twelfth of the estate to each of them. Because of that, Mariënwaerdt was unfortunately dispersed into several parts. Fortunately his second son, Frederik, married to Maria Johanna Munter, managed to buy out his brothers and sisters, enabling a unification of the property. From this time on, the family line has evolved from the van Bylandt (Otto Willem Arnold) to van Balveren (through the marriage of Susanna, daughter of Otto Willem Arnold to Willem Baron van Balveren) to van Verschuer, through the marriage of three van Balveren daughters to three van Verschuer brothers.

The van Verschuer family still owns Mariën-waerdt. The last direct descendants are Otto Willem Arnold Baron van Verschuer (b. 1927), his wife Catharina Theresia van Sminia (b. 1927) and their five children: Cornelie Charlotte, Bernard Frederik, Frans Jacob Albert, Otteline Marie and Catherine Marie Roline.

Throughout history, the family has always been very involved in politics and social issues. Several descendants have been Ministers and mayors. Various foundations focusing on social inequalities, education and cultural heritage have been established.

The house was built in 1734 on the remains of the abbey.

B. van Musscher

The estate still has a historic kitchen garden with many fruits and vegetables.

DESCRIPTION

A description of Mariënwaerdt Estate

When Count van Bylandt purchased the land in the 17th century, the main buildings were ruins. Van Bylandt started to build his house, but due to financial instabilities he was obliged to build it in several phases. First a square building was built, with the living room, the guests' room and the corridor. Afterwards, two additional rooms were built on the south side with blue stone stairs in the middle. The third phase was devoted to the north side with its "white room", the library, the study room and two bedrooms.

This different phasing is highly visible from the outside. Of particular interest are the library (consisting of 3337 books) and the vegetable garden, whose design was based on the old convent garden and which consists of pear trees, apple trees, many soft fruits, vegetables and greenhouses for grapes and an orangery.

Today Mariënwaerdt still is a family-run private enterprise, but has managed to remain a calm and peaceful place with beautiful landscape and diverse nature. The property presently consists of three stately homes, seventeen farms, of which fourteen have manor houses listed as national heritage monuments, and many hay and flood barns. The family combines entrepreneurship on one side with the conservation of nature and cultural heritage on the other. Nowadays, the eighth generation of the van Verschuer family is running the country estate of Heerlijkheid Mariënwaerdt.

Distribution of land-use

Marienwaedt Estate stands geographically within the locality of the Betuwe, in the river district of the Netherlands in the province of Gelderland. The Betuwe is situated between the rivers Lek and Waal. Mariënwaerdt borders a picturesque river called the Linge. It is very fertile land with river clay soil and therefore an area well known for its apple and pear orchards. In the spring it attracts thousands of tourists that come to see the blossom.

The largest and most important town in the area is Tiel. The estate is situated next to the village of Beesd, only five minutes from the highway. Therefore it is well located for tourism as it gives direct access for visitors wanting to come for a short visit.

The land consists of a total of 965 ha and is distributed as follows:

- 330 ha of woodland.
- 200 ha of arable land.
- 350 ha of grassland.
- 50 ha of fruit production.
- 35 ha of park land.

Soil characteristics

Mariënwaerdt has different types of soil. It varies from a light soil close to the riverbanks to a more heavy clay soil in the northern part. It is a combina-

Coat of arms of van Verschuer family.

B. van Musscher

The soils are rich in nutrients and well aerated.
There are 350 ha of grassland, 200 ha of arable land and 50 ha of apple and pear orchards.

The estate has 14 historic farm houses, that have several new functions. This farm in now a Bed and Breakfast.

tion of sand, silt, clay, minerals and organic matter that also contains some air and water.

Clay, because of its density, retains moisture well. It also tends to be more nutrient-rich than other soil types. The reason for this is that the particles that make up clay soil are negatively charged. They attract and pick up positively charged particles, such as calcium, potassium, and magnesium.

Mariënwaerdt Estate

The legal position: The NSW (Natuurschoonwet) of 1928

This Dutch legislation gives financial advantages to private landowners:

In order to obtain fiscal advantages, the estate has to consist of a minimum of 5 ha of uninterrupted land and 30% of forestry. An estate open to the public has to have 50 metres of path per hectare and 25 metres of path per hectare of other types of terrain.

The fiscal advantages are the following:

- The land belonging to an estate is exempted from property tax and income tax (only in Box 3).
- A residence belonging to an estate is considered to be a Box 1 tax category as far as property tax and income tax are concerned.
- A foundation or a private limited liability company (BV) owning an estate is sometimes allowed to pay less – or no – corporate tax.
- When an estate is sold, there is an exemption from transfer tax.
- When inherited or when given away there also is a tax exemption.

Forestry

The forestry at Mariënwaerdt Estate is essentially broadleaf. Poplar (*Populus* spp), Oak (*Quercus* spp), Beech (*Fagus* spp) and Elm (*Ulmus* spp) are the most represented species. Forestry has three important functions at Mariënwaerdt Estate, namely nature, production and recreation.

As mentioned above, according to Dutch law and the NSW, forestry has to cover one-third of the total land in order for fiscal advantages to be applied. In terms of harvest plans and reforestation, the forestry at Mariënwaerdt can be divided into four types:

1. **The lanes** with different types of trees: The lanes at Mariënwaerdt have been planted over the centuries with an enormous vary of different trees. The most famous is the beautiful lane with four rows of walnut trees. The trees were planted in 1925 by the late Baron van Verschuer when he needed the soil from the driveway in order to build his house. Nowadays all of the trees together are a national monument. Pruning may only take place under strict regulation. The public may collect the nuts when they fall in the autumn. One of the two

dykes (river banks) is planted with apple trees, with some of the trees now almost 100 years old. The apples are picked to produce the estate's own apple juice which is sold in the estate shop and other specialist shops all over the country. There is also a beautiful beech lane, with oak and white poplar.

2. The Willow (*Salix* **sp) forest** on the riverbanks in the southern part, and especially on the wetter areas in the northern part of the estate. They were planted on parts where it was too wet for agriculture or to plant other types of tree. In the old days the Willows were important as the wood was used for broomsticks and other domestic uses and also for restraining riverbanks. There is still a use for such river work although the production nowadays is much larger than the need. Because of this the branches are used for bio-fuel. The Willows are harvested every three years at a height of 30 cm up to 1 metre. Because this type of forest is very ancient the government subsidises the upkeep of Willows older than 25 years.

3. The old park with very old trees, some of them dating back over 200 years. When Count van Bylandt bought Mariënwaerdt in 1734 he found some beautiful trees around the remains of the old Monastery buildings. He also started planting trees around the site on which he built the present house of Mariënwaerdt. He was in love with Mariënwaerdt and with enormous precision and feeling for landscape architecture he planted a larger forest with beautiful trees, such as Plane (*Platanus* sp), oaks, beeches, elms, Limes (*Tilia* sp), Maples (*Acer* sp) and different types of nut trees such as the American Black Walnut *(Juglans nigra)* and Wingnuts (*Pterocarya* sp), as well as beautiful Ash (*Fraxinus* sp). The old wood is typical of river districts. Because the soil in the wood is extremely fertile the trees are of enormous height and width. The trees in the old forest are not harvested, but when for whatever reason they fall the wood is used to restore the old estate buildings. The wood is ranked as a highly protected site and because of that extra subsidy is claimed for the upkeep of the wood.

4. The productive forest mostly in the northern part of the estate. On Mariënwaerdt there are over 200 hectares of productive woodland. The soil in the northern part where this woodland is situated

B. van Musscher

is of a more clayish type and ideal for productive forestry. Very large yields are obtained. The main varieties are poplar and ash. Before harvesting a piece of woodland, permission must be obtained from the authorities. After felling, new planting has to take place within three years. Because of the NSW regulation for private estates one third of the total area has to be planted with trees or woodland. It is possible to vary the location of the woodland.

Farmland

Farming has always been important at Heerlijkheid Mariënwaerdt. The estate has a large mixed farm that covers all aspects of agriculture – arable, fruit, dairy and cattle. Besides farming, other activities have been developed, though always with respect for the tranquillity, culture and the environment. Marienwaerdt Estate farm converted to organic production in 2000. The dairy farm has about 250 milking cows that produce around 2 million kg of organic milk. This is all processed by the estate into cheese. All the cheese is sold to delicatessen and organic shops in the Netherlands and Germany.

Maize, sugar beet, pumpkins, potatoes, grass seed, wheat and barley are the arable crops in Mariënwaerdt.

Arable crops:
- Maize silage for the dairy farm.
- Sugar beet.
- Pumpkins.
- Potatoes.
- Grass seed.
- Wheat.
- Barley.

Agriculture at Mariënwaerdt Estate is completely organic and relies on crop rotation, green manure, compost, biological pest control and mechanical cultivation systems. This in turn maintains soil productivity and controls pests, limiting the use of synthetic fertilizers and synthetic pesticides, plant growth regulators, livestock feed additives and GMO's.

The organic agricultural sector has a quality mark – EKO. This quality mark is restricted to organic companies certified by Skal. The label is only allowed on products containing more than 95% organic ingredients. It cannot be used on agricultural products under conversion to organic production.

Besides organic farming, Mariënwaerdt increasingly focuses on the production of organic specialities such as
- Homemade jams, fruit curds, honey, juices.
- Sauces and chutneys.
- Biscuits and flour mixes for bread making.
- Cheese – natural, or with a variety of herbs.
- Angus beef.
- Game.
- Potatoes.
- Ice cream.

These products are sold in the country shop on the estate and in delicatessen and organic shops outside the estate.

A multi-functional farm turned into agri-tourism:

Visitors can enjoy a wide range of catering and recreational activities on the estate. There are two major events that take place on the estate: the Estate Fair (Country Fair) in August and the Christmas Fair in December.

Estate Fair (Country Fair): This attractive outdoor fair features over 130 stands with local produce, fashionable outdoor clothing, decorative garden accessories, country antiques and numerous activities such as animal demonstrations, competitions, food tastings and fashion shows.

Christmas Fair: During this winter fair there is a fairy tale atmosphere at Marienwaerdt. All the haystacks and sheds are beautifully illuminated. There is a live crib, various choirs sing Christmas carols and horses draw sleighs with little bells to make the Christmas Fair complete. There are over 70 stands with a wide assortment of festive articles, such as delicacies, Christmas decorations, table linens, clothes and much more.

Party locations

Mariënwaerdt offers a perfect location for weddings, private parties, business meetings and congresses. It is also possible to attend a cooking workshop under the supervision of a recognised chef. The old centre of the estate, with its historic

Brasserie Marie offers a menu of specialities made from the fresh produce of the estate and neighbouring farms.

Mariënwaerdt Estate

buildings, has recently been designated as a national monument. In this characteristic heart of Mariënwaerdt it is possible to rent one of the beautiful locations for well-prepared meetings, network drinks, staff parties or conferences.

How about a dinner at "De Nieuwe Refter", an afternoon tea at "De Hooiberg", a party at "De Hooge Schuur" or a meeting at "Het Koetshuis"? Each location has its own charm and is very suitable for any occasion.

De Hooge Schuur (The High Barn)

The name already indicates the original purpose of this shed: de Hooge Schuur (the High Barn) is a so-called flood shed built on an old artifical mound made for safety during floods. It is where the cattle of the estate used to seek refuge where the threat of flood was imminent. De Hooge Schuur is situated at the edge of the maintained woods of Heerlijkheid Mariënwaerdt in a meadow by the Linge River. Recent renovations have turned this shed into a beautiful place with plenty of space and a warm atmosphere. The double vaulting of the timber frame ceiling combined with elegant chandeliers and the large French doors to the terrace make De Hooge Schuur ideal for any type of special event, such as a meeting, reception, wedding party, staff party etc.

De Nieuw Refter (The New Refectory)

De Nieuwe Refter is an authentic shed and the name refers to the dining hall of the former abbey of Mariënwaerdt. It has a warm and distinctive ambiance. With a splendid view over the expansive grounds, this is a unique location for family as well as business gatherings. During the summer, the large terrace can be used as well. The Cookery School is also a true experience at the Nieuwe Refter. Under the professional guidance of the estate chef, people will prepare their own dinner with fresh and seasonal products in an easy-going atmosphere.

Koetshuis (The Coach House)

This location, where the carriages were once kept, has been thoroughly restored and has become a beautiful wedding venue. The civil Registrar of Geldermalsen will perform the marriage service with a view over Marienwaerdt Manor, the main house of the estate.

Mariënwaerdt Estate

De Grote Hooiberg and De Kleine Hooiberg (The Big and Small Haystacks)

Located next to the "De Nieuwe Refter" dining and party location are two hay stacks. In summertime, these authentic hay stacks offer an inspirational surrounding for smaller meetings or receptions. Both hay stacks have been left in their original state and offer a splendid view. The French doors of "De Grote Hooiberg" link up perfectly with the surrounding landscape.

B&B

For those who wish to stay longer at Mariënwaerdt, it is possible to spend the night at De Neust, a listed manor house on the estate dating from the 14th century. Visitors can come and stay at the Bed & Breakfast and enjoy the warm hospitality. Situated on the Appeldijk, close to the Linge

In the Estate Country Shop visitors can find all the wonderful delights of Mariënwaerdt.

The estate produced jams, chutneys, curds, sauces, cheeses and juices are very popular.

Mariënwaerdt Estate

A hunt at Mariënwaerdt.

River, this listed monument dating from 1329 combines a sense of tradition and history with contemporary service where the guest will be pampered by the house-keeper.

Multi-functional Centre

One of the homesteads on the estate has been converted into a multi-functional centre where a pancake house, a brasserie, the country shop and an information centre for tourists are all located. This is the ideal place from which you can set off on your walk or bicycle ride across the estate.

Pancake House de Stapelbakker & Brasserie Marie

For individual visitors, families and groups the pancake house known as de Stapelbakker is brimming over with the most delicious pancakes and other dishes that are made from organically grown products. Brasserie Marie offers a menu of specialities made from the fresh produce of the estate and neighbouring farms.

Landgoedwinkel/ Estate Country Shop

In the Country Shop visitors can find all the wonderful delights of Mariënwaerdt to take home. The estate-produced jams, chutneys, curds, sauces, cheeses and juices are very popular, as well as many more tasty things from the estate such as the famous walnut tarts made by Mrs van Verschuer herself, who bakes these in small quantities according to a secret family recipe. Mariënwaerdt Estate believes in the virtue of honesty and pureness and that is why the products sold on the estate do not contain any artificial additives. Shopping at Mariënwaerdt is like shopping in nature!

Paarden Heerlijkheid (Horses at Heerlijkheid)

Mariënwaerdt is an exceptional paradise for horse lovers. A beautiful route of 14 kilometres curls its way over more than 2200 acres amongst farms, fields, ponds, woods and tranquil water meadows. The route varies, depending on the season and the ground conditions. At Marienwaerdt, you are able to ride your horse in its purest form; the greatest way to discover the breathtaking beauty of the estate and its surroundings. The route starts and also ends at the Paarden Heerlijkheid, the centre for horses, horse riders and teamsters. The centre is fitted with large and light boxes, paddocks, a hot-water rinsing and washing area, plus – the dream of every horse – expansive fields of tender Betuwe grass.

Heerlijkheid Magazine – a magazine about living on an estate

Marienwaerdt also publishes a bi-monthly magazine called Heerlijkheid. Heerlijkheid is a life style magazine focusing on life on an estate. Real life is highlighted in an understandable, serious yet humorous way. The keywords are authenticity, stylish, core values and standards, and family traditions, but also the involvement of its owners with nature, history and their inheritance in this fast changing world, in which the importance of values and standards and attachments in particular are under increasing pressure.

Employed staff

The estate employs about 150 people:
- 68 in the restaurants.
- 8 in the shops.
- 35 in production and processing.

- 12 on the farm.
- 4 for events.
- 15 in the office (management).
  (3 on the magazine – 3 in the sales department – 9 in general management).
- 1 game-keeper.
- 3 for maintenance.
- 2 gardeners.

Tourism infrastructure

Walking and cycling

Mariënwaerdt is situated on an exceptional natural site in a river area. Visitors can take beautiful walks or bicycle rides, enjoying the wonderful scenery and splendid views. Four routes have been set out on the estate, which vary in distance.

There are also several routes, recognized by the ANWB (the Dutch automobile club) and the LAW (a Dutch platform for hikers), which cross the estate and allow people to see the Betuwe area at its best, particularly during the spring and autumn season when the fruit trees set the scene. From the dykes and paths the view of the rivers is often splendid. The maelstroms and pools show the battle against the water. The various villages that lie along these trails, like Leerdam, Beesd, Geldermalsen, Tiel, Kesteren and Opheusden, are also within easy reach by train.

In the future

Marienwaerdt still has several plans to grow its activities even further, which will help to earn income for the preservation of the estate. Future plans are based on new functions for the historic farms on the estate:

- A top-quality hotel.
- A farm museum (National Agricultural Museum) that will not be static but pragmatic, educating citizens about farming yesterday and today. Exhibitions of farm machinery (tractors, combines, etc.) are part of this museum.

The Society of "Vrienden van Mariënwaerdt" (Friends of Mariënwaerdt)

It takes enormous efforts to maintain a large country estate like Mariënwaerdt. Therefore anyone who would like to offer a helping hand is welcome. That is why the society 'Vrienden van Mariënwaerdt'was founded in 2002. The aim of the society is to make a contribution to the coherent and sensible management and offer help with the maintenance of this historic and national monument.

The society believes that Mariënwaerdt, together with its unique and natural beauty and its registered buildings, must be preserved for future generations. They aim to achieve this by organizing conferences, meetings, lectures, excursions and a broad range of other related activities.

The Hooge Schuur is one of the beautiful locations for meetings, weddings, staff parties or conferences.

Mariënwaerdt Estate

PRIVATE OPINION

Family vision

After 275 years of Mariënwaerdt, 15 years of the Estate Fair and the Estate Shop and 2 years of the Heerlijkheid magazine... People often ask us: "Do you still have more plans and dreams for Mariënwaerdt? Or is it enough as it is right now?"

In the past 275 years the different generations of our family have managed Mariënwaerdt in their own way. The first generations depended on the income from tenants, as they occupied the estate only in a limited way (the family used to live in Arnhem during the year and only came to the estate during summer), and except for a small profit from timber sales, the estate did not have its own commercial enterprises.

Since the 1950s, this has all changed. On the one hand out of necessity, because the costs kept on rising and the incomes from tenancies kept on falling, and on the other because the family moved to live on the estate permanently and as a consequence became more involved with agriculture. The production of fruit and arable crops were now managed by the family, under the supervision of a manager and a steward.

The current generation, in their turn, decided to manage Mariënwaerdt in yet another way. We started with a small dairy farm, after which four tenants quickly decided to surrender their farms. As a consequence our enterprise expanded extensively. Together with the fruit and arable crop production, we took up the daily management of other agricultural activities on Mariënwaerdt, not out of necessity but out of love for and belief in Mariënwaerdt. We believed that unity in management would benefit the conservation of the estate.

From 1995 onwards, the management changed once more, again not out of necessity but because we thought it would be a challenge to sell the products of Mariënwaerdt directly to our customers. We opened the Estate Shop ("de Landgoedwinkel"), started with the production of delicacies and the organisation of the Estate Fair ("de Landgoedfair"). Looking back, these developments have proved to be necessary as well, to be able to survive with an estate in these changing and challenging times. The first of the next generation have started, in their own way, to manage the estate.

What are the main lessons to draw from all of this? Above all it should be noted that the entrepreneurship on Mariënwaerdt is integral to our well-being. We love living on the estate and would deeply regret it if we were to leave it because of a job in the city. We have taken advantage of the opportunities to make a business out of Mariënwaerdt, driven by the feeling that we would be able to contribute to the well-being of our customers whenever they visit our estate. Whenever they come, they step into another world and experience what it is to be part of rural life, be it for a short moment. They can escape from their daily routines and they can go back to basics. We are convinced that the creation of new concepts, the courage of actually developing them and the hard work towards achieving them with heart and soul,

The van Verschuer family.

are the keys to success. In this ever-changing society you cannot afford to sit back and to just continue doing what you have always been doing. An estate is a treasure, with great historic and natural value. It is an art to conserve it by means of income from the estate itself but without damaging it. We are always searching for the balance between economic growth on the one hand and the preservation of the core values of Mariënwaerdt on the other. As my father likes to say: "I want my father to be able to recognise Mariënwaerdt if he were to stand up in his grave!"

We believe that the direct involvement of the family is essential to find this balance. Nobody else is as connected to the estate as the family is. An external party would maybe let the economic value prevail over the preservation of the historic values. Or, on the contrary, he would over-emphasise the aspect of nature conservation. Only the family can bear the responsibility of permanently dealing with the estate and its work. Our employees are definitely very involved, but do not share the rooted feelings we have. For us this is not a burden, but a part of our lives.

And to answer the question many people ask us: yes, we still have many plans and dreams!

Family Mariënwaerdt Vision

Mariënwaerdt Estate

HEERLIJKHEID MARIËNWAERDT ESTATE BELONGS TO:

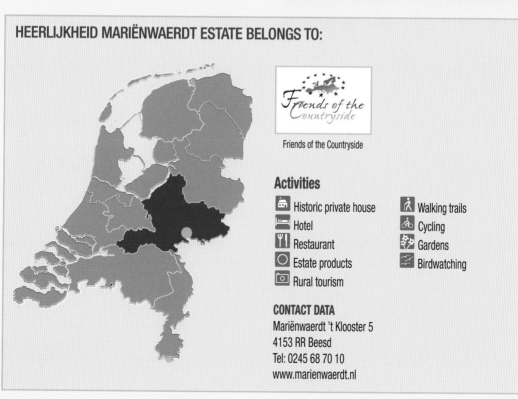

Friends of the Countryside

Activities

- 🏠 Historic private house
- 🛏 Hotel
- 🍴 Restaurant
- Ⓞ Estate products
- 📷 Rural tourism

- 🚶 Walking trails
- 🚲 Cycling
- Gardens
- Birdwatching

CONTACT DATA

Mariënwaerdt 't Klooster 5
4153 RR Beesd
Tel: 0245 68 70 10
www.marienwaerdt.nl

Isola dei Cipressi

Continental

Location: Lake Pusiano, Italy.
Surface: 2 ha.

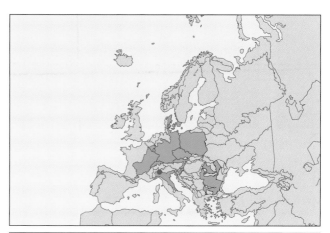

CLIMATIC DATA

Average rainfall
mm/cm²/year

Snow days: 7

1.000 mm

Temperature (ºC)

35,0 — max ■
15 — average ■
-5,0 — min ■

SUMMARY

Isola dei Cipressi Island is a natural 13 m high hill island, which, originally pointed, was enhanced in Medieval times by the addition of two great walls, that circle the peak to form a small plateau or embankment. The hill extends for approximately 18,000 sq m.

The northern slope and the eastern point of the hill are covered with woodlands. The rest is grass; but the entire circumference of the oval-shape island is made up of tress. The configuration and the vegetation of the island, therefore, allow the buildings and grassland to remain hidden from view, creating a sense of secrecy, a safe and precious hideaway. The island, in fact, appears very wild from far off, and also from the shores of the lakes, since all that can be seen is the dense, lush vegetation which gives the island the appearance of a huge, floating mass, a kind of sailing vessel on the peaceful waters of Pusiano. Pusiano Lake has a surface of 5,25 Km².

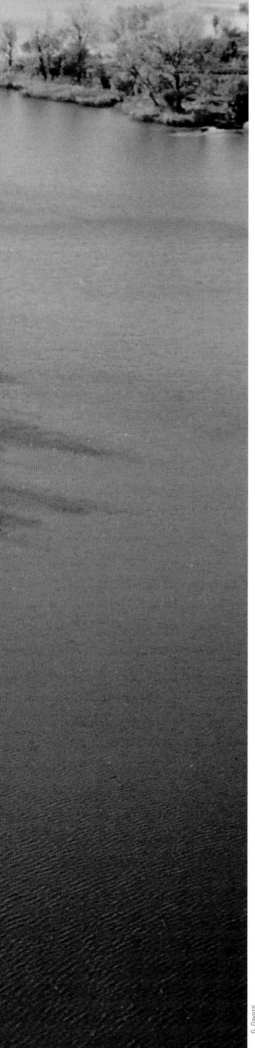

Aerial view of Isola dei Cipressi on Pusiano Lake.

G. Gavazzi

Antonio (right) and Egidio Gavazzi (below). The two bachelor brothers and silk industrialists of Valmadrera bought the property of Cypress Island and certain rights to the lake in 1877. Antonio and Egidio had an elder brother, Pietro, who married Ernestina Pascal, believed to be the natural daughter of Viceroy Eugene of Beauharnais, who had been the lover of Ernestina's mother.

G. Gavazzi

HISTORY

Both the island and the lake have always been owned by private nobility and there is an ancient history.

Prehistory

The island boasts an ancient history, dating back as far as the Neolithic period, approximately 10,000 years B.C. On the easternmost point were lake dwellings; moreover, it is still possible today to find stone axe-heads and flint tools left behind by prehistoric islanders.

The earliest building on the island dates from medieval times.

G. Gavazzi

During the last century, the remains of the lake dwellings were still present in abundance: tips of piles, buried in the lakebed, could still be seen, and the earth concealed innumerable carved flints.

Today no lake-dwellings remain visible; only by underwater exploration is it possible to glimpse small fragments sticking up from the lake bed.

The lake-dwellings, therefore, must also have been present in the Bronze Age (approximately 2200-1500 B.C).

From the Middle Ages to the 18th century

The history of the island is bound both to that of lake and to its succession of owners – the great landowning families of the area.

The lake and the island were privately owned until they were decreed public waters on May 5, 1922. Fishing, hunting, sailing and water deviation rights appeared always to be part of the property, and were separately leased out by the owner of the lake. In 1314 the Archbishop of Milan owned two thirds of the lake and the Island; the Collegiate of San Giovanni Battista of Monza owned the remaining third.

Later on, the ancient and important family of Carpani, previously counts and later marquises, were for centuries the landowners of the Plain of Erba.

They held the possession (originally by lease from the mentioned Curias, then as ownership), they held the ownership of Lake Pusiano and Cypress Island for around three centuries (from 1483 to 1765). During this period, the island was called Carpani Island on certain maps, and some notable events took place:

- *Notificatio in causa usurpationis:* Beginning from 1645, a dispute arises between the tax office and the Carpani family concerning the exemption of taxes regarding their ownership of Lake Pusiano. The dispute continues for years, until 1650 the private ownership of Lake Pusiano is finally recognized – it is defined as allodial land, and as such remains free of obligations and taxes.
- *Delictum fuit commissum:* On April 28, 1648 Andrea Carpani committed murder and was condemned to death. In consequence, his property was confiscated.
- In 1765 Marquis Francesco Carpani – a famous economist of the Dukedom of Milan,

and rival of Beccaria and of Alessandro and Pietro Verri – the last descendent of the Marquis branch of the Carpani family, passed on his entire estate (including the House at Pusiano, the lake and the island) to his niece Countess Marianna Grassi (daughter of his sister Gioseffa Carpani and Count Grassi). This transfer took place at the time of the wedding between Marianna Grassi and Marquis Giuseppe Antonio Molo. In exchange Francesco Carpani, later to pass away in 1777, received from his nephew and niece a life annuity and the payment of many of his debts.

- *Fishing in the lake:* Fishing was the object of special attention, both from private citizens and from the authorities. The Carpani brothers obtained numerous edits.

In around 1770 Marquis Molo, having magnificently restored the manor house of Pusiano, went on to make further improvements on the island, including the planting of cypress trees (along with poplars and willows). Apparently, however, in the early 1800s these trees, now ancient and noble, were felled, "profaned under the axe of greed".

These trees had probably stood since Medieval times, since even then the island is recorded to have been called "Cypress and Olive Island".

On March 5, 1785 Marquis Molo purchased the part pertaining to his wife and became the sole owner of the lake of Pusiano.

The manor house of Pusiano, the lake with Cypress Island and all that came with them were then leased out to Archduke Ferdinand of Hapsburg, Viceroy who married in Milan Maria Beatrice d'Este.

From 1785 to 1817

In 1805, all the property belonging to Marquis Giuseppe Antonio Molo, including the island, was sold by public auction to the Milanese marquis Gerolamo d'Adda, husband of noblewoman Felicina Meda.

In 1812 the Administration Fund of the Kingdom of Italy purchased the entire estate, and added it to the property given in apanage to the Viceroy of Italy, Prince Eugene Beauharnais.

In 1817 all the property of Pusiano, including the island, were transferred from Viceroy Eugene to the Royal Demesne, in other words, to the Hapsburg-Lorena Emperor.

Prince Eugene Beauharnais, Viceroy of Italy, who lived on the Island.

The 1800s

From 1817 to 1831 the manor house, the lake and the island belonged to the new Vice-regal family, which consisted, in 1818, of Viceroy Ranieri of Habsburg, Vicereine Elisabetta (born Princess of Savoy-Carignano and sister of Carlo Alberto, King of Sardinia) and their children.

The important events of this period were that the first steam boat in Italy was tested on the Lake of Pusiano, in 1820.

In 1831 the banking firm Pietro and the Marietti brothers (owners also of Villa Amalia in Erba) bought the lake of Pusiano and Cypress Island at public auction.

In 1864 the whole estate was made over to Ferdinando and Pietro Conti and to Pietro Gonzales.

On March 22, 1869 the estate was transferred to the Bosisio Town Council.

In 1874 the lake, the island and the property belonging to the island (wet docks, Diotti lock, etc.) were purchased by Antonio and Egidio Gavazzi, two rich unmarried brothers from the silk industry of Valmadrera.

From 1900s

In 1920 the lake and the island became the property of the State, but the rights to sail and fish were given to the Pusiano Lake Association, while the rights to shoot and sail for private use were given to the Island's owners.

Archduke Ranieri Giuseppe.

Winter concentrations of ducks on Pusiano Lake are very important, with many hundreds of individuals, mainly Mallard *(Anas platyrhynchos)*, Gadwall *(Anas strepera)*, Common Pochard *(Aythya ferina)* and Common Teal *(Anas crecca)*.

J.L. Rodriguez

DESCRIPTION

Isola dei Cipressi Island is situated in the central northwest part of Pusiano Lake. It extends for almost 2 hectares and forms a hill of 13 metres high.

Lake Pusiano, or Eupili, as it was called in Roman times, is a pre-Alpine lake set among the hills of the moraine amphitheatre of Brianza, at an altitude of 285 metres and with an area of 5,25 sq. km.

The river Lambro is both the river flowing from the lake and also, its tributary.

Flora and Fauna

Appealing and charming as Cypress Island is to man, it is undoubtedly at least as popular with wildlife. It is, in fact, a favorite haunt of birds, which obviously find it easiest to reach. It is not uncommon to see rare species, which are probably present in other parts of the territory also, but are easier to spot on the island.

In full show and in great quantities are water birds and marsh birds, which use the expanse of water and the reed beds for food and reproduction. Ducks, in particular, especially Mallard *(Anas platyrhynchos)*, Teal *(Anas crecca crecca)*, Gadwall

(Anas strepera), and divers such as Pochard *(Aythya ferina)* and Tufted Duck *(Aythya fuligula)*, along with Coots *(Fulica atra)* and grebes, may reach concentrations of over a thousand birds during the winter season.

Wrens *(Regulus regulus)* and Tits *(Parus caeruleus)* are also abundant on the island, and the kingfisher is not a rare visitor.

The reeds around the island are especially important for the wintering of the Bittern *(Botaurus stellaris)* and the Grey Heron *(Ardea cinerea)*, and every year a great colony of around 300 Cormorants *(Phalacrocorax auritus)* settles on the island for the winter (the tall Oaks *(Quercus ssp.)*, in fact, are now almost completely white with the guano of these birds).

The reeds are ideal nesting places for great reed warblers, marsh warblers and reed buntings.

The lake itself is especially rich in fish around the island, thanks to the tall tress which, now and then, brought down by strong winds or old age, fall into the water, creating a perfect habitat for the fish to feed and reproduce.

The fish are typically shallow-water fish, due to the limited depth of the lake (30 metres max.), and their species are determined by the quality of the water. The main species are Perch *(Perca fluviatilis)*, Tench *(Tinca tinca)*, Roach *(Gobio* sp.*)*, Chub *(Leuciscus cephalus)*, Pike *(Esox lucius)*, Large-mouthed Black Bass *(Micropterus salmoides)* etc...

Crayfish *(Austropotamobius pallipes)* are also found.

The plateau

In past years, the contours of the island were rendered more graceful by leveling the hilltop, which was probably pointed, to create a "plateau" with the construction of the wall referred to earlier.

The plateau, long and narrow and stretching from east to west, consists of grassland surrounded by rows of cypress trees planted parallel to the longitudinal walls. In one corner to the west, encircled by a crown of cypresses, is an octagonal shaped stone table with stone seats, frequently mentioned in the ancient descriptions of Cypress Island.

This is a truly enchanting place, and the highest point of the island, which offers a wonderful view southward over the lake.

The fish depository

As we mentioned earlier, in the first half of the 1800s Giuseppe Conti, the new owner of the island and the Beauharnais Manor House, trans-

formed the whole estate for the sole purpose of gaining financial profit. The House of Pusiano was thus debased by the opening of a spinning factory within its walls, and on the island a "fish depository" was constructed.

This consists of a canal cut in the rock and crossing the entire width of the eastern side of the island; it is 41 metres long, 1.5 metres wide and reaches an average depth of 1.6 metres. The two parts of the islands, thus separated, are connected by three small bridges.

The purpose of this painstaking work was to make it possible to store live fish which, after being caught in the lake, were transferred to the canal (closed at both ends with gratings) until ready to be sold.

The ice-house

One of the few remaining ancient ice-houses in Italy is found on the island. Still well-preserved, this peculiar building consists of a single room, a few square metres wide but very high, dug into the hill and accessed by means of a steep flight of steps, dark and narrow, which descend deep into the earth.

During the winter months, snow was packed into the room through a trapdoor at the top, and the pressure transformed it into ice. In this way, the ice was preserved until the warm season, guaranteeing the inhabitants of the islands the

The Reed Bunting *(Emberiza schoeniclus)* breeds in Central and Northern Europe. It is seen in winter in the south of Europe.

J.L. Rodríguez

benefits of a modern refrigerator (although, in those days, the ice was used mainly for the storage of fish and game).

This system was already in use as far back as Roman times.

The ice-rooms in the Brianza lake district were also fed with blocks of ice cut from the lake surfaces, alternated with layers of straw which served as thermal insulation. In this case, however, it is not feasible that such a system would have been used, as when the lake freezes (which generally happens first in the northern part, between the island and the northern shore) the island itself becomes inaccessible.

The houses

On the island there are a few small buildings and a small cottage, built in a style rather resembling that of the mountain chalets.

Apart from insignificant little brick constructions used as storage places for farm equipment, such as woodsheds, hen-houses, etc., the more "historical" buildings are those of the house and the annex.

The annex is the most ancient of the buildings, probably dating back to the 18th century or earlier; it consists of one single room with a large fireplace, and a bathroom with running water brought up from the lake by means of an electric pump. Originally built to store farm or fishing equipment, it is believed to have been the "niche" of Prince Eugene of Beauharnais.

The walls of this little building are completely covered with reeds from the lake, which serve as an effective insulation against the heat of summer and the cold of winter, and give it a very charming appearance.

The annex stands on the narrow side of the hill, on a level half-way between the lake and the hilltop, facing east.

The cottage, meanwhile was built in three stages.

It is believed that, at the beginning of the 19th Century, the original structure probably resembled the annex described above.

Later, in 1897, an upper floor was added to this structure. The result was most likely a small house with architecture typical of the Brianza region, very plain and sober with a whitewashed border around the doors and windows.

Still legible on this part of the house, facing east, is the date of construction, 1897.

Around the 1930s, a tenant of the island, a certain Mr. Hennsler, took it upon himself to make extensions to the house. This new part is typically Tyrolese in architecture, but blends extremely well with the previous style, and the resulting building as a whole is quite charming.

Since then, no other changes have been made to the house, which still consists of an entrance hall, living room, dining room and kitchen on the ground floor, and one large and two smaller bedrooms with a bathroom on the upper floor.

The house is situated on the same level as the previous building, but on the longer slope of the hill, facing south.

Electricity and telephone wires were not brought to the island until the 1960s.

Until then, paraffin lamps were used and bath water was heated by means of a special wood stove. Today, heating still depends on the use of fireplaces and an ancient wood stove.

Isola dei Cipressi.

G. Gavazzi

A LANDSCAPE WITH INSPIRATION

The young captain stood and watched as the boat sailed away towards the land, visible within shooting distance; the three trusted hussars headed for the landing place, where just a few steps away the horses were resting at the mill.

He was alone, finally!. Alone on the little island where he was to stay the night, under the hut behind the embankment.

Viceroy Eugene had given him leave, accompanying him as far as the gate of Villa at Pusiano.

The sun had gone down behind the mountains of Erba, and the air was vibrant with the romantic, late-summer sunset. The water of the lake, also, stirred by the evening breezes, rippled brightly in the moonlight.

A warm silence reigned over the whole landscape on both sides of the water and on the mountains, already shrouded in darkness.

The officer turned suddenly, as if beckoned, and headed towards the hut. Pushing aside the tall reeds which, together with a few willow trees, were all the vegetation the little island held, he reached the top of the embankment in moments and looked around him. In the gentle breeze, the water appeared to be pulled by a current and the island floated, without sail, towards a vain destination.

The officer pushed open door of the hut and cast a quick and approving eye over the wicker chairs, the table laden with flowers and the brightly-coloured mats, strewn randomly on the floors. Out of the little window, the jagged peaks of Mount Resegone stood out against the darkening sky.

The captain of the hussars unfastened his great belt, stood his sabre in the corner, took off his heavy headgear and quickly slipped off his jacket, richly decorated and clinking with medals.

With the air of a thoroughbred he shook his raven-black locks, looked once more through the window at the quiet face of the moon and then ran outside and down to the beach where a boat waited, rocking on the water.

Once on board and armed with oars, he heated towards the great shadows and little lights of Pusiano...

The boat sailed gently in, sliding onto the beach which rose up towards the small wall of a garden; concealed beneath a carpet of trailing plants was a little stone staircase. There was a rustle of silk,

G. Gavazzi

A warm silence covers the whole landscape on both sides of the water and on the mountains, already shrouded in darkness.

and there suddenly, silhouetted in the moonlight, appeared the figure of a woman. With one short, agile jump, she was on board.

The officer rowed out onto the lake once more, and headed back towards the little island. Not a word was spoken or a gesture made until they sailed into the bay and the oars were at last put down... how long then the two embraced silently in the moonlight!

"Oh, Renato, how I love this private little kingdom of ours".

"It will be yours always; I shall always wait for you here".

"Always! If only it would last, this ´always´!"

"Longer that life, Silvana, it will last. I feel that my promise will pledge me beyond my will itself, so great is the love that binds me to you, my divine beauty! Wars and great changes will count for nothing... The Faubard d´Etange family has an ancient tradition in Burgundy, and it shall be respected in Italy. I will stay here and wait for you always; do you understand me, Silvana? Always!".

At the foot of the willow tree, in a hole he had dug earlier, Renato placed a small metal box and covered it over with earth.

"Here we will come to renew the pledge of love that is written on the papers and in our hearts. Always!".

Always... The word was carried away on the wind, beyond the hut, beyond the island, until it was caught in the reeds of the lake and never ventured further.

Isola dei Cipressi (Italy)

The years marched on, and wars came and went; kings and viceroys passed away and others arose on the horizon.

Silvana herself was also blown away by life, to where , who knows...

Yet Renato remained true to his pledge and his dream.

The little island became his own; he planted a double festoon of young cypresses, like a call, a cry of love...

And every year he returned to wait, always, futilely. Beneath the willow, next to the hut, the little metal box was still there, with the vain pledge closed inside.

The tops of the cypresses had grown luxuriously over the years, and rose up to the sky like the masts of a motionless ship, anchored to hope and waiting faithfully.

One last time, the old hussar returned from the land of France, dug up the old box and on the fragment of paper inside he added a few lines. These were his last words of farewell. He would never again return, because in a little cemetery in Burgundy the name of Renato Faubard d'Etange was now engraved on a cross.

One day, however, an old lady in crinoline, accompanied by her servant, arrived on the island and, indicating with her parasol, she told the servant to dig in the spot where a scrap of paper lay folded inside a little metal tin. On this paper, now yellow with age, the old lady saw through her lorgnette that a few lines had been added at the foot of the vain promise:

"I know you will return, one day – I myself shall then be lying beneath the soil of Burgundy, But my promise is alive among the leafy branches of the cypresses that greet you. Listen to them. They too have learned to whisper «Always»".

(From "Ul Tivan", Como, 1951)

The sun had gone down behind the mountains of Erba, and the air was vibrant with the romantic, late-summer sunset.

G. Gavazzi

On the island is a small cottage built in a style that resembles a mountain chalet in the Adige valley.

G. Gavazzi

ISOLA DEI CIPRESSI BELONGS TO:

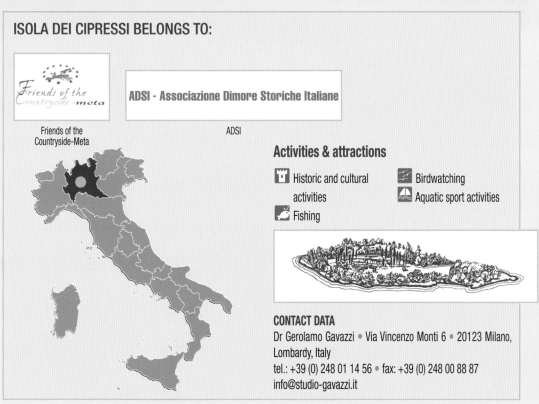

Friends of the Countryside-meta

Friends of the Countryside-Meta

ADSI - Associazione Dimore Storiche Italiane

ADSI

Activities & attractions

Historic and cultural activities

Fishing

Birdwatching

Aquatic sport activities

CONTACT DATA
Dr Gerolamo Gavazzi • Via Vincenzo Monti 6 • 20123 Milano, Lombardy, Italy
tel.: +39 (0) 248 01 14 56 • fax: +39 (0) 248 00 88 87
info@studio-gavazzi.it

Kullo Gård Estate

Kullo Gård

Boreal

Location: Borgå municipality, region of Ost-Nyland, Finland.
Surface: 650 ha.

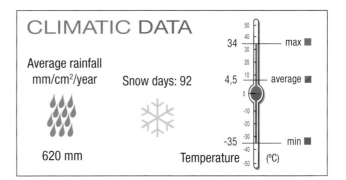

CLIMATIC DATA

Average rainfall
mm/cm²/year

Snow days: 92

620 mm

Temperature (ºC)

34 — max
4,5 — average
-35 — min

SUMMARY

Kullo Gård Estate is situated on the south coast of Finland, 10 kilometres west of the town of Borgå and 40 kilometres east of the capital, Helsinki. The history of the manor goes back to 1613 when the king Gustavus Adolphus II donated five holdings, which formed the start of what today is Kullo Gård.
Kullo Gård Estate is characterized by a "moving family working business". Apart from agriculture and forestry, the estate is a multi-functional farm with many different core activities such as golf, quarrying, shops, real estate and tourism. It is well kept and offers the prospect of stable long-term survival.

Kullo Gård Estate is a multifunctional farm with many core activities such as agriculture, forestry, golf, quarrying, shops, real estate and tourism.

The Frankenhaeuser family and the Shop Manager in the Kullo Gård Farm Shop.

Kullo Gård Estate

HISTORY

The present owner's family came from Schwanensee in Germany, when Carl Friedrich Christoff Frankenhaeuser arrived in the Swedish town of Wiborg in 1798.

Wiborg, situated at the eastern end of the Gulf of Finland, was a multilingual merchant town where German, Swedish, Russian, Finnish and French were frequently spoken. The administrative language however was Swedish. In 1809, Sweden lost Finland, and Wiborg, to Russia.

At the Diet of Borgå of 29th March 1809 which followed the Swedish defeat, and by the signing of the treaty of Fredrikshamn in September 1809, Finland became a true autonomous Grand Duchy as a part of the Russian Empire. The Russian Emperor, Alexander I of Russia, who ruled Finland as the Grand Duke of Finland then declared Finland to be elevated into a Nation among Nations. For 85 years, until 1898, Finland enjoyed a high degree of independence, with its own legislation, The Diet of Finland, its own senate and universities and its own languages, Swedish and Finnish. The Grand Duke of Finland was represented by the Governor-General of Finland, who resided in Helsinki.

In the 1899, the new Russian General-Governor in Helsinki, General Bobrikov, started the 20

years of attempted 'russification' of Finland and the Finnish people. This was heavily opposed by several groups in Finland. The young Carl Konstantin Frankenhaeuser moved from Wiborg to Helsinki where he studied to become an architect.

In 1910 he married Hanna Åström, and together they bought Kullo Gård from General Harald Åkerman.

The young couple were highly active in the underground fight against russification, financing the opposition and spreading propaganda brochures and imported weapons. Today one would certainly call them terrorists, because of their opposition to the legal Russian authorities through underground, even armed force. When the Bolshevik revolution took place in the motherland of Russia, Finland fell into civil war. The Reds wanted to join the new socialist Russia and the Whites fought for independence. Being better armed and organised the Whites won, and Finland was declared independent on 6th December 1917. From this date on we can find visitors' books in Kullo Gård.

The estate then consisted of 1300 ha, and from 1910 to 1912 began to produce milk in new dairies; there were also horse stables on three different sites. The estate was at that time run as three "profit centres".

In 1914 a new Corps de Logis, the main central part of the house, taken from drawings by the owner Carl Frankenhaeuser and done in white chalk-plastered brick, replaced the previous wooden one from 1798.. Interior details such as doors were taken from the old Corps de Logis and reused in the new one.

Before the end of World War II, the ownership was transferred to Carl's children, a daughter and four sons. Fifty per cent, the biggest share, was given to the daughter for political reasons.

In 1945, after World War II, Kullo Gård, like all of the larger estates in Finland, had to hand over land to the refugees from the land annexed by the Soviet Union. Because half of Kullo Gård then was owned by Cilla Johnsson (born Frankenhaeuser), a Swedish citizen, and because Kullo Gård was situated in a Swedish speaking area, only 11 plots (50 ha) were forcibly allocated to the refugees. The new inhabitants were fishermen from Tytärsaar island

The typical red buildings reflect the historical heritage of 1700-1800.

in the eastern part of the Gulf of Finland. Today these plots are mainly used as summer houses for their present owners. Because it was considered that giving away only 50 hectares was too little, Kullo Gård also financed clearances of new farmland in central Finland, which was successfully handed over as new home land to the farming refugees from the now Russian Karelia.

On behalf of the owners, the estate was managed by Carl's eldest son A.F.M. Hemming Frankenhaeuser, The brothers, who together had bought their sister's 50% share, passed their ownership to their own children in 1973. The ownership of Kullo Gård was now divided into small holding shares of between 4 to 15% each.

Hemming's eldest son, F.M Thomas, started to buy the shares in 1983. By 1993 he owned the main part of the estate with only minor parts still in co-ownership. The estate was its biggest since the 1930s and could again be managed by simple decision making without the conflicts of interest induced by complicated co-ownership.

In 2009 the main part of the estate was transferred to Thomas' son Jakob, who took over the management of the estate and still manages it today.

Kullo Manor is located near the town of Borgå, 40 km east of Helsinki.

The valley of Kullo Gård with golf, sweetcorn, red wooden buildings and its Corps de Logis.

Kullo Gård Estate

DESCRIPTION

A multifunctional farm and its infrastructure

Kullo Manor is situated on the south coast of Finland near the town of Borgå, 40 km east of the capital Helsinki. The estate covers 650 hectares of which 350 ha are forest, 100 ha are sundry land and 200 ha are arable land.

The farming is strongly affected by the split allocation of the fields in this typical southern Finnish coastal farmland, where comparatively small arable fields of irregular shape (average 5 ha) are mixed with rocky forest land. The soil is mainly clay to heavy clay, and drilling at the correct moment is critical because of the regular spring drought which often continues until mid June. This beautiful farm lies next to the biggest concentration of petrochemical plants in Scandinavia.

Through the estate run a four lane motorway, two highways, a railway, a main high voltage power line (and several smaller ones) and two gas pipelines. The construction of a new highway will start in 2010, and a railway and an oil pipeline are being planned. There are also plans to construct a new airport immediately north of the estate.

The private internal roads consist of two tarmac roads of 2.3 km, and 10 km of track leading from the main roads to the different houses. In addition to that there are a further 5 km of track specifically serving the forestry.

All this sets special demands on the planning and development of the estate in order to maintain the required green values and at the same time make use of the considerable development in the immediate surroundings.

The centre of the estate

The centre of the estate is situated on a rocky hill above the creek, and with views over the golf course and the fields of sweetcorn and strawberries. The main historic and cultural values are to be found in the concentration of preserved red-painted small wooden houses from the 18th/19th centuries.

The centre of the estate, combined with the valley below, is listed as a Cultural Monument of national value.

Landscape & Nature

There is an enormous variation in the landscape in different parts of the estate. It varies from

Typical 18th century red wooden buildings dominate the centre of the estate.

Kullo Gård Estate

In 2003 an 18 hole golf course was opened.

completely natural Natura 2000 wetland, forest land, normally cultivated arable land, man-made parkland (the golf course) and housing (both permanent residences as well as holiday homes), to rock crushing sites and industrial activities.

The Golf Course

In 2003 an 18 hole golf course was opened. Kullo Golf, with its corresponding Golf Academy, driving range and clubhouse, was 30% built on farm land and 70% on forest land. The golf course is designed to flow naturally through the landscape in wide circles, where you rarely meet other golfers and where the area of ground used is maximised. This of course uses more land than is needed (72ha) but it provides the opportunity in the future for building housing for golfers if so wanted. The golf course creates beautiful parkland around the centre of the estate.

Wetlands and Natura 2000

Out of a total of 80 ha of wetland, approximately 58 ha is a designated Natura 2000 site. The wetland consists of a deep layer of peat which averages 4 m in depth and is still growing. Of the peat 40% is of Spaghnum type, with 45% Acutifolia, 15% Palustria and 45% Cuspidata with a decomposition grade of 3.2 out of 10.

In the Natura 2000 decision, special account was taken of some rare butterflies present on this estate. The Natura 2000 site was established by the owners voluntarily, because of a threat from the environmental authorities that they would otherwise expropriate the land.

Originally the Natura 2000 decision was opposed by the town authorities, by the neighbouring petrochemical industry, and by the owner. The wetland is bordered by the big petrochemical site. A railway station for petrochemical products passes through it and a new highway is also due to be built across it. The unprotected part of the wetland is planned to be developed as an industrial storage area.

People are allowed (by "Every Man's Right") to walk and pick berries and mushrooms on the Natura 2000 site. For the landowner normal hunting is allowed. Otherwise the land has to be left untouched.

The golf course creates beautiful parkland around the centre of the estate.

Kullo Gård **(Finland)**

Kullo Gård Estate

Even if the Natura 2000 site removed some economic value (exploitable peat), it is positive for the image of the estate to have the Natura 2000 site included in the land use.

Creek, Dams and Ponds

This Natura 2000 site is a part of a bigger wetland from which a creek of 7 km length runs through the estate out to the Gulf of Finland.

On the estate three dams have been built in the creek to increase the water level, which the dams do by about 1.3 m each. These dams create sedimentation ponds, sites for wetland birds, and a source of irrigation water for farming.

The dams have been built so that they would promote the natural breeding of trout. Although the estate lies immediately on the Gulf of Finland, it only has a very short coastline of its own, with only one house located on the sea front.

Stone Exploitation and Rock Crushing

Another use of land is the exploitation of granite rock on some 24 ha, for the production of gravel. After the rock has been used, the site will be planned for industrial purposes. This site is situated about 4 km from the centre of the estate, and combines well with the intentions of the planning department of the community. In this area more land will be planned for industrial activities in the future. Here a new main road, which will serve the petrochemical and other industrial activities, is to be built in 2010-11.

ECONOMIC ACTIVITIES

Farmland & Agriculture

Since 2009 the farmed arable land has been worked as a separate activity, in cooperation with a neighbouring farm. In this cooperation Kullo Gård represents one-third and the other farm two-thirds of a total of 550 ha of arable land. The production in 2009 consisted of rye (27 ha), malting barley (120 ha), spring wheat (160 ha), rapeseed (80 ha), hay for horses (65 ha), nature conservation fields (70 ha) and water protection zones (27 ha). The goal is to rationalise bulk production and field operations, in order to (if at all possible in Finland) have a profitable production by 2015. The small size of Finnish farming estates is well shown by the fact that this farming activity of 550 ha is the tenth biggest in Finland. The goal is to increase the farmed area by leasing in more land.

Since 1995 when Finland joined the EU, there has been a production of sweetcorn (corn-on-the-cob) and strawberries mainly for self picking or Pick Your Own. As public interest in the self picking is declining, these activities will probably be shut down.

606

CROP PRODUCTION

Forest Type	Species	Average Yearly Growth of Pine
• OMT	Oxalis-Myrtillus-Type	7 m³/ha/year
• MT	Myrtillus-Type	6.5 m³/ha/year
• VT	Vaccinium-Type	5 m³/ha/year
• CT	Calluna-Type	3 m³/ha/year

Forest Management Plan for Kullo Gård Estate

The Forest Management Plan is set for a 10 year period (2009-2018), with a prognosis for the following 10 years.

The total forest land is 350 ha, including forest roads of 7 ha, and other land use (rock crushing) of 28 ha. In addition to this there are 80 ha of wetland, out of which 58 ha is a protected Natura 2000 area. In the action plan the forest is described in 275 stands or compartments for which different actions are recommended.

Of the forest land 81% is actual growing forest and 17% rocky scrubland with poor growth. The fertility is 6% OMT, 66% MT, 23% VT and 4% CT. The pine represents 42%, Norway spruce 30%, birch 23% and other broadleaf 5% of the standing stock. The average standing stock on forest land is 110 m³/ha. The growth is carefully estimated to be 4.6 m³ per ha, and the recommended felling 3.4 m³/ ha, that is 1200 m³ yearly.

Forestry in Finland

Finland is the most heavily forested country in Europe, two-thirds of the country being forest.

The fertility or production capacity for a specific forest stand compartment is classified using the botanical appearance, i.e. it is based on the typical species growing on the ground. The forest types are named after the Latin names of the typical plants growing on the ground of the compartment. This way the forest type, and a rough theoretical production capacity, can be determined very easily, by a quick look at what is growing on the ground, independently of what the actual tree growing situation is.

Forestry activities in Finland are regulated by the Forest Act of 1927. The basic principle is that a Forest Owner (FO) is not allowed to devastate or destroy forest and that good forestry management principles should be observed.

The good management principles are based on Periodic Cover Silviculture, with rotation periods in southern Finland of 60-80 years. The rotation period

ends in a regeneration felling, which is considered to be the start of forest regeneration. After the regeneration felling, new forest has to be established, either by planting or by natural seeding. The establishment of the new seedlings is then secured by a series of measures, such as cleaning, clearing and 2-3 consecutive thinnings, where you always leave the best trees and take away unnecessary seedlings or those that will cause the quality to deteriorate.

Two weeks before work in the forest is started, the FO has to deliver a *Notification of Forest Use* to the forest authorities.

This also means that so-called Continuous Forest Growth using the Selection Cutting method, where you remove only the largest trees from the

Red squirrel in Kullo Gård.

Mr. Ove on the timber pile. Finland is the most heavily forested country in Europe.

forest, is not accepted in our forests, where pine, Norway spruce and birch are the main species. The reason is that under continuous growth system, the biggest and best individuals are removed, leaving behind the less good individuals, which could lead to deterioration and decline of the genetic stock in the forest. Pictures and inventories made in early 1900s show extremely bad looking forests, with very low forestry value. The result of the new 1927 legislation principles, under which you let the best trees grow until a regeneration felling is made in order to establish new forest, is that the standing stock in the forests of Finland is bigger today than it ever has been and at the same time the volume harvested each year is bigger than ever. So during the last 80 years CO_2 sequestration has increased a huge amount due to increased forest growth.

In the Regeneration Felling, groups of Retention Trees also have to be left in order to increase the biodiversity.

Forest Owners Association (FOA) and Forestry Management

In the southern coastal part of Finland the FOA (Forest Owners Association) has been working for more than 70 years, with the aim of helping the Forest Owner to implement the activities required in his forest. The FOA is 100% owned by the FOs.

The FOA of which the estate of Kullo Gård is a member, Södra Skogsreviret, is active on the south coast of Finland and has 6,700 members with a total forest area of 225,000 ha.

The FOA handles all the necessary activities in the forest on behalf of the FO, namely soil preparation (mounding, harrowing), planting, clearing, thinning and final harvesting by the Nordic cut-to-length system.

On behalf of the Forest Owner, the FOA also handles the sales of the forest products to the saw mills and to the pulp and paper industries. If necessary, forest products are exported by the FO-owned export companies. The work in Södra Skogsreviret is done by employing some 45 entrepreneurs, using the latest technology of highly computerized forest harvesters and logging machines. The FOA also employs 75 forest workers, and some 50 instructors and administrators.

Forest residues for Bio-Energy production

The FOA is highly active in utilising forest residues for the production of bio-energy and the FOA now supplies several plants with forest fuel for heat production. As a result of a bio-energy project in 2008/09 there are now bio-energy plants built with a total effect of 28.5 MW. This means that the total forest residue used for energy

Retrieval of forest residues for Bio-Energy.

Kullo Gård Estate

has grown from a few thousand cubic metres 10 years ago to 250,000 lm3 in 2009. An important part of the residues comes from utilising the stumps in the final clear cuttings.

PEFC Certification

In 2004 the FOA decided to join the Finnish Forest Certification System, FFCS, which is a part of the PEFC Forest Certification system employed in Finland. The certification is voluntary for the FOs, but in the last certification period almost all the FO members (99.9%) of the FOA where certified by using the expertise and help of the FOA. The certification costs were covered by the FOA, so this was a very favourable way for the FO to get PEFC certification. Under the forestry laws a dozen key biotopes (springs, hills, brooks, small ponds, fertile swamps, brown peat, small groves, woodland islands in fields, gorges and precipices, sand fields, stone block fields, scarcely wooded peat land, flooded meadows) are protected which means that normal forestry is not applied. In the FFCS certification 24 habitats are recommended for protection.

Tourist attractions

Kullo Golf Club: (18 holes surrounding the private Manor)

A club house was erected in 2003 to receive shareholders and golf club members.

The clubhouse contains a 110 seat restaurant for members and guests, and, rather less common in a Golf Club, a 32 seat Fine Dining restaurant with ambitions to achieve Michelin recognition.

Real Estate

In addition to the Manor house, there are twelve houses suitable for year-round residence or for rural tourism. These small houses of about 60 to 100 square metres each, built between 1770 and 1930, were used to accommodate farm workers and their families until 1975. Normally, the houses did not include modern heating and other facilities apart from electricity, which was first introduced in 1910.

There is a total of forty-five buildings.

Since 1990, an average of one house every second year has been restored and refurbished, following traditional interior and exterior architec-

Kullo Gård Estate

ture and retaining the old atmosphere and materials.

Thanks to the proximity of Helsinki, demand for both year-round and holiday houses is increasing.

Activities on the estate are easy to market because the estate is well known after ten years of pick-your-own strawberries and sweetcorn.

The Farm Shop

Old traditional farm buildings beside the Manor have been restored for aesthetic and cultural purposes and the main Corps de Logis is in private use.

In 2001 the old horse stable was converted into a quality shop selling classical clothing and accessories for both ladies and gentlemen. The suppliers come mainly from across Europe and European quality production is favoured. In order to compete with the shops in Helsinki, the brands are exclusively chosen, often so that they cannot be found in the ordinary shops in Helsinki. The shop includes a log fire place where the lazier shopper can enjoy complimentary coffee and cake or some port wine and stilton.

Two generations
of Frankenhaeuser in
the Kullo Gård Farm Shop,
Butiken på Landet.

Kullo Gård Estate

Brands represented in the shop are for instance, from Austria: Habsburg, Schneiders, Gaisberger and Steinbock; from Germany: Hiltl, Gardeur, Voss, Golfino and Diplomant; from Britain and Scotland: Turnbull & Asser, Bonsoir, Hunter, Truefitt & Hill, Barbour, John Partridge and Glenn Garnock; from Ireland:

KLÄDER & PRYDNAD

BUTIKEN PÅ LANDET

Magee and Harris Tweed; from France: Saint James, Anne Fontaine, Galimard and Busnuel; from Italy: Beretta, Gardenia, Loro Piana and Eva Cavaletti; from Spain: T.ba; from Sweden: Stenströms, Oscar Jacobson and Hansen & Jacob; from America: Allen Edmonds, NYJD-Jeans and Sperry Topsider; and as a speciality the exclusive South African handmade ceramics Mustardseed & Moonshine by Kate Carlyle. For Christmas there is a selection of delicacies including foie gras, stilton, jams etc. The shop is open 7 days a week, all year round except on national holidays and has a regular staff of 4 people.

PERSONAL OPINION

The estate is surrounded by the activities of the community, activities that could be commercially viable but which are not so favourable when it comes to traditional farming and preserving landscape and nature.

The distance from the centre of the estate to the rock crushing gravel production is 4.5 km SW, to the oil refinery 2.5km S, to the petrochemical plants 4 km SW, to the waste handling area under construction 4 km W, to the eventual new airport 3 km N and to the eventual new railroad with a station 2 km N.

The parts of the estate which are situated close to the industrial and "hard" production zones and activities will in the long term be developed in the same direction.

The goal is however to keep a green, partly natural, partly man-made parkland zone around the centre of the estate, where only "softer" activities

should be developed. These activities should preferably be developed and run by the estate.

As far as planning is concerned, there may be some problems with the planning authorities, who in Finland have the monopoly on land-use planning. The landowner's own ideas and plans do not always coincide with the views of the planning bureaucrats. Sometimes the views of the authorities seem to be surprisingly short-sighted, and they are often also stained by the bureaucrat's personal or political opinions, without the necessary knowledge as a base. A developing problem is that the regional plans, which are supposed to be only advisory, are some times very strictly interpreted by lower planning authorities and even by the court.

There seems to be an attitude among the planners and some politicians that land owned by the original landowner should not be developed and planned. When the land is owned by the community or by a secondary owner, i.e. a developer, the planning is much speedier.

THE FUTURE

Kullo Gård lies only 30 minutes by car from the centre of Helsinki, 25 minutes from the main airport and 10 minutes from Borgå town centre.

The opportunities for Kullo Gård are to be found in its proximity to the capital city Helsinki and also the closeness to the historical centre of the old town of Borgå, combined with the cultural heritage of an old estate. Activities on the estate are easy to market because the estate is quite well-known thanks to a decade of pick-your-own strawberries and sweetcorn as well as the golf course with the well reputed fine dining restaurant. This gives opportunities for developing high quality tourism related activities, without diluting the owner's authority and ownership and without destroying the peacefulness and beauty of the estate centre. Of course this puts a pressure on the younger generation to make the right decisions.

The attractive surroundings of the estate centre support the growing shop activity, which could be easily expanded without destroying the atmosphere of an old estate. Correctly handled these activities could be of the utmost importance for the economy of the estate. The differences in concept compared to the city shops should give a good competitive edge. The risks with the shop activities lie mainly in possible bad management.

Even if the agricultural activities are not the real focus, they can be well handled due to the co-operation with neighbouring farms, which should provide as rational production as is possible within Finland.

The forestry will continue to be an important leg of the production. Due to the well-organised Forest Owners Association, the handling of the forestry is in good hands and the forests do give a good yearly profit. Even if the industrial use of forest products is global and cyclical, there will always be a long-term demand for forest products because of their versatility. The use can vary from traditional pulp and paper related products and energy use to nano-cellulose, which can be used for almost anything except food.

Of course it is economically important to develop the opportunities that ownership of the land intended for industrial use gives. Even if the land-use planning is in the hands of society, there are a lot of opportunities in this. These developments do in practice take a long time, sometimes even decades, to develop, but the crucial thing is to have the right contacts, have a good nose and make the right decisions.

Thomas Frankenhaeuser

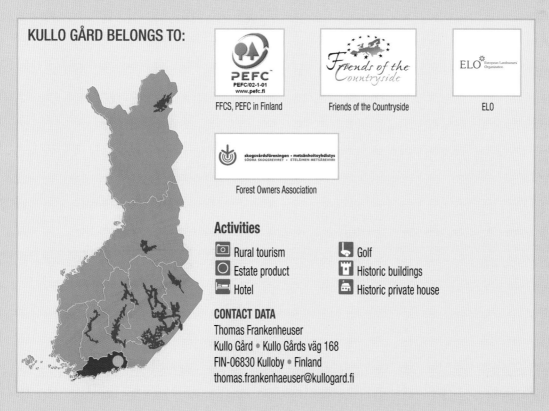

KULLO GÅRD BELONGS TO:

PEFC
PEFC/02-1-01
www.pefc.fi

FFCS, PEFC in Finland

Friends of the Countryside

Friends of the Countryside

ELO European Landowners Organization

ELO

skogsvårdsföreningen · metsänhoitoyhdistys
SÖDRA SKOGSREVIRET · ETELÄINEN METSÄREVIIRI

Forest Owners Association

Activities

🖾 Rural tourism   Golf

◎ Estate product   🏰 Historic buildings

🛏 Hotel   🏛 Historic private house

CONTACT DATA

Thomas Frankenheuser
Kullo Gård • Kullo Gårds väg 168
FIN-06830 Kulloby • Finland
thomas.frankenhaeuser@kullogard.fi

La Losilla

Mediterranean

Location: Villarejo de Salvanés and Belmonte del Tajo, Madrid, Spain.
Surface: 410 ha.

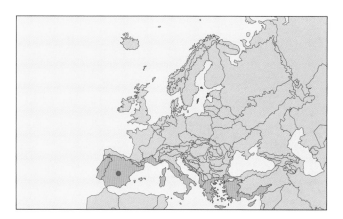

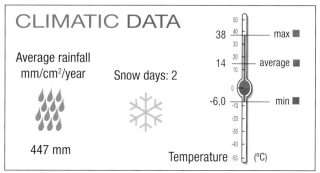

CLIMATIC DATA

Average rainfall
mm/cm²/year

Snow days: 2

447 mm

Temperature (ºC)

38 — max
14 — average
-6,0 — min

SUMMARY

La Losilla is situated between the villages of Villarejo de Salvanés and Belmonte del Tajo and about 6 km from the medieval town of Chinchón, world heritage, south-east of the Region of Madrid in Spain, and about 50 kilometres from the capital. The estate's outstanding feature is its potential for hunting, for which it was registered as a Commercial Reserve in 2006. On its somewhat more than 400 hectares there are over 20 driven partridge shoots each year as well as other small game.

The land is divided into several small blocks of Mediterranean woodland in which the Kermes Oak *(Quercus coccifera)* and the Holm Oak *(Quercus ilex)* are more abundant than the Aleppo Pine *(Pinus halepensis)*, but where there is also scrubland of Buckthorn *(Rhamnus lycioides)* and Rosemary *(Rosmarinus officinalis)* as well as areas of dry land cereal crops, all used not only by the game species which populate the estate but by non-game species such as seed-eating and insect-eating birds, small mammals and some Wild Boar *(Sus scrofa)*, Red Deer *(Cervus elaphus)* and Roe Deer *(Capreolus capreolus)* which have recently appeared in this habitat.

The management effort is therefore strongly focused on its use as a hunting resource, and the estate has a magnificent Manor House with 12 double rooms, a rest room, 3 reception rooms, a spa, tennis court and every possible comfort.

Red-legged partridge shoots at La Losilla usually begin with this drive when the higher part of the estate is being shot.

C. Otero

La Losilla **(Spain)**

The plains of El Chopo, with the boundary of La Encomienda in the background.

D. Ateca

HISTORY

La Losilla was part of the estates of La Encomienda Mayor de Castilla until the early 21st century. The *Encomiendas* were large areas of land which came into existence in the 12th century, given by the King to the Military Orders for them to colonise and Christianise the vast lands which at that time were situated on the borderline between his kingdom and that of the Moorish Kings who had occupied the Iberian Peninsula.

Among the duties conferred by the King was that of repopulating the lands, administering and governing them. The most important use of these lands was for livestock farming, using *merino* sheep and herds of goats. Agriculture developed gradually through the 13th and 14th centuries, reflected in the increase in ploughed land. Alongside livestock and cereals, vines and olive groves, the role played by beehives was just as important.

In the 15th century La Encomienda of Villarejo de Salvanés became the principal property of La Encomienda Mayor de Castilla, and in the 16th century the Chief Commander was Don Juan de Zúñiga y Avellaneda, the then guardian of Prince Philip, the son of the Emperor Charles V of Germany and I of Spain and future King Philip II.

Included among the rural properties of this Encomienda was that which is still called La Encomienda Mayor de Castilla y La Losilla to this day, a part of which is recorded as having been given by King Charles III to the Infante Don Fernando in 1766.

The estate passed to the Sanz Vives family through successive inheritances, and its present owner acquired La Losilla in 2003.

DESCRIPTION

Situation

La Losilla is situated between the villages of Villarejo de Salvanés and Belmonte del Tajo and about 6 km from the medieval town of Chinchón, world heritage, south-east of the Autonomous Region of Madrid in Spain, and about 50 kilometres from the capital. It is divided into an area of farmland of about 300 hectares and woodland zones which extend to about 100 hectares.

Boundaries

The natural boundaries of this estate are: to the north the village of Villarejo de Salvanés; to the east Villarejo de Salvanés and other private estates; to the south the road M-319 and La Encomienda

Mayor de Castilla; and to the west the village of Belmonte del Tajo, all of which are within the Region of Madrid as has been mentioned above.

Physical geography

The land is varied and diverse in character, areas of fertile land alternating with gentle slopes, hills and gullies amongst other features. The average height is 680 metres above sea level, rising to a maximum of 781 metres and with a minimum of 590 metres at the lowest point.

Vegetation

The vegetation found on the estate is typical of a Mediterranean climate on limestone soils. The most abundant species are the Kermes Oak *(Quercus coccifera)* and the Holm Oak *(Quercus ilex)*, with the presence of Aleppo Pine *(Pinus halepensis)* which forms compact areas of great interest.

Fauna

The wildlife on the estate of La Losilla is tremendously rich and varied. Everywhere there are rabbits and partridges, pigeons and doves. Hares can be seen in good numbers, as can thrushes, proven by the fact that large numbers of these are caught every year.

As well we can find magpies, jackdaws, foxes and wild boar, which even if they are not the prime subjects of the hunting resources are nonetheless species which are controlled so that they do not interfere or affect the populations of those that are of most interest.

However it is not just the game species that are so numerous on this estate. The management works hard to attract many non-game species.

Protected species are widely present on the estate; amongst these the most noteworthy in terms

D. Ateca

of their wildlife value are the golden eagle which uses La Losilla as a regular hunting ground along with Bonelli's eagle, and the eagle owl, of which there are at least two breeding pairs on this land.

João Filipe Espirito Santo de Brito e Cunha has clearly focused on sustainability based on service. Horse-breeding complements the offer of luxury accommodation and partridge shooting.

Equipment and machinery

The estate depends on the help of the following machinery in carrying out its work and aims:

- 100HP tractor with trailer
- 7,000 litre tank
- Backhoe excavator
- Horse-box
- Three pick-ups for maintenance and security works around the estate, among others smaller vehicles.

The Manor House is a traditional cosy and charming building.

It also has supplementary infrastructures for the employees, stables and agricultural warehouses.

The Manor House offers accommodation in 14 suites, spacious rooms and capacity for events of up to 400 guests.

D. Ateca

La Losilla **(Spain)**

G. Janssens

Main economic activities

As previously mentioned, the main economic activity on this estate is special events, commercial hunting and shooting of game. For this purpose it became a Commercial Reserve in 2006.

The king of all the species on the reserve is without doubt the Red-legged Partridge *(Alectoris rufa)*, for which driven shoots are organised.

The Wild Boar *(Sus scrofa)* is becoming more numerous in the area, spreading from adjacent estates and attracted by the feed made available on the estate, although this is a predatory species which has a negative influence on the partridge population and needs to be constantly controlled.

The estate has a stable of Lusitano horses looked after by specialist staff. The horses are schooled and trained at La Losilla where there is also an interesting collection of coaches used during the shooting season and in others social events.

The estate has 300 hectares dedicated to farming activities, with 150 ha of annual plots on

CATALOGUE OF BIRDS AT LA LOSILLA

BIRDS
- White Stork *(Ciconia ciconia)*
- Mallard *(Anas platyrhynchos)*
- Peregrine Falcon *(Falco peregrinus)*
- Kestrel *(Falco tinnunculus)*
- Hobby *(Falco subbuteo)*
- Merlin *(Falco columbarius)*
- Honey Buzzard *(Pernis apivorus)*
- Kite *(Milvus milvus)*
- Black Kite *(Milvus migrans)*
- Buzzard *(Buteo buteo)*
- Short-toed Eagle *(Circaetus gallicus)*
- Booted Eagle *(Hieraetus pennatus)*
- Bonelli's Eagle *(Hieraetus fasciatus)*
- Golden Eagle *(Aquila chrysaetos)*
- Sparrowhawk *(Accipiter nisus)*
- Goshawk *(Accipiter gentiles)*
- Red-legged Partridge *(Alectoris rufa)*
- Quail *(Coturnix coturnix)*
- Moorhen *(Gallinula chloropus)*
- Common Crane *(Grus grus)*
- Lapwing *(Vanellus vanellus)*
- Woodcock *(Scolopax rusticola)*
- Common Sandpiper *(Actitis hypoleucos)*
- Black-bellied Sand Grouse *(Pterocles orientalis)*
- Wood-pigeon *(Columba palumbus)*
- Stock Dove *(Columba oenas)*
- Rock Dove *(Columba livia)*
- Turtle Dove *(Streptopelia turtur)*
- Cuckoo *(Cuculus canorus)*
- Little Owl *(Athene noctua)*
- Scops Owl *(Otus scops)*
- Barn Owl *(Tyto alba)*
- Long-eared Owl *(Asio otus)*

- Tawny Owl *(Strix aluco)*
- Eagle Owl *(Bubo bubo)*
- Red-necked Nightjar *(Caprimulgus ruficollis)*
- Swift *(Apus apus)*
- Bee-eater *(Merops apiaster)*
- Hoopoe *(Upupa epops)*
- Wryneck *(Jynx torquilla)*
- Great-spotted Woodpecker *(Dendrocopos major)*
- Green Woodpecker *(Picus viridis)*
- Skylark *(Alauda arvensis)*
- Calandra Lark *(Melanocorypha calandra)*
- Woodlark *(Lullula arborea)*
- Crested Lark *(Galerida cristata)*
- Short-billed Crested Lark *(Galerida theklae)*
- House Martin *(Delichon urbica)*
- Swallow *(Hirundo rustica)*
- Red-rumped Swallow *(Hirundo daurica)*
- White Wagtail *(Motacilla alba)*
- Meadow Pipit *(Anthus pratensis)*
- Wren *(Troglodytes troglodytes)*
- Hedge Sparrow *(Prunella modularis)*
- Stonechat *(Saxicola torquata)*
- Black-eared Wheatear *(Oenanthe hispanica)*
- Wheatear *(Oenanthe oenanthe)*
- Robin *(Erithacus rubecula)*
- Blackbird *(Turdus merula)*
- Song Thrush *(Turdus philomelos)*
- Mistle Thrush *(Turdus viscivorus)*
- Redwing *(Turdus iliacus)*
- Black Redstart *(Phoenicurus ochruros)*
- Redstart *(Phoenicurus phoenicurus)*
- Cetti's Warbler *(Cettia cetti)*
- Nightingale *(Luscinia megarhynchos)*

- Garden Warbler *(Sylvia borin)*
- Whitethroat *(Sylvia communis)*
- Blackcap *(Sylvia atricapilla)*
- Subalpine Warbler *(Sylvia cantillans)*
- Dartford Warbler *(Sylvia undata)*
- Spectacled Warbler *(Sylvia conspicillata)*
- Chiffchaff *(Phylloscopus collybita)*
- Melodious Warbler *(Hippolais polyglotta)*
- Firecrest *(Regulus ignicapillus)*
- Pied Flycatcher *(Muscicapa hypoleuca)*
- Spotted Flycatcher *(Muscicapa striata)*
- Great Tit *(Parus major)*
- Blue Tit *(Parus caeruleus)*
- Long-tailed Tit *(Aegythalos caudatus)*
- Short-toed Treecreeper *(Certhia brachydactyla)*
- Golden Oriole *(Oriolus oriolus)*
- Woodchat Shrike *(Lanius senator)*
- Great Grey Shrike *(Lanius excubitor)*
- Magpie *(Pica pica)*
- Jackdaw *(Corvus monedula)*
- Raven *(Corvus corax)*
- Jay *(Garrulus glandarius)*
- Spotless Starling *(Sturnus unicolor)*
- Starling *(Sturnus vulgaris)*
- House Sparrow *(Passer domesticus)*
- Tree Sparrow *(Passer montanus)*
- Goldfinch *(Carduelis carduelis)*
- Greenfinch *(Carduelis chloris)*
- Chaffinch *(Fringilla coelebs)*
- Linnet *(Acanthis cannabina)*
- Serin *(Serinus serinus)*
- Rock Bunting *(Emberiza cia)*
- Corn Bunting *(Emberiza calandra)*

which wheat, barley and oats are grown for consumption on the estate: horse feed, natural feed of the fauna as well as a supplementary food source for the partridges, placed in feeders throughout the year.

The different plots are sown on the old Spanish system known as *año y vez*, a rotational system under which they are sown every second year and then left to rest, allowing the land to recover.

Red-legged partridge, rabbits and Iberian hares not are just the main game species, but also the main prey for predators.

D. Ateca

D. Ateca

Approximately 10,000 partridges are shot each year.

Landau carriage drawn by Frisian draught horses.

P. Pavia

Reception and dining room in the Manor House.

P. Pavia

La Losilla **(Spain)**

Living room.

FUTURE FOR LA LOSILLA

La Losilla is used and operated on the basis of two principal resources: driven shooting for red-legged partridge and special events.

Both these resources complement each other in the first instance, as the Manor House receives and welcomes the hunters and their companions with an incomparable standard of comfort and facilities. The house is also used for other events such as conferences, weddings and other social events.

To achieve this, the building offers 12 suites, with 24 beds in total, 3 reception rooms, a dining room, spa, chapel, tennis court and cellar. All of these are sited around a large central patio with garden.

Nearby are the garages, the coach house and the large stables for the Lusitano horses and the horses used on shoot days.

The first drives are tested in La Losilla in 2004, obtaining encouraging results.
In the picture the landlords, the cousins Manuel Fernando Espirito Santo and João F. Espirito Santo de Brito e Cunha with some friends and among them, the Prince Kubrat of Bulgarie.

Partridge shooting protocol at La Losilla

The red-legged partridge drives on the estate follow a strict protocol based over 30 years experience, and begin with the reception of the guests on the evening before the shoot.

Each season, some 20 days shooting are enjoyed at La Losilla in two periods: 6 or 8 days before Christmas, and 12 or 14 days at the end of the season.

The shoots are fundamentally based on stocked red-legged partridges, and the standard profile is 500 partridges/day, with 10 guns and 4 drives per day. Weekends normally include two days shooting for the same group.

The evening before

- A reception for the guests takes place in the Manor House, where they are offered a welcome drink and can settle into their suites, following the rules and preferences, provided by the group of hunters and guests.
- The guests' shotguns are moved to the armoury where they are labelled with the owner's name for convenience the following day and to avoid any confusion.
- The supplies of cartridges are checked so that there is sufficient ammunition for the shoot; one must bear in mind that a standard shoot of 500 birds/day might require some 2000-2500 cartridges each day.
- Hunting licences, insurances, gun licences and guidance notes are reviewed in order to rectify any shortcomings.

LA LOSILLA										
DRIVE FOR 10 GUNS										
Nr. of post	①	②	③	④	⑤	⑥	⑦	⑧	⑨	⑩
DRIVE A	1	10	2	9	3	8	4	7	5	6
DRIVE B	3	2	4	1	5	10	6	9	7	8
DRIVE C	5	4	6	3	7	2	8	1	9	10
DRIVE D	7	6	8	5	9	4	10	3	1	2
DRIVE E	9	8	10	7	1	6	2	5	3	4
(LEFT PUNTA)										(RIGTH PUNTA)

Tómelo. Simple reminder to occupy different positions during the day's shoot, so that positions alternate without ever having the same neighbour.

- Dinner in the Dining Room, with guests moving on to the Fireplace Room and Smoking Room for dessert.

During the evening a technical team from Renatur SA goes out to review at least six drives, ensuring that access is available and choosing the four best according to the density of partridges and the conditions for light and wind direction forecast for the following day.

Similarly the two groups of shoot assistants are reviewed. The first group consists of 20 specialists who undertake the tasks of loader *(cargador)* and clerk *(secretario)*, two for each shooting post and gun.

The *cargador* specialises in loading the guns, which are normally 12-bore or 20-bore side-by-side shotguns in the true tradition of Spanish partridge shooting.

The *secretario* marks down the partridges, which fall in rapid succession and which must be picked up completely. Both of these gentlemen also help in carrying the copious amounts of equipment to the shooting posts.

Finally there is another (second) group, much more varied in nature and comprising about 40 people. Of these, four are equipped with flags *(banderas)* and four are the *directores* of the drives, mounted on horses and each in charge of six beaters, meaning that there is a total of 32 engaged in the drive. In addition there are two dog-handlers to pick up partridges that have not been found, who start their work as soon as the drive has ended; two tractor drivers; two drivers of the 4x4 vehicles; and two reserves. All beaters are provided with protective glasses and fluorescent jackets, to be easily identified and located.

The list of staff is checked, the night previous, over to ensure that there are no gaps or to appoint replacements if the need arises.

Finally, the equipment at each individual shooting post is reviewed: canvas blinds, safety screens, a seat for the *cargador* and special cartridge box to allow him to load the shotguns efficiently, hooks to gather and hang the partridges, and plentiful supplies of cartridges.

Lastly, and before retiring to bed, checks are done with the kitchen staff on the supplies of food and drink and the logistics for the *taco* (refreshment break), and the radio sets are plugged in and charged.

Filling the *avispero* with cartridges. The *secretario* and *cargador* rapidly create a joint team effort with the shooter, establishing an unusual and enduring camaraderie.

The shoot

The shoot normally starts at 9.00-9.30 in the morning, before which breakfast is served in the Dining Room and the final guests have been welcomed.

During breakfast, and once the group is fully gathered together, the draw is made, in which each person shooting is assigned a number by whatever *Tómelos* process is in use and which he keeps for the whole day.

This number is quickly added to the labels on each gun and the ten teams of *cargador* and *secretario*, who are also given numbers from 1 to 10, are assigned logically to the shooter who has drawn their number.

Each shooter then meets his team, the *cargador* and *secretario* who will accompany him throughout the day, and they take personal care of the guns and ammunition. This is the moment when, with a firm handshake, the seal is set on a collaborative effort that will last the whole day and will be crucial in the smooth running of the shoot.

The game shooting plan started in 2005 with some magnificent days of shooting, consolidating one of the pillars of the sustainable exploitation of the estate.

La Losilla (Spain)

The record shoot at La Losilla on 7 March 2009 accounted for 1,145 birds in 4 drives with 8 guns.

C. Otero

It is altogether normal for *shooter*, *cargador* and *secretario* to build themselves very rapidly into a team, with plenty of camaraderie, affection, collaboration and understanding.

On their second day many shooters request 'their' same *cargador* and *secretario* as on the first day, refusing to accept any other team and even, year after year, claiming the same assistants in extraordinary and admirable faithfulness and friendship.

When the shooting party is ready to depart by car for the first drive, the two tractors and the 2 4x4 vehicles with the 60 beaters and assistants have preceded them and are already waiting, the *cargadores* and *secretarios* then accompanying the guests to their shooting posts.

The other 40 beaters have taken up their position at the start of the drive, usually about 1.5 kilo-metres from the shooting posts, ready to start beating as soon as they receive the order. This comes when the last shooting guest has taken his place, following the unwritten tradition of maximum speed and complete silence.

At that moment, and when fully in place at his post, this last person fires two shots into the air, which is the signal for the beaters to start moving through the drive. Up until this moment, absolutely nobody has been able to fire a single shot, even if a large flock of 500 partridges has flown straight over the top of him, as once happened on a day in March, 2008.

From the time at which the line of beaters – including the four riders – has started to move, to the moment at which the first shots are fired, some 20 or even 30 minutes may have elapsed, a period which seems to the person shooting as if it will

Each shoot day accounts for almost 80 wage packets, divided among *secretarios*, *cargadores*, beaters, *banderas*, game-keepers, 4x4 drivers, tractor drivers, auxiliaries and others. The family Espirito Santo is specially involved with development of the local communities.

C. Otero

620

never end and which fills the person directing the shoot with great anxiety given that he does not know whether the drive has, in one fateful moment, been 'emptied' of birds because of the presence of a herd of wild boar or for any other reason.

Some 60 minutes may pass between the start of the drive and its conclusion. Once it has ended, the birds are picked up and brought together for the first *tableau* of the day. Once the shooting posts have been vacated, it is time for the dogs – 4-6 labradors, cockers or spaniels – to start their search, always fruitful and productive, in which they usually find about 10% of the partridges which have been shot and not gathered by the *secretario* and the *shooter*.

At the end of each drive a note is made of the numbers shot, for statistical and administrative purposes.

After each drive a glass of sherry is taken, whilst ammunition supplies are replenished and whilst matters are reviewed by the teams. Between the second and third drives a *taco* is taken. This includes an endless number of appetising Spanish *tapas* among which there must always be a good Iberian *pata negra* ham and a glass of red *vino tinto*. This is usually the moment at which the wives and companions, who have remained quietly at the Manor House, come to join the shooting party. They are brought by horse and carriage, and remain with the group to participate in the two final drives of the day.

C. Otero

Once shot, the red-legged partridge are cleaned and sold for export.

Use of the Manor house

The Manor house at La Losilla currently has sufficient capacity to accommodate up to 24 people (in 12 suites) or to hold business conferences or functions for more than 400 guests.

It has two large reception rooms and a dining room capable of seating 40 people, although this can be extended onto the south patio to take 400.

This level of comfort, in the midst of natural scenery of enormous beauty yet only 50 kilometres from Madrid, the capital city, creates the ideal conditions for business meetings and tourism over 2-3, or more days in an atmosphere of quiet and isolation, or for celebrations and functions for many more people.

João Filipe Espírito Santo de Brito
e Cunha & Carlos Otero

LA LOSILLA BELONGS TO:

Rise Foundation — WE initiative — Aproca Madrid

Activities & attractions

- Shooting
- Social events
- Riding
- Rural Tourism
- Birdwatching
- Tennis
- Spa & Wellness

CONTACT DATA
La Losilla estate
fincalalosilla@gmail.com

Theme 7
Virgin Lands

INTRODUCTION

The three estates described, those of Las Trillas, Caraguay and Cañón Viejo, are framed into a single project: a joint initiative by two Spanish friends who are trying to develop a model of sustainable management in Argentine based on preservation, promotion of wildlife, and on social and human development. Centred on the economic resource of hunting, the select model is that of Wildlife Estates, which has been so successful in countries such as Spain, South Africa, United Kingdom, or even Argentine itself, where there already are comparable models.

We selected Sierra de Ancasti in response to ecological and social criteria. We needed an appropiate scenario and the mountain range has such beautiful landscapes, plentiful vegetation, a variety of ecosystems, water its average rainfall is bewtween 700 and 1200mm and human resources that are thirsty for knowledge and willing to work, to bring about a social model of sustainable development, exportable within many enclaves of the Andean Mountains.

The territory of Sierra de Ancasti, object of this initiative, has a surface area of approximately 13,500 ha, composed of eight separate smaller estates that already belong to four different owners: Las Trillas, Yunca Pampa, Corralito, Caraguay, Palo Labrado, Cañón Viejo del Paclín, Campogrande and Valle Viejo.

Carlos Otero

Trillas Estate and
Escondido. Sierra de Ancasti.

Situation

The territory of *Vertientes del Ancasti* is located in the southeast of the Province of Catamarca, 40 km from the capital city, and extends to about 13,500 ha. It is situated on the west side of the *Sierra de Ancasti* mountains, approximately between the villages of Amadores, on its northern boundary, and the boundary of the department of Valle Viejo on its southern side.

The layout of the estate can be compared to a long thin stripe orientated North-South. According to the title deeds of the different properties that make up the estate, its eastern boundary coincides with the peaks of the Ancasti mountain range, and its western boundary with the river Paclín.

This Wildlife Estate belongs to the departments of Paclín and Valle Viejo, both of which are part of the province of Catamarca.

The dimensions of the *Vertientes del Ancasti* stretch approximately 20 km along the main highway Ruta Nacional 38. The width of the estate is variable, from less than 4 km to over 10 km. Its eastern boundary, according to the property title deeds, would be delimited by the Cumbre Alta of the Ancasti.

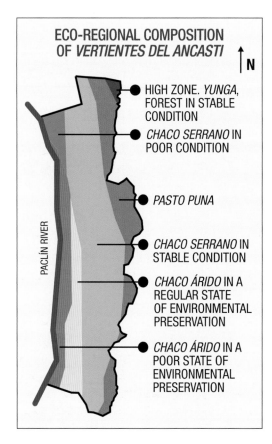

ECO-REGIONAL COMPOSITION OF *VERTIENTES DEL ANCASTI* ↑N

- HIGH ZONE. *YUNGA*, FOREST IN STABLE CONDITION
- *CHACO SERRANO* IN POOR CONDITION
- *PASTO PUNA*
- *CHACO SERRANO* IN STABLE CONDITION
- *CHACO ÁRIDO* IN A REGULAR STATE OF ENVIRONMENTAL PRESERVATION
- *CHACO ÁRIDO* IN A POOR STATE OF ENVIRONMENTAL PRESERVATION

PACLÍN RIVER

Soil Science

The soils of the *Vertientes del Ancasti* are heterogeneous in nature, in three distinct parts:

- The *low part* where accumulations of loess predominate. The soils are characterized by poor humidity retention capability, little organic matter and a low degree of mineralization, with a significant percentage of sand in their composition, leading to risk of erosion by water and wind, to the detriment of agriculture. The sides of the mountain ranges contain accumulations of thick sediments, allowing the development of better soils.

- The *middle part* where the hydrology and the soil are different. The characteristics of the river courses are typical of systems in mountainous areas, with important fluvial cones. In general the soils are superficial with predominance of thin sand and limes, strongly influenced by the rocky formations of the area.

- The *area of the high peaks* is a region in which the soils become more acid as rainfall and altitude increase. The soils are very rich in organic matter.

Vegetation

The wildlife reserve of *Vertientes del Ancasti*, presents high eco-regional variability providing great landscape and ecological value. The environmental elements of which it is composed are as follows:

Before starting to describe the vegetation, it is advisable to show, by means of a sketch of the bioclimatic sites, the structure of the altitudinal distribution present in the area.

Sketch of the bioclimatic sites of *Vertientes del Ancasti*

Therefore, if we started our description at the lowest altitudes, we would find an open forest with a dominance of White Quebracho *(Aspidosperma quebracho blanco)* and the Black Carob tree *(Prosopis nigra)*, accompanied by other species such as *Tala (Celtis tala)*, *Mistol (Zyzyphus mistol)* and *Cardón moro (Stetsonia coryne)*. However, in parts closest to the Ruta Nacional 38 highway, the vegetation is in a poor state of conservation and is increasingly distant from its climacic community. The causes are the clearings made in the past for purposes of agriculture or to extract firewood and timber, as well as processes of urbanisation.

Between the clearings there are usually some patches of forest left as protective belts, where the remains of the forest are very badly degraded. These patches have been subjected to forest extraction, or they are old clearings in which secondary growth processes have started and a lot of shrub is evident.

Moving to higher altitudes, a deciduous forest appears, in which the dominant species is the *Horco quebracho (Schinopsis haenkeana)*, accompanied by *Molle de beber (Lithraea ternifolia)*, *Sacha quince (Ruprechtia apetala)*, *Palo borracho (Seiba insignis)* and *Cardón* or *Achuma (Trichocereus terschekii)*; in the Gullies the *Viscote (Acacia visco)* dominates, whereas at the lower levels the commonest species are the *Tala (Celtis tala)*, the Black Carob tree *(Prosopis nigra)* and the White Quebracho *(Aspidosperma quebracho blanco)*. The Bull Shadow *(Jodina rhombifolia)* appears in lower

numbers and in more degraded areas there is a deciduous thorny shrub cover composed of *Churqui (Acacia caven)*, *Shinki (Mimosa farinosa)* and *Garabato (Acacia praecox)*, very far from their climacic community.

As we approach the high peaks, we start to notice small scattered and isolated stands, almost exclusively comprising the Hill Pine or *Pino del Cerro (Podocarpus parlatorei)* that endorses the good ecological status of the area by finding in the *Vertientes del Ancasti* its ecological niche.

Finally, at the highest altitudes, at about 2000 m above sea level, mountain pastures appear, mainly formed of grasses, showing marked growth seasonality in summer and winter. They are composed of species like *Festuca hieronymii*, *Stipa tenacísima* (straws) or *Piptochaetum* sp. The stocking density of cattle in this area was intense up until 2006, and it has suffered from frequent wild fires, which have partially modified the structure of the forest and where slight erosive processes in the soil can be observed.

Forests of Chaco Serrano on the slopes of the Sierra de Ancasti.

CATAMARCA HISTORY

Catamarca is a province of Argentine, located in the northwest region of the country, occupying a surface of 102,602 km². Its capital is San Fernando del Valle de Catamarca, usually shortened to Catamarca.

The word Catamarca is of Quechua origin and means fortress in the slope, alluding to the geographical situation of the city. *Cata* signifies slope or hillside and *Marca* stands for fortress or castle of the border.

Before the arrival of the Spanish conquerors, most of today's Catamarca was a part of the territories of Tucumán and was inhabited by Diaguitas indians. These indigenous people consisted of numerous tribes of which the Calchaquíes were the most renowned for their fierce resistance to the Spanish conquerors during the 17th and 18th centuries.

The Diaguitas formed a group of aborigines with an identical language, the *cacan*, similar customs and artistic manifestations. They were very skilful potters. When the circumstances demanded it, the tribes joined in common war against the Spanish.

These communities were governed by political and military chiefs. These leaders used to be polygamist while the rest of the population was monogamist. In order to inherit this position, being the son of a chief was not considered enough: the inheritor had to demonstrate that he had capacities to give orders. Thus, on the arrival of the Spanish, the Diaguitas territory was divided into headquarters and dominions. Their economy was based fundamentally on agriculture through artificial irrigation, for which dams and terraces were constructed along the sides of the mountains. Chiefs distributed the lands and organized the construction and care of the terraces. Land used to be exploited jointly and some of the crops were stocked in the communal warehouses.

Among the cultivated vegetables were papayas, gourds, corn and beans. Papayas and quínoa were sown in the highest zones (the terraces and platforms). Moreover, they brewed alcoholic drinks such as the *aloja* and the *añapa* based on the fruits of the *algarrobo* (carob) trees. Their meals were completed by hunting: ñandú, ducks, vicunas and guanacos.

In the 15th century the Incas incorporated Catamarca's western zones into the Collasuyu[1], forming the provinces of Chicoana and Quire-Quire. The most significant construction left by the Incas in Catamarca is the Aconquija de Pucará, one of the biggest fortresses of the south of the Empire. To form the Collasuyu, the Empire had to create a series of administrative entities that are nowadays known as provinces.

Initially, the Diaguitas fiercely resisted the Inca conquest; they then managed to resist the advance of the Spanish by more than a hundred years.

The *Spanish conquerors* reached the present-day province of Catamarca in about 1536 with Diego de Almagro's expedition, which after crossing the Calchaquies Valley in the Andes went directly to Chile.

The Spanish occupation of this region was based on a strategy of founding cities and guaranteeing commercial routes between High Peru and the southern part of South America. The principal reasons for the conquest of the Collasuyu was the existence of gold, silver, copper, lead, semi-precious stone and salt. These reasons led to the domination of the region by both Incas and Spanish. Lands were occupied with new types of crops and cattle and the indigenous people were forced to work for the conquerors.

When the Spanish conquest began in the 16th century, the Diaguitas formed a great army commanded by Juan Calchaquí. They managed to reject the invaders up to Santiago del Estero. However, in 1665 the conquerors had founded several cities around them, encircled them and finally managed to conquer them.

If practically all the Diaguitas who resisted the Spanish invasion were rooted out or deported when Calchaquí's War (Diaguitas's generalised revolution against the Spanish domination occurred between 1630 and 1665) was concluded, some tribes were treated with more indulgence for not having taken part in the conflict. This was the case of the Amaicha, who were allowed to remain in their ancestral territories.

Chile's supremacy reached a hundred miles eastwards of the Andes mountain, thus including an extensive part of the current province of Catamarca. In this zone, by mandate of the governor of Chile called García de Mendoza, the captain Juan Pérez de Zurita founded the first city in the current territory of Catamarca in 1558. This was in the valley of Quinmivil and was called Londres in honour of Mary Tudor, the spouse of Philip II of Spain. The city of Londres was refounded or moved four times, and finally, on the 5th July 1683, Fernando de Mendoza y Mate de Luna founded the city of San Fernando del Valle de Catamarca.

The economic activity of Catamarca during the colonial period was based on agricultural production of cotton, chilli, wheat, some vineyards and cane plantations. Moreover, minerals like gold, silver and copper and the textile industry allowed a great number of families to own a loom and equipment to spin and to comb.

According to Armando Bazán, the *mercedes de tierras* and the *encomiendas de indios*[2] were two funda-

---

[1] Collasuyu was the south-eastern provincial region of the Inca Empire. It related specifically to the Aymara territories which are now largely incorporated into the modern Latin American states of northern Chile, Peru, northeast Argentine and Bolivia.

---

[2] Control over land and Indians granted to an *encomendero*.

mental institutions in the economic and social life of Hispanic America.

There was plenty of legislation, often contradictory however, regulating the functioning of the institutions mentioned above. The legislation tried to harmonize the state's fiscal interest with the economic and political cravings of the conquerors, and to safeguard moral and religious principles relating to the evangelization and guardianship of the indigenous people. This was an impossible objective.

In reality, Spanish behaviour exceeded the juridical procedures, and a raw pragmatism always prevailed; an outstanding example was the relation of the Spanish with the native people.

Merced de tierras - Grant of Land

This institution already existed in Castilian law, and was an effective way for the Spanish Crown to reward subjects who took part in the reconquest of territories against the Moors.

When this was transplanted to America, its doctrine was to support the principle that control of the disclosed lands was the King's, as a conqueror's right.

The juridical term *gracia or merced* was the only one which allowed private individuals access to private ownership of land.

When a city was founded, the conquerors determined a place to build a square, a chapterhouse and a church. Moreover, they granted stables and lots to the religious orders and to those who accompanied the expedition. This occurred in Catamarca for the creation of the foundations of San Juan Bautista de la Ribera and San Fernando.

Mercedes were granted as well. These were granted to people reckoned by the crown as having been outstanding during the conquest. Furthermore, the aim of these benefits was to favour the development of villages and to give economic support to the development of Spanish farms and rural estates.

One of the first *mercedes* granted in Catamarca Valley was that of Pomangasta, granted in 1573 to Nuño Rodríguez Beltrán by the governor Jerónimo Luis de Cabrera. According to Gaspar Guzmán, the first estate of the valley was founded in this place, with houses, a chapel, farms and cotton fields. The primitive village of the Pomangasta Indians was in La Puerta, and Rodríguez Beltrán seated his estate in Pomancillo.

When Ramírez de Velazco founded the city of Todos Santos de la Nueva Rioja (1591), he gave titles of *merced* in Catamarca Valley. So did his successors Pedro Mercado de Peñaloza, Alonso de Ribera and Luis Quiñones Osorio. This gave birth to many *mercedes*, one of which was *Choya*, given to Luis de la Medina, that extended on both banks of the river and which included the seat of the present-day city of Catamarca. Another was *Autigasta*, given to Aslon Carrión, on lands

which correspond to the districts of El Portezuelo, Santa Cruz and Huaycama; *Motimo* was granted to Pedro de Maidana and is the site of the present-day San Isidro; *Alpatauca*, that is to say, San Antonio, was granted in 1621 to the priest Andrés de Guzmán; *Piedra Blanca* was granted to Antonio de Iriarte, grandson of Pedro de Maidana, who, in the middle of the 17th century, established himself here with his wife Maria de Nieva y Castilla.

This summarises how the Hispanic settlement of the current territory of Catamarca happened, with incentives of land given in the form of property by *merced real* (royal mercy).

Encomiendas

The Council of the Indies was a new institution previously unknown in Castilian law, born as a consequence of the new social American reality. It had different features in the different regions of the new world and its juridical profile was defined through burning polemics between theologians, moralists and politicians about the *justo titulo* of the Spanish to colonize the Indies and the social condition of the native peoples.

From the very start, two different criteria were clear: one was the legitimization of slavery, following the Aristotelian principle on the inferiority of some men; the other was praise of the respect of freedom of the indigenous people. Theoretically, the question was solved in favour of the second thesis.

The royal position, which decreed that the Indians were considered as free subjects of the Crown of Castile, was very explicit. But how could the Spanish have done without the indigenous workforce for the economic exploitation of new lands? These interests created a general situation where the native population was utilized without payment. As a result of this situation many abuses were recorded, showing neglect of the doctrine.

The Crown tried to resolve this by imposing a moderate tax on the Indians, as free subjects. This tax went directly to the conquerors, as agents, who perceived this tax as remuneration for their services. Lamentably, the institution's objective, defined by the Crown, was therefore spoilt. The agents preferred to use the Indians as free labourers on their farms and properties, thinking that they were bringing a major benefit. This was called the *personal service*.

When Ramirez de Velazco founded the province of La Rioja, he granted 56 commissions of Indian villages which were under his jurisdiction as encomendero or commissioner. These were assigned to members of the colonial community.

The system of commissions was legalized in Tucumán by the governor Gonzalo de Abreu, whose ordinances of 1576 approved the personal service of the Indians but included a series of collections to assure their religious indoctrination and to avoid certain abuses being commited.

Whatever the case, the king confirmed his decision by the certificate of the 10th of October 1618 and this was incorporated to the *Leyes de India (Laws of the Indies)*. Despite this, Tucumán was the region that least respected the Ordinances of Alfaro (1612). Regularly, bishops and missionaries reported abuse. This was deeply embedded in the mentality and habits of men.

The creation of the Viceroyalty of the Rio de la Plata in 1776 brought changes in political and economic aspects that influenced the daily life of the people of Catamarca. In 1783, the province was put under the administration of the governor of Salta.

The territories of Tucumán and Catamarca remained united until 1821, when Nicolás Avellaneda y Tula, who was the president of Catamarca under authority of the Republic of Tucuman, called the elite of Catamarca society to the Town Hall. He then solemnly declared that Catamarca and its territory were free. Independence from the Republic of Tucumán was thus achieved, and Nicolás Avellaneda y Tula was chosen as the first governor.

Catamarca contributed to the development of the Independence movement with men, supplies and provisions, and to its national organization through the words of the Orador de la Constitución of Brother Mamerto Esquiú, whose famous sermon *Laetamus de gloria vestra* ("We rejoice at your happiness") contained moderating and sensible words that called for a spirit of peace and order.

The 19th century was a period of progress for Catamarca's population with the flowering of the regional economies of the Northwest. Agriculture and cattle production, the exploitation of copper and gold mines, textile crafts and leather and intensive trade links with Chile, Peru and Buenos Aires brought a time of prosperity, with minor interruptions at times of national or regional conflict.

The demographic revolution in Argentine, starting in 1869 and provoked by the massive immigration of Europeans and the consequent intensive development of the Pampeana region, did not reach Catamarca. Instead it provoked disorganisation in the local economy and the beginning of the emigration of catamarqueños towards the new prosperous zones, similar characteristics being seen in the exodus of the 1970s.

History of the *Merced of Paquilingasta*

In the Quechua language, Paquilingasta means *divided village*. The first owner of Paclín or Paquilingasta was Diego de Vera (16th century), regent of the Council of San Miguel de Tucumán province since its foundation. According to the historian Juan Pablo Vera, the captain Diego de Vera was the first of that surname to come to Tucumán. He came in 1565 from Chile and was a member of Vera y Aragón family. He was part of the expedition of Francisco de Aguirre and participated in the foundation of San Miguel de Tucumán, thus obtaining the degree of mercedes and encomiendas in this territory.

Diego de Vera married Juana de Aguirre. After many years, he died without descendants. His widow married again in 1597, this time to Diego de Graneros de Alarcón, who looked after his wife's assets, one of them being Paquilingasta.

According to the prestigious historian of Catamarca Hugo Alaniz, Paquilingasta is already mentioned in documents from the 16th century. Its settlement began in that same century with the construction of a significant ranch. According to a document analysed by the historian Gaspar H. Guzmán, the old merced of Paquilingasta existed before 1589. Its dimensions *'are perfectly given only in its length; in relation to its width, it says that it clearly comprises all the valley of Paclín from the other side of the slope of Paquilingasta to the mountain ranges of Gracián, including when it talks about all of its hills. But the three leagues from North to South are few' '... And, as will be seen in other documents, this property comprises from the South of Balcozna to the current Villa de la Merced inclusive'.*

The concession made to Diego Graneros de Alarcón on the 15th July 1609 by the governor Alonso de Ribera is the document that informs us of the adjudication of Paquilingasta in 1589 to Diego de Vera.

This document, in its central part, says: *'...and because of your petition, you had informed me you have an estate and lands where you raise cattle from the other side of Cuesta de Paquilingasta, boundaries of this city where currently you have a lot of cattle, horses, cows... and you have them 12 years ago and this land is the same as Diego de Vera owned, your predecessor 20 years ago... I grant a merced of this estate and lands declared for use to Diego Graneros de Alarcón, which extend from where the corrals are to one league down the river and two leagues up the corrals and its width is the valley with the hillock, being remains of the valley for the Indians from Paquilingasta village, which declare it is enough for them...'*

The corrals mentioned by the previous document were in the present-day San Antonio, known after that as Las Beatas. The Indians who had been eradicated from this place a long time before the adjudication, had settled seven leagues to the south of La Merced, in present-day Amadores.

The centre of La Merced, where the principal residence of the estate was located, is nowadays the locality of San Antonio de Paclín. When Juana de Villegas died, her husband Diego Graneros de Alarcón married as his second wife Catalina Ramirez de Velazco, as is shown in his Will signed in 1630, in which he declared to have one only son, called Pedro de Velasco y Graneros de Alarcón and he gave as his properties the merced of Balcozna, as well as that of Paquilingasta.

The Ramírez de Velazco family owned the merced of Balcozna, on the northern border of Paquilingasta, and, as a result of Pedro's inheritance, passed its wealth to the Graneros de Alarcón family.

Both estates were acquired by Lucas de Figueroa y Mendoza, who bought a property in Sumalao known as Chacras de Las Beatas, where died in 1688. His descendants sold Balcozna in 1716 to the Jesuit fathers. Paquilingasta was inherited by another of his sons, Luis de Figueroa y Mendoza who kept it until his death. Then it was inherited by a daughter of Luis de Figueroa y Mendoza, called Catalina de Figueroa y Mendoza, wife of Carlos Villagrán, *'who donated all their properties to found a convent of noblewomen that would be a residence and school, as well as a home, and must be holden by Order of Our Lady of Mount Carmel or Carmelites'*.

According to Juan Pablo Vera, quoting Manuel Soria, amongst the properties included were the *merced* of Paquilingasta and the estate known as Las Chacras de Las Beatas in Sumalao, Valle Viejo. It is probable that they did not donate the entire merced, but just the part known as Las Beatas, because up until the last century there had been several properties in Paclín owned by descendants of the Figueroa family. With Villagrán's donation, the Carmelites founded the school of Our Lady of the Garden a few years later, in 1809.

Balcozna came into the property of the Jesuit Fathers, comprising the San Ignacio estate, which borders Balcozna on the east, Quilmilpa, Huacra, La Viña, and in the middle of XVIII century added the southern part of the merced of Paquilingasta, which is today known as La Merced.

In 1767 the Jesuits were expelled from the property, which was given to the authority of the *temporalidades* of Santiago del Estero. These were committees set up to administer the assets which had belonged to the Jesuits. From 1774 the committee started to sell off parts of the estate; in fact, it was divided into 15 estancias comprising three centres: Las Lajas and El Contador (the Varela family) in the north; Balcosna de Adentro in the west, where most of the land belonged to the Giménez family; and in the east where the Villafañe family owned the greater part. La Higuera and El Rosario belonged almost totally to the Vera family.

After numerous owners and several divisions due to sales and inheritances, and following the expulsion of the Jesuits, Paquilingasta had passed into the hands of the Fathers of Our Lady of Mercy (Nuestra Señora de la Merced) by 1821, but the area acquired the name of the congregation, in other words La Merced. From that time on, the town was consolidated on a plan drawn by the engineer who constructed the series of railway tunnels known as La Cuesta del Totoral.

This summary does not follow the exact detail of the succession of families that were, and are, the owners of lands that made up, or make up, the territory of the province. It is simply an attempt to establish how the basic system of landholding was shaped from its earliest days.

Hugo Alaniz & Flore Wittouck

Cathedral and Governor's Palace, San Fernando del Valle de Catamarca.

Caraguay
Neotropical

Location: Department of Paclín. Catamarca, Argentine.
Surface: 1,500 ha.

CLIMATIC DATA

Average rainfall
mm/cm²/year

Snow days: 0

760 mm

Temperature (°C)

41,0 — max
18,4 — average
-6,0 — min

SUMMARY

Estate located in the southeast of the province of Catamarca (Argentine), in the department of Paclín and parallel to the main highway Ruta Nacional 38. This is an estate of 1,500 hectares on the western face of the Sierra de Ancasti, bounded on the east by the estate of Las Trillas, on the west by the nearby village of Palo Labrado whose boundary is the previously mentioned Ruta Nacional 38, on the north by La Merced, and on the south by the 500 ha of the estate of Palo Labrado. The property was acquired in 2006 in order to plan a new model of sustainable development and conservation.

Once a model of conservation and sustainability, proven to be effective in other estates in Europe, has been started, an increase in biodiversity is evident; we would go from a model where one or two species are favoured to a new model where we protect threatened species such as the Darwin´s Rhea *(Pterocnemia pennata)*, Mountain Lion *(Puma concolor)*, the Gray Brocket *(Mazama goua-zoubira)*, the Red-winged Tinamou *(Rhynchotus rufescens)* and the Andean Condor *(Vultur gryphus)*, amongst others; and where we introduce new species such as Red Deer *(Cervus elaphus)*.

Sunflower crop under irrigation.
The water falls by gravitional force from the gully of El Cebil.

C. Otero

Red deer in Caraguay are specimens selected from New Zealand stock and crossed with Argentinian creole deer. The photo shows a four-year-old stag.

GAMEFARMING IN THE ANDEAN CORDILLERA

The Estate of Caraguay extends to 1,500 hectares, and presents a unique scenario for the development of a game farming model adapted to the landscape of the Andean foothills.

The longitudinal sectional profile of this estate starts (from west to east) with an almost flat line for the first two kilometres, before rising sharply at its eastern extremity, from a height of 800 m above sea level on the plain to 1,500 m at the summit (La Cumbre) in the space of just 8 km.

At the bottom of the valley runs the river Paclín, whose permanent but shallow waters meander over a bed of permeable sands. This is the western boundary of the property.

The river terraces and the lowest part of the foothills contain good fertile land, never cultivated, with generally deep soil and enough rainfall to allow two crops of sorghum, corn, oat or *porotos* (beans) to be harvested annually, or to irrigate alfalfa and walnut trees or pecan trees with the water which descends the slopes of La Cumbre.

These terraces and foothills start with a *Chaco Seco* or *Dry Chaco* forest type that evolves to a more humid *Chaco Serrano*. As the slope rises higher, it becomes an even more humid subtropical forest *(yunga)* which, finally, above the tree-line (>1,400 m above sea level), turns into *pasto puna* or Indian pasture, the typical Andean grazing of the high summits.

All these habitats just mentioned provide suitable conditions for populations of wild herbivores: native species which are present in the area (gray brocket deer and peccary), native species once present but now extinct (guanacos, rheas), and non-native species which are already present in other parts of Argentine and which now have their own "resident's permit" in the country (red deer, black antelope). However, it is the two extremes of this scenery, the low area and the high area, which provide the best conditions for developing a game farming model that is nowadays to be found in numerous corners of Europe, southern Africa, New Zealand, Chile and even in Argentine itself.

The model selected for the estate of Caraguay and the other estates situated on the slopes of the Sierra de Ancasti range involves three stages of development. Each phase can last between two and five years, and, little by little, aims to incorporate the diverse landscape elements into the conservation/game model.

In essence, the objective is to add value to these wooded hillsides of the Andean foothills, turning them from an excessive and sometimes anarchic cattle-grazing burden to a game farming area that develops in balance with the local wildlife, itself nowadays persecuted and decimated by uncontrolled hunting.

The model envisages the encouragement of non-native herbivores, in particular red deer, for exploitation by hunting (male specimens) or live

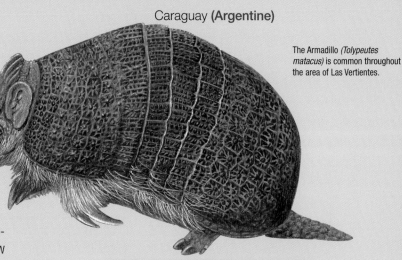

Caraguay (Argentine)

The Armadillo *(Tolypeutes matacus)* is common throughout the area of Las Vertientes.

STAFF OF VERTIENTES DEL ANCASTI
WITH THANKS TO THE KEEPER AND EMPLOYEES

Worker	Position	Estate
Guillaume Janssens	Manager	Vertientes del Ancasti
José Manuel Zafora	Chief Project Officer	Vertientes del Ancasti
Alberto Soria jr.	Administrator	Vertientes del Ancasti
Víctor Quintero	Gunsmith	Vertientes del Ancasti
Sebastián Peirano	Veterinary	Vertientes del Ancasti
Cristian Mejía	Head Game keeper	Vertientes del Ancasti
Ariel Noriega	Game Keeper	Caraguay
Justo Vallejo	Game Keeper	Las Trillas
Martín Guerrero	Game Keeper	Campogrande
José Noriega	Game Keeper	Cañón Viejo
Sergio Acosta	Game Keeper	Valle Viejo
Fabián Acosta	Game Keeper	Yunca Pampa
René Guerrero	Game Keeper	Corralito
Héctor Salcedo	Game Keeper	Cañón Viejo
Alberto Barrientos	Game Keeper	Taco Ralo
Gladys de Mejías	Housekeeper	Palo Labrado
Rosalía de Noriega	Housekeeper	Caraguay
Nena Leguizamón	Field Assistant	Vertientes del Ancasti

SCHEMATIC VEGETATION PROFILE ON THE ESTATE OF CARAGUAY

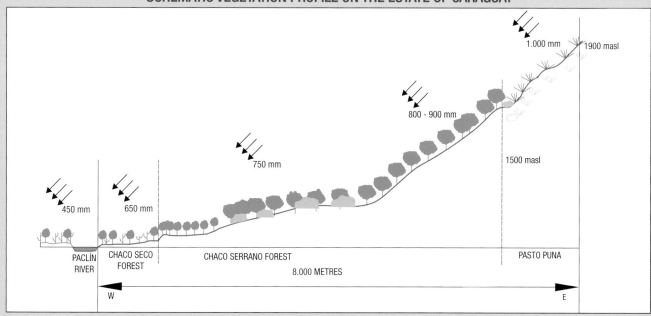

1.000 mm — 1900 masl

800 - 900 mm

750 mm

1500 masl

450 mm

650 mm

PACLÍN RIVER

CHACO SECO FOREST

CHACO SERRANO FOREST

PASTO PUNA

8.000 METRES

W

E

capture for purposes of repopulation (females as well as males), and the conservation of native species: peccary, gray brocket, mountain lion, ocelot, anteater and armadillo, amongst others.

A further aim is to restore local species that have disappeared, by reintroducing them into the river plains (rhea) or onto the high pastures of La Cumbre (rhea and guanaco).

The intermediate area of the humid *Chaco Serrano* and the *Yunga* is home to an extraordinarily diverse flora, which will be a reservoir and refuge for native species. The river terraces, foothills and peaks would house the non-native herbivores, the object of the game farm. Such activity gives value to these depressed areas, provides jobs in the countryside and creates natural space with the necessary peace and quiet for other species such as armadillos, vizcachas, ocelots and anteaters, dusky-legged guan and Chaco chachalaca, red-winged tinamou, black-and-chestnut eagles, Andean condor and king vulture to prosper.

At Caraguay the process began in September 2007, embracing 20% of the overall area. Several infrastructural improvements were made, such as: a network of internal paths, peripheral paths and firebreaks; a peripheral fence, 2 m high with metal posts; creation of firebreaks along every path; removing 30 ha of shrubs but retaining the trees, in order to sow buffalo grass, cereals (corn, sorghum, oats, barley) and alfalfa; creation of ponds and water holes, viewing points, hides,

feeders, salt blocks, handling pens, gravity irrigation system covering 20 ha, using water coming from the slopes and springs on the estate; planting 3 ha of local Walnut Trees *(Juglans australis)* and Pecan Tree *(Carya illinoinnensis)*; restoring the Casa de Ariel and Casa de Los Venados (200 m^2), of a shed/warehouse (120 m^2) and construction of 7 bungalows to accommodate visitors with typical *quincho* eating area (300 m^2) and camp-fire. Besides, 200 head of red deer with a sex-ratio of 1:1 were introduced.

Two European technicians are involved in implementing this project: José Manuel Zafora and Guillaume Janssens. In addition an Argentinian technician, Alberto Soria, and local keepers Cristian Mejía (Head Game Keeper) and Ariel Noriega (Game Keeper), all highly enthusiastic and motivated, are in charge of Caraguay, helped by the rest of the keepers and a local team that, at some moments, amounts to a total of 47 people.

This first stage was completed in the record time of 6 months, its official inauguration taking place in March 2008.

The second stage deals with the development of the high peaks area, which accounts for 40% of the overall estate. It is home to a magnificent area

The Eared Dove *(Zenaida auriculata)* is extraordinarily abundant on the 35,000 hectares of farmland managed by Coto Caraguay, and offers a natural resource of enormous potential.

of *puna* or Indian pasture that extends to 600 ha. In the little gulleys and in the most sheltered hollows, this area houses a true botanic treasure, forests of Pine *(Podocarpus parlatorei)* in small woods and isolated stands.

This area would be wonderful for developing an ecological model that would be reminiscent of the Scottish Highlands but in a much milder climate. This scenery would be perfect ground for red deer as a game-farming species, living side by side with reintroduced populations of rheas and guanacos. There is a super-predator living in this area, the puma, or *león* as it is locally known, as well as an extraordinary beautiful scavenger, the Andean condor.

The development of this stage would be envisaged around 2012, once the low ground is consolidated and the trophy heads of the red deer have developed satisfactorily.

Carlos Otero

Southern winter of 2007: Arnaud de Merode and Jean Cristophe de Lantsheere finishing their placement in Las Vertientes del Ancasti. Here seen in the agricultural land where the eared dove abounds.

Las Trillas

Neotropical

Location: Department of Paclín. Catamarca, Argentine.
Surface: 1,600 ha.

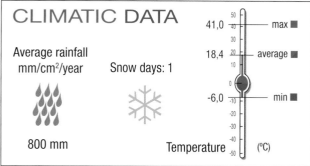

CLIMATIC DATA

Average rainfall
mm/cm²/year

Snow days: 1

800 mm

Temperature (ºC)

41,0 — max ■
18,4 — average ■
-6,0 — min ■

SUMMARY

The estate is located in the southeast of the province of Catamarca (Argentine), on the border of the departments of Paclín and El Alto. It is situated 40 km from the capital city of the province, San Fernando del Valle de Catamarca. It extends to 1,600 ha and its average altitude is 1,200 m above sea level. It has an astonishingly rich ecology. The estate was acquired in 2005 with the purpose of offering a new model for sustainable development and conservation.

Since the property was acquired, its network of tracks and paths has been improved and it can be accessed by 4x4 vehicle from Alijilán village.

The intention is to change the direction of the land management, moving from traditional livestock to a model of conservation and wildlife which is more respectful of, and committed to, the existing natural resources, promotes biodiversity and guarantees sustainable development, following the philosophy of Wildlife Estates.

Southern slopes of Las Trillas above the Sauce Mayo or Carpintería river.
In the bottom, Yunga woodland. In the foreground, specimens
of Pino del Cerro (Podocarpus parlatorei).

C. Otero

Guillaume Janssens and Pancho Maza reconnoitring Las Trillas.

Caraguay Es

Plateaus covered by Indian pasture (*Stipa* sp., *Festuca* sp.), the habitat of guaypo, rheas and

A SUSTAINABLE MODEL FOR THE ANDES

The native *criollo* horse, a placid, agile, strong, comfortable animal, stumbled as we crossed a small stream, and woke me from the drowsiness which our slow uphill walk had brought on. We had ridden almost three hours of the way up to Cumbre Baja. Behind us, the *chaco serrano* woodland of the Vizcote ravine, on the estate of Cañón Viejo del Paclín, and now, after crossing a transitional area of dry scrub land at an altitude of 1,500 metres where thickets of scrub and a few isolated *horco molle* trees grew, we were heading for the top, and passing through a vast limitless grassland of *pasto puna* or *pasto indio.*

The fescue grasses sway in the gusts from La Cumbre's peaks, and a sea of grass moves gently back and forth, like waves in an inlet. Still yellow at the end of the southern winter, the peaks seem like a smooth golden grassy tapestry, gently moved by the air.

The surprise came when we reached the Cumbre Baja, because after a Cumbre Baja logically there always has to be a ...Cumbre Alta!

From the valley of the River Paclín, 1,600 metres below, it had seemed that the Cumbre Baja and the Cumbre Alta were the same thing, just one huge mountain slope. They had not revealed the fact that between them there was a *hidden valley*. I felt as if this moment could not be real. How had that valley appeared there? It was hidden from sight. Not even Pablo Leguizamon, the mountain guide who is accompanying me and has led us up these winding paths, had told me anything about it. However, there it was, a valley almost 2,000 hectares in size, in the shape of a large triangle 12 km in length, its top corner pointing towards the Southern Cross. And in that far corner was the source of the San Martín river that runs through the bottom of that *hidden valley*, from south to north, more than 10 km in length.

The western slope was formed by the Cumbre Baja, where we had just arrived on those little native horses, and it was soft and undulating land, covered by thin Indian upland pasture. In the centre of the valley, the course of the San Martín river, at this stage of its course a noisy mountain creek, and on the opposite side, to the east, the slope that rose up to the Cumbre Alta. And between the creek and the Cumbre Alta, thick *yunga*, typical mountain forest of the subtropical north of Argentine; real, genuine rainforest.

After crossing the San Martín valley, it took a further two hours to reach the Cumbre Alta, nearly 2,000 metres above sea level, following a track made by cattle, winding between the yunga at a spot called Cuesta de la Esperanza.

Footprints of Gray Brocket Deer *(Mazama gouazoubira)* on the same bank of the San Martín river, sometimes hidden under those of the puma or mountain lion. The lion was abundant in those parts and we had counted as many as seven carcases on the way up from Cañón Viejo; they were calves, some old, others more recent, but all of them, said Martín Guerrero, eaten by the mountain lions.

Going up the Cuesta de la Esperanza we had frightened away a flock of nervous Dusky-Legged Guan *(Penelope obscura),* that disappeared into the thick cover of Coco *(Fagara coco)* and Horco Molle *(Blepharocalyx gigantea)* trees.

And when we reached the top of the Cumbre Alta, we witnessed an impressive show of Andean

C. Otero

Condor *(Vultur griphus)*, with more than twelve birds perched in the sunshine on a cliff at Potrero de la Lechuza.

The Cumbre Alta presented us with another surprise because it was in fact an extensive plateau of almost 2,000 ha, with a gentle downhill slope from west to east, crossed by Sauce Mayo or Carpintería river, which rises here and is fed by hundreds of little streams and springs that channel the rainwater with which the grazing of the high Andean *puna* uplands is saturated.

And finally, to the south, like a backdrop to this tableland, the peak of Cerro Alto de Corralito, at a height of almost 2,000 metres. It marked the limit of this fantastic view.

At that moment I knew, instantly, that after a search that had taken me to visit 84 different estates in this province and in the neighbouring provinces of Tucumán, Salta and Santiago del Estero over the last 6 months (with monthly trips from Europe that had seldom lasted more than 10 days), I had found the estate where I could develop this overseas initiative.

It sounded a bit pretentious at that point in my life to look for "virgin land", with all its potential still intact, where I could develop a sustainable model and could transfer the strict rules that we have been using in Europe to those lands of far horizons and immeasurable dimensions.

The model that we were hoping to achieve was ambitious but at the same time simple and quite basic. It is a model that we have tested a thousand times – to keep a long story short – during 30 years of professional life with RENATUR S.A. in Spain, Portugal, Morocco, France, Mexico…

We were not therefore starting out from a base in utopia but on an integrated management model that defines values which are both sustainable and renewable.

The almost 750 head of livestock – cattle and horses – present at Las Trillas at that time will be replaced by wild herbivores such as Guanaco *(Lama guanicoe)*, Greater Rhea *(Rhea americana)*, and the already almost indigenous Red Deer *(Cervus elaphus)*.

The first two were species that had existed here until a dozen years ago, and the third should spread into this region sooner or later from adjacent areas in Santiago, Córdoba or Tucumán.

Once the process of restoring the populations of guanaco and great rhea, and red deer as well, is complete, the presence of easier food supplies will lead to a further process of encouragement and establishment of the Puma, the lion of these mountains, as well as the Andean condor, which nests in the inaccessible cliffs of the Cumbre Alta,

C. Otero

more to the south of Las Trillas in the fluvial valley of the river Paclín.

And, to continue with the logical sequence of effect, cause, and effect, we would achieve the profile of a Wildlife Estate, cataloguing some 6 quarry species and about 200 species of protected vertebrates.

In addition, those peaks include another fantastic wildlife treasure, the guaypo or Red-Winged Tinamou *(Rhynchotus rufescens)*, which, in the eyes of Europeans, would equate without doubt to the Scottish grouse as the equivalent game species in the Old World.

C. Otero

The soils of Yunca Pampa are very rich and deep. They have never been cultivated. They represent a tapestry of highland pastures, composed of *Stipa* sp and *Festuca* sp.

Cañón Viejo del Paclín

Neotropical

Location: Paclín Department. Catamarca, Argentine.
Surface: 1,736 ha.

CLIMATIC DATA

Average rainfall
mm/cm²/year

Snow days: 0

41,0 — max ■

17 — average ■

-6,0 — min ■

750 mm

Temperature (°C)

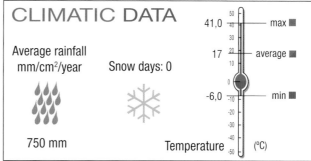

SUMMARY

The estate of *Cañón Viejo del Paclín* lies in Vertientes del Ancasti, in the province of Catamarca, Argentine.

Cañón Viejo has a surface area of 1,736 hectares on the slopes of the Sierra de Ancasti range, between La Cumbre (1,800 m above sea level) and the Paclín river (700 m).

Its western edge runs 3,000 metres along the main highway (Ruta Nacional 38) from Catamarca to Tucumán. Its northern and southern boundaries, adjoining other estates of Vertientes del Ancasti, are 7,000 m (Palo Labrado) and 6,500 m (Campogrande) in length. The eastern limit is marked by the summit of La Cumbre Alta in the Ancasti mountains, and borders the estate of Corralito.

It contains two types of forest, Chaco and Yunga, and its average annual rainfall of 750 mm means that some streams run with water throughout the year.

Cañón Viejo belongs to the Valle de Servicios SRL company.

Slopes of the Sierra de Ancasti range
on the Estate Cañón Viejo del Paclín.

G. Janssens

CAÑÓN DEL PACLÍN: A MODEL OF HOW TO PLAN AND MANAGE NATURAL RESOURCES SUSTAINABLY

The Sierra de Ancasti is located in the *Chaco* eco-region, or more precisely the sub-region known as the *Chaco Serrano* which represents the forest area in the province of Catamarca.

The advance of deforestation and accompanying progressive decrease in biodiversity determine the urgency and need to undertake projects such as that being implemented by the Valle de Servicios SRL company, in Vertientes del Ancasti, a territory of approximately 13,500 ha located in the southeast of Catamarca, in the western sector of the Sierra de Ancasti range.

Elevations in this area range from 700 m in the west to 2,000 m to the east, and reflect the diversity in landscape and ecology.

The richness of the wildlife of Las Vertientes is shown by the fact that, of the 314 potential species for this area, 102 of them would be found in one or other of the conservation categories such as one of the lists included in Law 22.421 (1981), the Convention on International Trade in Endangered Species of Wild Fauna and Flora (CITES, 1995), or the International Union for Conservation of Nature (IUCN, 1996).

The richness and complexity of the natural environment of Las Vertientes, and the size of the area it occupies, coupled with its location in a region particularly threatened by problems of deforestation and progressive environmental degradation, makes this area an ideal place in which to develop a management strategy such as the one set out by the Valle de Servicios SRL company, in which conservation and the sustainable use of renewable natural resources are very closely linked.

One of the most serious consequences of deforestation is the fragmentation of natural habitats and the consequential barrier effect on wildlife communities. This represents one of the main causes of loss of biodiversity and is one of the factors that should be particularly acted upon by those involved in the conservation and management of these lands.

Specifically to avoid the consequences of this problem in the region of Catamarca, our company has started to implement the Vertientes del Ancasti Project following the guidelines on Wildlife Estates promoted by the European Commission (Copenhagen, September 2006; Tor, March 2008).

This far-reaching project represents an important reference model of a new strategy for land management, which, from a global perspective, integrates aspects of conservation, sustainable development and social responsibility. It has been necessary to establish a clear set of values and goals which the sustainability strategy of our company must adhere to, so that the Project is an open window on each of the commitments undertaken by the Company, and an expression of its social and

The Chaco Seco (Dry Chaco) vegetation of the foothills gives way higher up to heavy and dense rainforest, the *Yunga*.

C. Otero

environmental dimensions. The project has been developed with an integrated and coherent vision in mind, with a clear understanding of how it operates and works as well as what it contributes to sustainability and its international influence. The outline of its various component functions is as follows:

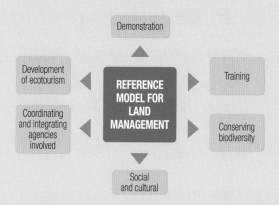

- ■ **Demonstration:** The project has been conceived as an international reference model for the sustainable management of land in which conservation and the improvement of natural resources is inextricably linked to improving the living conditions of local people.
- ■ **Development of Ecotourism:** The creation of accessible and open spaces will be promoted for the purpose of such activities as birdwatching and productive hunting (non-extractive), following the model of the Network of Wildlife Estates from the European Union, in which dedicated hunting areas are placed next to areas used as a wildlife sanctuary. In the case of Cañón Viejo del Paclín, hunting would not affect the indigenous wildlife, but would focus only on non-native species (red deer, axis deer, black antelope) which would replace cattle, thereby creating a new and renewable resource under the heading of "hunting stock".
- ■ **Training:** This will include the creation of a Rural Training School and capacity building measures, with special emphasis on the more significant aspects of the sustainable management of resources.

- ■ **Social and Cultural:** This will promote the participation and involvement of the surrounding population in the management of the project, and will be a model of Corporate Social Responsibility (CSR)
- ■ **Conserving biodiversity:** Wildlife Conservation Centre and central point of action for matters relating to the active conservation of nature on privately owned property and landscapes, tracking the most up-to-date trends in the world.

To achieve the functions listed above and to validate the project as a Model of International Reference, agreements are set up with local and European NGOs, conservation plans are carried out through partnerships with local authorities, Argentinian universities, social partners and other internationally recognised and prestigious organisations from the European Union and elsewhere.

Although Vertientes del Ancasti Project, of which Cañón Viejo Estate is one of its exponents, has an indefinite timeline, in reality it is based on a time frame of 15 years, during which we will try to carry out our measures for conservation and management based on factual and adequate knowledge of the current problems and future prospects of these estates.

José María Romero

The Collared Anteater
(Tamandua tetradactyla),
lives in trees and
is present on the Cañón Viejo Estate.

VERTIENTES DEL ANCASTI ESTATE

The clear and constant waters of the Paclín river flow through the bottom of the valley, forming the western boundary of Las Vertientes.

CONSERVATION PLANS

The extinction of plant and animal species is one of the most worrying symptoms of the environmental deterioration that we are witnessing in Argentine, because it constitutes an irreversible process that deprives us forever of a unique and irreplaceable genetic material.

The *San Carlos Foundation for the Stewardship of Land* is deeply worried by this situation and strongly committed to the conservation of endangered species. With excellent results obtained from other sites across the world, it strives for a land management model that promotes biodiversity and guarantees sustainable development.

The lands under this management model will be called *Wildlife Estates*, and will be those where traditional livestock is replaced by game animals, respecting existing natural resources and committed, by means of Promotion and Conservation Plans, to endangered and protected species in Argentine, and specifically in the province of Catamarca.

The conservation plans implemented in Las Vertientes, with the help of researchers Edward Campbell, María Encina Aulló and Gonzalo Díaz, and highlighted here by the San Carlos Foundation are the following:

1. Conservation Plan for the Andean Condor *(Vultur gryphus)*.
2. Conservation Plan for the Pino del cerro *(Podocarpus parlatorei)*.
3. Conservation Plan for the Red-winged Tinamou *(Rhynchotus rufescens)*.
4. Conservation Plan for the Guanaco *(Lama guanicoe)*.
5. Conservation Plan for the Rhea *(Rhea americana)*.
6. Conservation Plan for the Mountain Lion *(Puma concolor)*.
7. Conservation Plan for the Dusky-legged Guan *(Penelope obscura)*.
8. Conservation Plan for the Gray Brocket Deer *(Mazama gouazoubira)*.
9. Conservation Plan for the Ocelot *(Leopardus pardalis)*.
10. Planned creation of a native flora nursery.

We shall briefly describe each of these plans:

C. Ote

1. Conservation Plan for the Andean Condor (*Vultur gryphus*)

The Andean condor belongs to the Cathartidae family, as do many others that feed on carrion. Acknowledged as the biggest bird on the planet, it reaches a height of 1.3 m and has a wingspan of 3.3 m.

The Condor's favourite habitat is the highest and steepest cliffs. They nest in caves in vertical rocky walls protected from the wind and the open air. However, the roosting sites are located in high cliffs protected from the rain, the wind and potential predators.

Condors require a habitat with at least three conditions:

- Winds or rising air currents that allow them to fly high.
- Open ground so that carrion can be seen from height.
- An adequate supply of dead animals.

The development of this conservation plan is based on the classification of the Andean Condor as a protected species in the province of Catamarca, and an emblematic species of the wildlife existing in Las Vertientes. This is the strategic and conceptual context for the conservation plan for the Andean Condor *(Vultur gryphus)* on the land managed by the San Carlos Foundation for the Stewardship of Land.

The plan's objectives are:

1. To eliminate the mortality of condors from human activity in the Sierra de Ancasti range.
2. To maintain the increase in population.
3. To achieve an occupied area of land of at least 400 km² or 40,000 ha on which the San Carlos Foundation is active.
4. To reach a population of at least 60 breeding pairs across this same land area over the next 10 years. (2009-2019).

The action points are:

1. Reducing non-natural death factors.
2. Monitoring the population.
3. Protecting and improving the habitat.
4. Promoting research activities designed to acquire deeper knowledge of the species - its habitat, behaviour or any other characteristic that may help towards improving its conservation.
5. Increasing the populatioon of wild herbivores

C. Otero

Bañadero del Cóndor (the Condor's bathing place) at the source of the Carpintería river.

(red deer, black antelope, rhea and guanaco) as a food source.

2. Conservation Plan for the Pino del Cerro (*Podocarpus parlatorei*)

Also known as the white pine or the mountain pine, it is distributed across the south of Perú, Bolivia and the northwest of Argentina, where its southernmost boundary is in Catamarca. This gives incalculable value to the populations under study.

It is an evergreen tree that reaches 10m to 15 m in height, and is very slow-growing. It takes 50 years to reach reproductive maturity.

The objectives to be followed in this plan are:

To expand the *pino del cerro* stock present on the Wildlife Estate as well as to collaborate on a possible Global Plan for this species where knowledge of the genetic variability of populations, together with detailed knowledge of their distribution, could provide valuable information about the geobotany of the species.

In addition, there is a mutualism between the *Podocarpus parlatorei* and other endangered species, or species with limited distribution, such as the Dusky-legged Guan *(Penelope obscura)* and Red-faced Guan *(Penelope dabbenei)* or the Alder Parrot *(Amazona tucumana)*. This mutualism is based on the important dispersal tasks (or zoochory) that they carry out when they eat its fruits and seeds.

C. Otero

Relics of old pino del cerro woodlands on tops of Yunca Pampa.

This species is primarily a ground-dwelling bird, a forager, with short wings and legs. It weighs approximately one kilogram and can reach 42 centimetres in length. It derives its name from the fact that, in flight and especially against the sun, its wings have a very pronounced red tone. The head and the breast are a cinnamon colour, and it has dark brown spots or stripes on its back.

The red-winged tinamou is omnivorous. It feeds on plant material (green shoots, seeds, roots and fruits), larvae and insects, and its diet varies depending on the season. In summer, it feeds on insects and other small animals (including small mammals), changing to plant material such as fruits, shoots, tubers *(Cyperus sp.)* in winter.

Its natural predators are birds of prey, foxes, felines and reptiles.

It is one of the most coveted birds and therefore the most pursued, because of its exquisite meat.

The action plan will be as follows:

- Conservation of the pampas in the whole area of Cumbre Alta and Cumbre Baja.
- Monitoring and control of the populations, by means of periodic census.
- Game-keeper work to avoid illegal hunting (poaching) of this species.
- Controlling opportunist predators, especially in the nesting season.

Action points are:

At a general level, maximum protection will be established in places where the pino del cerro is located, with consideration being given to a protective margin around these populations. The management of these peripheral areas will be a key element for natural regeneration and the expansion of the existing woodland sites.

At a local level:

1. Trying to improve the current populations in Las Trillas, Yunca Pampa, Corralito, Palo Labrado and Cañón Viejo by creating inventories to indicate the density of the mature pines and their natural regeneration.
2. To promote the critical stage of plant recruitment, due to the fact that the mortality rate of seeds and seedlings is at its highest level within the mature forests. With this purpose in mind, an attempt will be made to develop areas along the margins of these plots where plenty of light is available. In addition, creating areas of preferred habitat for its main dispersers, such as the Alder Parrot, would be very important.
3. Creating a nursery with 1500 small plants of *Podocarpus parlatorei*.

3. Conservation Plan for the Red-Winged Tinamou *(Rhynchotus rufescens)*

Endemic bird of Argentine, belonging to the Tinamiformes order (Tinamidae Family), usually known as *Tinamous*. Its local name is the *Guaypo*.

4. Conservation Plan for the Guanaco *(Lama guanicoe)*

Wild elegant camelid, with an approximate height of one metre at the shoulder and weighing almost 100kg. Covered by a thick protective double coat. It has a dark head and white under parts and legs. It can reach a speed of 50km/h, which gives it security against predators, since it lives in open places without shelter. In Argentine it is considered a wild animal and has certain protection.

The main reasons for the decrease in its distribution are:

- Competition for food with other livestock.
- Habitat change.
- Uncontrolled hunting for its meat, skin or wool.
- Lack of protection and management plan that would assure its conservation.
- Natural predators, especially the puma.

The main objective is to create an extensive breeding herd in order to establish a permanent population in Las Trillas, Yunca Pampa and Corra-

The Guaypo or Red-winged Tinamou, a game species which in the eyes of Europeans would equate without doubt to the Grouse of the Scottish Highlands.

lito and, at the same time, to provide specimens to other areas where it will be introduced.

It is worth mentioning that studies carried out in some populations of guanaco living at low density have shown 40% of the overall mortality to be caused by the puma.

The action plan will consist of:

1. Creation of a core population of over 500 individuals within 10-12 years.
2. Control and monitoring of the specimens reintroduced.
3. Health analysis.
4. Informative programs.

5. Reintroduction and Conservation Plan for the Rhea *(Rhea americana)*

Also known locally as the *Ñandú* or *Suri*, it is a flightless bird with long legs, each with three toes. It has a long neck and small head. Gregarious and living in families, the male incubates the eggs laid by the female. There are usually between 9 and 25 eggs in each clutch. The incubation lasts from 34 to 40 days, the principal hatching season being in the period from January and March. It is a herbivore with a predominant intake of grasses *(Stipa spp)*. Its legs enable it to be a strong runner, reaching speeds of 60 km/h.

Currently it is considered as a vulnerable species due to:

- Pressure from hunting because of the international demand for its feathers and skin.
- Belief that it is a potential competitor of domestic livestock for grazing.
- Encroachment of the livestock/agricultural boundary into its natural habitat.

Objectives

The creation of an extensive breeding flock is planned, to establish a permanent population in Las Trillas, Yunca Pampa and Corralito and, at the same time, to provide specimens to other areas where it will be introduced.

This plan will start with the introduction of 100 individuals within the next five years.

Action plan:

1. Control of fox populations.
2. Control and monitoring of the individuals reintroduced, by means of annual census. Special attention will be given to the nests in

C. M. Martín / J.L. Rodríguez

an attempt to minimize losses during the first years of the plan.

3. Development of habitat improvements through:
- Conservation of primary grazing areas.
- Conservation of shrub patches for shelter.
- Health analysis.

The guanaco will be reintroduced in Yunca Pampa and Las Trillas in 2010-2011.

6. Conservation Plan for the Puma or Mountain Lion *(Puma concolor)*

The Puma or Mountain Lion is a solitary species of nocturnal habit which makes use of a great variety of habitats, including planted woodland, forest areas both at low and high altitudes, meadows, swamps and anywhere where there is appropriate prey. The principal elements of its carnivorous diet are: red deer, cattle, horses, peccaries and smaller animals.

Adults stand about 60 to 76 cm tall at the shoulders. Adult males measure around 2.4 m in length, from nose to tail, with overall ranges between 1.5 and 2.75 m for the species in general. Males have an average weight of between 53 and 72 kg. In rare cases, some may reach over 118 kg. The average weight of the female is between 34 and 48 kg.

The mountain lion requires a large territory for its survival. According to different authors, individuals occupy areas of between 13 and 62 km^2 (1300 to 6200 ha) although adult males range from 83.3 to 85 km^2 (8,330 to 8,500 ha). This depends on the abundance of food, habitat and breeding status of the individual.

C. Otero

Locally the Puma is known as the *León* and is abundant throughout the Sierra de Ancasti. The photograph depicts the place known as *El Monte del León* (the Puma's Wood).

The objectives of the plan have been:

1. To ensure that there are always four-five pairs of puma across the entire *Vertientes del Ancasti* range.
2. To develop a system of control and surveillance measures to prevent damage to the habitat of the species.
3. Direct management measures and habitat restoration through the development of technical criteria for management, conservation and restoration.
4. Any hunting practised, both in areas of big game as well as small game, must be compatible in the medium and long term with the maintenance of puma populations.
5. To encourage a form of sustainable hunting management that is compatible with the puma.
6. To develop coordinated technical management criteria, reflected in Hunting Plans (habitat management, forestry and agri-environmental measures) in order to encourage populations of potential prey.
7. To analyse areas that are capable of functioning as potential sites for the long term conservation of puma populations.

Action Plan

1. Run a powerful campaign to increase awareness of the delicate status of the species in the region of Catamarca, emphasising its important role in the ecosystem, its place at the top of the food chain and its contribution to richer biodiversity.
2. Furthermore, by encouraging and establishing significant populations of red deer black antelope, guanaco, peccary, armadillo, rhea and several species of marsupials across the estate, the food chain would be restored, providing the puma with more than enough food resources.
3. The increase and encouragement of game species will bring immeasurable nutritional benefit to this predator.
4. At the same time, implementing a Wildlife Estate would assure habitat conservation that would favour the presence of all native species associated with this region.
5. And finally, constant vigilance by the estate game keepers would offer security and peace against poachers.

7. Conservation Plan for the Dusky-legged Guan *(Penelope obscura)*

The bird measures an average of 70-75 centimetres in length and weighs an average of 1.2 kilograms. Its beak is black and its legs dark grey. The unfeathered skin on its face is grey and the throat is red. The forehead and crown are black. The neck, chest and back are brown with green tinges and feathers edged in white. The rest of the plumage is brown with green tinges. The tail is dark brown.

It eats fruit, flowers and buds taken from the ground or plucked from branches of trees, and it acts as a seed disperser for various species of trees and palms, such as the endangered Palm *Euterpe edulis*, or the Palms of the *Syagrus* genus (e.g. Queen Palm and Licuri).

The nest is shaped like a platform, and is placed in trees. It is built with sticks, stems of climbing plants or shrubs, with leaves lining the inside. It lays 3 white eggs.

Their habits are predominantly arboreal, being particularly active in the twilight hours. Little is known about their voices and their ability to produce a dull humming or drumming sound by vibrating their outer wing feathers.

Objectives

The importance of the Dusky-legged Guan can be summarised by:

- Its important role in seed dispersal, helping the maintenance of forests. The dusky-legged guan, and all members of the Cracidae family in general, can be said to be *key indicator species of healthy ecosystems wherever they live*.
- Its role as a biological indicator of habitat.
- An important protein resource for local communities.
- A valuable resource for ecotourism.

The threats to which they are exposed are essentially the loss of their habitat due to deforestation, the growing development of agriculture, and trafficking in wildlife (illegal and unsustainable poaching).

The *San Carlos Foundation for the Stewardship of Land* has extensive knowledge of this problem, and one of the conservation objectives introduced is to achieve a population of at least 600 Dusky-legged Guan *(Penelope obscura)* in Las Vertientes, having established (through transect surveys) that there are already about 3 individuals in each 100 ha.

Action Plan

The conservation and encouragement of the Dusky-legged Guan population will be achieved as a result of the following measures:

- Control and monitoring of the bird through population censuses as well as identifying the locations of roosting areas.
- Installing grain feeders and water troughs in the roosting areas.
- Control and constant vigilance by the estate keepers to prevent poaching.
- Control of specific predators
- Conservation and maintenance of woodland and gallery forest.

8. Conservation Plan for the Gray Brocket Deer *(Mazama gouazoubira)*

A species of brocket deer, between 55 and 65 cm in height and 140 cm in length. It can weigh up to 25 kg. At a year old, males develop un-branched horns that reach a length of 15 cm. It lives in open, or semi-open, wooded areas. Solitary or in pairs, it is notably territorial and marks the perimeter of its area with faeces, urine, etc.

Nocturnal and crepuscular in habit. At the hottest times of the day it retreats to thicker forest or pasture to rest.

Objective

The main objective would be to consolidate a population of 1,000 gray brocket in the Wildlife Estate Vertientes del Ancasti, to achieve a density of 7.5 individuals per 100 hectares within a time-frame of 5 years (2009-2014).

At the same time, its increase will facilitate the completion of the food chain, helping the populations of predators such as ocelot and mountain lion.

Action Plan

1. As the most important and fundamental measure towards conserving the gray brocket, we will pursue the best possible maintenance of the 'threshold of stillness'

Waterfall of Las Trillas, source of the Carpintería river, which is here still known as the El Zarzo stream. Wonderful habitat for Puma Lion and Gray Brocket Deer.

C. Otero

and the habitat in which these animals will live.

2. At the same time we will undertake annual censuses to monitor the status of the population over the course of time.

3. Likewise we will sow seed and specific crops, and install selective watering and feeding equipment, in order to provide supplementary food in times of shortage.

9. Conservation plan for the Ocelot
(Leopardus pardalis)

Also known locally as the *Gato Onza*, it is a medium size cat of between 115 and 165 cm in length, weighing between 11 and 16 kg.

The ocelot is mostly nocturnal and highly territorial. It will fight fiercely in territorial disputes, sometimes to the death. Like most felines, it is solitary, usually meeting only to mate. However, during the day it rests in trees or other dense foliage, and will occasionally share its lair with another Ocelot of the same sex. After mating, the female will find a den in a cave in a rocky bluff, a hollow tree, or a dense (preferably thorny) thicket. The gestation period is estimated to be 70 days. Generally the female will have 2-3 kittens, born in the autumn with their eyes closed and with a thin covering of hair.

In Argentine it is found in specific jungle habitat in the region of Chaco and in the yungas of norwest of the country.

It feeds on cavies, young gray brocket kids, peccaries, birds, small birds...

The presence of Ocelot *(Leopardus pardalis mitis)* is linked to the *Yunga* forest in Las Vertientes.

The reduction in population size and the fact of its isolation leads to loss of genetic variability which means in turn that it loses the ability to adapt to environmental changes and increases its vulnerability to parasites and disease.

Objectives

This conservation plan aims to ensure a continuous population of up to six pairs across the whole of *Vertientes del Ancasti* range.

Action Plan

The establishment of significant populations of medium-sized birds, rodents, and even European hare and gray brocket in the area would consolidate the food chain, thereby providing the Ocelot with food resources that help the process of conserving this predator.

At the same time, the implementation of a *Wildlife Estate* means that the "threshold of stillness" of the whole ecosystem is ensured, and its habitat conserved, promoting the presence of all native species associated with these eco-regions.

And finally, the constant vigilance of the estates' gamekeepers would offer the security, peace and quiet necessary to combat poachers for whom this species can provide the lure of a hide, and trophy, still in great demand today.

10. Planned creation of a native flora nursery

The creation of the nursery will try to achieve the following objectives:

- Developing species like the *Pino del Cerro* or the *Pacara* Tree *(Enterolobium contortisi-liquum)*, of particular interest in this area, attempting to gather as much information as possible about their needs for possible reintroduction in areas within their historic range.

- Production of high value timber species by promoting the use of valuable natural varieties as well as diversified rural investment.

- Developing new techniques for growing tree species, concentrating on their morphological and physiological requirements.

The nursery will be approximately 1000 m² in size, and will be divided into four sectors described as follows:

1. The first section is devoted to the cultivation and production of orchids, the two native

species present in Catamarca: *Sacoila lanceolata* and *Oncidium bifolium*.

2. The second sector, between 250-300 m², will be divided into 8 beds, each sub-divided into two plots that will be irrigated. Each plot will be irrigated independently. The species selected for this sector will be the Floss Silk Tree *(Chorisia speciosa)*, the Quebracho *(Schinopsis balansae)*, the carob tree, and others.

3. The third sector, of similar size to the previous one, will be devoted to typical species of the Yunga with showy flowers: *pacara*, *jacaranda*, *tipa and lapacho*.

4. The fourth sector will be composed of six beds each with a shaded area and workbench (with an electric power supply) for research, handling and other tasks. This area will be aimed at the *Pino del Cerro (Podocarpus parlatorei)*.

Besides being considered a conservation measure in its own right, the nursery will act as a support tool in carrying out many of the conservation plans described above.

It is estimated that the capacity of the nursery, in terms of number of plants, and encompassing all growth stages, could be of the order of up to 35,000 plants.

The species on which more emphasis would be placed are:

- The *Pino del Cerro (Podocarpus parlatorei)*.
- The Pacara Tree *(Enterolobium contortisiliquum)*.
- Native orchids belonging to the Orchidaceae family.
- The jacaranda, lapacho and tipa, representing trees with striking blooms.
- The Floss Silk Tree *(Chorisia speciosa)*, Quebracho Colorado *(Schinopsis balansae)*, the carob tree and others.

THE VIRGIN LANDS BELONGS TO:

San Carlos Foundation for the Stewardship of Land

Vertientes del Ancasti

RENATUR, S.A.
Recursos Naturales

Renatur, S.A.

FORESTARIA
SOCIEDAD DE SERVICIOS FORESTALES INTEGRADOS

Forestaria, S.A.

Activities offer in Vertientes del Ancasti:

- Country park
- Cycling
- Equestrian
- Restaurant
- Rural tourism

- Walking trails
- Birdwatching
- Hunting
- Shooting
- Fishing

- Research
- Wildlife Management School

CONTACT DATA

Argentine
LA QUEBRADA AGROPECUARIA SRL
C/ Sarmiento 83, 4700 S. Fernando del Valle de Catamarca (Argentina)
(0054 3833 422 573, lic.soria@arnet.com.ar

Spain
RENATUR, S.A.,
Urb. La Cabaña, C/ Burgos, 107, 28223 Pozuelo de Alarcón, Madrid. (Spain)
(0034 917 990 542 / 520). renatur@arrakis.es

FORESTARIA SL
C/ Atarazanas, 2 - 4ª planta • 29005 Málaga. (Spain)
(0034 952 219 996)
dirección@mediterraneoasesores.net

Theme 8

Transmissions & Foundations

PUBLIC GOODS FROM PRIVATE LAND

Corrado Pirzio-Biroli

THE CORE IDEAS

1. The core ideas of this paper are summarised in the following statements.

- The majority of European land is in a managed state. Europe has little truly natural, unmanaged environment. Most land management is performed by farmers and foresters who provide a range of environmental services in addition to the food and fibre they supply through markets.

- Because there are no spontaneously occurring markets for environmental services they are not provided to the extent society would like. The under-provision of rural environmental services is a classic, and pervasive, case of market failure which affects the majority of the European land area.

- European society is highly concerned about these failures especially biodiversity loss, landscape degradation, and pollution of water and atmosphere. In short, European land managers are providing insufficient environmental "goods" and too many environmental "bads". The scale of the failures has been grossly underestimated, our policy responses are inadequate.

- There are reasons to expect these failures and concerns to grow, especially if climate change is not slowed, and if farm supports are not suitably amended.

- A constructive way to look at these failures is to view them as public environmental services which can be delivered by suitably incentivised land managers.

- This then turns our attention to the policy measures which can create the conditions and appropriate incentive structure for delivery of the services. If the demand for the services can be effectively created then private operators will step up to supply.

- Given the transboundary nature of nature and the institutional structures in Europe we are dealing with European Public Goods. This suggests that EU policy must be at the core of the response to these challenges.

2. The world is undergoing a **transition** reflecting the new demographic, climatic, ecological and economic reality. This new reality results from a number of trends: population explosion, mushrooming urbanisation, market globalisation, changing life styles, resource limitations such as oil and minerals, fertile soil, clean water and healthy air, growing energy demand with clean-energy shortage, and climate change. These trends are changing the environment as well as the food picture, not only as regards food production, but also food consumption and food markets. In dealing with two of the world's major, interconnected challenges – food security and environmental security – this report focuses on the delivery of public environmental goods and services (in short: public goods). It highlights the role of private land in the production of these public goods, and seeks ways to enhance that role in order to help land managers to better respond to these challenges.

3. Food insecurity. Globally, there are over one billion undernourished and two billion malnourished, not to mention two billion overweight people (nearly a quarter of who are obese). Nearly one billion people live on less than one USD a day, more than three quarters living in the developing countries' rural areas. Some 50% of the hungry are small farmers, who can't feed themselves and lack the money to buy food. A number of factors point towards worsening food scarcity as the world is expected to add nearly 2.5-3bn people by 2050, with most being born in developing countries. This would require up to a doubling of food production. The challenge is of a tall order. Cultivated land is diminishing, not just because of expanding deserts, but because much is lost to urbanization. Potential new land for cultivation is insufficient. Much of it is either inappropriate because of: lack of water or poor or polluted soils; or difficult to use due to doubtful property rights, government mismanagement, lacking transport infrastructure, unattractive local food prices or poor finance. World demand cannot be met without a bigger rise in the productivity of today's cultivated land than currently projected. It remains to be seen to what extent the looming food challenge will be driven more by demand or by supply constraints. This depends on many factors such as changes in technology, purchasing power, life styles, and public opinion.

4. **Environmental insecurity.** The challenge here is to stop and reverse soil degradation, water pollution, and biodiversity loss, and drastically reduce greenhouse gas (GHG) emissions. It has been calculated than some 2bn of the world's hectares, or 22% of all cropland pasture, forests and woodland have been degraded since the 1950s and 5-10 million hectares of agricultural land are being lost every year due to severe degradation. Fertilizers and pesticides not taken up by crops, pollute surface and ground water as well as the sea. As regards GHG emissions (carbon dioxide, methane, and nitrous oxide) agriculture and land use change can help or harm the environment. Globally, including land use change, particularly deforestation, it accounts for 30% of man-made emissions. There are further emissions in the rest of the food chain. However, through the process of photosynthesis, plants are the most efficient vehicles of carbon capture on earth and so, suitably incentivised, some forms of agriculture and land use change can permanently store carbon.

5. A further factor affecting our achievement of food security and environmental security is represented by the **effects of affluence on life-styles**. Affluent people tend to eat less carbohydrate and more high-value products such as fruits and vegetables, meat, dairy products, eggs and fish. Livestock production shifts land from food to feed crops. FAO calculates that global livestock-production emits more than transportation. The damage to the environment from livestock-produced methane and nitrous oxide (particularly by dairy cows) is high because these gases have much

higher global warming effects than carbon dioxide. The shift to ready-to-cook and ready-to-eat food, in particular in urban areas, also tends to increase the environmental imprint notably due to processing. More generally, the human imprint on nature grows more strongly where income growth is higher.

6. A new paradigm is rapidly being adopted to try and better integrate the interaction between man's activities and nature. This is based on the concept of so-called ecosystem services. These are the benefits people obtain from ecosystems which include *provisioning services*, e.g. food and water, *regulating services,* e.g. floods and drought, *supporting services,* e.g. soil formation, and *cultural services* such as recreational, spiritual, religious and other non-material benefits. This framework explicitly allows the two-way interactions between food production and the environment to be considered.

MARKET FAILURES

7. Europe's land is mostly privately owned and managed by farmers and foresters. Pervasive market failures arise from the fact that land management for farming or forestry purposes has the capacity to both conserve and enhance aspects of the environment or harm it. Modern science and technology and mechanized agriculture have dramatically increased the capacity of man to manipulate 'nature' to provide food, feed and other materials. While land managers have generally proved able to provide much more food and materials, they have been producing insufficient environmental services. European society is highly concerned about the resulting ecosystem deterioration: biodiversity loss, landscape degradation, and pollution of water and atmosphere. With growing affluence, its demand for environmental services has grown.

8. While there are well functioning, albeit imperfect markets in the food and fibre chains, there are no spontaneously occurring markets for environmental services. These are therefore not supplied to the extent society would like. Quite naturally farmers will respond to the market signals for their food and other saleable outputs, and pay less attention to the impacts of their activities where there

are no markets. They will tend to provide fewer "goods" such as habitats, species and cultural landscapes, which no one pays for; and too many "bads" such as pollution of the atmosphere, soil and water, as long as they are not required to pay the relevant full social or environmental costs. As the reformed CAP incentivises market behaviour, European farmers increasingly focus on what pays them as a business as against nature, which does not pay. The under-provision of rural environmental services is a classic, and pervasive, case of market failure that affects the majority of the European land area. The scale of these failures has been grossly underestimated. Our policy responses are inadequate. There are reasons to expect these failures and concerns to grow, especially if climate change is not slowed, and farm support contracts.

9. These market failures are extraordinarily difficult to deal with. This is because they are diffuse in the extreme covering a high proportion of the total territory. They are complex, with strong interactions between biodiversity, landscape and soil, water and atmospheric quality. They are highly interconnected with farming and forestry. A new response is therefore needed

10. A constructive way to look at these market failures is to view them as public environmental services that can be delivered by suitably incentivised land managers. But to that effect, it is necessary to make a clear definition of what we mean by the required services and make an estimate of their value and the costs of delivering them. This then turns attention to the policy measures that can create the conditions and appropriate incentive structure for delivery of the services. If the demand for the environmental services can be effectively created then private operators will step up to supply. Given the transboundary nature of nature and the institutional structures in Europe it is argued that we are dealing with European Public Goods. This suggests that EU policy must be at the core of the response to these challenges.

VALUING ECOSYSTEM SERVICES

11. Estimating the value of ecosystem services is controversial. Some believe it cannot be done. Others think it is infinite. Whatever the difficulties in measuring the value of the ecosystem services,

Les Amerois Estate.

C. Otero

the few studies undertaken so far, which are reviewed in this paper, indicate that that value could be colossal, and that the welfare losses of their degradation are huge. According to one all encompassing empirical study, the value of annual global flows of 16 ecosystem services ranged from US$ 16-54 trillion, one third of which were attributed to eleven terrestrial ecosystems (as against five marine ecosystems). The UN Millennium Ecosystem Assessment of the World Bank and UNEP (2003) indicates that 60% of ecosystem services are being degraded or used unsustainably, that "more dramatic negative impacts on the capacity of the ecosystem to provide future services" are in the offing, and that it is therefore "essential that proper measures be undertaken in the present time". The conclusion of the Stern Review on the economics of climate change concludes that the latter "is the greatest and widest-ranging market failure ever seen". The on-going TEEB study, The Economics of Ecosystems and Biodiversity, suggests that the welfare losses from the loss of biodiversity from terrestrial systems is of the order of €50bn per year or about just under 1% of GDP, but €14tr (14 trillion) or 7% of estimated GDP in 2050. The results of these studies, with all their uncertainties, suggest that the gross value of environmental services may well be of comparable order of magnitude as the value of conventionally measured goods and services in the economy.

12. It is instructive to refer to the experience with the Common Agricultural Policy (CAP), which has set the pace in establishing environmental conditions for farm support and offering payments for environmental service delivery. The latter are still a small share of total CAP support, and no effort has been made to calibrate rural development payments on the basis of objective information about the demand for the services, their values, or the costs of their delivery. The proposed increase of funds for rural development in 2005 for the current period (2007-2013), about half of which go to the environment, was annulled by the European Council, not because of other priority objectives, but due to overall budgetary considerations. An exercise of systematically valuing environmental services and their delivery costs can play a useful role in reforming the CAP and better informing such future decisions.

HOW COULD ENVIRONMENTAL PUBLIC GOODS BE DELIVERED?

13. One way to deliver environmental public goods is the **direct delivery** by clubs and societies, such as environmental NGOs, Trusts and Nature Clubs which supply a range of environmental and cultural landscape services through, for example, the purchasing or leasing of land and property, and managing it specifically with their environmental objectives in mind. The main limit to the expansion of this approach is the ability of such clubs to find the resources to buy, lease and manage more land.

14. Another way is to incorporate environmental services into commercially marketed goods and services. These supplies can be natural, planned or unplanned **by-products of normal commercial farming**, consciously **chosen farming systems** (such as organic, conservation agriculture, and integrated farm management) and services delivered **in conjunction with** countryside **sporting activities** (such as sporting shooting and hunting). These all already provide some contribution, and it is not clear how much more environmental service could be delivered through these routes in practice.

15. A more important delivery measure is **public payments**. Its use became systemic in the EU when it was integrated into the CAP at the turn of the century with the MacSharry and Fischler reforms gradually focusing on means to take appropriate care for the environment. However, the programmes for agri-environmental delivery in the EU Member States vary considerably in type and effectiveness. The role of public payments to farmers to provide public environmental services is expected to expand and perhaps by a very large margin. However, there is a long way to go to persuade citizens that just as they contribute tax revenues annually to enable publicly funded health and education services, they will not enjoy the standard of environment care they desire unless they are prepared to contribute similarly (but on a far lower scale of course) to the provision of environmental services. No matter how persuasive these arguments can be made, as public finances will be recovering for some considerable time with the aftermath of the 2008/09 financial crisis, it is wise not to rely entirely on this source to make up the deficit.

16. So another possible approach to environmental delivery is to try and create the circumstances in which environmental services can be supplied through business to business transactions (rather than state to business transactions). This means trying to simulate a market approach to environmental services, or in shorthand, environmental markets. The key is to apply regulations or allocate property rights such that a class of potential purchasers of environmental services seeks to strike contracts with the suppliers of those services. In this way Government regulation can help incentivise potential parties to act, setting reference levels, allocating rights, and allowing them to operate within a framework of contract law. The question remains what the nature of such regula-

Het Loo Estate.

tion would be, where the balance between prohibitions or prescriptions and incentives would lie and how to enforce it.

17. There are several broad approaches to set this process in motion: cap and trade, floor and trade, offsets and contracts for services. The most important example of **cap and trade** is the European Emission Trading Scheme for carbon. There is also a UN scheme, a number of regional schemes in the US and pending mandatory federal legislation in the US Congress. A regulation sets emission limits for companies in designated sectors. Those that overshoot the limits must buy emission certificates or be sanctioned; those who reduce their emissions below those limits can sell C credits to firms who could not respect their targets. While cap and trade is used to control environmental bads that are over-supplied, **floor and trade** is an analogous approach, which might be employed for an environmental good that is under-provided. It has not been tried so far. One could for instance establish for all farms a minimum (floor) proportion of managed land to be devoted to biodiversity, allowing farms exceeding that proportion to trade credits with those preferring to focus on food production. The idea of **offsets** is to reduce the environmental costs of economic development. A regulation requires that developers must offset environmental degradation resulting from their project by purchasing equivalent environmental services, i.e. offsets, which are offered by land managers who undertake to supply such services in perpetuity. This approach is in use in the USA and Australia, and permitted under certain conditions under the EU Birds and Habitats Directives.

18. Another approach, **contracts for services**, refers to the idea of finding opportunities for private sector purchase of environmental services supplied by farmers or other land managers. There are already operational examples of this. For instance, there are private water companies contracting with farmers or foresters in their catchments to manage their land in such a way as to reduce costs of water treatment. This approach can provide a cheaper way of dealing with the pollutant than the alternative of removing the pollutant in a water treatment works. This approach might be equally used for positive environmental services provided by the 'upstream' land managers, for example providing flood relief by creating fields permitted to flood (wash lands) in order to prevent downstream flooding of a village or commercial facility. The purchaser in this case would be a local authority on behalf of householders, or the private operator of the facility.

Het Loo Estate

WHO PAYS FOR THE ENVIRONMENT?

19. This is a key question. Currently it is **European citizens** who pay by suffering the consequences of the environmental market failures that are the subject of this report. The costs are large, but diffuse. Individuals cannot measure them, and do not know what they can do about them. If all citizens pay for environmental degradation, who should pay to reverse it: farmers, food and forest product consumers, or taxpayers? How could the costs be best distributed in order to incentivise the actions required?

20. The *polluter pays principle* suggests that the negative environmental impacts of farming should be dealt with by regulations ensuring that the costs are initially borne by **farmers**. This is the current state of affairs in Europe, but it is not very effective. The farming industry puts up strong resistance to additional regulatory costs on the grounds that returns on capital in agriculture are low compared to other industries, they have limited ability to pass regulatory costs up or down the food chain, and they are in competition with regions with lower environmental standards. While it is not unreasonable in principle to require through regulation that farmers do not pollute, the costs and effectiveness of policing diffuse pollution pose practical challenges. But in any case this approach will not induce them to provide additional environmental services that demand additional management and resources.

21. Can one then turn to the **consumers** to pay the full social costs of the food they are purchasing, such as those regarding environmental damage and diminishing biodiversity? This can be done, but policies raising food prices are regressive, that is, it puts more of the costs of the environment onto the lower paid and disadvantaged in society who typically spend more of their incomes on food.

22. If it proves possible to create **environmental markets**, the cost of the environmental services will be borne by the shareholders and customers of the businesses that are buying the carbon, biodiversity or water quality credits. This could be a better way of distributing environmental costs, avoiding regressivity concerns and food-price sensitivity, and offers better possibilities to share costs up and down the product chains.

23. Although this may be a difficult time to propose it, there are also sound arguments why it is fair and reasonable that **the taxpayer** should fund a significant part of environmental delivery. If a reasonable part of the costs is borne by producers as well as by food consumers, it is normal that taxpayers contribute the remainder of the costs in meeting the environmental standards that the citizens have chosen through their legislative process.

24. If it can be agreed that there should be substantial taxpayer contribution to the delivery of European environmental services, it has then to be debated whether this portion should be done **through the EU or the Member State budgets**. This is a matter for the next EU budget review in connection with the new EU financial perspective for 2014 to 2020. Some Member States such as the UK and Sweden are advocating a substantial cut in the CAP budget by abolishing the first pillar of the CAP. The net contributors to the EU budget (the two above plus The Netherlands, Germany and France) would like to forget the EU budget limit formally agreed by Council 25 years ago limiting EU budget commitments to 2.4% of GNI, and if possible even reduce the maximum level of EU payments currently set at 1.14% of GNI. Several of these governments may claim that environment is by definition 'local' so that environmental services should be funded as locally as possible. Quite a few, mostly new member states, while supportive of rural development, would like to reduce the second pillar of the CAP because they have difficulties in putting up their co-financing part.

25. However there are strong arguments that support a substantial contribution of EU funding for environmental public services: these are that the services are often cross-boundary in character, they are EU common interests, and competitiveness, cohesion, and competence all also suggest EU funding. Co-funding these services between EU and member states is sensible although co-financing rates may have to change, with lower co-financing by states with lower ability to contribute to what is in the common interest. The total amount of public funds that would be necessary to deal with the objective also will depend on the degree of success in creating environmental markets.

IN SUMMARY

26. It is often observed that political action to deal with climate change was galvanised by the publication of the Stern Review of the economics of climate change showing that the costs of averting further change are considerably less than the costs of taking no action. This has been a powerful motivating force to collect information on the comparable benefits and costs globally of halting biodiversity loss. The thrust of this paper is that if we are to really grasp the challenge of delivering the rural environmental services which could be provided by land managers in the EU then efforts should be made to define and describe these services and show their value and what it would cost to deliver them.

27. Of course, precisely because there are no directly observable market values for environmental services, such valuations are not straightforward. The point is that evidence-based policy demands that the best estimates should be made. There has been strong progress in the development of the analytical frameworks for doing this, notably in the concept of ecosystem services. The strength of this approach is that it neatly embraces the provisioning services of food and energy as well as all the other vital services mankind derives from the environment. Correspondingly there have been great strides in the development and implementation of valuation techniques. To mobilise the actions and budgets necessary to induce the delivery of the desired quantum of environmental services, it is important to devote more effort to quantify Europe's demand for these services. There are a number of studies taking place but more remains to be done and should be a priority for research.

28. This is particularly relevant to the on-going EU review of its Budget and Policies. It is vital that decisions on the scale of EU budget resources are made in the light of the tasks policies are expected to fulfil. There is a strong danger that in decisions about the future CAP the budget resources will be decided before it is agreed what the real objectives of the policy are and the costs of delivering those objectives.

29. Agricultural support through pillar 1 constitutes an important instrument to meet the Treaty objectives of the CAP. Any significant reduction would produce a productivity drop. But such support needs to be better targeted and complemented by measures tackling market failures and climate change.

30. The discussion paper submitted by the Swedish Presidency for the informal agricultural Council in Växiö in September 2009 calls for a raft of measures to compensate for market failures. It notably stresses the role EU agriculture can play in mitigating climate change and the relevant role of CAP instruments. It suggests three questions as an agenda for further research: a) what should be the role of the EU regarding mitigation and adaptation in agriculture and the key areas of cooperation, b) how can opportunities such as R&D investments and the new challenges addressed by the Health Check be utilised and lessons learned, and c) should common EU policies and strategies be developed further in order to meet the challenges of changed patterns of dissemination of pathogens and diseases. This is a hopeful sign of an awakening, and a call for action.

De Hoge Veluwe N.P.

De Hoge Veluwe National Park

Atlantic

Location: Hoenderloo, The Netherlands.
Surface: 5,400 ha.

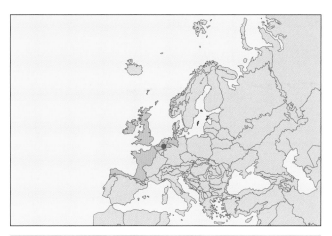

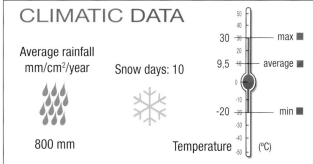

CLIMATIC DATA

Average rainfall
mm/cm²/year

Snow days: 10

800 mm

Temperature (ºC)

max ■
30
9,5 average ■
-20 min ■

SUMMARY

De Hoge Veluwe National Park is one of the largest nature reserves in the Netherlands. It covers about 5,400 hectares of which 5,000 hectares are enclosed by fencing, and consists of 3,200 hectares of woodland and 2,100 hectares of open terrain, including heathland and about 60 hectares of drift sand. The woods are mostly made up of first generation scots pine stands, but also include older mixed forests with tracks and rides. Within the heathland, several peat bogs and fens occur, formed as a result of local water stagnation.

Due to its central position in the Netherlands, De Hoge Veluwe National Park plays a key role in the country's National Ecological Network. The Park is also part of the European Natura 2000 network. The careful and systematic, long-continued management has led to a large diversity in biotopes, which together form a sanctuary for many floral and faunal species that today are rare and protected. For several of these the Park constitutes the last refuge in the Netherlands.

Aerial view of Sint Hubertus.

The Kröller-Müller couple.

Kröller-Muller Museum.

HISTORY

The legacy of an inspiring couple

In 2005 the prime minister of the Netherlands, Jan-Peter Balkenende, described De Hoge Veluwe National Park as a treasure-house of Dutch nature, making specific reference to the Park's unique combination of art and nature. The Park is a rare enclave of unspoilt nature in our otherwise highly urbanised country. In the heart of that enclave lies the world-famous Kröller-Müller Museum. This Museum holds a large collection of outstanding modern art, including paintings by Vincent van Gogh and Pablo Picasso, and sculptures by Auguste Rodin and Henry Moore. The unique combination of art and nature represents the joint vision of the founders, Anton Kröller and Helene Müller.

In 1888, the Dutch captain of industry Anton Kröller married the German Helene Müller, a woman with broad intellectual and spiritual interests. Anton Kröller's purchase of the Veluwe's Hoenderloo country estate in 1909 formed a crucial step towards the foundation of the National Park as we know it today. A substantial portion of the couple's wealth was used to purchase art and hunting grounds and to fund the construction of the Sint Hubertus Country Residence. Kröller, a nature lover and fervent hunter, continued to buy land until the advent of the global economic crisis in the thirties. At that point in time, the Kröller-Müllers were one of the Veluwe's biggest private landowners.

Long before the Great Depression started, the couple had expressed the idea of preserving the estate and the art collection for the citizens of the Netherlands. In 1928, this led to the creation of the Kröller-Müller Foundation, which became the new owner of the art collection. As the economic crisis worsened, there was a risk that the estate and art collection would be split up and sold. To prevent this, the State of the Netherlands was awarded the art collection. An agreement with the estate held that the collection would be exhibited in a museum inside the Park, to be constructed by the State, and that Park and Museum would be open to the public.

The estate was transferred to an independent De Hoge Veluwe National Park Foundation, which was created in 1935 and which has owned the Park since that time.

Terrace by Night, painted by Vicent van Gogh.

This is how an inspiring couple's legacy became a national park that is unique in Europe. It is a Park in which nature, art and architecture are truly interwoven. Rooted in history, the Park has now become a modern organisation with a unique task: the diligent stewardship of the Kröller-Müllers' legacy, preserving it for future generations and ensuring that it remains open to paying visitors.

DESCRIPTION

The Park: A gem to be cherished

De Hoge Veluwe National Park is one of the largest nature reserves in the Netherlands. It covers about 5,400 hectares of which 5,000 hectares are enclosed by fencing, and consists of 3,200 hectares of woodland and 2,100 hectares of open terrain, including heathland and about 60 hectares of drift sand. The woods are mostly made up of first generation scots pine stands, but also include older mixed forests with tracks and rides. Within the heathland, several peat bogs and fens occur that formed as a result of local water stagnation.

The park's name "Hoge Veluwe" refers to the dry and high core of the Veluwe, with sandy soils and a rather hilly relief. This relief is due to the huge Fenno-Scandinavian glaciers that reached the Netherlands during the penultimate Ice Age, approximately 200,000 years ago. The pushing action of the ice formed large ridges (push moraines), such as the large ridge immediately east of the Park and a smaller one – the Oud-Reemster ridge – in the southern part.

The current landscape and vegetation reflect the history of land use, characteristic of the dry sand landscapes of the Veluwe. This history started during the Neolithic period (about 2500 BC) with the gradual clearance of forest and its replacement by heathland and scant grassland, used for sheep and cattle grazing. By the Middle Ages, the growing population and concurrent overexploitation had already induced such destruction of the vegetation and soil that sands started to drift. In the eighteenth century, most of the area had become drift sand with sparse groups of trees and small settlements that fought a fierce battle against the drifting sand. This situation continued until the end of the nineteenth century. At that time, fertilizer became available,

wealthy merchants and new captains of industry provided capital that was needed for afforestation, and the old agricultural system became obsolete. It is particularly on the slightly more fertile soils of the moraines that forests were planted, often in the form of large blocks of coniferous trees, separated by tracks and rides which are lined by broad-leaved species such as American Oak *(Quercus rubra)* and Beech *(Fagus sylvatica).* On the poorer drift sands, afforestation was more limited and largely consists of pine monocultures. Later on, pine forests expanded considerably through natural regeneration from seeds.

The Park consists of large tracts of well-preserved open landscape with heath and drift sand, with lesser-sized but still impressive old woodland linked to the late nineteenth and early twentieth century estates. It thus consists of a mosaic of old, pre-industrial man-made landscapes that are known to host a highly diverse flora and fauna. Unlike most of the Veluwe, the Park is hardly affected by the large-scale reclamation of heathland for modern agriculture (based on fertilizer), nor massively planted with pine or other popular coniferous trees. It thus is a kind of 'museum of cultural landscapes' for the Veluwe at large.

Contrary to other major nature reserves in the Netherlands, De Hoge Veluwe is private land. This allows the foundation to manage the Park according to its own philosophy and aims. One important assertion the foundation makes is that there is no

The Park hosts a healthy herd of about 200 mouflons.

De Hoge Veluwe N.P.

The black grouse was reintroduced into the Park in 2006, and good results were obtained.

Photography during the red deer rutting season.

E. Marek

work. The careful and systematic, long-continued management has led to a large diversity in biotopes, which together form a sanctuary for many floral and faunal species that today are rare and protected. For several of these the Park constitutes the last refuge in the Netherlands. This consistent approach allowed us in 2006 to reintroduce the Black Grouse *(Tetrao tetrix)*, a bird species that was once a native inhabitant of the Veluwe. It requires a habitat such as is found in the Park and adjacent areas (with extensive agriculture) to survive and nearly became extinct because of the poor conservation of this type of habitat throughout the Netherlands.

Through this intensive management, and aided by volunteers that together form the active Flora & Fauna Group, De Hoge Veluwe has become one of the most studied nature reserves in the Netherlands. Year after year, a large number of observations are made, evidence indeed that the Park's flora and fauna is highly varied: rare orchids and unusual lichens; insects like the Wart-biter Bush Cricket *(Decticus verrucivorus)*, Fritillaries (family Nymphalidae) and Silver-studded Blues *(Plebeius argus)*; birds such as Stone-Curlews *(Burhinus oedicnemus)*, Ravens *(Corvus corax)*, Nightjars *(Caprimulgus europaeus)* and Yellowhammers *(Emberiza citrinella)*; and many species of native amphibians and reptiles. Indeed, De Hoge Veluwe is an especially rich habitat for species that thrive on poor sandy soils.

longer "primeval nature" in the Netherlands. The management does not therefore strive for such a thing, but aims to protect the existing mosaic of man-made, semi-natural landscapes and to maintain its high ecological values through an active management. This means, for instance, that young tree shoots are removed from the heathland (by hand!), that the drift sand areas are reactivated when overgrown by mosses and grass, and that numbers of larger mammals are controlled by hunting to prevent over-grazing.

Due to its central position in the Netherlands, De Hoge Veluwe National Park plays a key role in the country's National Ecological Network. The Park is also part of the European Natura 2000 net-

Wildlife

Many species of fauna live in De Hoge Veluwe National Park. Some are hunted.

1. Red deer *(Cervus elaphus)*

The red deer is the showpiece of the Park, with people coming from far and near to admire them, particularly during their rut when they can be easily spotted on pastures laid out near the main roads. The mating season is about two weeks earlier than in the surrounding areas, probably as a result of genetic differences.

Taking into account the size of the park and its vegetation, the optimal deer population is about 200 animals (spring numbers) with a specific population structure, based on extensive population dynamic studies of these large herbivores. Manage-

De Hoge Veluwe N.P.

ment consists of culling to maintain this population size and structure, focussing on the female population to reduce the number of births and on male animals of up to 5 years of age and older than 12.

2. Wild Boar *(Sus scrofa)*

If winter is mild and food is abundant during summer, as has often happened in the last decade, wild boar populations may grow rapidly. This recently led to a massive increase in wild boar on the Veluwe and an outcry from farmers because of the danage done by these voracious animals. The Park tries to regulate their number by culling, as with the red deer, but has problems in assessing the required culling because of large fluctuations in population size, and in hunting the animals satisfactorily using current legal methods.

It also faces a dilemma regarding animal welfare. A year with abundant mast results in high fitness levels, causing high litter numbers in the following year. When the piglets are born, or in the following summer, the food situation may be unfavourable, with insufficient food and possibly even serious starvation of the piglets. The obvious decision would be to provide additional food early on in the season, as well as increasing the culling effort. However, such a decision impedes quick reduction of the population and requires considerable extra effort later in the season to achieve the optimal numbers.

The question is what alternatives are practically and ethically acceptable in order to reach this objective (trap cages?). Hunting with silencers has been tested and appeared to be very effective, but the Ministry of Justice denied extension of the dispensation for the silencer trial and the Police consider the use of silencers to be in breach of the Weapons and Ammunition Act.

Although European legislation provides for various exceptions – after all, silencers are used elsewhere in Europe – the Ministry claims that Benelux regulation prohibits the use of silencers. It is primarily for this reason that the Park is attempting to find a legal way to obtain permission.

3. Mouflon *(Ovis musimon)*

The Park hosts a healthy herd of about 200 mouflons and is the only Dutch nature area with such a herd. The animals formerly used to have quite severe health and breeding problems. Veterinary research showed that this was due to a cobalt deficiency disorder. A spectacular improvement has been achieved by spreading the grassland with salt containing cobalt, and by introducing cobalt salt licks.

4. Sale of game and antlers

The Park traditionally sold its cull animals to game dealers. In 2005, because of falling prices, the Park started to sell game, mostly venison and wild boar, to the public. Initially it feared negative publicity and campaigns by anti-hunting groups. However, the opposite appeared to be true, since

Red deer.

the reaction from most of the media was very positive. Moreover demands by customers exceeded the Park's supply, which is largely sold through its Park shop. As well as game the shop also sells the discarded antlers collected by the Park's personnel.

Today, the Park is achieving a much better price. The Park only sells game shot in the Park and the culling plan is the main element of this. Although total game production varies, average production is such that the investment required to meet EU regulations (cooling and slaughter facilities) can be recovered.

5. Roe Deer (Capreolus capreolus)

Spring numbers of roe deer are approximately 300. Roe have not been hunted since 2004 as there was no reason to do so. However, any weak animals are shot and sent to Utrecht University for research purposes.

This research may indicate a need to reintroduce some form of control of Roe Deer numbers.

6. Also of interest

Red fox: variable numbers – foxes are hunted when black grouse are released into the wild.

Pine marten: approximately 5 nests.

Badger: approximately 70 animals

There are various small creatures, such as the dark green fritillary, niobe fritillary and heath fritillary, the adder, smooth snake, hobby and nightjar. The Park's flora and fauna are particularly well served by the areas of open terrain.

What does the Park offer to the visitors?

De Hoge Veluwe National Park attracts roughly half a million visitors a year. These guests are encouraged to explore the terrain in depth, on foot, by bike or by horse. For the latter, the Park features a network of 43 kilometres of well-maintained cycle paths. Contrary to many other nature reserves in the Netherlands, visitors are not obliged to stick to the designated paths, but are allowed to stray from them. This also applies to horse riders. It is very unconventional in our regulated Dutch society to tread beyond the beaten paths and this is one of the Park's major charms, along with rest areas.

The Dutch and many international visitors particularly associate "De Hoge Veluwe" with its large mammals: red deer, mouflon, roe deer and wild boar. In fact, the red deer's rutting season in the au-

tumn is the traditional climax in the tourist calendar. The complex network of walking and cycling paths ensures that visitors to the Park are very likely to see large mammals during their stay. There are seven observation posts, which provide a view over various grazing areas. Rangers provide tours and there is also the option of getting to know the terrain more intimately on a small-group safari with one of the Park's rangers. One unique feature of the Park is its online "large mammal forecast": taking account of the weather and other variable factors, the ranger regularly indicates at which locations visitors have the greatest chance of seeing these animals. The webcam on one of our observation posts is also a well-visited section of our website.

The population of large mammals is actively managed by culling. The Park discourages feeding of these wild animals and knows precisely how many healthy animals the vegetation can support. In spring, optimal numbers are 200 red deer, 50 wild boar, 200 mouflons and 300 roe deer. Based on annual counts and also reckoning with our vegetation management and forest rejuvenation, the Park determines how many red deer, wild boar and mouflon need to be culled. The Park employs five full-time game wardens who supervise the Anton Kröller Guest Hunters Society (12 paying hunters) which carries out the annual cull. Hunts are subject to fixed rules and agreements, with individual annual contracts being terminated if hunters fail to comply. The Park also invites a few of its own guests to hunt. Such active management maintains a healthy balance between De Hoge Veluwe's populations of large mammals and their habitat.

Remarkably, the half million visitors attracted to the Park each year tend not to disrupt the sense of space and tranquillity in and around the Park. This is partly due to traffic management. Visitors are encouraged to leave their cars outside the Park and to explore the terrain on foot or by bike, but cars are still welcome. Bike racks are located at the Park's three entrances for the famous White Bikes, which may be used for free within the Park's boundaries. The White Bike is an 'alternative' idea that originated in Amsterdam in the 1960s as a free form of city transport. De Hoge Veluwe is the only place in the Netherlands where our national mode of transport is used in this way. The 1,700 White Bikes are maintained by a professional bike repair workshop located at the centre of the Park. If the Park happens to be covered in snow, there are 50 White Sleighs!

Most activities take place in the Park's central area, which is where you will find the Kröller-Müller Museum, with its major collection of modern art, and Europe's largest Sculpture Garden. In addition, the Park has a Visitor Centre, with its Museonder (an underground nature museum), an exhibition area and a museum shop where you can buy many local products from the Veluwe. The shop is one of the most successful museum shops in the Netherlands. Behind the Visitor Centre lies the Landscapes Garden, which introduces you in miniature to the different types of landscape you might encounter on the Veluwe. The large central restaurant, the Koperen Kop, also lies in the Park's central area.

Funding and organisation

De Hoge Veluwe National Park is an independent, not-for-profit foundation that does not receive regular subsidies. It applies the principle that paying visitors should provide the lion's share of the Park's income. Supplementary income is generated by sales from the museum shop, leasing refreshment facilities, timber yields, hunting, Park restaurants, field rentals and house rentals. This form of financing enables the foundation to pursue its own path, perpetuating the spirit of the Kröller-Müller couple, the Park's founders. This couple consistently fought for the Park's autonomous status, and the organisation's successive directors have managed to turn this dream into reality.

The Park welcomes between 500,000 and 600,000 paying visitors a year, generating annual sales of €4.4 million. A study carried out in 2004 demonstrated that the Park forms a key element of the region's economy, in total employing 700 people and generating roughly €34 million in recreational spending.

Despite its historical roots and attachment to tradition, De Hoge Veluwe National Park is a modern and professional organisation. It is small (53 FTE / 80 staff) and efficiently structured. Executive leadership is in the hands of a managing director, assisted by a management team consisting of the heads of three departments. The Supervisory Board exercises control over policies and finances, an Advisory Board acts as a sounding board and consultant for policy decisions, and a Nature Management Advisory Committee is consulted in relation to nature management issues. The organisation aims to operate in a manner that reflects its environmental and social awareness and is transparent in accordance with the principles of Corporate Governance, in order to successfully navigate the often quite complex administrative and political waters of Dutch society. This also translates into an active approach with regard to national and international cooperation. As to the latter, De Hoge Veluwe participates in international networks such as the European Landowners' Organization, Friends of the Countryside, Wildlife Estates Initiative, Europarc Federation and The Green Key.

The White Bike is an "alternative" idea that originated in Amsterdam in the 1960s as a free form of city transport. De Hoge Veluwe is the only place in the Netherlands where our national mode of transport is used in this way.

P. Leuthold

De Hoge Veluwe National Park **(The Netherlands)**

CHALLENGES OF THE FOUNDATION: CONTINUITY OR CHANGE?

For as long as the Park has existed, which is now almost a century, its appearance has hardly changed. The same holds for the aim of the Park, which continues to be "the preservation of the old Veluwe landscape and the attendant flora and fauna". Outside the Park this old nineteenth-century Veluwe landscape can hardly be found any longer, not least because it was only much later that it was recognised and managed as a valuable landscape of high biodiversity. Another reason is the some-

times entirely different vision of other nature management agencies active in the Veluwe, such as Natuurmonumenten and the State Forestry Service, which have contributed to its transformation through such things as extensive grazing by large herbivores in order to create large open park-like landscapes.

Over the years, there has also been an immense increase in the scale of legislation and policy. Whereas in the early twentieth century conservation was still about private estates, forestry owners and economic returns from forestry, nowadays it is regional and national nature policy, with a complex funding and rulings structure. Moreover, the influ-

MANAGEMENT TYPE	Experience	Cultural history	FUNCTION Nature preservation	Production	Landscape
Protected woodland			+++		
Native selection forest	+	+	++	+	
Exotics selection forest	+	++	+	++	
Cultural-historic woodland	++	+++		+	+
Acidic grassland	+++	+++	+++		+++
Dry calcareous grassland	++	++	+++		+++
Wet grassland & damp calcareous grassland	++	+++	+++		+++
Peat bogs	++	+	+++		+++
Drift sand	+++	+++	+++		+++
Farmland	+	++	++	+	+
Wildlife food plots	+		++		

Drifting Sand.

H. van Holland

S.E. van Voorst tot Voorst, managing director of Stichting Het Nationale Park De Hoge Veluwe.

De Hoge Veluwe N.P.

Forest landscape.

ence of EU policy is increasing. This means that the Park has to take the 'outside' world and plans for the future of the Veluwe far more into account than before. These plans include, for example, Veluwe 2010 and the Endless Veluwe (Province of Gelderland), the Ecological Exploration of the Veluwe (1997), and Natura 2000.

Key phrases in future plans include "making the Veluwe less fragmented" by removing impediments like fences, roads etc.; space for more "natural development"; "reducing traffic and disturbance" and "improving environmental excellence". A more recent key phrase is derived from Natura 2000: "conservation of biodiversity". The proposed outline for the future is a Veluwe consisting of an uninterrupted and extensive nature reserve of high environmental excellence in which other functions – traffic, residential use, agriculture, industry and military training zones – are reduced to a minimum. The Park management is also aiming for high-quality nature and sees the importance of collaboration with other managers of the Veluwe landscape. However, in the past not all managers and policymakers have held the same view on what constitutes 'high-quality nature' and how to achieve it. This led to quite serious controversies. More recently, and linked to the change in policy induced by Natura 2000, relations have become much more relaxed, the focus now being on main-taining biodiversity, which matches the Park's aims much more strongly.

The main issues in current and future management

1. Making the Veluwe less fragmented

A first major step is to make the Veluwe less fragmented by removing fences, closing off roads and introducing all kinds of facilities such as animal passages and eco-ducts to ease the movements of animals, especially the larger mammals. The most important arguments for doing this are to reactivate the natural migration of these mammals and to combat inbreeding.

Such plans cost a great deal of money and have immense consequences for local traffic, since roads have to be closed due to the increased risk of accidents, or tunnels/viaducts have to be built ensuring safe passage. They will also have serious repercussions for the building plans of local councils in the Veluwezoom, since red deer and boar are hardly going to migrate through built-up or industrial areas. Furthermore it is likely that a mass migration of red deer and wild boar to the river area will occur at times when food is scarce, so that animal densities in the higher and poor parts of the Veluwe, like the Park, will be dramatically reduced. Another potential problem is live-

De Hoge Veluwe National Park (The Netherlands)

The philosophy of the Park can be summed up as traffic reduction and disturbance improving the environmental excellence.

stock diseases, such as swine fever and foot-and-mouth (aphthous fever), which can spread and get out of control more easily.

Most policymakers are aware that making the

Veluwe less fragmented is not a simple issue, but the idea is extremely appealing – large scale, one manager and one policy – as evidenced by the recent plan for an "Endless Veluwe". For the

Park the situation is different, since it would be faced immediately with the negative consequences. Removing the Park's fence might induce the larger mammals to move elsewhere.

Anyone could enter the Park, thereby posing a threat to security and seclusion, and the income from admission charges, which funds the management of the Park will decline (and who will make up the difference?). In short, there are quite a few problems associated with the ostensibly straightforward idea of removing the fences. Moreover, the legitimate problem of inbreeding can be resolved by creating in-and-out jumps so that in the event of a disease such as foot-and-mouth breaking out, it would still be possible to isolate and save large numbers of animals. These jumps are in fact currently under construction, though traffic problems have not yet been adequately solved.

2. Natural development

More natural development needed? In terms of policy that means several issues such as cutting down on culling, combating exotic flora, developing "natural woodlands" and reducing various types of intensive nature conservation schemes. Sometimes one has the sense that biologists and policymakers are falling over themselves in their urge to think up new ideas that will lead to "natural development". Here are just a few examples from an extremely large and complex whole:

a) "Culling is unnatural and not animal friendly". Opponents often interpret the idea of culling to regulate populations as "hunting", and they strongly oppose hunting. It is often left unsaid that without culling or introducing predators into an "Endless Veluwe", populations of large mammals will become so large that they will have to be regulated. Some experts claim that food shortages and the deteriorating capacity of an area to sustain its animals prevent large populations occurring, but it is doubtful whether the general public would appreciate being faced with starving wild animals or their carcasses. Another solution is to introduce predators like the wolf, which regulates the wildlife naturally. This is not at all fantasy, as some conservationists have seriously proposed introducing wolves on the Veluwe. Is that what the Dutch people want and will they want to pay for it? Or should the large mammal population simply be regulated via culling? Opposition against hunting used to be very strong, but culling is becoming more and more accepted as a management tool.

b) Heath reverts to woodland if wild shoots are not removed and it is not grazed or regularly mowed, or if the sods are not cut. Such measures are expensive and are able to be carried out due to subsidies provided by the government as part of its nature policy. However, the government is currently less prepared to subsidise the management of heathland. Thus virtually all managers of heathland are faced with a major problem and it is doubtful whether they can continue to maintain the heath in the long term. For supporters of "natural development" it is obviously not a problem if the heath reverts to forest. However the Park will then lose unique heathland communities.

Flocks of sheep can be reintroduced on the heath, although shepherds are expensive so this does not solve the problem of costs involved. "Then use cows or other large grazing animals", you might be thinking. "They do not have to be tended and are much cheaper." The trouble is of course that cattle do not always go together with an average sized wild population of large mammals, and the propensity of cows to breed easily could totally devastate an entire area, resulting in food shortages and malnourishment of the herd unless you provide supplementary food again. This is hardly a natural situation anymore and the Park winds up simply breeding cattle.

c) Another good example of quite contradictory rulings concerns the general attitude towards exotic or non-indigenous species. Mouflon *(Ovis musimon)* and Fallow Deer *(Dama dama)* are not indigenous animals, but fortunately there are few people who really object to their presence in nature reserves. Some biologists do, however, and are for their ruthless removal. There is also opposition to the introduction of black grouse bred in captivity, though largely originating from wild populations from adjoining countries. The true inhabitants of the Veluwe are the Dutch heath sheep, but that is a heavily domesticated beast, like the aforementioned cows, with very little in common, genetically, with the original wild animal. Based on current regulations, the releasing of Badger *(Meles meles)* into the wild, as happened in the past in the Park, is now completely illegal and would incur hefty penalties.

3. Reducing traffic and disturbance, improving environmental excellence

These three elements are intertwined and are linked to the increasing degradation and fragmentation of areas of outstanding natural beauty through recreation, dwellings, roads and so on. Reducing traffic and disturbance and improving environmental excellence by controlling the number of caravan and camping sites, closing secondary roads, placing sound buffers along existing and new roads, curbing housing development and banning business extensions as well as closing down existing industries around towns and villages on the Veluwe itself, is all to be welcomed.

These are measures universally supported by local governing bodies, residents and nature managers, albeit with the proviso for the first two groups that these are sensibly adopted and that any policy measure does not result in large areas of the region being inaccessible, or the economic basis for a large portion of the local population being jeopardised. Not all planners seem to be taking these wishes into account, as is evident from the scheme to introduce Veluwe "rangers" and create park-and-ride sites on the edge of the area from where people will make – accompanied – visits to the nature reserves. These kind of schemes threaten the continued survival of businesses and facilities in local villages that depend on tourists and leisure seekers, and thus on the Park, especially if access is prevented by private car. So the Park would prefer not to have an extensive, inaccessible and uniform-looking nature reserve, but a tranquil yet accessible, large-scale and homogeneous Veluwe landscape.

Brief description of the functions:

- Experience: a free translation of the task upon us is that visitors must enjoy a new experience at every turn.
- Cultural history: care not only of the Park's surviving original structures, but also of those built by Kröller.
- Nature: preservation of the Park's unique elements and an attempt to recover that which is lost.

Managing Director with game-keepers and field staff.

De Hoge Veluwe N.P.

- Production: the Park is managed on the basis of the wise-use principle.
- Landscape preservation: protecting the landscape also safeguards biodiversity.

A couple of principles are central and a couple supportive. Production, for instance, should be seen as supportive (generating as much income as possible from the sale of products derived from preservation and conservation activities), and nature as central (partly due to statutory obligations).

A very healthy degree of biodiversity has been ensured by consistent and diverse forms of intervention, in terms of the timescale, scope and nature of given activities.

De Hoge Veluwe N.P.

Frank Schreve, chairman Supervisory Board.

NP HOGE VELUWE BELONGS TO:

| Federatie Particulier Grondbezit | Wildlife Estates Initiative | ELO | Friends of the Countryside | Europarc Federation | The Green Key |

Activities

- Birdwatching
- Museum
- Country Park
- Campsite
- Country residence
- Kids
- Walking Trails
- Cycling
- Garden
- Restaurant
- Equestrian
- Estate products
- Boutique

CONTACT DATA
Stichting Het Nationale Park De Hoge Veluwe
Seger E. baron van Voorst tot Voorst, managing director
www.hogeveluwe.nl
information@hogeveluwe

El Palomar

Mediterranean

Flores family land-holdings

Location:

- La Cañada del Quintanar (Albacete, Spain).
- El Pinar del Boticario (Albacete, Spain).
- La Casa de la Torre y El Cepillo (Albacete, Spain).
- El Coto Camilo (Ciudad Real, Spain).
- El Castillo de Montizón (Ciudad Real, Spain).
- El Villar y El Coto de la Casa del Río (Jaén-Albacete, Spain).
- Peñascosa (Albacete, Spain).
- El Ateril del Cuerno y La Carnicera (Jaén, Spain).
- La Cuesta del Gatillo (Jaén, Spain).
- Los Alarcones (Jaén, Spain).
- Sardina (Jaén, Spain).
- San Agustín (Jaén, Spain).

Total area of the family land-holdings: 28,685.24 ha.

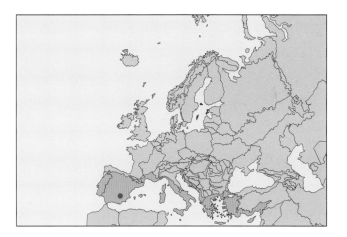

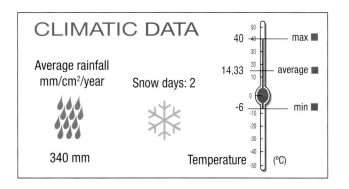

CLIMATIC DATA

Average rainfall
mm/cm²/year

Snow days: 2

340 mm

Temperature (°C)

40 — max
14,33 — average
-6 — min

The fighting bulls of the Samuel Flores stock are branded with special marks.
The oldest was designed by Gil Flores at the end of the 17th century.

HISTORY

The different generations of the Flores family through time

I belong to the eighth generation of the Flores family, who in the mid-18th century settled in the locality of Peñascosa, in the Sierra de Alcazar, 80 kilometers from Albacete (Castilla-La Mancha, Spain).

The family's main activities were livestock breeding and agriculture. Through their constant day-to-day work over the years, they were able to buy land not only in the province of Albacete but also in Ciudad Real, and from there looked to the south, where they acquired land in Jaén (Andalucía) for warm winter pastures for the livestock. Thus it was that they were able to build up and establish their agricultural family-based land holding.

In 1970, when I was only 26 years old, there was a jump in the generations for family reasons, and I took on (in my mother's name and in my own name) the responsibility of looking after the estates. From that moment on, and for the next 40 years, I have fought with the greatest keenness and enthusiasm to maintain these estates, transforming them and adapting them to the socio-economic requirements of the time. Even more importantly, I have transmitted this hope and dedication to my children, Isabel, Samuel and Carlos, so that they, who will represent the ninth generation, can continue to honour the memory of the first members of the Flores family who took on this valuable work of conserving the natural environment and, through it, nature itself.

The greatest expansion of the estates occurred during the life of my great-grandfather, Agustín Flores, a well-known figure who was clearly intelligent and capable of very hard work. He was able to carry on this job with the help of his brother, Samuel Flores y Flores (my great-uncle), from whom I have inherited my love for the countryside in all its aspects. He was a man who always put his vocation and his position ahead of any economic interests. In those days, farmers and livestock breeders were able to buy land with the profits they earned from their previous agricultural enterprises. The value of an estate was a result of its capitalization, which in itself was made more favourable by the great amount of land on offer as a consequence of the economic needs of the nobility who had to maintain their castles and their way of life at court. It was also a time when church lands became available as a result of the financial policies of Mendizábal. Today it is a very different picture, since estates have an added value that stems from leisure activities and the expectations of investing in fixed assets.

My great-uncle was a wonderful person with a fine sense of humour. He used to tell us that he had never got married because he did not have the time to go looking for girl friends. He was able to take the animals acquired in 1926 from Palma del Río (Sevilla) – Parladé-Vista Hermosa pure-breds – to great success in the 1940s, '50s and part of the '60s.

In 1944 Luis Miguel Dominguín "graduated" as a bullfighter *(matador)* with our livestock in La Coruña, and specifically with our bull named "Cuenco." In the 1950s, important bullfighters such as Antonio Ordoñéz, Dominguín, Antonio Chenel *(Antoñete)*, etc. demonstrated their bullfighting skills with bulls bred on our estates. In 1963 the bullfighter Manuel Benitez *(el Cordobés)*, also graduated to *matador* in Córdoba with our bulls, and won both ears and the tail of the bull called "Berlinés." In 1966 Santiago Martín *(El Viti)*, rose to fame in Seville with a bull called "Peina feas."

Since the 1970s, when my great-uncle was impaired by a stroke and I took on the management of the bulls, I have maintained both the genotype and phenotype of the herd, known by every aficionado in Spain, France and America as *Los Samueles*: bulls with the conformation of a male lion, strong, vigorous, with well-developed humps, bulls which command respect by their class and which, at the same time, generate real nobility that increases as the fight goes on.

I will never cross-breed; in other words, I will always keep this blood pure, because I am conscious of my responsibility of having kept alight the torch

Samuel Flores y Flores, great uncle of Samuel Flores Romano, from whom he got his love of the countryside.

El Palomar Estate

of this genetic heritage in my youth, and my strong desire is one day to hand over this torch, shining just as brightly, to my children who themselves, like the previous generations, have been helping me since they successfully completed their university studies. Perhaps it is also the fact that, at the age of 64, I cannot continue to manage this business in such a dynamic way without their help.

I have had the pleasure of experiencing some very special and historic evenings as a breeder of fighting bulls, such as being carried from the arena shoulder high with the bullfighters Ortega Cano and Cesar Rincón in Madrid in 1991, when each bullfighter won three ears; or the prize for the best bullfight during the fiesta of San Isidro, Madrid in 1990 and 1995; the prize for the best bullfight in Bilbao in 1993, 1994, 1997 and 2006; and the historic bullfights of San Isidro in Madrid in 1996, fought by Joselito, Enrique Ponce and Rivera Ordóñez, and in Dax (France) in 1999, fought by Enrique Ponce, Morante de la Puebla and Miguel Abellán, in which the bullfighters won 11 ears and 1 tail from the six bulls. The achievements in this ring were repeated in August 2008 with an exceptional bullfight in which Enrique Ponce was awarded the four ears of his two bulls. I have also had

El Palomar Estate

the honour of being the first breeder to be awarded the gold medal from the Bullfighting Club of New York City in 1998.

A breeder's most beautiful and precious sense is that of knowing that bullfighting festivals have a huge cultural tradition. The ancestral link between Mediterranean man and the fighting bull goes back throughout the history of the entire area surrounding this "mare nostrum". Proof of this is the iconography from the various periods: Altamira, the paintings in the Cretan palaces in Mesopotamia, the myth of Theseus and the invincible Minotaur. The ancient tradition spread from the island of Crete to Greece and

Samuel Flores and his mother in the Plaza de Toros of Las Ventas (Madrid) in 1990 unveiling a plaque to commemorate the best bullfight in the Feria de San Isidro in that year, awarded to bulls of his herd.

Samuel Flores fighting a young bull in the bullring of Peñas de San Pedro (Albacete) during the festivals of 1983.
He fought with Julio Aparicio (father) and Sebastian Palomo Linares (father).

El Palomar Estate

El Palomar in the 1950s. Even the fiercest bulls allow themselves to be tempted.

Samuel father with his three children Isabel, Samuel and Carlos in the pastures of El Palomar Estate.

Rome and throughout Western Europe. In ancient Hispania the bull was a mythical animal with religious connotations similar to those in ancient Carthage, which was founded using the hide of a bull as a measure and where the bull had a clear impact on culture and society and where it often occurs in the social and industrial world in its role as a symbol of enterprise and great economic impact.

We should not forget, for example, that the Emperor Charles I of Spain (who was Charles V of Germany) killed a bull in the festival organized in 1527 to celebrate the birth of his son Felipe II.

DESCRIPTION

LA CAÑADA DEL QUINTANAR

Area: 912.29 ha.
Location: Municipality of El Pozuelo,
La Herrera, Albacete. Spain
Main activities: Irrigation agriculture,
breeding La Mancha sheep, and shooting.

EL PINAR DEL BOTICARIO

Area: 747.83 ha.
Location: Municipality of Peñas
de San Pedro, Pozohondo and Alcadozo,
Albacete, Spain.
Main activities: Organic almond production and
forestry.

LA CASA DE LA TORRE Y EL CEPILLO

Area: 2,059.64 ha.
Location: Municipality of Alcaráz Villanueva de la
Fuente, Povedilla and Viveros Albacete, Spain.
Main activities: Irrigated and non-irrigated agri-
culture, with La Mancha sheep and shooting.

PEÑASCOSA

Area: 1,271.34 ha.
Location: Municipality of Peñascosa
and Alcaráz, Albacete, Spain.
Main activities: Irrigated and non-irrigated agriculture and forestry.

EL PALOMAR

Area: 2,883.56 ha
Location: Municipality of Povedilla
and Alcaráz, Albacete, Spain.
Main activities: Semi-intensive shooting of
Red-legged Partridge *(Alectoris rufa)*, breeding of
fighting bulls, irrigated and non-irrigated agriculture, big game hunting, children's summer camp.

EL COTO CAMILO

Area: 1,713.36 ha.
Location: Municipality of Villahermosa
and Montiel, Ciudad Real, Spain.
Main activities: Irrigated and non-irrigated agriculture.

EL CASTILLO DE MONTIZÓN

Area: 1,423.65 ha.
Location: Municipality of Villamanrique,
Ciudad Real, Spain.
Main activities: Non-irrigated agriculture, shoot-
ing, and breeding fighting bulls.

SARDINA

Area: 2,233.61 ha.
Location: Municipality of Andújar, Jaén, Spain.
Main activities: Organic cattle breeding
and big game hunting.

EL VILLAR Y EL COTO DE LA CASA DEL RÍO

Area: 1,332.62 ha.
Location: Municipality of Torres de Albanchéz
(Jaén), Biensevida and Alcaráz (Albacete), Spain
Main activities: Organic cropping,
goat breeding, organic olive production.

EL ATERIL DEL CUERNO Y LA CARNICERA

Area: 1,405 ha.
Location: Municipality of Navas de San Juan,
Jaén, Spain.
Main activities: Cattle breeding and big game
hunting.

LA CUESTA DEL GATILLO

Area: 831.36 ha.
Location: Municipality of Baños
de la Encima, Jaén, Spain.
Main activities: Organic cattle breeding
and big game hunting.

LOS ALARCONES

Area: 6,200 ha.
Location: Municipality of Andújar, Baños de la
Encina and Villanueva de la Reina, Jaén, Spain.
Main activities: Organic cattle breeding
and big game hunting.

SAN AGUSTÍN (LA LOMA DE LA PUENTE, LA MARAÑOSA Y EL CRESPILLO DE ABAJO)

Area: 5,670.98 ha.
Location: Municipality of Orcera,
La Puerta del Segura and Siles, Jaén, Spain.
Main activities: Big game hunting,
crops and forestry.

But it is no less precious for a breeder to know that a bull, from the time he is born until the moment he dies fighting in the ring, is the only animal apart from wild animals to enjoy a free life in the extensive pastures and fields where he is bred. Bulls are cared for until the moment at which the fight begins. Without this there could be no justification for the very existence of such a marvelous animal and the care given to it. The bull is the only animal capable of growing stronger in the face of punishment and of fighting to his death.

At the end of the Middle Ages, the jousting tournaments between knights began to bore people, and they began to look for various animals against which the knight could fight in order to make the shows more attractive. They soon found the most appropriate one in the form of the Iberian bull, which in those times was wild but not fierce despite his aggressiveness and size.

With Philip V of Bourbon's rise to the Spanish throne, horse races began to disappear. The nobility left the army and were substituted by gentlemen (hidalgos). Their assistants, who helped them when they fell off their horses, became the real protagonists of the party: bull fighters on foot. This is how the Fiestas were born.

As a consequence, the breeders of those bulls started to select for fiercer and more aggressive animals, which would provide a greater show. They therefore began a process of genetic selection and became breeders of fighting bulls. As this selective breeding went on, more and better bloodlines came to be developed. A new concept arose, that of defining the bravery of the bull. The word used for this today is *commitment*, and it can refer to the man just as much as to the bull. It embraces the qualities which make the bull committed to the fight, his natural sense of self-preservation, his nobility and praiseworthiness. This has been an essential part in creating the art of bullfighting. For me, full commitment and nobility means bravery, bloodlines and aggressiveness.

For me and my children it is wonderful to be able to live in the countryside, from the countryside, and for the countryside, because it assumes, without any doubt, that we are always in touch with nature, and makes mankind feel a creature of God.

Samuel Flores Romano

Fighting bulls

We have three brands for our bulls:

1º "El Redondo," advertised under the name of Samuel Flores with an emblem of blue, red or old gold, dating back to 22nd April 1928.

Our bulls fight mainly in the most important festivals of Spain and France, and are frequently seen in the bullrings of Madrid, Nimes, Dax, Arles, Valencia, Bilbao, Albacete or Seville.**Historical Background:** In 1914, the Flores brothers formed their herd from animals acquired from Don Eduardo Olea. They later added a group of cows and a stud bull from Don José Vega, and advertising them under the name of Samuel Hermanos. In 1925, they acquired animals from the heirs of Don Luis Gamero Cívico y Torres that were sold to Don Juan Domínguez Delgado, from whom the Flores brothers acquired them. When the Civil War ended, Don Samuel Flores, who continued advertising under the name of "Samuel Hermanos," reorganized the herd. In 1968 the herd was given to "Agropecuaria Sierra Morena. S.A." in which Don Samuel Flores Romano has served as chief executive since 1969.
Current Source: "Samuel Flores".

2º The "F", advertised under the name of Manuela López-Flores, has a white, blue, and red emblem that dates back to 25th September 1864.
Historical Background: Founded by Don Gil Flores at the end of the 17th century with "Jijona" animals. In 1840 a part of the herd passed to Don Agustín Flores from whom his son, Don Melquíades, inherited it in 1921. It was later inherited by his children Don Leonardo, Don Samuel and Doña Carmen Flores. When Don Leonardo died in 1941, it was passed on to Manuela Agustina López Flores. The herd is comprised solely of animals from the herd of Don Samuel Flores. In 1968, it became the property of the "Agropecuaria Sierra Morena", preserving its name.
Current Source: "Samuel Flores".

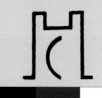

3º The third is that of Castillo de Montizón, with a black, blue, and white emblem.
Historical Background: It was registered into the Association in 1969 with the purchase of the animals belonging to Gómez Rangel and de Vera. It consists of cows and stud bulls from the Gamero Cívico line of Parladé.
Current Source: "Samuel Flores".

ce the 1970s Samuel Flores has maintained both the genotype and phenotype
e herd, known by the *aficionados* as *Los Samueles* bulls.

685

The Flores family has been linked to the countryside for over eight generations. Originally livestock breeders, our ancestors accumulated many hectares of land, from Albacete to Jaén (Andalucía, Spain) in order to feed their livestock during the different times of the year.

However, life evolves and we, the current generation, have had to confront important changes in the countryside in order to be able to maintain it, and only by anticipating these changes have we been, and will we be, able to keep living in it, from it, and for it.

These continual changes are the means by which we adapt to new times and are able to maintain the heritage of the countryside which we still conserve; it is the same in any sector or branch of industry, with the particular difference that a change in the countryside takes several years to yield any fruit, and that if the decision is wrong the consequences are very difficult to rectify quickly.

My great-grandfather Samuel Flores y Flores continually bought land. My father, who from an early age had to take charge of the management of the estates, hardly bought any land, and dedicated himself to consolidating what he had, making great changes in farming – in particular irrigation – on the one hand, whilst on the other hand pioneering the intensification of red-legged partridge shooting. My brothers and I are presently exploring ways to reduce costs, create products with added value, and diversify into other technologies related to the land.

But let us now analyze the management as a whole and see how it is structured nowadays. The different activities or lines of business are:

Agriculture

Irrigated agriculture: We grow alfalfa (lucerne), barley (for malting and feed), wheat, oilseed rape (colza), and poppies.

We plan to experiment with peppers in the fertile alluvial land of El Palomar. The problem is the shortage of water since the ground water level is very deep and the cost of electricity for the irrigation is very high.

Main House of El Palomar.
Fighting bulls in the foreground.

El Palomar Estate

The challenge is to find crops that consume less water, such as woody-stemmed plants watered by droplets, or to produce crops of greater added value than cereals.

Non-irrigated agriculture: Mainly barley, wheat and oats, besides the organic olive and almond trees and the recently planted lavender.

We are also studying the idea of growing thistles to supply a biomass plant, and holm oaks injected with mychorrhizal fungi to produce truffles, as well as intensive olive tree plantations.

The problem is low cereal prices as well as low prices for agricultural products in general, and the high price of fuel, fertilizers and in particular certain plant protection products.

The challenge is on the one hand to find an appropriate method of crop rotation to minimize the use of fertilizers and plant protection products, and on the other, to experiment with crops of greater added value.

The average production volumes in recent years are:

- 7,500,000 kg of cereal.
- 80,000 kg of olives.
- 200,000 kg of almonds.
- 140,000 kg of poppy.
- 200,000 kg of rape (colza).

Stockbreeding

Organic beef cattle

We currently have an extensive herd of 1,000 Limousin suckler cows in Andalucía, registered as organic. They are spread over the estates of Los Alarcones, La Cuesta del Gatillo, Sardina and El Ateril.

The challenge for the future of organic beef is to close the cycle and to be in a position to sell the meat for immediate consumption.

Sheep

Pure-bred La Mancha sheep for meat production (Lamb of La Mancha). For years we have been crossing them with "improved" males with the thought of milking the ewes in the medium term.

Goats

We produce meat from the kids of the Negras serranas goats, which are currently considered an endangered species. They originate from the so-called "flower goats" that have grazed in the Sierra de Alcaraz since time immemorial.

Horses

We have a herd of pure-bred Spanish horses (in Spanish known as PRE) which are making a name for themselves in this sector. We also breed piebald donkeys, which are also an endangered species, because of a certain romanticism in making sure that they do not become extinct.

Hunting and shooting

This is one of our principal enterprises and specifically the one that has allowed us to maintain the profitability of the property in the last few years.

One of our best decisions has been to intensify the hunting and shooting activity. My father was one of the pioneers in this, as partridge shooting days on the El Palomar Estate have been sold to groups of foreign visitors since the late 1960s. In the early years, partridges were bred on one dedicated farm; this was later dismantled, however, when some commercial enterprises started to rear partridges of higher quality. Ever since then, year after year, we have had groups of hunters coming to El Palomar from different parts of the world. In particular, we have one group that has come every year for the past 28 years; others have come for 20 consecutive years to enjoy the tradition of shooting in El Palomar.

Parallel to this, the management of game on the family estates has been recognized by multiple prizes and trophies for way it is organized and the trophies achieved. In particular, the estate of El Palomar has held the Spanish record for red deer since 1988, twice breaking its own record during this period. We also have mouflons and roe deer that have been among the best 20 trophies shot in Spain.

Renewable energy

Renewable energies is an area that currently offers enormous possibilities to the owners of rural estates.

We ourselves have only carried out one project in renewable energy. We are in the midst of creating a photovoltaic solar park of 2MW in the municipality of La Herrera (Albacete). However, we have several projects in hand, such as various photovoltaic installations in warehouses, some biomass plants, and wind farms for which we have requested for a licence.

El Palomar Estate

Group of red deer
in Los Alarcones, in
Sierra Mereno (Andalucia).

Olive oil

In December 2008 we began to produce organic extra virgin olive oil in the new oil mill located in Alcaraz (Albacete). It is one of the vanguard-design mills producing bottled commercial organic extra virgin olive oil of the highest quality. The oil of this region is of very high quality, and the olives that we have will permit excellent blends.

The project embraces the majority of organic olive producers of the region (many of whom are partners in the oil mill). The short-term aim is to produce a little over 2,000,000 kg in each harvest. This year for the first time we will bottle oil from the 2008/09 harvest.

The agricultural firm of San Antón, 84, S.C.L

This was founded in 1984 in collaboration with other well-known farmers from Albacete in order to dry the maize corn that in those days was starting to be produced in the province as result of high prices, low energy costs, and the availability of underground water resources.

Today it is one of the most prestigious companies in the sector and in terms of volume ranks as the leading business in the area of Albacete. As one of the major partners, we participate actively in the management.

Carlos Flores Santos Suárez

STAFF

Estate	Employers (Nº)
La Cuesta del Gatillo	1
Peñascosa	3
La Cañada del Quintanar	4
El Pinar del Boticario	1
El Villar y El Coto de la Casa del Río	6
La Torre y El Cepillo	9
El Coto Camilo	5
El Castillo de Montizón	5
El Ateril y La Carnicera	2
Sardina	1
San Agustín	2
El Palomar	17
Los Alarcones	6
Central Administrative services	6
Total	**68**

FROM THE MANAGER'S POINT OF VIEW...

To be a game manager, farmer or livestock breeder these days is without doubt not an easy task. To make the countryside profitable each day is becoming more of a challenge in a world in which the authorities focus more on the big cities and abandon a population that still lives in the rural areas and refuses to leave it. Those who govern us are not aware that the primary sectors must be supported because they are the basis and the future of any country. Middle-aged people who were born in small towns and who have no intention of migrating to the big cities, which are full of traffic, pollution and a quality of life that is incomparable with life in the small towns see themselves daily under more and more pressure to migrate. The love of their environment, however, makes them stronger every day. Young people have no other choice than to emigrate.

Living in the countryside is a way of life for a few people. It requires many sacrifices, but for people who enjoy the countryside at weekends thanks to better communications the countryside is closer than it has ever been. Nature is without doubt something that we should respect and from which we should learn. The awareness and sensibility that a person who lives in that environment has is not learned in a city. The real ecologists are those of us who live in, for, and from the countryside. Nobody is more interested in looking after nature than the people who live in its midst.

We are the ones who keep the land in good shape, the ones who put out the fires in the summertime so that the forests do not burn, the ones who control the caterpillars so that the trees do not die, the ones who work the soil so that the weeds don't grow, the ones who select and care for the animals so that they grow bigger and healthier, the ones who feed those animals in times of drought to prevent them from dying, the ones who replant trees for future generations. In the end, we are the guardians and guarantors of nature, so that our sons and grandsons can enjoy it. I assure you that if it were not for the hunters we would not have the great variety of animals and game species in our Peninsula; and if it were not for the livestock breeders, we would not have the bulls, and if it were not for the farmers, the lands would be abandoned and would die in the same way as the forests. People with responsibility should recognize us as the protagonists that we are and deserve to be, and should not treat us like rare animals, to be constantly controlled by bureaucracy and interference. It is clear that we all pay justly for the sins of others, for as in everything there are people who in doing things badly cause harm to those who are trying to manage things to perfection. Fortunately there are very few of the former.

Hunting is a very significant economic activity for everyone. In autonomous Spanish regions such as Castilla-La Mancha, Castilla y León, Extremadura, and Andalucía, where there are no major economic enterprises in the towns and rural areas, hunting and shooting has become a fundamental and necessary activity for the survival of hundreds of thousands of families, mainly in the autumn and winter months. Hunting brings many millions of Euros to Spain every year, and involves many thousands of people. In parallel with it run the prosperities of an endless number of businesses, such as the catering trade, restaurants, the automobile sector, the armoury and gunsmith businesses, outfitters, trailer manufacturers, country sports shops, organics, management firms, meat industries, etc. We, the reserve owners, have seen ourselves obliged to transform hunting into an economic activity in order to be able to maintain our heritage in the countryside.

More than thirty years ago, my father started another economic activity in the estates known as game and wildlife tourism. There are several estates dedicated to it. El Palomar is one of the most valued ones for its partridge, as are Los Alarcones, Sardina or San Agustín for their Spanish red deer, mouflon, and fallow deer.

El Palomar is a privileged estate for the production of game species, for its enormous quantity of Mediterranean fauna and flora, together with its cereal farming. Holm oak, Portuguese oak, rockrose, gum rockrose, thyme and spanish broom mix with large plantations of wheat, barley, oats, rape and alfalfa. The different animals in these estates have access to these areas: Spanish red deer, mouflons, fallow deer, Spanish ibex, roe deer, wild boar, red-legged partridges, quail, rabbits, Iberian hares, wood pigeons, wild ducks, thrushes etc. are the game species that form El Palomar's ecosystem. Every animal has its place on the estate and they are all looked after to perfection. But the one animal that without doubt is more important or is given more attention is the fighting bull. It is here where one of the most essential species of Spanish livestock grazes, the herds of Samuel Flores.

Let us discuss small game shooting. The red partridge is highly regarded by hunters because of its nervous and varied flight. Between the months of October and February, we receive between 15 and 20 groups of hunters from different foreign countries to shoot red legged partridge. The guest house of El Palomar is perfectly conditioned for its visitors, and equipped with every type of luxury for 30 people. Usually the groups come to shoot two days of driven birds. Here partridge beats are varied and intense. Visitors can shoot more than 1,000 partridges per day at the beginning of the season. We do not skimp on looking after our visitors, and ensure that they always leave delighted. The best marketing one can have is that these groups keep coming back year after year, and the fact is that 80% of our clients have done so for the past 20 years. The personal attention of every member of the family is valued by the clients, friends in many cases, just as much as the shooting is.

The month of September is one of the most magical and passionate moments of the year. The roaring begins. After timidly wandering and only coming out at night, the stags, the king of the sierra breaks the silence. Its broken voice is heard kilometres away and sends shivers to everything that hears it. The stag comes into action; it is his moment and he knows it. The older stags take up position in the best places to attract their hinds. The fights between males in these places are tough and sometimes deadly. This is the best moment to record the herd because they can be seen more

easily. With a pair of binoculars and a lot of patience those in charge of the countryside take a census of the males in all the estates where big game lives.

This census will be necessary to determine the quantity and quality of hunting drives that can be achieved that year. In a good year, which means that it has rained enough and there is enough grass so that the stags' horns have developed and in consequence the number of trophies is high, we can have around 8 or 10 such *monterías* on the estates of Los Alarcones, Sardina, El Crespillo and La Cuesta del Gatillo. All of these estates belong to the Flores family and are dedicated to the hunting of big game and to extensive agriculture, making the most of the excellent feeding conditions that they enjoy through the excellent and large areas of grazing land and mild climate. Here in Spain the hunting of big game species is approached in a different way than in the rest of Europe. Although it is also marked by its own traditions, hunting is done differently. It is the Spanish *montería*. To begin with, one cuts an extensive area that will be covered by hundreds of dogs (known as the pack) rented by the organizers. These dogs comb the 1,000 or 2,000 hectares where the hunters are and move the animals forward so that they pass close to the places where they are positioned. The animals are shot on the move, and there are some long-range and difficult shots. When the hunt is over, the hunters return to lodge where a traditional and replenishing meal awaits them and where stories are exchanged – the exaggerations, the occasional tall tale and the chapter and verse of every move, just as hunters do in every country.

Stalking is probably more pure and traditional. It is a form of hunting that heightens your predatory instinct, and very profound feelings and emotions can be aroused. Here the wind plays an important role. Like a sailor who always attempts to position his boat to windward, the hunter takes out his cigarette and lights it, because he must always smell the smoke. An animal's sense of smell should not be underestimated. Patience is a virtue that anyone who hunts in this way must have. This is how we hunt on El Palomar. Here stalking only takes place during the period of the rut, when the stags are roaring, a moment that one can use in order to be very selective indeed, something that my father established 45 years ago. The first young deer arrived on the estates of Sardina and Los Alarcones 50 years ago. El Palomar, with its 3,000 hectares, is enclosed

The first mares and stallions arrived at Los Alarcones in the 1970s. Pure Cartujano horses. In 2002 the breeding of Spanish horses moved to El Palomar.

along its entire perimeter by a two-metre high wire mesh fence. All the game species found here have access the whole year round to the cereal land that we plant, often for the purpose of feeding them. The deer can thus choose a varied menu of wheat, barley, oats, alfalfa, beans or chickpeas that together with the natural trefoil and the rich grasses and varied scrubland found here supplies them with an abundance of food. In order to breed big males, it is also very important not to have a high number of individuals and to have a proportionate number of males and females. This ensures that only physically healthy stags will be available to cover the females.

In conclusion, it has been selection, good nutrition and equal numbers of males to females, together with years of work, that have made the estate prosperous. In El Palomar the record for red deer in Spain has been achieved on three consecutive occasions. We have had the honour of accompanying His Majesty the King of Spain on various occasions. We have also made numerous friends with whom we have broadened our relationship by sharing long periods together, full of emotions, perched on top of a cliff. Stalking at the height of the rut leaves its mark on you, and is a magical experience.

At El Palomar we also breed pure thoroughbred Spanish horses. The PRE is an animal that stands out because of its beauty and nobility. A war horse and a riding horse for great kings and noblemen, it has been preserved and selected down the centuries by breeders who love the breed. My father purchased the first mares and stallions in the 1970s. Mares from Fernández Daza and Marqués de Borja were in those days the purest representation of the Cartujano horse, as it is also known, which arrived at Los Alarcones in 1971. There they were bred and nurtured for many years until finally they were brought to El Palomar six years ago because El Palomar had better facilities with which to continue their breeding. From then on the selection has been more carefully controlled and studied. Today we have 20 young mares and 4 stallions with excellent conformation and movements. Horses bred at El Palomar have won many breed shows. Mares such as Faenera, Iluminada, Kalinga, Llovizna, Llanera IV, Níspola, Pastora VII, Rebeca 2 or Rameada have been the main pillars of this success, together with stallions such as Romancero I and V, Glauco or Banderín III, which have already

El Palomar Estate

produced a select and consolidated progeny from El Palomar. Horses and mares of appropriate size, with strong bones, well-filled faces, excellent movements as well as class, elegance, and nobility are the result of more than 35 years of selective breeding.

My brothers and I are the ninth generation of a family that cares for and works this land. We continue to look after it in the traditional way even as we introduce new methods and new technologies. What counts the most is the knowledge and experience transmitted by earlier generations. In our case, it was the wise advice that our dear father has always given us. He has always been, and continues to be, a lover of the countryside. He has lived passionately through each spring, summer, autumn, and winter, always looking at the sky and praying for rain, or not for rain, depending on the needs of the moment. He has lived through good, bad, and even worse years, but thanks to his determination, everything he has done has resulted in success. He knew how to pass on to my brothers and me the intense love of the countryside and of animals. He learned from his great-uncle Samuel's example as well as from his mother, our grandmother Noli, how to live a noble and admirable life. Now all of us Flores form a great team and will keep fighting to maintain what was, eight generations ago, started through effort and hard work. We owe it to them.

Samuel Flores Santos-Suárez

El Palomar has held the Spanish record for red deer since 1988, twice breaking its own record during this period.

DECOY PARTRIDGE SHOOTING AT "EL PALOMAR"

The day broke calm, with a soft wind and air that was fresh and easy to breathe. It had been a cold night, one of those freezing nights of La Mancha that leaves you breathless and makes icicles hang from the bulrushes and covers the sown fields with frost. When I reached the entrance of "El Palomar," Juan, the gamekeeper, a good friend of mine, was waiting for me. It was eight in the morning, the sky was bright and clear, and the sun rose over the tops of the Alcaraz mountain range, lighting with gold and happiness the estate where I was coming to shoot.

Juan had already made a hide for me, where I could sit quietly, as if in my own lair, and witness what was happening on both sides of the "Cerro de las Madroñeras". He recommended the site to me, perhaps because he knew it was my favourite spot. After we had greeted each other, I took the lane that passes in front of the "Cortijo Nuevo" and separates the dense thicket of evergreen oak trees and shrubs from the farmlands that climb to the top of the hill. There I left the four-wheel-drive and took a short path, an easy walk, to the place where Juan had prepared the hide. I had my bird on my back, the cage covered with baize and held tightly with hooks. I also had my hat, warm clothes, and knife strapped to my waist. I was carrying my folding bed, shotgun, and cartridges, all the necessary equipment that an experienced bird partridge hunter.

When I arrived at the hide, I could already hear the partridges on the rough mountain top, so I didn't want to lose any time. I put the decoy a live male red-legged partridge partridge to one side and went slowly towards the hide where I could survey everything. I inserted my folding bed and shotgun through the observation hole, from which, once inside, I could watch the whole area. Even before managing to get into a comfortable position, my decoy had begun a few trial verses of his song. Then, adopting the upright stance of a fighter, he turned up the volume and launched into full song, making himself heard all across the hill. It was his way of saying "Here I am", a warlike gesture in which he issued an open challenge to all comers.

To my left, about two hundred meters away, a partridge male with a strong, hoarse, jealous voice answered him. He was defending the territory, which he had claimed as owner and hero. He was not going to tolerate any intruder and was ready to fight to the death for his mate and his turf. On hearing him, the caged bird turned around and faced him. Battle began. From that moment on, they entangled themselves in an exchange of threats in which they both expressed their coolness and their ferocity. From my hide I could sense the wild bird coming closer to us. After a few moments, during which my bird sang loudly (I called it El Carbonero and he was at the height of his extraordinary powers), the wild bird appeared on the edge of the clearing, his feathers puffed up with fiery indignation. When he saw my bird, he made a gesture as if sharpening his beak on a rock and then, quickly crossing the green area, he moved towards him, prepared to fight. When he reached the spot where the intruder was waiting in his cage, he made several turns, displaying his wings in a show of power and majesty, those two defining characteristics of wild creatures. El Carbonero, the decoy bird, also arched his body, hollow as a turkey, stuck up his neck feathers, and willingly accepted the challenge, engaging with the enemy at the top of the rise where I had secured the cage with the hooks. It was glorious to watch them.

After the faena (which is what the attack is called), I was ready to forgive such a beautiful and arrogant creature as this wild bird, in the same way that a fierce bull is forgiven. However, that isn't possible in this game. The decoy wants to see his enemy defeated, humiliated, and at his feet when the fight is over, so you have to help him feel victorious. If not, he will not only remain frustrated, downhearted, and quiet for the rest of the day, but he will never again want to confront a partridge. A bad faena can ruin a red legged partridge forever.

Even if a cuquillero ("cuckoo hunter" – the name given to decoy hunters) has years of experience, his pulse still races and his heart throbs each time a fierce cock challenges and attacks his bird. Anyone reading this who is fond of this kind of hunting knows that's how it is. Those who are not familiar with it (probably the majority of those reading this article) will ask themselves: What is it about this peculiar and thrilling adventure that fascinates people who practise this type of hunting?

In my book "Sierras, perdices y Olivares" (Mountains, Partridges, and Olive Groves), published in 1996 but now out of print, I write (and ask you to forgive me for quoting my own work):

"The partridge does not have fans or supporters, but devotees, and, like flamenco, it carries within it a hidden cloak of mystery that affects only those who have been fortunate enough to feel the shiver."

To begin with, I have to mention that we are dealing here with the most ancient way of confronting our red legged partridge. Xenophon, over two thousand years ago, already tells us about the nets and devices used to trap the partridges that the Greeks attracted with their decoy skills. During my years as ambassador in Greece, I was able to discover five anonymous fables from the Hellenistic Era that told of this type of hunting. They spoke of a pact made between a humble farmer and a partridge that he had captured. "Let us respect life", said the creature, "and I will work for you." Something similar to the agreement put forward by the dog, according to various Eastern mythologies, in order to obtain man's protection in exchange for helping him in the difficult work of hunting, at a time in history when you were either a hunter or you were nothing. Dante himself wrote in his Divine Comedy the verses with which I begin the fourth chapter of my book:

"In similar wise the evil seed of Adam
Throw themselves from that margin one by one
As signals, as a bird onto its lure. "

Let me give another example. Froylán Troche Zúñiga, in her famous treatise on the art of hunting written in 1563, notes that at that time a pair of oxen were valued at 4 ducados, a dead partridge at only 12 maravedi, but a live partridge could be sold for 550 real. In those days, 550 real constituted an important sum of money with which one could buy a decent house, a good vegetable garden, or a herd of livestock. This gives us an idea of how much people valued this kind of hunting. They were willing to pay a high price for a captive bird, which if it remained healthy had no more than seven or eight months of useful life left.

I have practiced this sport since I was young, and have had the opportunity to do so amongst the stony outcrops and scrubland and oak forests of "El Palomar" as a guest of Samuel Flores for more than twenty-five years. I have never missed our annual meeting. To start with, we used to do it at "El Calderón" in the morning or at "Aza de la Iglesia" in the afternoon, two places full of partridge, fierce and abundant, where I have enjoyed some of my best shoots. On one of these occasions I experienced something I will never forget. A bold male came up, furious and enraged, to fight with my decoy. I wanted him to get down because he could harm my bird. However, it was impossible. He was entangled in battle and for that reason did not hear my loud coughs or notice the pebbles, nor even the empty cartridge, I threw at him. He was so blind. He just wanted to defeat the bird in the cage, banish him from his territory, and punish him for challenging for his female companion who was watching the battle attentively from the ground.

With the passing of time, my hunting extended to the more mountainous areas of the property: the "Collado de los Perules," the so-called "Cerro de las Madroñeras," the "Vereda de los Ateros," and "Los Pizarrales." Everywhere is the same. The partridges are the same, and the pleasure of enjoying my bird in the solitary space and pure air of the mountains is identical.

I know very well that it is impossible to summarize in only a few lines a technique and an art that one perfects over the course of an entire lifetime. It is also impossible to mention all the strategies needed to enjoy this sport, which can be practiced in the evening, daytime or at dawn. Similarly, it is impossible to mention every aspect of the selection, detailed training and care of a caged decoy bird. It all requires a great deal of careful attention. I have simply tried to sketch, with the briefest strokes of my brush, the enormous attraction of this kind of hunting. It is a sport that you undertake in the lap of mountains, submerged in nature, surrounded by the thousand-and-one noises of the countryside, and the deep and nutritious aromas of the earth. You do it at the same time as the sap starts to rise once again, when the newly planted crops promise us the ears of corn of June and when they begin to paint, between the new green growth, the tender, insecure and fragile flowers of February.

I have wanted, above all, to transmit to whoever reads this the emotions of decoy hunting: that chaotic passion, that madness.

José Cuenca

EL PALOMAR AND FLORES FAMILY LAND-HOLDINGS BELONG TO:

Agropecuaria Ecológica
Sierra de Alcaraz

Asociación Ecológica
Sierra de Alcaraz

Agricultura ecológica

Fundación Amigos
del Águila Imperial

Grupo de Empresas
Agrarias

Friends of the
Countrside

Asaja

Aproca
Castilla-La Mancha

Ademac

Junta Central de Regantes
de la Mancha Oriental

Fundación Consejo Regulador
de la IGP Cordero Manchego

Asociación Española de
Amigos de los Castillos

WE initiative

Parque Natural Sierra
de Andújar

ANCCE
Asociación Nacional de
Criadores Caballos de
Pura Raza Española

Asociación Nacional de
Criadores de Ganado
Caprino Raza Negra
Serrano Castiza

Asociación de Castilla-La Mancha
de Pura Raza Española

Asociación de la
Industria Fotovoltaica

D.O. Aceites Monte
de Alcaraz

Unión de Criadores
de Toros de Lidia

Asociación Nacional de
Criadores de Toros de Lidia

Cooperativa Frutos
Secos del Mañan

Activities

 Hunting

Shooting

Birdwatching

Estate products

Historic buildings

Educational activities

Country Park

Rural tourism

Walking trails

Olive Oil

Equestrian

CONTACT DATA
D. Samuel Flores Romano
C/ San Antonio, 7 • E-02001 Albacete • SPAIN
Finca El Palomar
Povedilla, Albacete
Tel.: (+34) 967 39 20 09 / Fax: (+34) 967 39 66 77
info@el-palomar.com
www.el-palomar.com/

1. La Cañada del Quintanar (Albacete, Spain)
2. El Pinar del Boticario (Albacete, Spain)
3. La Casa de la Torre y El Cepillo (Albacete, Spain)
4. El Coto Camilo (Ciudad Real, Spain)
5. El Castillo de Montizón (Ciudad Real, Spain)
6. El Palomar (Albacete, Spain)
7. El Villar and El Coto de la Casa del Río (Jaén-Albacete, Spain)
8. Peñascosa (Albacete, Spain)
9. El Ateril del Cuerno and La Carnicera (Jaén, Spain)
10. La Cuesta del Gatillo (Jaén, Spain)
11. Los Alarcones (Jaén, Spain)
12. Sardina (Jaén, Spain)
13. San Agustín (Jaén, Spain)

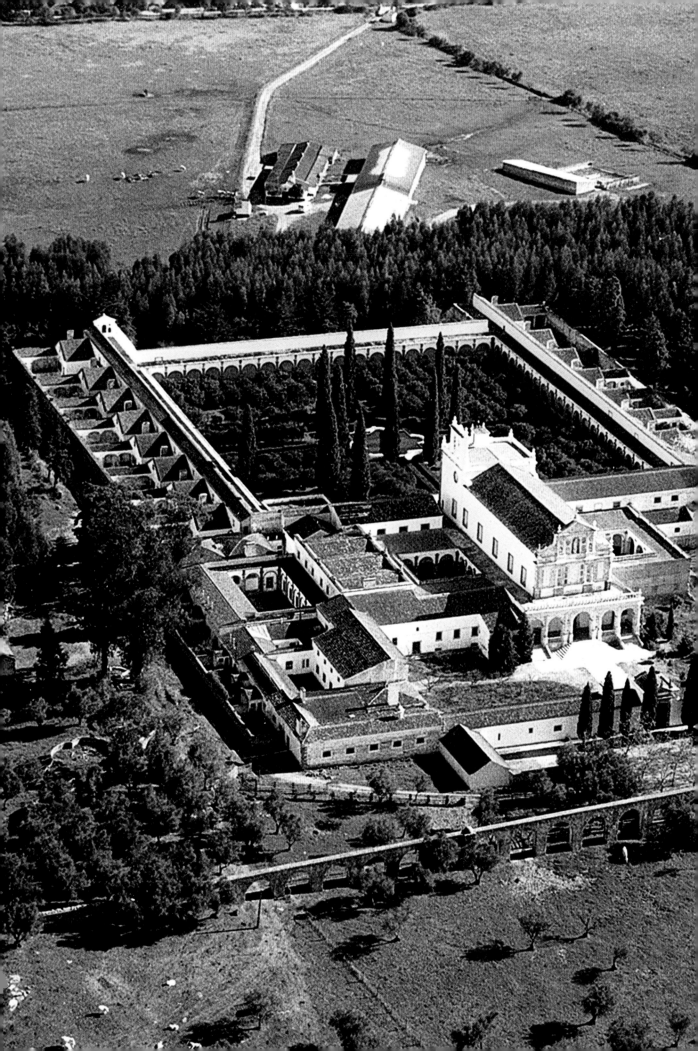

Fundação Eugénio de Almeida

Fundação Eugénio de Almeida

and its properties

Mediterranean

Location: Évora and Lisbon, Portugal.
Surface: 6,500 ha.

CLIMATIC DATA

Average rainfall
mm/cm²/year

Snow days: 0

716 mm

Temperature (°C)

39.5 — max ■
15.5 — average ■
-0.2 — min ■

SUMMARY

Comprising rural estate assets of over 6,500 hectares and a wide range of different productive enterprises, the Eugénio de Almeida Foundation has been developing its agricultural and industrial business models by making use of the most up-to-date production technologies. Within its proactive strategy of sustainable development, improvement of its environmental standards and maintenance of its landscape values are a feature of everything that it does.

Its agricultural and commercial activities are highlighted by cattle-rearing on the natural grazing lands of the Alentejo as well as cereals, cork harvesting and the production of high-quality olive oil. However the Foundation's main national and international recognition comes as a result of the development of its wine-making projects. The wines it produces are nowadays recognised as a point of reference in the highly competitive markets into which they have penetrated.

Furthermore the Foundation owns and administers a large number of properties that are of great historical and cultural value, located in Évora and Lisbon (Portugal).

Amongst these the Palace of the Condes de Basto in Évora, whose origins date back to the times of the Romans and Visigoths, has been listed as a National Monument since 1922. Other Évora properties include the Chapel of S. Miguel, the Palace of the Inquisition in which the Court of the Holy Office operated from 1536 until the early 19th century, the Convent of Cartuxa founded at the end of the 16th century for the Order of S. Bruno, the Painted Houses (Casas Pintadas) and the Eugénio de Almeida Forum founded in 2002. In Lisbon the Foundation owns the House of Santa Gertrudes and two buildings in Lisbon.

Convent of Cartuxa, founded in the late 16th century for the Order of S. Bruno.
Bought in 1869 by Eugenio's family from the National Estate. Carthusian monks
returned in 1960 once the reconstruction and restoration work was completed.

Vasco Maria Eugénio de Almeida (1913-1975), a person of strong Christian and humanist convictions with a vocation for philanthropic works, created the Foundation in 1963.

THE FOUNDER

Vasco Maria Eugénio de Almeida was born on the 30th August 1913. He studied in the Higher Institute of Agronomy, completing his studies in 1936. He died in Lisbon on the 11th August 1975.

A person of strong Christian and humanist convictions, with a vocation for philanthropic works and cultural patronage and sensitive to educational and social needs, he soon placed his fortune at the service of Évora and its inhabitants.

Among the countless works for which he was responsible we highlight, for reasons of their importance and the impact which they had, the rebuilding and restoration of the Convent of Cartuxa and the founding of ISESE – Évora's Higher Institute of Economics and Social Sciences, the harbinger of the resumption of university teaching in the city. He supported the creation of the Patrocínio Hospital, of a social housing estate, of the municipal aerodrome, as well as various institutions of social aid in Évora. His activities were equally extended to Lisbon, where he managed, transformed and gave financial help to the D. Pedro V Orphanage, having also made the Santa Gertrudes Park available for the first Lisbon Fair in 1943, the proceeds from which were used to finance the Summer Camp for children of "O Século".

He gave particular attention to the protection and preservation of heritage, going on to restore carefully and painstakingly the historic buildings which were his property and which are now a part of the assets of the Eugénio de Almeida Foundation. His interest in culture also led him to donate funds to various institutions in the city with links to the musical and theatrical arts.

At the beginning of the 1960s, Vasco Maria Eugénio de Almeida transformed what was a personal aim to help others into a long-term purpose by founding the Eugénio de Almeida Foundation, leaving behind a legacy of values, set objectives and the means to achieve these in full.

THE FOUNDATION

The Eugénio de Almeida Foundation, based in Évora (Portugal), is a private law institution in the public interest. Its founder drew up its statutes at the time of its creation in 1963.

The initial period of the Foundation bears the stamp of Vasco Maria Eugénio de Almeida's personality who, until his death in 1975, guaranteed the effective management of the institution.

During this period the aims set out in the statutes became reality through the restoration of the Cartuxa Convent as a centre of spiritual life, the building of the S. José Oratory in 1964 for the purposes of giving schooling and vocational training to thousands of children, and the upkeep, in collaboration with the Jesuit Order, of ISESE – Évora's Higher Institute of Economics and Social Sciences – which was the trigger for the resump-

The most representative architectural feature, still evident in the most recent construction in the exterior of the Palace – perhaps the pretext of the residence of the young King Sebastião (1570) – is the two covered galleries.

tion of Évora University and which trained hundreds of professionals who took up posts or went on to top-level management in the public and private sectors.

The downturn in the activities of the Foundation, which were a result of the occupation and expropriation of its estates after the Portuguese Revolution of 1974, coincided with the death of Vasco Maria Eugénio de Almeida.

After the return of its assets in the 1980s the Foundation began a new phase of heritage management which has allowed it to continue the task inspired by the Christian values embodied by its Founder, in the present day and in a new context, and which has become a point of convergence and aggregation of efforts to promote the region.

The Board of Trustees of the Eugénio de Almeida Foundation consists of a five-man committee. It includes one representative from the Archdiocese of Évora, who chairs the Board, one representative from Évora University, one delegate from the teaching staff at the Évora Higher Institute of Theology and two delegates co-opted by the above.

Its Board of Auditors is composed of three members. It is chaired by the Canon of Évora Cathedral and includes a delegate from the Santa Casa da Misericórdia de Évora (a private social welfare institution) and one delegate co-opted by the other two.

MISSION

The mission statement of the Eugénio de Almeida Foundation is evident in the spheres of culture, education, social welfare and aid, and spirituality, especially in its aims to develop and promote the Évora region.

To carry out these aims, the Foundation promotes and puts into action a series of initiatives, either on its own or with other partners, and will support the projects of other public or private organisations in a wide range of activities covering the areas in which it itself operates.

The knowledge it has acquired and its interest in the diverse reality around it has led the Foundation to share its means, efforts and resources with various entities at national and international level as part of its commitment to achieve economic development and a greater social and cultural balance in the Évora region.

C. Otero

Its ever-strengthening ties with the local community are the result of the same determination which has given it its leading position in the area of projects relevant to the region, projects which always carry the standards of quality and excellence.

Being by definition an institution created for perpetuity, the Foundation has tried to remain faithful to its origins, adapted to the present and prepared to meet the challenges posed by a world in constant change.

AIMS

Culture and education

The Eugénio de Almeida Foundation is open to many forms in which culture is actually expressed and lived. From artistic expression to the promotion of knowledge, from discussion and debate of ideas to the upkeep and improvement of heritage, the Foundation seeks to start, and involve itself in, projects which, in an effective manner, help to take up culture in its fullest form as a factor in realizing

View from the 16th century gallery of the Palace of the Condes de Basto and Patio of S. Miguel – important historic Heritage properties belonging to the Fundação Eugénio de Almeida in the centre of Évora (Portugal).

The Count of Vill'Alva made use of ancient masonry work of inestimable aesthetic value, like a granite double window in the Moorish style.

Palace of the Inquisition where the Court of the Holy Office sat from 1563 until the early 19th century. Future instalations of the museum of contemporary art.

the human potential and in its role as a mainstay of progress in society.

In this area, the role of the Eugénio de Almeida Foundation can be seen in the holding of exhibitions and other arts projects, seminars, conferences and events, as well as its grants programmes for Masters and Doctorates as an incentive to scientific research and innovation. Equally the Foundation places a great focus on the maintenance and improvement of heritage, especially the heritage left by its Founder which has great architectural and cultural value and is strongly linked to the life and history of the city and the country.

In order to develop the region through the training and qualification of its human resources, the Foundation has invested in the preparation of a professional work-force through continuous collaboration with Évora University, the Évora Higher Institute of Theology and other institutions concerned with university education and post-graduate studies.

With the same aim in mind, there is also de Eugénio de Almeida Prize, which each year is given to the best students in the Business Management, Economics and Sociology courses at Évora University.

At the same time the Foundation develops and supports educational projects at other levels of education, namely through its special relationship with the S. José Oratory day-school in Évora.

The Foundation has also developed its own publishing and printing press, highlighting those publications linked to its arts projects and other cultural themes.

SOCIAL WELFARE AND AID

Driven by the core aims set out in its statutes, the Eugénio de Almeida Foundation wholly and effectively fulfils its commitment to contribute towards the creation of a caring society which upholds human dignity in all its aspects.

The Foundation develops projects, on its own or with other entities, mainly through training schemes and by helping to improve community organisations and their workers, and by forward-looking studies on topics concerned with values, attitudes and customs which help to provide an intimate knowledge of social conditions, especially of those in the Alentejo.

The Foundation's activities are also directed towards those in most need, trying to ensure that the support given meets the nature and situation of each case, in accordance with the principles of justice and equality, encouraging not only the search for solutions within the community, but also the willingness to take part in and live these solutions.

Hence, support is given to private entities which are actually working in the area of community care. This support takes the form of financial help and promotion of discussion groups, with priority given to those aimed at social groups most at risk of social exclusion. The Foundation also has a first-degree grants programme which aims to encourage and support students doing courses in higher education who come from low-income households.

SPIRITUALITY

Through its activities the Foundation, based since its inception on the core ethical values of Christianity, hopes for a balanced and complete development of each person's potential and of the community of which he/she is part.

Certain that Christian values and concerns also provide a solid base for an organisational project, and that these form a basis for the renewal of personal and social lives, the Foundation is a regular backer of organisations with Christian values, regardless of whether these are of a religious nature or not, respecting their identity, character and autonomy. This type of activity, developed within the terms of a cooperation protocol with the Archdiocese of Évora, aims especially to encourage the training of people into pastoral work, promote worship, improve places of worship and contribute towards the restoration, maintenance and preservation of the religious art heritage.

In keeping with one of the priority aims set out in the statutes written by the founder, the Eugénio de Almeida Foundation guarantees the upkeep of the Cartuxa de Santa Maria Scala Coeli Convent, hoping that this ensures it remains unchanging and faithful to its ideals of contemplation and prayer.

Moreover, the Foundation undertakes to keep alive Christian values by making them part of its organisational culture.

ASSETS

Donated by the founder as the financial basis for the promotion of the Foundation's aims, the assets owned by the Eugénio de Almeida Foundation include estates in the Évora district and a series of buildings of great cultural and historic interest in Évora and in Lisbon.

Chief among these is the Patio de S. Miguel and the architectural complex which includes the Palace of the Condes de Basto and the Chapel of S. Miguel. It is here that one finds the headquarters of the Eugénio de Almeida Foundation.

The Palace of the Condes de Basto, dating from the Roman-Visigoth period, has been classed as a National Monument since 1922. Great names from the Portughese history lived there, such as D. Fernando, D. Nuno Álvares Pereira, D. Joao III, D. Sebastião and D. João IV. The series of 15th century frescoes by Francisco Campos are worthy of particular note.

The Chapel of S. Miguel, a listed building since 1939, was founded in the 12th century by Gonça-

FUNDAÇÃO
EUGÉNIO
Ð ALMEIDA

Herdade de Pinheiros:
The modern equipment installed in the new winery at Cartuxa produce fine wines under the Pêra-Manca, Cartuxa, Foral de Évora, Scala Coeli and EA labels.

The Foundation breeds thoroughbred Lusitanian horses. The photo shows the stallion Guizo, the winner of several prizes.

lo Viegas, son of Egas Moniz and Master of the Order of S. Bento de Calatrava.

The Palace of the Inquisition, where the Court of the Holy Office operated from 1536 until the beginning of the 19th century, was acquired by Vasco Maria Eugénio de Almeida in 1963 with a view to setting up the ISESE – Évora's Higher Institute of Economics and Social Sciences.

The Cartuxa Convent was founded at the end of the 16th century to receive the Order of S. Bruno. It was closed in 1834 and became state property. It was bought thirty-five years later by the Eugénio de Almeida family. The Carthusian monks moved back in 1960, invited by the Founder, who, with this aim in mind, undertook great rebuilding and restoration works.

The Painted Houses (Casas Pintadas), formerly the property of a family with links to the Discoveries, contain frescoes from the 16th century with figurative and fantastic motifs.

The Eugénio de Almeida Fórum, founded in 2002, restored and made use of a building which formed part of the assets of the Foundation. Nowadays it is the centre for Foundation projects and events and those of other entities, aiming to develop and dynamise the city and the region from a socio-cultural, educational, economical and spiritual perspective.

In Lisbon, the Foundation owns the Casa de Santa Gertrudes and two buildings in Rua Rodrigo da Fonseca, which it rents to private individuals and organisations.

Rural assets owned by the Eugénio de Almeida Foundation comprise some 6,500 ha in the Évora district, spread over various estates. Close to the city the Foundation also owns Quinta de Valbom, where the old Cartuxa Winery is situated, and Quinta da Cartuxa, where the Cartuxa de Santa Maria Scala Coeli Convent is located.

ASSET MANAGEMENT

The Foundation has direct control of its estates through livestock farming and industrial activities which, by raising funds, allow the institution to be financially independent and to guarantee that it will continue to pursue its aims and perpetuate its existence. On the other hand, the development of

The herd of purebred Alentejan cattle consists of almost 900 cows.

HERDADE DE PINHEIROS

Area: 1,134ha
Location: Évora
Main Activities: Charolais and Alentejan cattle, thoroughbred Lusitano horses, vineyards, cereals and forage.

HERDADE DO FREIXO

Area: 677 ha
Location: Évora
Main Activities: Irrigated crops, grazings, beef cattle.

HERDADE DO ÁLAMO DE CIMA

Area: 539 ha
Location: Évora
Main Activities: Livestock, olives and vines.

HERDADE DO ÁLAMO DA HORTA

Area: 453 ha
Location: Évora
Main Activities: Vineyards and olives, production of olive oil.

ZAMBUJAL DO CALADO E ZAMBUJALINHO

Area: 533 ha
Location: Évora
Main Activities: Merino sheep mediterranean forest.

HERDADE DO PAÇO E ALGARVÉUS

Area: 679 ha
Location: Évora
Main Activities: Alentejan cattle, livestock grazing, forage.

HERDADE DA CABIDA

Area: 749 ha
Location: Évora
Main Activities: Cattle and irrigated crops.

HERDADE DE CABAÇOS

Area: 243 ha
Location: Évora
Main Activities: Dry land crops, cattle grazing.

HERDADE DAS MURTEIRAS

Area: 1,458 ha
Location: Évora
Main Activities: Alentejan pigs, Merino sheep, grazing and cork oak trees.

QUINTA DA CARTUXA E VALBOM

Area: 79 ha
Location: Évora
Main Activities: Enoturismo and Charolais cattle.

these assets, innovative from a technological point of view and a job creator, is also in itself an effective contributor in terms of encouraging economic and social development in the region.

The most important part of these assets comprises the estates known as Pinheiros, Paço e Algarvéus, Murteiras, Álamo de Cima, Álamo da Horta, Freixo, Cabida and Cabaços,

Herdade das Murteiras: Montado landscape of cork oaks. There are 2,000 merino sheep.

Almost 400 ha of vineyards are found at Herdade de Pinheiros, Herdade do Álamo de Cima, Herdade do Álamo da Horta and Quinta Valbom.

Autumn landscape on the Herdade do Álamo da Horta, which has 66 ha of old olive trees and 33 ha of vines planted in 1984.

Zambujal do Calado and Quinta da Cartuxa e Valbom.

The objectives of the Foundation's investment and production policies in the agricultural sector have set out, above all, to exchange traditional Alentejo crops for profit-making crops in terms of the market place, from a perspective of both quality and competitiveness. Dry arable land used for growing cereals has been changed into tilled, irrigated field systems, into new vineyards and into new forestry areas.

The Eugénio de Almeida Foundation uses about 1,900 ha of forest which contain, among other uses, areas of Cork Oak *(Quercus suber)* and Holm Oak *(Q. ilex)* in the traditional Alentejan landscape and land use known as montado.

The extensive pastures are used for livestock farming, native breeds of cattle and sheep predominating, these being destined for the production of quality meat. Also worthy of note is the thoroughbred Lusitanian horse, breeding having started at the beginning of the 1980s.

The Foundation's economic project is also characterised by its opening up to diversification

of the product offer, be it new or complementary to products already in existence, namely in the growing of olives for oil production and in viniculture. As far as vineyards are concerned, an activity in this region since time immemorial, the Eugénio de Almeida Foundation is also heir to a long history of viniculture in the area, as vine-growing has been part of the traditional agricultural products of the Casa Agrícola Eugénio de Almeida since the end of the 19th century

In the 1980s the Foundation started to restructure the Cartuxa Winery and to plant new vineyards from which the white and red wines of Pêra-Manca, Cartuxa, Foral de Évora, Scala Coeli and EA are produced.

Included in the Évora sub-region of the DOC (Denomination of Controlled Origin) of Alentejo, these wines follow the pattern of wines from the region, showing the characteristics of the varieties that give rise to them. The best-known reds undergo a controlled process of aging in wood and a period of bottling in the cellars of the Cartuxa Convent. They are prized by consumers because of the quality maintained by the vinification process, the good raw material, the use of advanced technology and the care given right up to the point they reach the markets.

Fundação Eugénio de Almeida

Neolithic constructions on the Herdade das Murteiras testify to the ancient occupation of these lands.

Fundação Eugénio de Almeida

Pigs of the Alentejo breed resemble the Iberian *Pata Negra*.

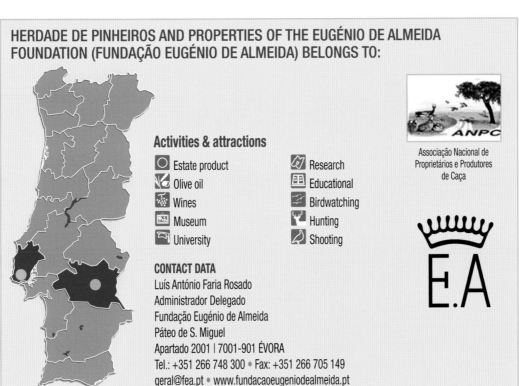

HERDADE DE PINHEIROS AND PROPERTIES OF THE EUGÉNIO DE ALMEIDA FOUNDATION (FUNDAÇÃO EUGÉNIO DE ALMEIDA) BELONGS TO:

Activities & attractions

- ◎ Estate product
- 🥖 Olive oil
- 🍇 Wines
- 🏛 Museum
- 🎓 University
- 📖 Research
- 📚 Educational
- 🦅 Birdwatching
- 🦌 Hunting
- 🔫 Shooting

ANPC

Associação Nacional de Proprietários e Produtores de Caça

CONTACT DATA
Luís António Faria Rosado
Administrador Delegado
Fundação Eugénio de Almeida
Páteo de S. Miguel
Apartado 2001 | 7001-901 ÉVORA
Tel.: +351 266 748 300 • Fax: +351 266 705 149
geral@fea.pt • www.fundacaoeugeniodealmeida.pt

E.A

Gisselfeld Kloster

Continental

Location: Locality of Gisselfeld, Haslev region, Denmark.
Surface: 3,850 ha.

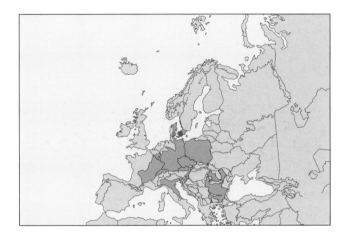

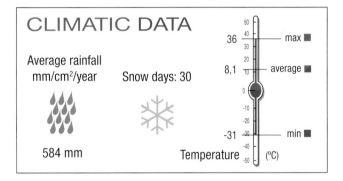

CLIMATIC DATA

Average rainfall
mm/cm²/year

Snow days: 30

584 mm

Temperature (°C)

36 max
8,1 average
-31 min

SUMMARY

Gisselfeld Kloster is one of Denmark's largest estates, founded by Peder Oxe and built between 1547 and 1575.

Many celebrities have over time been attracted by the beautiful landscape around the main house. The former monastery has been converted in a profitable business due to extremely well organised management.

This rural business has many facets operating under modern management principles, respecting the long and significant history they represent. The very high values of natural and cultural history are perceived today as a very important tool to develop future operations.

Peder Oxe founded the castle in 1575. In 1699 Christian Gyldenlove established a charter, from which it appeared that the estate was to be transformed from a privately owned estate to a monastery foundation.

HISTORY

Peder Oxe founded the present castle. The castle was built in the period 1547 to 1575. In 1699 Christian Gyldenlove (the son of Christian V and Sophia Amalie Moth) took over Gisselfeld. Christian Gyldenlove died shortly after establishing a charter, from which it appeared that the estate was to be transformed from a privately owned estate to a monastery foundation. According to a will of 1701, his descendants inherited the position as hereditary Director of the Commercial Foundation.

The Foundation

The objects of the Commercial Foundation are to own, operate and maintain the activities, hold Gisselfeld Kloster (Abbey), and to maintain and preserve the estate's collections of art, furniture, porcelain etc.

Moreover, financial support is given in the form of grants to non-profit organisations and various scholarships. The estate is operated according to modern management principles; respect for the long and significant history of the place being an important part of the philosophy.

The estate of Gisselfeld Kloster operates 3850 hectares of land and forestry, leases hunting and fishing rights, operates a park, an events department and a restaurant, and leases 125 houses. The day-to-day management consists of a managing director, a financial manager and a farming manager. The general idea is also to create an economy based on the estate's environmental and ecological aspects. Centralisation of all activities has be one of the keys to good management practice.

The estate management is organised and structured as a traditional company, with a board of directors, a managing director, managers and representatives. This means that the necessary managerial skills are retained and used, and can therefore focus on the business itself in order to achieve best results.

Today Gisselfeld Estate employs 25 full-time workers and another 40 to 50 seasonal workers. The permanent staff attached to the various operational activities are: farming (5); forestry (6); property (5); wildlife (1); administration/tourism/events (5); gardeners (3). Apart from being responsible for their activity, they are all involved, interconnected and available when needed. All employees are flexible and work across department boundaries.

Specific operational plans are established to create objectives for all divisions so that all targets are used as part of the overall goal. All business plans are based on sustainability. This applies both to the estate's cultural, natural and long historical aspects, and also – especially – to its economics.

Retaining as many employees as possible is another principle on which the estate works. It wishes to have and keep as many employees as possible to create momentum and dynamism.

The Foundation Fund's purpose and its origin

The Foundation fund was founded in 1701 by Gisselfeld Estate's last owner, Christian Gyldenløves, and his three children – Christian Count Danneskiold-Samsoe, Fredrich Count Danneskiold-Samsoe and Frederica Louisa Duchess of Schleswig-Holstein-Sundborg.

Then, in 1924, a new charter was created to adopt different aims and objectives with a set of principles:

This charter consists of five main objectives to be achieved:

- **1.** To own, possess, operate and maintain the monastery belonging to Gisselfeld Estate.
- **2.** To provide financial support for the unmarried daughters of Danish noble families, or daughters of families that are in the top three ranks.
- **3.** To provide financial support for girls living in Haslev municipality.
- **4.** To provide financial support to socially disadvantaged residents of Haslev municipality.
- **5.** To provide financial support to other charitable and philanthropic including cultural, scientific, social and educational purposes.

Gisselfeld awards around 100,000 Euros each year in grants for various purposes, partly through grants which specifically focus on the area of education or through so-called operation scholarships which support different regional social, economical and environmental projects which are entrepreneurial and dynamic.

HISTORICAL HERITAGE AND GENERAL INFRASTRUCTURE

The Park

The park was designed and created in the 1800s and resembles an English landscape garden. It is known to be one of northern Europe's most beautiful and still contains many rare botanical species. It is approximately 40 hectares in area, half of which are carp ponds. The lakes are both an important landscape element that creates space and nature, and from the very earliest time they have been a part of an extensive fish farming business, which dates from Peter Oxe's time in the 1500s. Gisselfeld was among the first to introduce carp farming, and to this day some of the best carp fishing is to be had on the estate. There are fountains and waterfalls created in the late 1800s by both Danish and foreign experts – notably the architects Nyrop (fountains) and Pullham (waterfall). Pullham worked at the same time for the British royal family. Park maintenance and reconstruction is carefully planned. Both the planting and restoration of the many elements will, over the coming years, ensure that this unique culture will be preserved and improved for posterity.

Together with the park and the castle, the Parade House is the "brand image" of what is today the true value and "guest's impression" of Gisselfeld Estate.

The Parade House

One of Gisselfeld Park's absolute highlights is the Parade House. This "Orangery" was created in 1876 by the Danish architect Herholt. The architect drew his inspiration from the Great Exhibition in London in 1851, where he saw the Crystal Palace. The Parade House, as well as being protected, is today the only one of its kind in private ownership in Denmark. The house had to be restored in 2004 and received the 2007 Europa Nostra Prize for this. It was originally built to keep exotic plants and vegetation, and was equipped with 3 different "climate rooms", representing tropical, subtropical and temperate climates.

At that time, the purpose of a greenhouse was not only for grand entertainment but also to impress and show power and wealth to those who visited Gisselfeld. The place was also used for small exhibitions, workshops and private events. Nowadays the house is run by two well-known architects and partly used as a showroom of a fine collection of plants. Furthermore, plants and all kinds of exclusive accessories for gardens and parks are sold here.

Surrounding area

Gisselfeld Estate still owns approximately 125 houses that are leased for private and commercial purposes. The estate has its own carpentry department with four employees who work exclusively to maintain the estate's old and valuable buildings.

Beautifully situated, many of these houses were built in the 1800s and renovated some years ago. Many are of half-timbered construction, with thatched roofs and special decorations on the soffit and woodwork.

The Parade House: this "Orangery" was created in 1876 by the Danish architect Herholt and had to be restored in 2004. It received the Europa Nostra award in 2007.

Gisselfeld castle is beautifully placed in the 40 ha Park.

All these elements, together with the distinctive colour, give an immediate signal that these houses belong to Gisselfeld Estate. The emphasis is on maintaining this special heritage in good shape, and a framework for renovation, maintenance and colour has therefore been established.

DEVELOPMENT OF THE LAND AND LANDSCAPE SETTING

The area around Gisselfeld manor is a perfect combination of classical landscape and unspoiled nature. The overall terrain is characterised by undulating small hills where small valleys cut through the magnificence of the forest. Between the lakes, some parts of the large forest have been converted into wetlands and meadows, which create a whole range and diversity of natural habitats.

A Sustainable Management Plan which considers programmes for the landscape, the environment and conservation is projected every 10 years. This sets a number of guidelines and goals to be achieved, following given rules which evaluate nature and its biodiversity.

Based on conservation projects and development of landscape and habitats, Gisselfeld Estate was the first estate in Denmark to prepare a comprehensive "sustainable management plan". This plan contains general and detailed data on flora and fauna, as well as information on particular protected habitats, special operating conditions, etc.

The plan is used as a tool to relate good management practices and principles with the estate's economic operations, combining environmental principles with efficient agricultural and forestry activities. The estate is aware that such a plan can not remain fixed and that it should be continuously updated in line with operational, strategic and regulatory conditions.

In collaboration with the Danish government, Gisselfeld Estate and its neighbours have in recent years re-naturalised large areas. The project consisted of the conversion of farmland into wetland. The estate agreed to include 90 hectares and is today one of the best bird areas on Zealand.

The same kind of project has happened with the local authorities and the Forest and Nature Agency in connection with the restoration of Holmegaard Bog, where the estate included 33 hectares in the project.

In 2009, the management team is planning and designing a project involving the conversion of around 100 ha of grassland into wetland with special measures of care for different protected species of flora and fauna. The project is being carefully planned in order to create maximum value in the long term for both Gisselfeld Estate and society as a whole. The project will include the river, and will be ready in December 2009.

The wild garden consists of more than 400 different species of trees. This *arboretum* of 2.5 ha is currently being improved and reconstructed for public entertainment. At the entrance, a small renovated Danish wooden house will be used as a museum to introduce the existence of the many plants and trees in the garden.

ECONOMIC ACTIVITIES

Tourism and events

With the proximity of Copenhagen (60 km), Gisselfeld Estate offers an opportunity to escape easily from the city. Thanks to good logistics and great infrastructure, about 12,000-15,000 visitors come to Gisselfeld Kloster Park annually.

However, over the past 10 years, the estate has renovated several old buildings for public, private and business purposes where the park and surrounding land and forest are part of the whole picture.

Training courses, conferences, product exhibitions, motor shows, weddings, country fairs etc., are part of the day to day management of the estate. The biggest event is the annual Christmas Fair, to which 20,000-25,000 visitors come over two week-ends. These events organised at Gisselfeld Estate contribute significantly to the economic revenue of the estate.

Real estate

As mentioned earlier, Gisselfeld Estate owns 125 large and small houses and buildings, representing two-thirds of the small village of Vester Egede. About 90 percent of the houses are leased as single-family homes. These houses are beautifully located, situated in small groups or placed individually in the beautiful surrounding landscape. Besides their unique location, many of them are characteristic of their architecture and with a special "Gisselfeld expression".

The larger tenanted farms, in particular former farm buildings that are no longer in use, are rented out to IT companies and for storage and production purposes.

On the maintenance side, the estate works with its own craftsmen as much as possible. This creates a good dialogue between tenants and the estate, while the very old houses require particular attention to maintain and preserve the required personal expressions.

Entrance to the wild garden.

Gisselfeld Kloster Estate

In terms of benefits, real estate management at Gisselfeld Estate creates ways in which people are connected to the property, gives personality, stimulates objectives, and is by far the greatest economic basis in which the estate has invested.

Farming

At Gisselfeld Kloster, farming activities including set-aside land cover 1350 hectares, of which 350 hectares are considered to be wetlands. Soil conditions are extremely varied and strongly characterised by the undulating moraine terrain created during the last Ice Age, where high hills and low areas succeed each other, with soil types varying from mainly sandy, with large deposits of stone and lime flakes.

The estate has nine farms, with a centralised operational point at Gisselfeld home farm, which is centrally located. Gisselfeld home farm has modern facilities for drying and storing the annual crop production. The storage capacity is 7000 tonnes of cereals which represents about one year's harvest. 30 tonnes of cereals can be dried per hour, down to about 4%.

In terms of quality, 40% of the agricultural land is of soil type 5 and 60% of soil types 3-4. The

Gisselfeld Estate still owns 125 houses. About 90 percent of the houses are leased as single-family homes, and many of them are characteristic of their architecture and with a special "Gisselfeld expression".

Gisselfeld Kloster Estate

G. Janssens

good soil is primarily situated in the northern part of the estate, where the fields are relatively flat and regular, while the poorer soil types are situated in the southern part, in undulating terrain with the largest deposits of stone, lime and sand.

The estate has a wide range of machinery, the main focus being on a system where most land is ploughed. The estate practices plough-free cultivation in a small area, which it aims to extend in the coming years. In terms of reinvestment, the establishment of auto-steering and permanent wheel traces is being contemplated.

Farming operations on the estate are done by three tractor drivers, one blacksmith and a farm manager. Labour remains the same for both farming and forestry operations, e.g. harvesting and handling the Christmas trees and ornamental foliage.

The main crops harvested are:

- Wheat, spring barley, peas for canning, rape, rye (Gisselfeld is one of Denmark's biggest producer of rye).

The straw is delivered to the local energy plant, but a large part of the straw is left on the ground nowadays for the sake of nutrient content and soil structure. The estate has deliberately chosen not to breed animals after taking into consideration the negative consequences this can have on operational activities connected with property rentals and tourism.

Meadows

The agricultural area includes extensive natural grassland. During the past ten years, adaptation and optimisation have been made in agricultural and set-aside land, and drainage schemes on 120 hectares have been changed. It is expected that another 58 hectares will soon be transferred from set-aside land to a nature restoration project in connection with the Susaa River which flows through the estate.

This will bring the total area of the various environmental schemes, including grass areas, to 360 hectares. The areas require grazing combined with hay-making/grass-cutting in order to maintain them. The agreements made mean that, from 2009 and for a limited number of years, it will be possible to buy additional land equating to 160 hectares, an option the estate is very interested in exercising.

Another 58 hectares of set-aside land will soon be transferred to a nature restoration project in connection with the Susaa River which crosses the estate.

711

WILDLIFE CONSERVATION / HUNTING & FISHING

Gisselfeld Estate within its mosaic landscape, with a good mix of crop production, meadows, forests, wetlands and lakes, provides very good natural conditions for nature conservation and for the creation of diversified habitats and biotopes for wildlife. The re-naturalisation of the river is creating natural wetlands and a perfect area for migrating birds and local wildlife.

There is strong emphasis on developing the whole estate in order to improve these great and optimal conditions for wildlife and nature. This means planting new small biotopes, hedgerows, set-aside areas, small reserves etc. all around the property.

The hunting area covers the entire estate and has been continuously improved, in particular in marginal areas. Hunting rights are leased under contract for 5 years, and follow a long-term vision based on maintenance, improvement and sustainability on an ongoing basis.

The estate has a significant population of Fallow Deer *(Dama dama)*, which since 1993 has been managed through a controlled shooting policy. The stock is currently approximately 500 animals and has evolved not just quantitatively but also qualitatively. The Roe Deer *(Capreolus capreolus)* is strong and spread throughout the estate. It is by far

Brent Goose *(Branta bernicla)*. Flocks are often on water, upending like ducks in order to feed eelgrass and algae on mudflats, and cereal grass.

the most numerous of the large population of deer species.

From 2008, the introduction of Red Deer *(Cervus elaphus)* has provided both hunting interest and new conservation practices. The gamekeeper is studying the population and how they adapt, in order to predict the future; the aim is to try to maintain a reasonable population taking into account the agricultural and forestry interests.

The estate now provides supplementary feed to all deer species from October until April, to dissuade and prevent them from damaging agriculture and forestry and to keep them in good shape.

Biotopes for small game species, for example hedgerows, small woods and lakes, together with the undulating landscape create natural habitats for an excellent quality of bird and small game shooting, especially wild pheasants and wild ducks. Geese and pigeons are also becoming numerous. For some years now, after several years of dramatic decline, the population of wild partridges and hares has been constantly increasing as a result of considerable improvement in game management and habitat creation.

Since these measures started, birds such as the Sea Eagle *(Haliaetus albicilla)*, Osprey *(Pandion haliaetus)*, Red Kite *(Milvus milvus)*, Marsh Harrier *(Circus aeruginosus)*, Hen Harrier *(Circus cyaneus)*, Peregrine Falcon *(Falco peregrinus)*, Kestrel *(Falco tinnunculus)*, Hobby *(Falco subbuteo)*, Buzzard *(Buteo buteo)*, Honey Buzzard *(Pernis apivorus)*, Raven *(Corvus corax)*, Rook *(Corvus frugilegus)*, Hooded Crow *(Corvus cornix)*, Magpie *(Pica pica)*, many species of duck, grebe and merganser, a colony of Black-headed Gull *(Larus ridibundus)*, Heron *(Ardea cinerea)*, Greylag Goose *(Anser anser)*, Bean Goose *(Anser fabalis)*, Canada Goose *(Branta canadensis)*, Barnacle Goose *(Branta leucopsis)* and Brent Goose *(Branta bernicla)* visit the estate. In addition, a myriad of smaller birds associated with the various biotopes, including more water species such as Kingfisher *(Alcedo atthis)* and Sand Martin *(Riparia riparia)*, can be seen on a daily basis.

Fishing

The many lakes and streams present on the estate provide good fishing opportunities. Carp *(Cyprinus carpio)*, Pike *(Esox lucius)*, Walleye *(Sander vitreus)*, Perch *(Perca fluviatilis)*, Trout *(Salmo trutta)* and Crayfish *(Astacus astacus)* are common species encountered in the natural and artificial lakes and rivers. In the many ancient carp ponds (23 units), water levels may still be regularly drained, either to manage fish stocks or to improve the bottom and water quality, to allow continuous maintenance of fish, water and plants to ensure a good quality of aquatic flora and fauna.

The estate's largest lake is 66 hectares and up to 23 metres deep. This lake, a Natura 2000 site, offers the best fishing spot in the region.

Forestry

The forestry at Gisselfeld Estate is based on quality production and a desire to comply with high international environmental standards.

Maintenance of the rivers, roads, stands, improvements etc., is also at the forefront of the basic management.

Beech *(Fagus* sp.*)*, Oak *(Quercus* sp.*)*, Ash *(Fraxinus* sp.*)* and Norwiepian spruce are the four species commonly grown and sold. 60% of the stock is hardwood and 40% is coniferous, according to conditions of geography and soil and the desire to have a broad range of different products to be more competitive in the market.

Growth rate is approximately 16,000 m³/year which corresponds to an average of 8 m³/ha/year. Conifers, for example, grow at over 20 m³/ha/year. In future, the estate expects to harvest about 10,000 m³, with more logging in good economic times. Because of an increase in the production of Christmas trees (70,000-100,000 trees/year), and the above requirements on quality standards, the staff necessary can be maintained.

The estate's forestry was in PEFC certified in 2004. This involves sustainability and traceability of the entire range of forest products. The forestry covers 2360 hectares of which 2011 are economically operated. The rest are lakes, marshes, reserves and wetlands which are very sensitive habitats, of high importance for biodiversity. The

Perch *(Perca fluviatilis)* is present in lakes and streams and it provides good fishing opportunities.

estate has designated some area of its forestry as sensitive and of exceptional ecological interest. Therefore, these are kept outside normal forest operations and untouched by human presence. Unfortunately, no subsidies are given by local authorities nor by the EU, but many aspects of forestry are influenced by restrictions imposed by Danish legislation.

The forest is in geographical terms mostly situated on the western and southern flank of the estate. The rest is distributed in about 15 large and small areas spread between arable land and meadows.

The large forest has difficult access due to the typical topography of the South and East Zealand. Forestry operations are heavily influenced by the disastrous windfalls which have occurred during the last 10-15 years, especially the most valuable coniferous zone. In response to these hurricanes, hardwood has been the main emphasis. Beech, Oak and Ash make up more than 80% of the planted area and will affect forestry operations far into the future.

To counter this, and to allow profitability in the forestry operations, approximately 30 hectares of land were planted with Christmas trees and ornamental foliage, to reinforce economic activities.

The annual production of Christmas trees is currently 25,000 units. Ornamental foliage production is about 150 tonnes, with an emphasis on Nobilis.

• Beech	650 ha
• Oak	350 ha
• Other broadleaf trees	290 ha
• Conifers	430 ha
• Annual Growth	16,000 m³
• Annual Felling	10,000 m³
• Decorative Greenery	150 tonnes/year
• Christmas trees	25,000-70,000 trees/year

With the proximity
of Copenhagen, the estate
offers a way to escape
easily from the city.

PRIVATE OPINION

The endless challenge to implement the values of Gisselfeld Estate successfully – that is
what ownership means. Managerial and operational activities are continuously adapted in the
light of market opportunities and expectations
from society. Society has an influence on the
long-term strategy of Gisselfeld Estate.

It is important to keep in mind that the entire estate is of exceptional cultural and natural heritage.
Land managers, rural entrepreneurs and land owners manage some of the most prestigious assets.

Underlying this, the asset must be profitable in order to be sustainable.

The estate plays an important role for the surrounding communities and these communities on
the other hand influence the management of the
estate. Historically, the estate was the 'dynamo' of
these communities but unfortunately many factors, such as successions, regulations, and external pressures challenge the goodwill and become
a heavy burden instead of an asset which blooms
and evolves positively into the future.

G. Janssens

Gisselfeld therefore has over time become a small but dynamic and entrepreneurial business which is forward looking, not only to preserve and maintain the great cultural and natural values but to improve them so that they are more competitive in meeting the needs of the market.

Investing in people has become our greatest resource; the estate believes that human skill across all departments is crucial for new opportunities and to create success. This does not only mean a good, competent and loyal workforce in the various sectors; this is obviously a basic prerequisite, but it is especially so at managerial and strategic levels. Large estates, along with all other companies, continuously face major challenges: legislation which restricts opportunities, uncertainties about funding opportunities within the EU, lack of understanding from the outside world, and much more.

Our tasks include, through close cooperation and with national and international focus, an understanding firstly of the value created by what we produce, but secondly of the importance of the values that already exist wherever history, culture and nature are managed properly and appropriately. Also, that society has a great interest in this.

We must remember that large estates have always had great importance in rural life. Expressed another way, we have perhaps the "world's best brand".

Jens Risom

GISSELFELD KLOSTER BELONGS TO:

PEFC, Programme for the
Endorsement of Forest Certification

Friends of the Countryside

Activities & attractions

- Historic buildings
- Rural tourism
- Fishing
- Hunting
- Shooting
- Country Park
- Estate products

CONTACT DATA
Godskontoret • Gisselfeldvej 12 A • 4690 Haslev
Telefon: +45 - 56 32 60 32 • Fax: +45 - 56 32 64 25
jr@gisselfeld-kloster.dk • www.gisselfeld-kloster.dk

La Quéjola

Mediterranean

Location: San Pedro, Albacete, La Mancha region, Spain.
Surface: 2,000 ha.

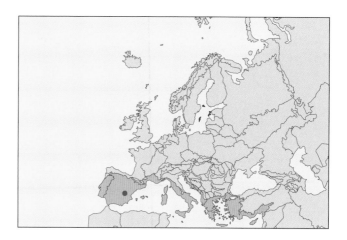

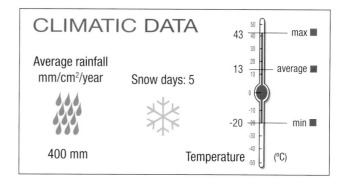

CLIMATIC DATA

Average rainfall
mm/cm²/year

Snow days: 5

400 mm

Temperature (°C)

43 — max
13 — average
-20 — min

SUMMARY

La Quéjola is a Wildlife Estate of just over 2,000 hectares situated in the foothills of the Sierra de Alcaraz, province of Albacete, in the La Mancha region of central Spain. This land has an important history and has belonged to the Melgarejo family for 350 years.

Its management system, which strikes a perfect balance between hunting, arable and livestock resources, has enabled the estate to create a family atmosphere in the midst of historically traditional lands where friends, guests and numerous hunters can be accommodated, hunt and enjoy its now restored magnificent manor house.

The estate is dedicated to organised shooting of Red-legged Partridge *(Alectoris rufa)* and Rabbit *(Oryctolagus cuniculus)*. There is also an area of 600 hectares fenced for hunting large game species.

Aerial view of the main buildings at La Quéjola,
which is bordered by the river of the same name.

C. Otero

HISTORY

The rural properties owned by the Marquis of Melgarejo in the La Mancha region of south-east Spain derive from two families, the Melgarejos and the Valdeguerreros, who were later united through marriage. Their settlement of the region dates from the 14th Century War of Reconquest, when King Ferdinand III "The Saint," and later his son Alfonso X "The Wise", embarked on the successful recovery of these lands from the Moors, who had occupied them since the 8th century.

The first member of the Melgarejo family (Marquises of Melgarejo and Dukes of San Fernando) to settle in La Mancha was Ruy-Fernán Melgarejo, commander of the fortress of Belmonte in Cuenca at the end of the 14th century. This family established a series of interconnected fortresses in the various administrative centres of the region, including Belmonte, Santa María de los Llanos, Pinarejo, Castillo de Garcimuñoz, San Clemente, and Pozoamargo in the Province of Cuenca, and Villanueva de los Infantes in the Province of Ciudad Real. These properties were maintained undivided and practically intact until the death of José Mª Melgarejo, Duke of San Fernando (1826-1896).

The properties of the Valdeguerrero family also remained intact throughout the various generations until the death of the tenth holder of the title, Mrs Pilar Sandoval y Melgarejo, Marchioness of Valdeguerrero and Countess of Buenavista (1853-1922). The history of these properties is curious, however. For several generations it was only the eldest brother who married, having his residence in the family seat of San Clemente (Cuenca). The other brothers lived in the "Bachelors House" in the villa of Vara de Rey, and, when they died, the properties they possessed and enjoyed while alive reverted to the person who succeeded the eldest brother.

Today, the properties in the possession of the current Marquis of Melgarejo, the lineal descendant of these two families, comprise a rural heritage which has been improved and turned into a productive business. They have been divided into five operations, based at San Clemente, Belmonte, and Iniesta in the Province of Cuenca; San Pedro in the Province of Albacete, and Villanueva de los Infantes in the Province of Ciudad Real. They all embrace diverse activities – including agriculture, wine production, livestock, hunting, and tourism – and all of them together form a natural heritage whose beauty and richness have remained intact.

La Quéjola, in the region of La Mancha, Province of Albacete, among the foothills of the Sierra de Alcaraz, is noted for both its natural beauty and its varied plant and animal life, for which reasons it has been selected to be featured in this book.

Valdeguerrero Palace, located in San Clemente (Cuenca).

La Quéjola Estate

Entrance hall of the main house at La Quéjola, with the coat of arms of the Valdeguerrero family.

DESCRIPTION

The estate of La Quéjola was one of the properties in the Sierra de Alcaraz owned by the Sandoval family (the Marquises of Valdeguerrero) 350 years ago.

The ancient tower known as the Torre de Albar-Ruiz was originally the principal residence for all the properties, but today no longer belongs to the family.

The current owner of La Quéjola is Joaquín Melgarejo Martínez del Peral, Baillo y Sandoval, Marquis of Melgarejo, a son of La Mancha through all four branches of his family and a direct descendent of the lineage that goes back to the 14th century. It is he who is responsible for the conservation and management of more than 2,000 hectares which makes up the estate of La Quéjola.

La Quéjola is located on a site of great environmental value between the River Jardín and the River Quéjola or Montemayor, whose waters flow into the River Júcar. The banks of both rivers have fertile lowlands which produce a variety of irrigatted crops.

The land is hilly and undulating and reaches elevations of more than 1,100 metres above sea level, the lowest levels being at 850 metres in the fertile lowlands of the riverbanks.

La Quéjola possesses a variety of vegetation. Tree species include the traditional Holm Oak *(Quercus ilex)*, Portuguese Oak *(Quercus faginea)* (few specimens but of considerable size), Spanish Juniper *(Juniperus thurifera)* (scattered in

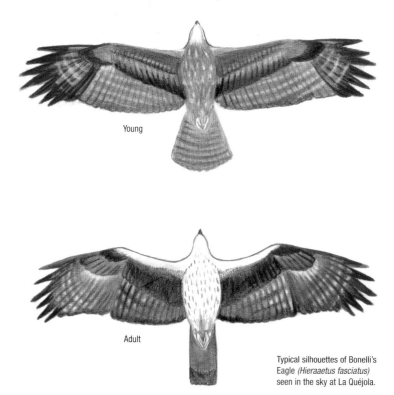

Typical silhouettes of Bonelli's Eagle *(Hieraaetus fasciatus)* seen in the sky at La Quéjola.

La Quéjola (Spain)

La Quéjola Estate

Red carpet of poppies
in a Mediterranean landscape
of Holm Oaks.

Animal life includes an abundance of Red-Legged Partridge *(Alectoris rufa)* (the queen of game birds), a plentiful amount of Rabbits *(Oryctolagus cuniculus)*, and Hares *(Lepus granatensis)*, whose population density is declining. One also finds wild boar, whose habitat is in the thicker wooded areas but which feeds in the fertile lowlands. Among migratory birds, the Woodpigeon *(Columba palumbus)* is abundant, and in the summer Turtle Dove *(Streptopelia turtur)* and Quail *(Coturnix coturnix)* are found.

The estate has a flock of native La Mancha sheep which graze in the fields at La Quéjola, although their breeding and milking centre is at San Clemente (Cuenca). The sheep enterprise is a member of *AGRAMA (Asociación de Ganaderos de Raza Manchega Selecta)*, the association of breeders of La Mancha sheep.

various places), and a dense forest with Mediterranean (or Aleppo) pines *(Pinus halepensis)* together with the Gum Rockrose *(Cistus ladanifer)* and Prickly Juniper *(Juniperus oxycedrus)*. Shrubs are also very abundant, including Sage-Leaf Rockrose *(Cistus salvifolius)*, Rosemary *(Rosmarinus officinalis)*, Lavender *(Lavandula angustifolia)*, Retama *(Retama sphaerocarpa)*, and many more.

Special and particular mention should be made of the protected species present at La Quéjola, which have high ecological value. These include the Iberian Imperial Eagle, also known as the Spanish Imperial Eagle *(Aquila adalberti)*, and the Eagle Owl *(Bubo bubo)*. La Quéjola is a member of the *Fundación de Amigos del Águila Imperial Ibérica* (Foundation of the Friends of the Iberian Impe-

La Quéjola

Palace of the Marquis of
Valdeguerrero, with a beautiful
Renaissance courtyard in the
town of Vara del Rey (Cuenca).

rial Eagle), whose goal is to protect and preserve this and other species of similar value, as well as the habitats in which they coexist.

Currently, the buildings at La Quéjola consist of three houses of simple construction that overlook the fertile lowland area. One of these has a small chapel in which Catholic Masses are celebrated for the residents of the villages and the estate employees. On the banks of the La Quéjola River there is an old flour mill operated by water channels created for that purpose. The mill has been restored and is used to accommodate guests, clients, hunters and tourists.

The principal activities of La Quéjola today are farming, livestock, hunting, tourism, and conservation.

The agriculture is extensive in character and based on techniques of conservation and minimum cultivation, in order to achieve the best possible environmental outcomes. Cereals, legumes, and oilseeds are grown. Hunting is also a popular activity, its purpose being both to contribute to profitability and to promote the conservation of the estate. Organised days include driven partridge, walked-up shooting for partridge, rabbits and hares using dogs for both ground game and feathered game, and wild boar, both driven or stalked.

In light of the rich variety of plant and animal life, guided tours have also become an important activity at La Quéjola.

Ghosts of La Quéjola

In the middle of the 20th century, people in the area began to report a light that supposedly accompanied walkers and vehicles travelling between the towns of Casas de Lázaro and San Pedro in the Province of Albecete, but principally at La Quéjola.

It seems that the first people who saw this mysterious light were members of the Cuerda family, old employees of La Quéjola. One of their sons, Cristino, described it on his first encounter as a large ball of fire that moved rapidly to a nearby grove, but later he reported many more sightings, of which nearby village residents were also witnesses. Others in the neighbourhood have related how these lights accompany them while they walk late at night, floating about a metre above the ground and one and a half metres in front of them, and then disappearing among the almond trees of La Quéjola.

What truth lies behind these reports? The owners of the property have maintained a prudent skepticism about these ghost stories. However, as a Galician proverb says, "Me? Believe in ghosts? No, I don't believe in them. But they do exist!"

A tractor preparing the land for sowing.

Red-Legged Partridge (*Alectoris rufa*), the queen of game birds.

LA QUÉJOLA THESAUROS (SAN PEDRO, ALBACETE)

Another curiosity of La Quéjola is an ancient Iberian village situated on the property. The remains of this settlement can be seen on the so-called Cerro del Peñón. The walled rectangular village, with a small tower located at its only point of entrance, covered a surface of almost one hectare and dates back to the end of the 6th century or beginning of the 5th century BC.

Excavations that have taken place in the Iberian village of La Quéjola over the past few decades have brought to light a particularly interesting building. After analyzing its construction and the materials used to build it, experts have identified it as a *thesauros*, or *treasure house*. Such a building blends perfectly into the urban nature of the settlement. The *thesauros* was used for storage and contained a significant selection of representative materials of prestige and power in Iberian society, including objects of religious value such as images representing gods and goddesses.

The remains of the Iberian village, like similar sites, is located in the interior of the Iberian peninsular, in the south-east portion of the Iberian plain. It appears to have existed for about a century, from approximately the end of the 6th century, or beginnings of the 5th century BC, until the end of the 5th century BC, judging by the remains of imported, black varnished ceramic found in the village, a material which only did not last into the following century, but also is not found in other archaeological sites throughout Spain or indeed the whole of the western Mediterranean. It seems clear that this settlement depended for its existence on storage and, probably, on the production and sale of wine, implying that the political organization of the town and surrounding region was probably structured hierarchically because such a specialized economy can only function in a structure based on politics and area. This suggests that La Quéjola can be seen as the best equivalent in form to the well-known archaeological site of L'Alt de Benamaquía (Denia, Alicante).

Archaeological examination of the town's main features as well as analysis of the ceramic materials excavated allow experts to deduce some of its representative aspects and to argue, for example, that one of its houses is a particular *singular space* of sacred character that some have dubbed a *thesauros*.

The site is located on a small spur of the so-called Cerro del Peñón on a modest elevation rising about 20 metres above the surrounding valley. The mineral wealth of the area is negligible, with nothing but an abundance of gypsum and porous limestone, both unsuitable for stonecutting. The ancient vegetation of the Iberian period, identified from systematic analysis of seeds and pollen, consisted of oak trees, walnut trees, and junipers mixed with areas of pine groves and ligneous shrub, in the wet low-lying land along the fertile valley of the Quéjola River.

The town was rectangular in shape (approximately 150 metres x 50 metres) and walled, with a small tower guarding the only entrance. Its total area was less than one hectare. This is one of only a small group of known fortified towns from the Iberian period, known as Oppida. One of the most interesting characteristics of the town at La Quéjola is that it was built during a single phase of construction, its builders following a pre-established design. It fits well with a clearly intended economic specialization based on wine, since provision was made for the storage of wine in quantities exceeding those needed by the town's resident population. The existence of such a pre-established plan, undertaken in a short period of time, has also been observed in other important Iberian towns of the period, for example El Oral and, at the middle of the 5th century BC, El Puig de la Nau in Benicarló.

The wall of La Quéjola, together with its single tower at the entrance, not only played a defensive role, but also had an ideological purpose at the same time. On the one hand, it limited and protected the urban space, and on the other (and no less important) it lent prestige to the inhabitants' territory at a time when Iberian populations were immersed in competitive effort to create impressive urban spaces. The wall had an average thickness of 1.30 metres and did not exceed 4 metres in height, the last 1.5 metres of which may have been constructed of adobe. (The absence of adobe remains in the four extramural quadrant, however, suggests that this may not have been the case). In the case of the tower at the entrance of the town, its walls were more than six metres thick, and since it was raised above the wall of the town, its construction was probably completed with adobe. Nevertheless, the tower was probably not joined to the wall, as was standard practice in the patterns of construction noted in other sites with which the town of La Quéjola has many similarities.

It has only been possible to excavate the town's interior in the western half of the site, on account of the other half having been demolished. It has allowed archaeologists to document a total of 16 divisions of the town, all but one contiguous with the wall. The excavation uncovered a total of eight buildings with various functions: the "singular space" (or *thesauros*) (building n° 2), warehouses for wine storage (buildings n° 1, n° 6, and n° 8), two spaces for industrial activity (buildings n° 3 and n° 4), a guardhouse (building n° 7), and finally a building (n° 5) which was not excavated. All of them, with the exception of building n° 8, backed on to the wall and had a noticeably communal character detected in other important Iberian sites such as Alt de Benimaquía and El Oral. The residential spaces that certainly existed in La Quéjola must have been located in an area that has not been preserved. In no case, however, would they correspond to more than seven or eight family units (based on an estimate of five members per family). This estimate derives from an understanding and evaluation of the characteristics and plan of the town's sacred space, in building n° 2.

The ceramic materials found in the rooms excavated correspond to typical Iberian amphorae and were probably made locally. Typologically, they are a clear continuation of the old Phoenician-Punic forms, although with their own formal characteristics.

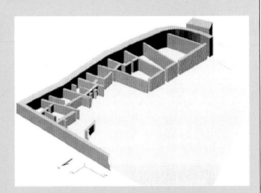

Reconstruction of the plan of the survived Iberian village of La Quéjola, dating from the sixth century BC.

Only in building n° 2, the sacred space identified with political power, has a more ample ceramic repertoire been documented, with examples of decorated tableware (dishes, earthen bowls, etc.) and storage containers (covered pithoi, wide-mouthed containers, etc.). Some of these have significant bichrome and polychrome decorations. Together with these a significant number of ceramic pieces made from clay and intended for cooking were also found, some of them decorated with white paint. The question arises whether these may have been used for sacred purposes in the light of their location in building number n° 2.

STAFF AT LA QUÉJOLA

WORKER	POSITION	LENGTH OF SERVICE	LOCATION	NATIONALITY
LUIS MARCOS NUÑO PÉREZ	Technician	04.06.2007		Spanish
ADOLFO SEGOVIA UTIEL	Manager	01.01.1954	Iniesta	Spanish
ANTONIO ALMODÓVAR MARTÍNEZ	Manager	01.10.1964	Belmonte	Spanish
JOSÉ MANUEL MARTÍNEZ REDONDO	Manager	01.08.1989	San Clemente	Spanish
RICARDO PAÑOS PÉREZ	Manager	15.09.2002	La Quéjola	Spanish
LUIS ARCAS GALLEGO	Administrative Assistant	01.04.1995	San Clemente	Spanish
MARTA FRESNEDA LÓPEZ	Administrative Assistant	20.05.1999	Belmonte	Spanish
MARI LUZ CABRERA SAIZ	Commercial	20.01.2006	San Clemente	Spanish
LUIS YÁÑEZ OREJÓN	Game Head Keeper	15.05.1992	San Clemente	Spanish
RAMÓN CHILLERON GARCÍA	Game Keeper	01.06.1970	Infantes	Spanish
JULIÁN CATENA POZA	Game Keeper	15.05.1997	La Quéjola	Spanish
SEBASTIÁN GARCÍA MARTÍNEZ	Game Keeper	01.04.1998	San Clemente	Spanish
ENRIQUE BENÍTEZ ROIBAL	Game Keeper	02.02.2004	Belmonte	Spanish
LUIS CHAPARRO YÁÑEZ	Game Keeper	21.05.2007	La Quéjola	Spanish
JOSÉ MANUEL MARTÍNEZ SEVILLA	Manager	19.02.1996	San Clemente	Spanish
WILDER KLEBER MONAR	Manager	16.07.2007	San Clemente	Ecuadorian
AMPARO MARTÍNEZ OLMEDA	Housekeeper	12.12.2002	San Clemente	Spanish
ÁNGELA MOLINES GUERRERO	Housekeeper	01.07.2003	La Quéjola	Spanish
ENCARNA ROJAS GIL	Housekeeper	01.03.2003	Vara de Rey	Spanish
CAROLINA URRA ROCUANT	Housekeeper	01.03.2006	Belmonte	Chilean
ARMIDA PATRICIA VIGO DE SALVATIERRA	Housekeeper	28.03.2006	San Clemente	Bolivian
ALEXANDRA SILVA SILVA	Housekeeper	16.07.2007	San Clemente	Ecuadorian
CARMEN GÓMEZ TORRIJOS	Housekeeper	04.10.2007	La Quéjola	Spanish
ÁNGELA CATENA MOLINES	Housekeeper	Eventual	La Quéjola	Spanish
MIGUELCABRERA MORENO	Tractor Driver	01.02.1989	San Clemente	Spanish
FRANCISCO CUÉLLIGA MARTÍNEZ	Tractor Driver	12.11.1990	San Clemente	Spanish
JOSÉ ROBERTO CAROCA CÁCERES	Tractor Driver	22.02.2005	San Clemente	Chilean
ÁNGEL PORRAS MORENO	Tractor Driver	01.06.2000	Belmonte	Spanish
SANTIAGO CAMPOS GRANDE	Tractor Driver	06.10.2003	Belmonte	Spanish
JOSÉ AGUSTO CAROCA CÁCERES	Tractor Driver	01.03.2006	Belmonte	Chilean
JUAN SÁNCHEZ GÓMEZ	Tractor Driver	01.08.2007	La Quéjola	Spanish
JUAN ANTONIO CRISPÍN	Tractor Driver	01.09.2000	Iniesta	Spanish
JOSÉ MORATALLA MONTERO	Farm Manager	01.02.1996	San Clemente	Spanish
IVÁN CIRO SALVATIERRA GARCÍA	Shepherd	27.03.2006	San Clemente	Bolivian
AHMED ABADLIA BAGHDAD	Shepherd	26.11.2007	San Clemente	Algerian
BACHIR ABADLIA ALI	Shepherd	01.03.2007	San Clemente	Algerian
JULIÁN SEVILLA MORENO	Labourer	Eventual	San Clemente	Spanish
LUIS YÁÑEZ NOTARIO	Labourer	Eventual	San Clemente	Spanish
ANA BELÉN BAUTISTA CARREÑO	Labourer	Eventual	San Clemente	Spanish
JOSÉ LUIS JIMÉNEZ CRUZ	Labourer	Eventual	San Clemente	Spanish
ARGIMIRO MONTELLANO ALMODÓVAR	Labourer	Eventual	Belmonte	Spanish
JOSÉ MIGUEL ALMODÓVAR MARTÍNEZ	Labourer	Eventual	Belmonte	Spanish
ESPERANZA MONTELLANO DELGADO	Labourer	Eventual	Belmonte	Spanish

La Quéjola Estate

Three generations of the Melgarejo family at the Palace of the Marquis of Valdeguerrero.

La Quéjola Estate

Head Game Keeper, Luis Yáñez, with the staff ready for a shooting day.

A collection of shotguns are available at La Quéjola so that guests enjoy an excellent day's shooting.

La Quéjola Estate

WORK COMPATIBLE WITH THE ENVIRONMENT

When, in 1981, I started to work in this family business, I understood that our forebears had left us a legacy whose principal value was in conserving the environment.

Since then, I have fought to make agricultural development compatible with an absolute respect for the environment in which we operate.

Many things have been done in recent years to make the work both profitable and capable of protecting and conserving our heritage. These have included transforming the way in which we irrigate land; vineyards on trellises; advances in the facilities for raising livestock and modern means of selective breeding; cultivation of new crops; changes in methodology in the areas of agriculture, conservation, and direct drilling of seed; prevention of erosion; increased use of organic material; the establishment of associations of agricultural producers in order to improve the trade in products, and a long list of other developments.

But the widely acknowledged drop in the profitability of the countryside has forced us to embark on other activities whose development is both possible and necessary today in order to keep the environment in good shape, with its Mediterranean woodland and wildlife conserved and enhanced. I am speaking here of hunting and tourism activities.

Today, these activities constitute a means of support that cannot be underrated in balancing simple agricultural production with a new, hard-working, but highly creative world.

I would like to take this opportunity to express my gratitude to our employees who, with us, have made this transformation possible and who have been able to "retool" themselves in order to meet the challenges that present times demand.

Antonio Melgarejo Nárdiz

An old Holm Oak with stakes placed around it to protect it from pesticides used on the land.

C. Oté

Quéjola Estate

A comfortable lounge used by guests on shooting days.

At La Quéjola and in the surrounding countryside there is a mosaic of crops, meadows and grazing land.

La Quéjola Estate

DEHESA LA QUÉJOLA BELONGS TO:

AGRAMA

APROCA
Castilla-La Mancha

Friends of the Countryside

WE initiative

Fundación amigos
del Águila Impreial

ASAJA

ADEMAC

GEA

Activities & attractions

🐗 Hunting   🍴 Restaurant
🦆 Shooting   📷 Rural Tourism
🐟 Fishing   🚶 Walking trails
🏞 Country Park   🦅 Birdwatching
🐎 Equestrian

CONTACT DATA

D. Antonio Melgarejo
DEHESA Y FAUNA
C/ Arrabal, 2. 16600, San Clemente
CUENCA
info@dehesayfauna.es
Tel.: +34 637 825 053 • +34 969 301 561
Fax: +34 969 307 054

725

Symondsbury

Atlantic

Location: Bridport, Dorset, United Kingdom.
Surface: 700 ha.

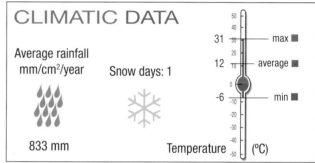

CLIMATIC DATA

Average rainfall
mm/cm²/year

Snow days: 1

833 mm

Temperature (ºC)

31 — max ■
12 — average ■
-6 — min ■

SUMMARY

Symondsbury Estate is of such beauty that its landscape has been pre-approved for classification as Heritage Landscape of National Importance. Such beautiful landscape carries a large financial premium in excess of its already high earning capacity. Buyers compete in order to live here or simply to own it and thus pay more to buy it than it will earn. Therefore it is impossible to make a normal financial return on capital.

Owning such land is a rich man's business. Only during and shortly after serious global wars – such as the Napoleonic or 20th century World Wars – has it been possible for the property to make a normal financial return. The effect of this long business cycle can be seen in the dates of the farm buildings and of the beautiful hedgerows. Fine agricultural barns and farmhouses, if they do not date from 500 years ago, were usually built during the period of serious farming prosperity 200 years ago. Examples on our estate are at Crepe Farm, Manor Farm, Duck Street, Symondsbury House, etc

Our landscape here at Symondsbury is full of such rich variety and beauty because of the steep hills, varied topography and fine soils, but it cannot make money when food and raw materials are imported from the Great Plains of the Americas, continental Europe and Australia where land is plentiful and huge machines can travel wherever they like.

In our landscape, land management is a micro-business and our land products must therefore be of high value and detailed, and leverage the heritage and beauty of the setting, location, wildlife etc.

The hill owes its fame to the trees at the top of the hill which were planted around 1920 by the then owner.
Major (W) Philip Colfox MC MP (later Sir Philip Colfox Bt).

ifphotos.com

DESCRIPTION

The Symondsbury Estate near Bridport, Dorset is owned by the Colfox family, and covers 700 hectares. It is set in an Area of Outstanding Natural Beauty, less than two kilometres from the Jurassic Coast, which has World Heritage status. Its backdrop is the area's iconic Colmers Hill, visible from afar. The estate consists of farmland, forestry, residential and commercial property.

People living and working in the village, and visitors are encouraged to share the tradition and beauty of Symondsbury, with its charming church, pub and yellow stone cottages. The many footpaths enable people to explore geology-rich locations such as Ryeberry and Watton Hill. The views of the six hills of Symondsbury from the village remind visitors and residents of the six hills of Rome: Colmer's, Old Warren, Allington, Ryberry, Sloes and Legg's Hills.

THE VILLAGE

At the heart of Symondsbury Estate lies the delightful traditional village of Symondsbury. The historical relationship between the village and the estate is unusual as the Manor of Symondsbury was broken up in c. 1669 by the Dowager Duchess of Somerset, whose husband's family had bought it from the Abbots of Cerne during the Dissolution of the Monasteries in c. 1536. The Duchess sold it to its tenants, only retaining the Dinhay (Denhay) and Colmer's tenements. The Colfox family consolidated much of the ownership, and brought in more land from other Manors which were broken up, e.g. Allington and, Netherbury, and parts of Chideock Castle – the Manors of Moorbath and Atrim – in the late 19th and early 20th centuries.

In the early 20th century the newly reformed Symondsbury Manor Estate's four farms and smallholdings within the village (Shutes, Crepe, Sloes and Manor) and those outlying (e.g. Higher and Lower Moorbath, Axen, Barbridge, Broadoak, Higher and Lower Denhay, Venlands, Henwood, North End, Lower and Higher Atrim, Atrim Gore, Bilshay, Bilshay Dairy, Colly, Home, Hole, Magdalen and Watton Farms and Lease Acre) were the mainstay of the village, with agricultural and farm rentals being its main income. The majority of the tenants worked on the estate or in associated employment. The estate provided water, electricity (through a joint venture company) and sewerage systems to most of the village. As a result of diversification, the estate now farms the majority of the land in hand. Redundant farm buildings have been converted into business units, empty farm houses and cottages have been turned into holiday lets and a commercial shoot has been reintroduced.

At the heart of the estate lies the delightful traditional village of Symondsbury.

Symondsbury is now regarded as a 'destination' village with four large holiday accommodation businesses, where both visitors and local people can enjoy the tradition and charm of the place, and some notable estate buildings and landmarks. The estate intends soon to provide a specialist wedding venue in the centre of the village next to the medieval church.

Shutes Farmhouse

Shutes Farmhouse was built from a single oak felled in c. 1446 and formed the court house for the abbots of Cerne and later owners of the manorial rights (first the Duke of Somerset and later the Earl of Ilchester). During the 17th century it formed part of the Colmer's Tenement and ceased to be an active farmhouse in the 1950s. The estate intends to make the best use of its historic potential.

Abbey Barn

Built in the 14th century by the Abbot of Cerne, the Abbey Barn is the second oldest barn in Dorset and prior to its refurbishment (and demolition of two bays) in the 20th century was the largest (it is now the third largest). The original thatch was replaced by a tiled roof in the 1930s, with gable end finials from Sir Charles Barry's House of Commons. A painted board on the beams bearing the inscription "God save The King" is the subject of much discussion amongst historians as to which King the board refers. The estate intends greatly to expand the use of the Abbey Barn for wedding parties in order to secure the economic future of the building and the associated thatched courtyard.

Symondsbury House

Symondsbury House has an interesting history. Previous residents include a world famous haematologist as well as Mr. Alfred Johnson, an eminent local farmer who developed the Dorset Horn sheep breed and was the first farmer to export rams to Australia; he was also the first person to sell a ram for 100 guineas. Symondsbury House is now the home of Sir John and Lady Frederica Colfox.

Colmer's Hill

The 140 m Colmers Hill overlooks Symonds-

Symondsbury Estate

The Estate combines a commercial farming enterprise with full environmental responsibility.

bury and dominates the area. It is named after the family of the widow Elizabeth Lush (nee Colmer) who farmed the Colmer's tenement in the 17th century. Perhaps she was of the same family as the Rev. John Colmer, Symondsbury Rector in 1805-06. The hill owes its fame to the trees at the top of the hill which were planted around 1920 by the then owner Major Philip Colfox to celebrate the birth of his first son, Andrew. Colmers Hill is a very popular subject for artists and photographers, capturing this iconic Symondsbury Estate vista in many paintings and photographs.

Other Places of Interest

The Church of St. John the Baptist stands in the centre of the village. Originally Gothic with perpendicular pillars, the first Rector's records were in 1325. The church register dates back to 1558.

Symondsbury Church of England Primary School was built in 1868, originally as a charity school. One of the early headmasters appointed had been a missionary in Australia, and arrived accompanied by a native Australian and a kangaroo.

The Ilchester Arms, built in the 16th century, was named after the Earl of Ilchester. Down the years publicans have offered baking, shop keeping, butcher and coal merchant services as well as inn keeping.

Crepe Farmhouse

Crepe Farmhouse is a luxury Holiday Farmhouse sleeping 17, with sole use of the heated indoor swimming pool, sauna, jacuzzi and games room. It is the perfect setting for shooting parties and corporate events, large family holidays, families sharing, and party weekends. It is situated three kilometres from the sea, between rolling hills in the beautiful countryside of West Dorset.

PROPERTY

The Symondsbury Estate has a range of residential and commercial properties to let.

Nestled at the heart of Symondsbury village, the **Crepe Farm Business Park** was started just over nine years ago when Symondsbury Estate ceased dairy milking and pig farming. The redundant farm buildings were converted into a mixture of offices and workshops. After the successful re-invention of the area the Business Park is now home to many local businesses. The rural setting is the perfect base for over 19 local businesses including a plumber, builder and caterer.

The estate owns a number of **residential properties** in and around Symondsbury. Letting vacancies occasionally occur.

THE COUNTRYSIDE

The oaks, above all those that are a century or more old, are the object of special attention.

The mission of the business managers is to create a prosperous and forward-looking estate that successfully encourages the pleasures of rural li-

ving complying with the necessity to be a commercially economic and sustainable enterprise. It acts as guardian of the countryside, the land, the properties, the wildlife and its environs. It preserves rural heritage and strives to create a 'destination village' that is enjoyed by those that live, work and visit.

In April 2007, with considerable funding from Natural England, the estate produced a Heritage Management Plan. It was put together by Dr Nicola Bannister and includes recommended policies on the management of all aspects of the estate including flora and fauna. It is supported by a number of specialist reports. The estate is now managed in accordance with the recommendations of that Plan.

The Executive Summary at the beginning of the Heritage Management Plan states:-

"The Symondsbury Estate lies within the Marshwood Vale of West Dorset, on the western side of the town of Bridport. It is an agricultural estate with farming stretching back to the prehistoric period. Today the enclosure landscape of fields comprising an intimate mix of woods and woody hedges has a medieval origin in which are areas of post medieval agrarian expansion and development".

"Scattered farmsteads set within their fields of arable and pasture are a characteristic feature of the landscape with the central Domesday village of Symondsbury lying within a sheltered vale between two hills Colmer's Hill and Sloes Hill. These hills with Alington to the east and Jan's to the north are a striking topographical feature of the landscape as are the sunken lanes which wind through the fields to the higher ground to the north".

"The Colfox Family have had connections with Symondsbury and Bridport since the medieval period, but their ownership of the Symondsbury Estate dates from the mid-nineteenth century when Thomas and William Colfox, grandsons of Thomas Collins Colfox a businessman in the wool and shipping industry, began to purchase land from the Ilchester Estate and other landowners to form part of what is now the Symondsbury Estate.

The game cover woods were planted by Sir Philip Colfox, and Sir John Colfox has undertaken further planting of trees in hedgerows, withy beds and odd corners creating the rich tapestry of woodlands and trees amongst the fields".

C.Otero

FARMING

Symondsbury Estate combines a commercial farming enterprise with full environmental responsibility. The objective is to run a profitable farming business in a balanced and sustainable manner with complete consideration for the land, the environment, wildlife and the local community in and around Symondsbury.

The estate farms some 555 hectares, of which 58% is arable and the remaining 42% is grassland.

Arable Crops

Large modern machinery facilitates rapid cultivation and harvesting which means that wheat can be grown as a profitable cash crop but only when prices are above €160 per tonne and the summer weather is good, which is no longer guaranteed. Wheat is sown in September/October, harvested in the following August and retained in the estate's recently built grain store.

Maize for cattle feed is grown as a "break" crop within the rotation – it is sown in April/May for harvest in September.

Potatoes are planted in March/April and then lifted in August/September. Once harvested, the potatoes are retained in contractors' refrigerated stores.

Grassland for Grazing

The 235 hectares of grassland is located on the steeper, wetter areas of the estate. Most are rented out as grazing for livestock belonging to three main tenants. A small amount of grassland is used for the estate's horses.

Farming Practices

Symondsbury Estate is a member of the UK's Entry Level Stewardship (ELS) Scheme. In return for a yearly payment per hectare (from Pillar II of the European Agricultural Policy), ELS requires that farms deliver specific environmental management solutions appropriate to the needs of the particular area. For example, one of the key issues for the Symondsbury area is soil erosion, requiring the estate's careful management of field operation and crop rotation to meet both Pillar I and Pillar II stipulations.

It is paramount to the estate that whilst running a profitable farming business in Dorset's Area of Outstanding Natural Beauty, all aspects of the environment are protected, sustained and enhanced.

The estate farms some 555 hectares, of which 58% is arable and the remaining 42% is grassland.

Potatoes are planted in March/April and then lifted in August/September.

Once harvested, the potatoes are retained in contractors' refrigerated stores.

Carpet of bluebells.

FORESTRY

Symondsbury Estate's woodland management combines the production of quality timber with enhancement of the conservation wildlife status and habitat biodiversity.

Of the total woodland area of just over 57 hectares, Symondsbury Estate has some 23 hectares of Planted Ancient Woodland Sites (PAWS) which consists of planted broadleaf and conifer species,. The woodland consists of 30% conifer: Douglas Fir *(Pseudotsuga menziesii)*, Japanese Larch *(Larix kaempferi)* and Spruce *(Picea abies)*, 58% broadleaf (oak, ash and mixed broadleaves), and open ground of nearly 7 hectares (12%). A gradual 'fell and replant' strategy will be employed to create a mosaic of uneven aged coupes, with native broadleaf species such as oak and ash replanted. There are some specific areas that have been designated in three categories: Natural Reserves, which are often areas of open ground such as water meadows and substantial canopy gaps within woods; Long Term Retention, which are more specifically areas of trees that have a substantial ecological value that would benefit from being left to natural occurring events; and Non-Intervention, in areas where any potential management operations may have a detrimental impact on the status of the habitat. The latter are generally steep and inaccessible.

Symondsbury Estate is set in an Area of Outstanding Beauty, with rolling hills, steep banks and valleys. Most of the woodland exists in these valleys. The iconic Dorset landmark, Colmers Hill, was replanted in 2007 with Monterey Pine *(Pinus radiata)* to retain the beauty spot's famous pine cover.

Woodland Management is carried out in consultation with all appropriate parties, both local and national. A key consideration is the local community, both socially and economically. Footpaths and walks are well maintained, and woodland management operations aim to pro-

732

vide employment opportunities for local workers.

As an endorsement of its approach to woodland stewardship, the estate is undergoing UK Woodland Assurance Standard (UKWAS) certification. UKWAS is an independent standard for verifying sustainable woodland management in the United Kingdom. Management practices, documentation and records are audited on an ongoing basis to ensure adherence to the standard, providing assurance that timber from certification holders is sourced from sustainably managed woodlands.

ECOLOGY

Symondsbury Estate has a huge and varied range of natural habitats, creating a patchwork of areas across the landscape to explore and enjoy. This includes ancient woodland, land that has never been used as farmland, dry grasslands, beautifully varied watercourses, intricate networks of weaving hedgerows and old trees, all thriving with an abundance of wildlife.

Mammals

As well as the working farm animals grazing throughout the estate, the land boasts a large number of wild mammals that, with a keen eye, can be spotted darting throughout the surroundings.

Otters

The old woodland tributaries from the river Simene provide the ideal habitat for one of the country's most beautiful mammals. Otters *(Lutra lutra)* use the networks of damp grassland fields, hedges and woods to cross from one watercourse to the next in their search for food, companionship and shelter. The otter has a soft under-fur, which is protected by their outer layer of guard hair, keeping them warm and dry in their search for fish. The otter is renowned for its playful nature – in English a group of otters is known as a romp, a word which also means "to play".

Dormice

Dormice *(Muscardinus avellanarius)* are nocturnal animals and use the estate's twisting wild hedgerows to find their nourishment from flowers, fruit, pollen, seeds, nuts and insects. Mouse-like in appearance, the dormouse has a furry tail and is perfectly adapted to climbing. The dormouse population is thriving, thanks to the estate's policy of rotational hedge trimming, and enjoys the freedom to roam across the whole estate in order to find the perfect spot for their lengthy hibernation period, just like the sleepy dormouse which "Alice" came across in "Wonderland".

Greater Horseshoe Bat

The Greater Horseshoe Bat *(Rhinolophus ferrumequinum)* is an endangered mammal which requires insect-rich cattle pastures, tall hedges and overhanging branches to hunt, mate and live, all of which Symondsbury has to offer. The bats are confirmed as residents in Manor Cottages and many locals have spotted the winged creatures flitting above their heads at dusk, especially during the mating season in spring.

Birds

All the following birds are confirmed residents of the varied landscape that spreads throughout the estate. However, we welcome any avid bird-spotters who want to let us know of any other elusive species flitting across our old English skyline.

Goldcrests (Regulus regulus)

These beautiful birds nest in the village and on Colmer's Hill.

Yellowhammer (Emberiza citronella)

The Yellowhammer is 15.5-17cm long, with a strong seed-eating beak. As with most birds the male is a brighter colour than the female with more defined markings. Building nests on the ground, the yellowhammers live primarily in hedgerows with a decent patch of grass on either side. On the Symondsbury Estate, the rape and turnip fields grown for over-wintering sheep provide the yellowhammers with much of their food source. However, to increase the numbers of these beautiful birds, plans are in place to grow kale or a similar plant to provide the yellowhammer with a more abundant food source.

Linnet (Carduelis cannabina)

Taking its name from linen (the Linnet feeds on flax seeds used to make linen) the orange-brown bird has been sighted in large flocks over the Symondsbury landscape. Linnets have similar requirements to the Yellowhammers and are perfectly suited to the local habitat, feeding on seeds and using the hedgerows for shelter. A slim bird with a long tale, the male has a red breast in the summer whereas the female remains white throughout the year. They build their nests in hedgerows just off of the ground laying between 5-7 eggs in a season.

Song Thrush (Turdus philomelos)

Strolling through the Symondsbury Estate is never better than when the song thrush's song is floating across the landscape, creating a quintessentially English experience. The brownish speckled bird prefers the taller hedges on the estate for nesting, feeding and song-posts. The damp pastures littered throughout the area also allow the bird to satisfy its omnivorous lifestyle, providing worms and snails to be devoured or fed to the young. In the winter months the song thrush survives on berries from the wild bushes. The monogamous birds are known to stay in Symondsbury all year round, with the male establishing his territory and singing to ward off competition.

Barn Owl (Tyto alba)

With only around 4,400 breeding pairs of barn owls in the UK, Symondsbury is ideal for the nocturnal birds, with plenty of nesting opportunities (old trees and buildings) and hunting grounds (rough grassland). Its cry can be heard across the estate at dusk. With their acute hearing and silent flight, the barn owl is a formidable hunter of small rodents. Its white face and effortless hovering, has earned the bird many nicknames, including "Ghost Owl". Work is being undertaken on some of the larger trees on the estate to ensure a growth in potential nesting sites for the graceful night hunter and known nests in barns are protected with nesting boxes.

Greater & Lesser Spotted Woodpeckers (Dendrocopos major & Picoides minor)

The main difference between the two birds is

their size. The greater spotted woodpecker is much larger and is much more frequently seen across the estate. They also 'drum' in shorter bursts than the lesser spotted woodpecker and nest in the main stems of woodland trees. The lesser prefers to nest on the side branches of individual trees. The varied and diverse landscape of the Symondsbury Estate means that both types of the woodpecker can find everything they require to increase their numbers, including large amounts of lying deadwood from which they feed on insects with their long barbed tongues.

SHOOTING

The Symondsbury Estate Shoot offers full day packages for pheasant and partridge shooting.

DAYS OUT

The Symondsbury Estate in Bridport is set in an Area of Outstanding Natural Beauty, only a few miles from the Jurassic Coast, which has World Heritage status. The market town of Bridport is 3 kilometres away and offers a wonderful variety of shops and restaurants as well as a traditional street market on Wednesdays and Saturdays. There are many outlets supplying local produce and a regular monthly Farmers Market in the centre of the town. The sandy beaches of West Bay, Charmouth and Lyme Regis, as well as the small coves at Eype and Seatown, are all within easy reach, offering breathtaking coastal walks, fossil hunting, fishing trips, scuba diving, paragliding, river boating, power boat trips, golf and much more.

Visitors and people living in the village are encouraged to share the beauty and charm of Symondsbury.

The Symondsbury Estate Shoot offers full day packages for pheasant and partridge shooting.

SUPPORT AND KEEP FAMILY RELATIONSHIPS

Professional land managers often advise families (who own and live on the land) that there is a mythical creature called "the Estate" which has a life of its own and must be protected from the dangers of younger brothers and sisters, divorce, tax and business disaster. Landowners often believe that transmission of the land from one generation to the next is a basic need of the lowest order on Maslow's "Hierarchy of Needs," along with food and reproduction. The interests of fee-earning professionals and landowners often, therefore coincide to perpetuate a myth of the need for estates to be kept together and for eldest sons to inherit. This preserves intact the professional's fee base (the property) and it is part of the conspiracy of primogeniture where oldest sons conspire father-to-son against the rest of the family.

The prime importance of transmission of property from one generation to another is a fallacy. Taking an inter-generational view is only a lobbying code for defending inherited wealth and those who wish to influence the world from beyond the grave do so because of pride, self-respect and personal ambition. These are luxuries, not needs at all (and near the very top of Maslow's Hierarchy.) Such ambition is not necessarily bad, but an excess is highly damaging to the family and to society as a whole. It might be very good for the environment and biodiversity, but if the whole of Europe were managed in accordance with practices imposed from beyond the grave it is doubtful if we would be able to feed ourselves and we would still be wearing clogs like they did in China until recently.

Where, in reality, the family does not have sufficient resources to pay for taxes, sisters, younger brothers, business disasters and divorce, the ambition of keeping the es-

Another ambition of CBK is to run a project to restore the Black Grouse *(Tetrao tetrix)* to favourable conservation status.

tate together is a high risk strategy at every level – financial, family, environmental.

Furthermore the history of landownership has been one of tension between those who have it and those who want it. Respect for property rights, on policy grounds, needs to be balanced against common sense, that it is wrong for property owners to be able to survive and live rich lives without doing anything at all to deserve it. Countries with finely tuned methods of making unsuccessful landowners gradually lose their land are those that have not seen revolution in recent centuries. The UK, for instance, has an optional wealth tax, which is charged on transmission from one generation to another. This sometimes leads to the break-up of properties, but can be avoided by the able and well advised. The three routes to avoiding the tax are all pro-business, pro-change and pro-good management. They are: (1) to run your property as a real trading business; (2) to transmit it to and empower the next generation as early as possible; and (3) to create a near-perpetual vehicle that uses the best trustees/directors/managers that you can afford.

Furthermore, change and balance is good. Good family relations are even better and the world needs the best possible and most innovative entrepreneurs and businessmen to be custodians of the world's primary resources. Families need the best people for the job of running the family's money as well.

Thus there are five children in my generation, and sixteen of the next generation. All are based here (or in the parish) with their spouses. I have control of the strategic direction via the "ownership function" and have put in place a structure that empowers the best possible managers and will enable perpetual succession if the family so wish it. However I have tried to share the benefits of landownership with my immediate family and they are therefore contributing their bit to the common good and to the prosperity of the area as well as, incidentally, to its vibrancy and biodiversity. With my parents and spouses (less one divorced), a total of twenty six members of the family are based on the estate.

During the years whilst I have been of influence I have taken the view that the survival of the estate should not be the primary objective of the investment philosophy. The primary objective is the survival of the family and the role of the estate includes that of assisting members of the family to project themselves to the highest level possible in their careers. This might be by helping them to pay their university fees or by allowing them to use the wonderful landscape to entertain their friends and contacts.

In dealing with the next generation I am considering adopting a method used in a globally important family whereby the members of that family are given basic assistance, but those who excel are given far more – each according to their success. This is the opposite of the welfare system whereby failure is rewarded – an easy mistake for all families if they think of their wealth as a charity to be applied for the benefit of the less fortunate or less able or less inspired members of their family.

Thus the old-fashioned (and largely British) habit of sending children to boarding schools, which in other contexts and because of its extreme expense I have called a "mechanism for the self-destruction of the class system", here is used, as far as we can afford it, as a method of propelling some members of the family into the wider world where they can network and make contacts and thereby be a success and one day repay the estate for this assistance in life.

However this assistance is exceedingly expensive, especially if there are a large number of children and cousins. Thus if the family and the estate are tied together by a tradition of primogeniture the only way that the estate will be a success is if the people who own it are rich and successful as a result of their own achievement. No estate of this size can generate cash on a scale that, on its own, would be self-supporting across the generations. The estate therefore has to be a tool to project the family forward and not the capital asset out of which they can live – not even, as we have seen above, as farmers. Furthermore a mechanism is needed so that if members of the family are successful they have the opportunity to put something back. Whether this is done by way of creating a mini-estate out of the main estate, or by joining the management structure, is a matter to suit each individual on their merits.

For estates to be transmitted down the generations the business has to be very successful. Key to this is the management and ownership structure. Families can either organise themselves so that they choose the best businessmen to be the owners, or, if they want to follow some pre-ordained theoretical inheritance pathway – for instance to keep the land and the title together – they can use a structural solution, for instance a trust or a company. The self-management solution is an evolutionary solution the estate will only survive when the "fittest" members of the family are chosen to run it. This solution would suit a family that always passed their money to the person most qualified to look after it and who has no emotional tie to the land or the area. But properly set up and operated, the structural solution can have that evolutionary benefit as well. Key to the structural solution is to find the best – normally professional – managers of the structure. Normally a structural solution will divide management from ownership. This can be done by contract (as at Symondsbury) or by company or by trust. The beauty of a contractual solution (which allows a hybrid between a structural solution and a self-managed solution) is that the contract is temporary and each new generation of the family can decide whether or not to renew the business plan. As stated above, change is good for everyone – the family, the land and society – so it is important not to be too perfect with your structural solution!

Our family is proud of its boast to be connected with this village for 800 years, but on investigation I found it was not true! This family's earliest written ties with the estate date back to 1396 and with the area in general to 1280. However we did not put the land together until the late 19th and early 20th century, buying it in small parcels. Nevertheless the formula of putting the family first and not making the estate a millstone around the neck of the oldest son and a source of jealousy for the rest, appears to be one that has worked for us. As a result we were able to take part in the industrial revolution in Birmingham and global trade in London and make enough money to buy the estate. The end result is that we have been able to benefit the surrounding area: a school that educates all the townsfolk is named after my father (who is still alive), two hospitals, other schools, the harbour defences and the railway were all built with family money. The importance of looking after those around you as well as the family is that, if you look after them, they will look after you. However, without the people there will be nobody to look after the land or the estate.

When my grandfather started farming in 1936 there were 25 farms and approximately 100 workers on the land. Now there are no full-time agricultural workers employed by the estate – though there are people employed by the shoot and the commercial tenants. That means that there are very few people to do the work of protecting the biodiversity, recording what we have and tending the landscape. The importance of having family nearby running their own businesses in the global-electronic-super-highway cannot be underestimated, for without them and people like them the land will die. But it does not have to be my family who have the opportunity. If we cannot do it, we can sell, reallocate our resources and someone else can have a go.

Rich Man's Toy and Estate Reflects the Success of the Family

So the key to the future of the estate under my tenure is firstly to make sure that the very large cash drain (from servicing the rich heritage) is not too big and that the off-estate business is exceedingly successful to keep pace with the financial needs of a very hungry family.

To prevent the estate being a cash-drain requires the very highest quality of management and, indeed, today this is fully delegated to the best that can be identified (liberating me to work full-time where the real money can be earned). It also requires close cooperation and work with the local authorities. They need to appreciate our vision and our spirit of working together in partnership to achieve their goals. The estate is in the business of

Philip Colfox and Lety.

C. Otero

land and property as well as that of delivering what users of land and property want. It is not just about food and environment; it is also about employment, holidays, business premises, roads, houses, schools, hospitals and now clean energy as well. Whatever it is that is needed by landusers, we can supply it.

The off-estate business leverages our financial collateral, our expensive educations and our network of contacts built up by the family over generations with our prestige trophy asset, namely the sheer desirability of this superlative landscape. I helped to set up a network of prominent individuals in business and public life and specialise in organising deals on their behalf. This business, called OneBridge Limited, has the potential to make enough money through commissions to keep this "rich man's estate" in the good order in which it should be kept. Additionally, as well as trading on its own behalf, OneBridge is developing a number of investment vehicles specifically aimed at helping landowner to maximise the potential of their land. These will either be in the form of a collective vehicle where many landowners participate in one scheme or schemes specifically tailored to the needs of one family. These products and services will be rolled out on both an UK and pan-European basis. The prestige of this very beautiful estate gives me the credibility to do these and other deals with very rich men in far-away countries and the superlative shoot allows me to invite them back here to be indulged in a luxury that they love and which often helps to clinch the deal. So the beauty of the estate reflects the prestige and success of the family and is a critical factor in ensuring the family will be successful in the future and be able to subsidise this very beautiful place for a long time to come.

One of my ambitions is to create an endowment or "backing fund" for the Estate – in reality, for the family. By getting off the estate and doing deals, I and my business colleagues uncover exceptionally good investments from time to time with upside potential to underwrite the family (or any other investor) for another 150 years. If I was sitting at home driving my combine-harvester or arguing with my tenants or local government, I would not be able to do this. This innovative activity is also exceedingly beneficial to the economy as a whole.

I have also set up a second off-estate business – CBK[1] – which is modelled on my experience as a landowner, and especially my experience working with Thierry de l'Escaille of the European Landowners Organisation in Brussels and our team here headed by Antony Lumby of Savills and Andrew Dyke of Pineapple. CBK brings our on-estate innovations to other landowners and also links landowners to very big global businesses who want to do business with them and help them to unlock seriously large amounts of money from their property – obviously to the considerable benefit of the environment, biodiversity, business, employment, education, health and housing. Very considerable sums of money can be unlocked by some landowners if the very best dealmakers, who are used to dealing with global businesses and government, are given sufficient leeway, considerable incentives and clear parameters.

To raise its profile, CBK has also organised some very exciting landowner-based "outreach" projects. We are running the Red Squirrel South West Project to help reintroduce this threatened native Red Squirrel *(Sciurus vulgaris)* to the mainland of south west Britain. This has considerable benefits for woodland as the invasive competitor Grey Squirrel *(Sciurus carolinensis)* badly damages commercial plantations. In addition it utilises our networking skills and

understanding of landowners to the full. The project also demonstrates that landowners, when they work together, can achieve that which the bureaucrats have failed to achieve in over 100 years. We are using methods successfully developed by politician and landowner Lord Redesdale in Northumbria and Dr. Craig Shuttle worth in Anglesea.

Another ambition of CBK is to run a project to restore the Black Grouse *(Tetrao tetrix)* to favourable conservation status throughout its natural range in the UK. The UK subspecies is not protected under the Birds Directive and can still be hunted. This is an opportunity for hunters and landowners to demonstrate how, when they work together, they can achieve a near-impossibility that every Green NGO would love them to do. Black grouse were present in every county in England until about 100 years ago but have been disturbed by increasing number of walkers and by less than totally excellent forestry management which they must have. The last black grouse in the South West were shot about 10 years ago. There are thought to be only 200 breeding pairs in Wales. The remaining UK population is in the north of England and Scotland and is about 2,000-4,000 in number. This is potentially a very exciting political and environmental project. If suitable habitats were developed for this key indicator species, just think what side benefits that would produce for biodiversity.

Philip Colfox

---

[1] Colfox.Buchanan.Knospe Research and Innovation Ltd - CBK.

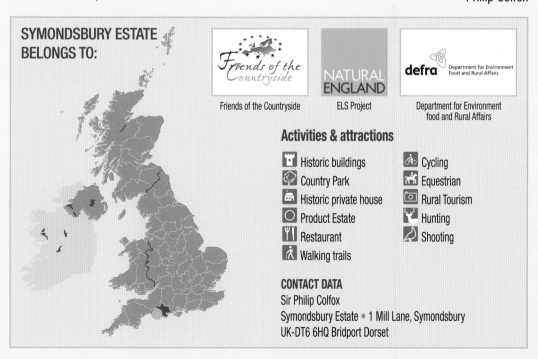

SYMONDSBURY ESTATE BELONGS TO:

Friends of the Countryside

ELS Project

Department for Environment food and Rural Affairs

Activities & attractions

- Historic buildings
- Country Park
- Historic private house
- Product Estate
- Restaurant
- Walking trails
- Cycling
- Equestrian
- Rural Tourism
- Hunting
- Shooting

CONTACT DATA
Sir Philip Colfox
Symondsbury Estate • 1 Mill Lane, Symondsbury
UK-DT6 6HQ Bridport Dorset

Tenuta di Collalto

Continental

Location: Susegana, province of Treviso, Veneto region, Italy.
Surface: 1,500 ha.

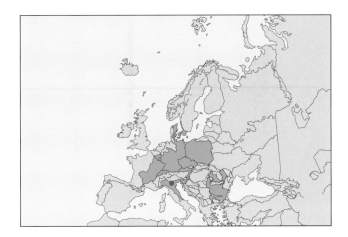

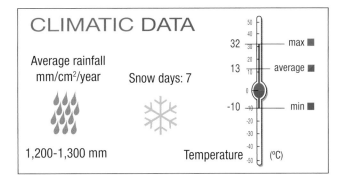

CLIMATIC DATA

Average rainfall
mm/cm²/year

Snow days: 7

1,200-1,300 mm

Temperature (°C)

32 — max
13 — average
-10 — min

SUMMARY

Not far from Susegana rises the Castle of San Salvatore majestically evoking the memory of the Collalto family, whose roots have been deeply rooted in the Veneto region for around a thousand years.
The Castle dominates the hills and countryside that slope down towards the bank of the Piave river. Situated in the heart of an area where wine has been made for centuries, the Collalto Estate lies amongst vineyards, woods, hill-side meadows with free-roaming cattle, and flat arable land in the plain; a unique ecosystem with extraordinary biodiversity.

The Castle of San Salvatore dominates the hills and countryside
that slope down towards the bank of the Piave river.

San Salvatore Castle was built in the 12th century, although the property had already been in the hands of the Count of Treviso, then Collalto, since 994 AD.

Tenuta di Collalto Estate

HISTORY

Collalto is a reminder of heroic deeds and memorable events from the early age of the Lombards to the Holy Roman Empire, to the magnificence of the Venetian Republic and the Austrian Empire of Veneto.

The coat of arms of the Collalto family is one of the oldest known in heraldry, with its Sable (black) and Argent (white, silver) shield of four quarters. The family is known to have used this banner since before 1000 AD.

The family of the Count of Treviso later took the name Collalto. The medieval "Nervesa Document" records that in 994 AD the Germanic Ottone III, Emperor of the Holy Roman Empire, gave land to "Regimbaldo di Treviso" for his administrative and political commitment as imperial official. The family resettled in the Susegana hills and always managed to secure important positions and consequently played an influential role in local political life.

From the 12th century the family extended its fiefdom to the left bank of the Piave river and built the Castles of Collalto and San Salvatore. By the end of the Middle Ages San Salvatore had become one of the biggest castles in northern Italy.

During the long periods of peace that Venice experienced, the castle remained unconquered and flourished in a time in which many artists and musicians visited and wrote about it.

The 1800s was a thriving period for San Salvatore Castle and the region. The estate became even more active, and new agricultural methods and experimental techniques were skilfully developed and applied in the agricultural pursuits of the family.

The early 1900s were marred by the First World War, with the River Piave becoming the centrepiece of some of the most barbarous battles seen in that war. The castle, which had been forcibly occupied by the Austrian army, was extensively bombed and destroyed by the Italian artillery, leaving a desolate landscape with only a part of its glorious buildings intact. The churches on the estate, the big tower, the hamlet and its enclosure walls were all devastated and turned into mere rubble.

The Count Rambaldo's sense of honour and responsibility ensured that he could not accept such a situation, and he immèdiately started a long and demanding period of reconstruction and restoration of the castle and its surrounding land.

This onerous task was undertaken by the late Prince Manfredo of Collalto, and the gargantuan task was only concluded in 2003 when the Palazzo Odoardo in the castle was finally refurbished and restored to its original splendour.

The estate's extensive lands have been preserved throughout the centuries thanks to the entrepreneurial approach of the Collalto family, combined with a profound respect for biodiversity.

Coat of arms of the Collalto family.

DESCRIPTION

The estate has an estimated height of between 30 m and 300 m above sea-level, and has a variety of landscapes with different geological characteristics, ranging from gravel – due to the proximity of the Piave river – to clay.

The property is well-known for the diversified equilibrium achieved through its integrated rural activities and management. With its extraordinary variety of flora and fauna, the Collalto Estate is a unique ecological oasis amidst the ecosystems of northern Italy.

The property is characterised by its harmonious variety of biodiversity, which ensures that the land is well-balanced and remarkably well-preserved. Of the total area, 200 ha are dedicated directly to the historical vineyard, 600 ha are cultivated arable fields, 200 ha are grazing pastures, 420 ha are woodlands and there is an additional 80 ha of walnuts.

Significant investments over the years have helped enhance the natural environment by applying only the most suitable forms of land conservation. The past is brought into the present thanks to the wise way in which the rich traditional heritage has been combined with the most sensitive ecological concerns.

Tenuta di Collalto Estate

From farm to fork

Extensive traditional farming at Collalto Estate is based on quality production. Animals such as cattle (1000 head) and pigs are treated respectfully and humanely. The livestock is fed naturally with maize, wheat, soya and barley, produced and harvested within the estate.

The farm supplies high quality controlled and traceable fresh products that are sold directly to the consumer.

The property is well-known for the diversified equilibrium achieved through its integrated rural activities and management.

After the almost complete destruction of the historical heritage at the start of the 21st century, the late Prince Manfredo of Collalto completed the restoration of the Palazzo Odoardo.

Tenuta di Collalto Estate

About 1,000 cattle are raised on an extensive system.

Horses, pigs and cows are reared extensively.

Tenuta di Collalto Estate

A shop is available on the farm giving consumers the opportunity to be in contact with their supplier and to experience traditional farming by watching a farmer in his day-to-day work in meeting the high quality standards.

Wine Production

Collalto is an estate which has not forgotten the importance of the soil, the value of caring for the vine and the production of outstanding wines by using modern, up-to-date equipment and methods – but methods where family traditions and experience are also integrated to produce a wine which is not only an icon of its place and vintage but also an ambassador for the patience and skills of its maker and the traditions of the family which has helped to create it.

The sun-filled hills of the Collalto Estate are located approximately 48 km from the sea. This means that even though the climate is continental the moderating effect of the sea breezes play a positive role in the surrounding nature and ensure that grapes get the full benefit of a long, slow ripening process, which is typical of a cooler climate.

The vineyards lie between the plain and the hills, embedded in the territory of three demarcated DOC areas: Prosecco di Conegliano e Valdobbiadene, Piave and Colli di Conegliano e Valdobbiadene. The famous Prosecco grows in these areas, as well as single grape varietals such as Cabernet, Merlot and Pinot Grigio that produce important blends of both red and white grapes.

Agrotourism

By being located at the very centre of the *Marca Trevigiana,* a very suitable geographical position for travellers who wish to visit the Veneto region and its small historical cities famous for their art treasures and traditions, the management of the estate saw and invested in a future promise: agritourism.

Two old farmhouses immersed in the green countryside with a private ecological swimming pool are surrounded by hills, woods and vineyards and are available for guests to experience new senses of natural splendours.

These houses have been fully restored, respecting the traditional style and features of rural architecture. They are characterised by their old roof tiles and the traditional colours of the Collalto properties, with their yellow ochre and broad red stripes, while the interiors retain the wooden floors or handmade terracotta paving and ceilings with oak beams that recreate the atmosphere of a bygone age.

Tenuta di Collalto Estate is the ideal place to enjoy a holiday in contact with nature. Peaceful walks or rides on bicycles or horseback in the midst of woods, gently rolling hills and vineyards let people discover centuries-old magical, uncontaminated places. Visitors can enjoy and relax in and around an ecological, cement-free and chlorine-free swimming pool surrounded by lawns and trees.

Events and Congresses

Despite the damage suffered during WWI, the masterly restoration work conducted by Prince Manfredo has bought the Palazzo Odoardo inside the castle back to its ancient magnificence and it constitutes today a splendid location for exclusive

Tenuta di Collalto Estate

The famous Prosecco grows in these areas, as well as Cabernet, Merlot and Pinot Grigio.

Tenuta di Collalto Estate

receptions, private busines smeetings and important conferences. The charm of history and tradition combines indissolubly with impeccable service to make any event unique.

The spacious frescoed halls are equipped with the most advanced technology and highly qualified staff, thus constituting the ideal location for events, meetings or even weddings. San Salvatore Castle provides an extremely high standard of quality, and customized management of each event.

Interactive education programmes

Visitors and schools are able to experience art and nature by visiting Tenuta di Collato Estate. Educational programmes are organized to make adults and children aware of the cultural heritage.

Within its farm education project, Tenuta di Collalto offers groups of youngsters and students the chance of spending a day in the countryside, immersed in the wildlife and in contact with animals.

Expert restoration work has brought the building back to its former magnificence.

Tenuta di Collalto Estate

Tenuta di Collalto (Italy)

Castello of San Salvatore.

At the Casa Forcolera, choosing between various teaching laboratories, it is possible to discover the many details of the agricultural world. And a visit to the historical castle will make the day even more fascinating. Built in 1245 it includes marvellous works of art and architecture; young visitors can trace back the most important dates in the territory's history, from the Romans to the Middle Ages, from the Renaissance to the 17th century and the Great War.

Bio-Energy

The estate is implementing agri-environmental measures through good environmentally friendly practices and the creation of clean energy through bio-mass. The castle for example is partially heated by bio-mass energy. The estate is about to invest in bio-digestive energy created from ecological and animal waste.

CHALLENGES

Fields, pastures, woods, orchards, vineyards, livestock breeding, rural houses, etc. For many generations the Collalto family has demonstrated their love and passion for all of these. Our first thought is to show respect towards our ancestors who for centuries have cared for, protected and preserved these lands, now given to my sisters and me, with their charming landscape and environment and their efficient and functional organization.

Those same fields, woods, orchards, vineyards, livestock, rural houses, etc. are the pieces of the marvellous puzzle that our farm comprises nowadays. Each piece expresses its historical, environmental or agricultural value, all of which are brought together in a multifunctional business that simultaneously carries out more activities among its synergies.

With this large area of land, the estate's biodiversity, and the help of our husbands, today we are committed to making our territory emerge and develop its potential. Our basic principles are landscape and environmental conservation, animal welfare, and quality and security of food products. We plan to expand the variety of agricultural products, with vertical integration and the development of more local sales.

There is a trend toward, and a new demand for, authenticity and natural products being expressed by the consumers today. Direct sales are a strategic route to increase the added value of our products and transform the estate into an attractive tourist destination. Sales of beef, pork, salami, flour and walnuts are developing very well, and our goal in the near future is to establish a herd of water buffalo and adjacent cheese factory for the production of mozzarella and ricotta.

Our next challenge has to do with renewable energies. For this we are installing a plant for the production of bio-gas electric energy, transforming organic residues and cereals into electricity.

Nowadays it is not easy to be a farmer because there are thousands of problems, large and small, that one has to confront every day. These include staffing, equipment, pathologies, the market, and the weather (!), by which sometimes we even feel overwhelmed. Demands, statements, permissions, authorizations, etc. are necessary for the smallest initiative. Truly, only great passion and enthusiasm keep one moving forward.

We want always to look towards the future with regard to the market, the consumer, and the consumer's needs. It is certain that on the Collalto Estate there are still many important projects to undertake in order to pass on to our children a land that will always be loved.

Maria Trinidad di Collalto

Principessa Trinidad di Collalto
and her daugthers (from the left)
Isabella, Alessandra, Caterina,
Giuliana and Maria Trinidad.

TENUTA DI COLLALTO BELONGS TO:

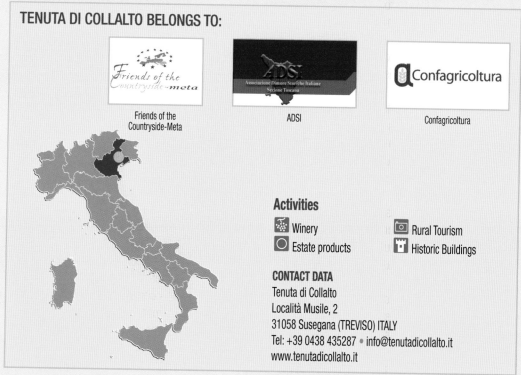

Friends of the
Countryside-Meta

ADSI

Confagricoltura

Activities

- Winery
- Estate products
- Rural Tourism
- Historic Buildings

CONTACT DATA
Tenuta di Collalto
Località Musile, 2
31058 Susegana (TREVISO) ITALY
Tel: +39 0438 435287 • info@tenutadicollalto.it
www.tenutadicollalto.it

Twickel

Atlantic

Location: Mostly in the community of Hof van Twente and partly in Hengelo, Borne, Almelo, Wierden and Haakbergen. Province of Overijssel, The Netherlands.
Surface: 4,000 ha.

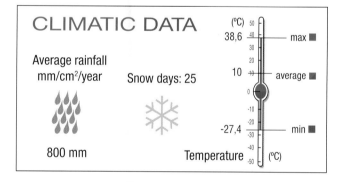

CLIMATIC DATA

Average rainfall
mm/cm²/year

Snow days: 25

800 mm

Temperature (°C)

(°C) 50
38,6 40
30
20
10 10 — average ■
0
-10
-20
-27,4 -30 — min ■
-40
-50

max ■

SUMMARY

Twickel Castle lies in the middle of a beautiful estate, reaching out over five parishes. The estate covers more than 4,000 hectares and includes 150 farms with agricultural land and meadows, interspersed with moorland, fens and woods. The oak woods have long been famous, not just because of their beauty, but also because of the quality of the wood they produce. The characteristic farms can be recognised by their black and white shutters.
The building of the present house goes back to 1551 when the front gable was built. In the 17th century a south wing was added and the main building enlarged. Both buildings on the forecourt were built in the 18th century and in 1847 a north wing was added. On the estate several buildings, most of them farms, were purchased. Among them other castles, like Weldam and Dieren. Nowadays some 250 other buildings like farms (both agricultural and dwellings), houses, restaurants, watermills, a saw-mill, schools, offices and a hospital are on the grounds of the state.

Twickel Estate

Panoramic view of the beautiful Twickel Castle.

The Baroness van Heeckeren van Wassenaer.

Twickel Estate

HISTORY

From 1347 until 1953 the estate belonged to successive members of the Van Twickelo, Van Raesfelt, Van Wassenaer Obdam and Van Heeckeren families. In 1953 the last private owner, Baroness van Heeckeren van Wassenaer, also Countess van Aldenburg Bentinck, set up a private foundation (the "Stichting Twickel") which took over the estate, including the house and all its contents. After her death in 1975 the other family estates came into possession of the same foundation.

In 1347 Herman van Twickelo bought a farmstead near Delden, and built a new house which formed the foundation of the present castle. After six generations of the van Twickelo dynasty, the last daughter, Agnes, married Goosen van Raesfelt. They built the present façade of the house and placed their coat of arms above the main entrance. For three generations the van Raesfelts took residence until Agnes van Raesfelt married the rich and powerful Count Jacob van Wassenaer whose descendants used the house as a summer residence while their professional duties kept them in The Hague or abroad. They brought in their properties in the West of the country which are still part of the Foundation.

Although they only resided temporarily at Twickel, they had a good eye for the region's economy. Marie Cornélie van Wassenaer, the last member of the Van Wassenaer dynasty was said to be the richest woman in the country when her father died. She

married Jacob Derk Carel van Heeckeren van Kell, who changed his name into van Heeckeren van Wassenaer. After his wife died childless, he married as his second wife Isabelle Sloet van Toutenburg who gave birth to three children. After the eldest son died rather young, his younger brother Rodolphe Frédéric succeeded him. He married his niece when he was already in his sixties. Marie Amélie Mechtild Agnès, Countess van Aldenburg Bentinck, was more than 20 years his junior. Unfortunately they did not have any children. After 14 years of marriage and, for almost 40 years, she lived in the house as a widow and last owner of the largest private estate in the Netherlands. She turned out to be a very keen and interested preservationist. One of her major challenges was to look ahead into the future and find ways and means to preserve the estate and its natural and cultural values after her death. With her decision to set up a foundation in 1953 she took a very important step towards safeguarding one of the last large private estates in the Netherlands. For more than 20 years, until her death in 1975, she was a passionate Chairman of the Board. In her last will she bequeathed the other properties to the Foundation which increased the total surface more than 60 square kilometres.

DESCRIPTION

The main area of the estate is situated in the eastern part of the country. The soil consists mainly of sand and partly of clay. This area consists primarily of wood and farmland and some untouched heath land. The land is used for agricultural, forestry and leisure purposes. Some parts around the castle are laid out as a park and gardens. Small streams and a canal run through the grounds with some water storage areas to retain the water in periods of drought.

There are three other estates that form part of the property. These are located in different parts of the country. In these areas more grassland is found, especially along the rivers (IJssel and Rhine) and their side arms. On the largest nature reserve in the Netherlands, the "Veluwe" (see the other estate in this book: De Hoge Veluwe) some hilly and wooded grounds are found, belonging to the "Hof te Dieren". The western parts of the estate are situated near

Wassenaar which has a large area of meadows next to the royal grounds and forms a "green lung" in the built-up area.

The most famous and extended garden surrounds Twickel Castle. This garden, which was designed and executed by many generations of people and garden designers from various countries over long periods of time, is an excellent example of garden creation through the ages dating from the 17th until the 21st century. On the north side of the house a French Neo-Baroque garden was designed by Marot with an Orangery built in the first half of the 19th century as a winter garden for (sub-) tropical plants, including 300 year old orange trees. The surrounding landscape garden dates from 1790 and was extended by J.D. Zocher in 1830. In 1888 the German landscape architect E. Petzold came to Holland from the Puckler Muskau Estate and carried out his last and major duty by extending the park around the castle into the extended grounds outside the fence. A special water park was created around 1870 by J.D. Zocher at some distance from the house, the Breeriet, now a nature reserve which is closed to the public. Unfortunately Petzold died before he could finish his work. The park remained unchanged for more than a century. At the end of the

Twickel Estate

20th century, one of the leading garden designers in the Netherlands, Michael van Gessel, was asked to finish and restore this project with modern additions. His masterplan took several years to be carried out and was completed by the end of 2008. Another fine garden is found at the Hof te Dieren in the province of Gelderland. After the purchase of this estate, in 1822, a garden was laid out in a romantic English landscape style by J.D. Zocher. Before Petzold came to Twickel he went to Dieren in 1877

Twickel Estate is situated very close to communities such as Almelo, Hengelo, Enschede, Borne, Hof van Twenthe and others.

The orangery, built in the first half of the 19th century as a winter garden for (sub-) tropical plants, including 300 year old orange trees.

ickel Estate

View of the west side of the Castle.

where he made some alterations which are still visible around the remains of the burned down house.

One last garden is found at Zuidwijk near Wassenaar, originally dating from the 18th century.

Some two hundred farms are dotted all around the estate, most of which can be found around Delden. At present, only one out of every three farms is still in use for agricultural purposes. These active farms took over the land of two other farms which were turned into residences for tenants. Many farms are listed, but even when they are not, they are preserved in a traditional way. Essential modern extensions, like huge stables or storage buildings and silos, are designed to blend in with the landscape and the adjacent buildings. Farms in other parts of the estate are more related to their areas but still easily recognised as part of the estate by their black and white shutters.

The Castle seen from the rock-garden.

The orangery is used as a tea room during the summer.

CHALLENGES OF THE FOUNDATION: AN OLD ESTATE IN A NEW WORLD

Continuity

It was the spirit of the last Baroness, who owned the estate privately and who was a widow without offspring, that solved the problem she had to face during her life: what should happen after her death which would put an end to the more than six centuries old unbroken family line. With the help of influential people in the field of cultural heritage she took the major decision to endow the estate to a private foundation: the "Stichting Twickel".

The guidelines were written down in the statutes of the foundation. The main target was to preserve the estate as a nature reserve and a cultural heritage for people who are interested in nature and culture and want to safeguard its historical value. The upkeep of Twickel's natural beauty and its typical landscape through the ages is the prime objective. The running of the estate is carried out by the "rentmeester" (Estate Manager) and almost 50 people from different backgrounds who work in different parts of the estate but who have one aim in common: preserving the estate.

Preservation

The landscape preservation policy is not hostile towards new additions. The values of the past are reinterpreted as they have been throughout the centuries. Restoration often includes modernisation. The farms which are used for agricultural purposes still keep their original exteriors but the tenants have also added modern stables. Old and new blend together in a manner that pleases both the farmer and the visitor. Extension of farmland is possible by merging together land from two or three farms and turning it into one single farm. The former farmhouses were transformed into very attractive places to live in. The park around the house has recently been restored by the landscape architect Michael van Gessel who kept close to the design of previous garden architects and who gave it his own modern touch by adding four bridges as modern artefacts in an old landscape topped by a traditional cupola, designed almost 200 years ago but never built until now. Other aims include restoring the relationship between Delden and Twickel (see below) and a reconstruc-

Twickel Estate

tion of the central building in the Hof te Dieren. Here, a new house will be (re)built in traditional style on the empty space where the previous house was burned down after the Second World War and which was demolished thereafter. The remaining estate was neglected for a long period and many plans were made but never executed. Now a complete recovery plan, both for the house and for the estate, is being worked on.

A separate walled vegetable garden was used for its original purpose during the time the house was lived in. After the last Baroness died in 1975, the garden was neglected for several years until a point where it was almost decided to turn it into a car park – behind the old wall – for the increasing number of cars of the many visitors. This plan was fortunately overruled by the enthusiasm of the gardeners on the estate who started a small scale restoration project in part of the old garden. Another part was rented out to a commercial gardener who acted as a "green" partner in the reuse of the plot. The old and severely damaged greenhouses were put into use again. Some of the Victorian greenhouses are being restored now and the smaller pits will be restored in the next few years. The vegetable garden is back in full swing with many volunteers working in shifts with great enthusiasm and with the professional help of the gardeners who share the same spirit. Vegetables are sold to the public twice weekly as are fresh cut flowers. Every autumn, a special Sunday Market is organised in the vegetable garden with small scale "green" activities (that fit in with the green surroundings within the wall). Next year, the last remaining part of the wall will be restored.

Some of the Victorian greenhouses are being restored now and the smaller pits will be restored in the next few years.

A variety of wildlife finds its natural habitat in different parts of the estate. Among the large game species are: roe, fox, wild boar and deer (in the Hof te Dieren only) and among the small game species are: pheasant, hare, rabbit, some species of wild ducks and geese and wood pigeon. Hunting is a regular activity but done within the strict boundaries of Dutch law. Some traditional hunting is done by the members of the Board, accompanied by employees, tenants and relatives. The estate is used for foxhunting parties as well. In this sport also traditional values are kept up, but within the strict rules of the law.

The Forestry Management has been modernised over the past decades. The timber is mainly conifer, oak, and other deciduous trees and all of these are timber-yielding species. A large part of the timber is sawn on the estate itself. An old fashioned and traditional sawmill is run by volunteers producing a variety of products made of wood. A modern wood factory next to the old mill demonstrates that old and new can co-exist quite happily. This factory sells increasing amounts of traditional wood of a very high quality, suited to many purposes such as different kinds of wood flooring. The development of this factory is significant and generates a profit for the whole estate.

As the map shows, the Twickel Estate is situated very close to communities like Almelo (72,000), Hengelo (81,500) and, further afield, Enschede (155,000) and the smaller town of Borne (21,000), the rural community of Hof van Twenthe (35,000) and others making up a total of about half a million people who consider the estate as their back-garden.

Although on the one hand the pressure of urbanisation plans is growing, the estate has, on the other hand, a major role in providing a green belt for many people. The pressure is felt most specifically in the parts of the estate to the east of the A35 motorway, linking Almelo, Borne and Hengelo to Enschede. These areas feel the pressure of urbanisation and, even more dangerously, industrialisation. Large industrial estates are planned for the area south of Almelo and west of Borne which border on the estate. This makes it necessary to be alert at all times and to keep continuous discussions going with both representatives of society and the local and regional authorities. A strategic and pro-active policy is put forward, which chal-

lenges strategic partners in the field to start with the plans and carry them out to satisfaction for all partners and people involved.

A good example of working the land in conjunction with nature conservation is the clay zone in the southernmost part of the Foundation, the Geldersche Waard, which lies between two old arms of the river Rhine. This area of 330 hectares is partly used for agricultural purposes by two large farms and partly worked for clay-mining for the brick industry. After the clay is extracted, the holes are filled with water creating a new natural habitat and new possibilities for flora and fauna. In the end all parties are happy with the new situation and Twickel has gained some income from the sale of the clay

On the Twickel Estate water retention is not a new phenomenon. In the 18th and 19th centuries,

Twickel Estate

it was necessary to let water flow into the Twickel canal during dry periods to keep it open to ships. Until the railway was constructed, it was the only link with the west of the country.

At the end of the 19th century water was needed again for drinking purposes (after the last Baron's brother died from typhus), as well as new sanitary installations in the house and fire extinguishers. For these purposes a water network was created and a watertower was built just outside the park, as a real "château d'eau". In the beginning of the 20th century the first Dutch environmental conflict against the industrial town of Enschede was won by the Baron. And at the end of the last century new water retention areas were created near the urban areas to collect rainwater in times of heavy rainfall. This area functions as a buffer between the built-up areas and the estate.

One of the issues about running a large estate is that the area covers many different local communities. The main part of the Twickel Estate lies within six local communities, each one of them with its own policy, priorities, strategy, rules, subsidies, etc. The other parts of the estate are located in another seven local communities scattered over three different provinces and even two countries (Germany). Having to deal with so many authorities and institutions makes many things much more complicated. Some improvements were reached in 2001 when five small rural communities merged into a new community named Hof van Twente. Twenty percent of the surface of this new community is in the hands of private estates; Twickel itself covers 10%.

The building of the present house goes back to 1551. New buildings were built in the 17th, 18th and 19th centuries.

The old sawmill,
still in use by volunteers.

Profitabilty

Management of visitors to the park

The park around the house is open to the public in the summer season from May until October and attracts about 15,000 visitors a year. A special public entrance has been created as well as a large car park – catering for around 200 cars – which features as an element of the new layout of the park. Three ladies work in the department of "Public Activities" answering questions and arranging group visits, mainly for the garden, but also for the house during some weeks of the year. Furthermore, a group of enthusiastic volunteers work in the garden and give guided tours. Visitors are free to walk around on their own and the team of (four) gardeners are most willing to answer their questions. The amount of visitors does not create many difficulties as the park is quite large (25 hectares), but car parking both for visitors to the garden and other people visiting the grounds is an increasing problem. The parking charge is only one Euro (to create a fund for the upkeep of the park), but nevertheless it is the case that people try to park elsewhere to avoid paying.

In 2008 a new and sophisticated shop was opened at the entrance of the park. The main purpose of this shop was to create a market for farm products from the estate (such as cheese, meat, wine, etc.). A larger shop now sells everything related to the estate. A special design was made for products such as table linen, oven gloves, egg warmers etc. Books on different subjects (history, garden design, flora and fauna, cooking, walking) are on sale. Some products from the sawmill are also sold here.

At the beginning of the seventies a protest group (who were against the then newly planned motorway crossing the estate) evolved into a large society of Friends of Twickel with about 2,000 members, after successfully achieving their aim. With this society a shared newsletter was issued 17 years ago. This has developed into a glossy, colourful quarterly magazine of 24 pages publishing all kinds of facts and news about the estate and the people who live and work on it. A voluntary group of people edit the magazine and there is no need for any advertisements.

An important amount – about 34% – of the income of the estate is generated by renting out the buildings on about 65 farms. These 200 houses and farms are rented by people who consider themselves part of a large family. In many cases the farm remains in one family over many generations. Houses are rented to employees, and farms which are not used in the traditional way are 'sold' without the land. Some buildings are rented out as offices or schools. Among them is the American school in Wassenaar near The Hague. On the estate there are several hotels, restaurants, inns, pancake restaurants with different classifications and some of the farms offer "bed & breakfast".

One farm and its grounds are in use by a golf club. This club was originally located between Hengelo and Enschede but did not have enough space for an 18 hole course. After some negotiations it was decided that a part of the estate could be used for a new course which would create a good balance between nature and sports. Additionally, some sports fields are found on the estate as well, which all add to the considerable recreational value the estate offers to a large area and to many people.

RECOVERY OF THE HISTORICAL LINK BETWEEN DELDEN AND TWICKEL

When the first house at Twickel was built in 1347 the nearby settlement small, then called Delden, had obtained its 'town rights' 14 years previously, which allowed it to build a wall and to dig a moat. The course of this wall can still be found in the circular "Noordwal" and "Zuidwal"; the canal around it was situated between this street and the parallel "Noorderhagen" and "Zuiderhagen" and beyond it

From May to October the park attracts about 15,000 visitors per year.

were nothing other than little private vegetable gardens. The house of Twickel was built less than 500 metres from the centre of this little town of Delden.

Although the town did not grow very extensively, the small area between the town and the estate remained a green buffer due to the vegetable plots, until the seventies, when unfortunately a much-needed by-pass was planned to run between the two. Many of the objections were ignored as the only alternative around the southern edge of the town was too expensive because of the need to build two bridges or tunnels. Only when, some years later, a motorway became the preferred option instead of this by-pass, which was meant to connect the nearby urban areas of Hengelo and Enschede to the west of the country, were plans made to make this intervention as least obtrusive as possible. To create this, a plan was designed - by landscape architect Michael van Gessel – to lower the surface of the road to such an extent that cars (and vans?) are no longer visible from the grounds above. This also creates opportunities to reconnect parts that had previously been connected, by bridges for pedestrians and cyclists. By carrying out this project, Twickel and Delden can be reconnected after a period of 35 years. Subsidies have been requested to turn this into reality, and possibilities present themselves through the National "Belvedere Project" for public-private cultural environmental planning projects.

Both the (ca. 7000) inhabitants of Delden and the people working for the Twickel Foundation are striving to convince politicians to reinstate the historical link between Delden and Twickel that has existed for more than 600 years. After a very short separation of less than 40 years, Delden and Twickel will embrace the future together.

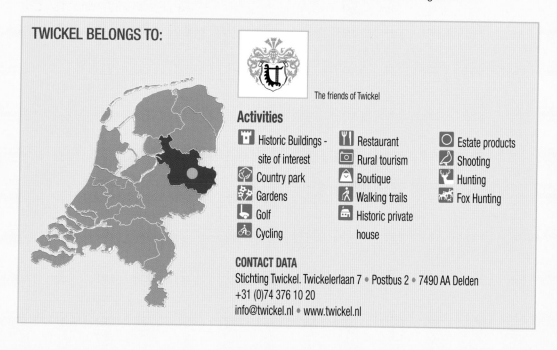

TWICKEL BELONGS TO:

The friends of Twickel

Activities

- 🏰 Historic Buildings - site of interest
- 🌳 Country park
- 🌷 Gardens
- ⛳ Golf
- 🚴 Cycling
- 🍴 Restaurant
- 📷 Rural tourism
- 🏠 Boutique
- 🚶 Walking trails
- 🧹 Historic private house
- ⚪ Estate products
- 🦫 Shooting
- 🐾 Hunting
- 🦊 Fox Hunting

CONTACT DATA

Stichting Twickel. Twickelerlaan 7 • Postbus 2 • 7490 AA Delden
+31 (0)74 376 10 20
info@twickel.nl • www.twickel.nl

THE PRIVATE OFFER

Thierry de l'ESCAILLE
CEO & Secretary General

Businesses and private properties are offering the framework for a prosperous countryside all over Europe, with a balanced approach to social, environmental and economic considerations. It is not one at the expense of the others; it is a global approach which allows the countryside to develop its own richness and to be a unique asset for society as a whole. The livelihood of the countryside is only possible because public actions and expectations are implemented by numerous private managers delivering this service. It is our belief that the future of Europe's countryside is largely dependent on the individual management decisions of its millions of entrepreneurs and landowners. Burdensome regulations make little sense.

Throughout European history these regulations have demonstrated their total inefficiency whereas private enterprise and property are the best guarantee for economic, social and environmental protection and development, especially at a time when we are facing the first food crisis in decades. As a matter of fact the current discussions about halting the loss of biodiversity or mitigating climate change are leading reasonable people to understand that without the voluntary contribution of millions of European landowners and rural users it will be impossible to make a success of these crucial challenges.

As a landowner, on the one hand it is relevant for my ability to produce that I keep my freedom of action as flexible as possible; on the other hand, due to my commitment to my corporate social responsibility, I like to see my management being recognised, as long as it will not set my activities in aspic and as a consequence destroy the nature which the public authority was hoping to protect.

We recognise that without land management, society and nature are in trouble. This works in both directions: land management and society need nature; and in crowded areas such as ours, nature needs the care of land management, farming and society. We are seeking to jolt the already

outdated philosophy that the best way to tackle environmental problems is through more and more regulation. We suggest it isn't, and that a far more effective way is to engage all the good volunteers from the private sector. It is no coincidence that in 2007 the ELO was officially recognised as an environmental NGO by the European Commission.

The role of the private manager as the key provider of public environmental services in the countryside has, at last, been publicly acknowledged at the EU level. Combined with the tremendous developments in food processing, retailing and food service, European land managers can satisfy the coming world food deficit. However, not surprisingly, we have to recognise that modern science-based agriculture may have resulted in some loss of biodiversity and some damage to our natural resources of soil, water and air. This sets an even greater challenge for modern land managers. We are asked to continue to innovate and produce the high quality food required, and at the same time to reduce pollution, as well as to increase the delivery of the environmental services of biodiversity and landscape. In addition to this, society expects us to produce more of Europe's energy supplies without creating exaggerated tensions on the world food markets, and maybe even some additional flood protection and carbon sequestration too! Just to make this more interesting there is a drift in agricultural policy towards reducing the public financial support that this sector has enjoyed for the last half century and to expose Europe to more competition from imports from areas of the world which appear to have less concern for the environment.

These are indeed major challenges, and it is clear that they can only be met by the efforts of private land managers working within a public policy framework suited for the task. To tackle those challenges we advocate that one should initially understand three considerations. Firstly, land management is like no other sector of the economy; it provides a complex and constantly changing balance of private goods and public environmental services. Secondly, these activities are spatially defined and climatically and biologically determined. Each plot of land is a unique mix of soil, water, climatic and ecological characteristics and is set into business structures defined by the local social and legal structures. Thirdly, private businesses deliver both private and public goods, and because of this they should secure some payment for a small part of the total value of the public goods that they deliver. At least seven principles should underlie sustainable land management and should guide public food and environmental policies. They are:

1. AN INTER-GENERATIONAL PERSPECTIVE

Land management is an inter-generational business and sustainability is also an inter-generational concept. The effects of human activity on the environment must be viewed over a long timeframe, because the effects of such activity may take a long time to appear, and adaptation also takes time. We recognise that cars, refrigerators and houses are now far more energy efficient than their forbears. Land management businesses display a long-term view in three key ways:

- First, continuity of management allows land managers to adapt to current and expected change, in new technology, in public policies and to wider environmental or economic developments, such as climate change;
- Second, land managers have an interest in conserving the resources of soil, water, biodiversity and landscape which support their businesses;
- Third, they are often more prepared to invest in the long-term, for example in forests and landscapes or farm buildings, with benefits for succeeding generations.

2. A SCIENCE-BASED APPROACH

Standards of rigour should apply not only to scientific research but also to its interpretation.

The tendency for politicians and the media to view the countryside as a refuge from the modern world may inhibit the desirable application of science or technology to rural areas.

Authoritative reassurances from scientists to allay an alarmist news story are not as newsworthy as the original story, nor are reports that indicate that aspects of our lives are getting better, not worse. The accurate communication of sound science to land managers, politicians and the public is as important as the science itself. The science on which environmental policy depends must look beyond the physical world and test the economic and social effects of policies, to see which policies produce environmental benefit while working in sympathy with society and business. Risk assessment, necessitated by the uncertainties of biological and economic relationships, is important for land managers and policy makers.

Too readily falling back on the precautionary principle denies an assessment of risk (this incompatibility was recently demonstrated in the revision of the Pesticides Directive), and is an unreliable policy tool.

3. VOLUNTARY PARTICIPATION

Conservation is most effective when land managers share the goal to tackle environmental problems, help to propose solutions and participate voluntarily in implementation. Information, education, advice and training are the key. Land managers may then begin to see benefits from participation. One attraction of a voluntary initiative to minimise pesticide usage is the prospect of cost reductions. Governments are tempted by one-size-fits-all regulation, but that is a blunt instrument to deal with diffuse pollution which is often the problem for agriculture. Here the willing participation of practitioners is needed, not least because regulatory costs of monitoring and policing diffuse pollution are prohibitive. Delivery of positive environmental services, such as biodiversity and landscape management, also requires motivation, care and local knowledge – these are not deliverable by administrative order.

4. PROPORTIONALITY

Regulation to deal with environmental problems should be scaled in relation to the problem. For example the costs of removing the last traces of a pollutant often rise to levels far greater than the damage they cause. Proportionality also requires the burden of regulation to be in line with the capacity of businesses, especially small or micro-businesses, to cope. Otherwise, regulation will have the effect of accelerating the process of business size enlargement, with consequences for consumer choice and, in some circumstances, the environment. Agreement on standards should be reached at the appropriate regional, national or international level, depending upon the tradability or cross-border effects of the goods or services in question. Otherwise regulation of local production will lead to displacement by imports from less regulated sources abroad.

5. A DECENTRALISED APPROACH

The ELO's perception of environmental problems is that they are, at root, the result of missing markets and market failure. The aim should be to assign property rights (where they do not already exist) and incentives which induce behaviour in the desired direction – reducing environmental "bads" and increasing environmental "goods". The idea is to use elements of the tax and incentives or payments systems to "correct" for the divergence between private and social costs or benefits.

For this to work, the measure(s) must be targeted and must be the most cost-effective option, and any process or material to be taxed must be reasonably sensitive to price. Examples are the agri- and forest environment schemes which are becoming a larger part of EU rural policy and which pay land managers to deliver public environmental benefits. Another possible example could be relief from VAT on the maintenance of historic buildings, where there is public benefit from private heritage property.

6. WORKING WITH NATURAL CYCLES

Some aspects of modern farming have come to resemble industrial practices in their linear reliance on external inputs of renewable and non-renewable resources (such as fossil fuels and crop protection products) and creation of waste. Land man-

agers are aware of natural cycles such as those of the seasons, water, carbon, nitrogen and other nutrients associated with crop growth and soil fertility.

The natural carbon cycle creates no waste. CO_2 taken from the atmosphere as plants grow is returned when these materials are consumed and oxidised by animals, fungi and microbes, but we need to know more about man's impact on the carbon cycle. In principle, food production could be part of this carbon cycle, but the part of the cycle where dead matter is returned to the soil as organic matter tends to be overlooked. Disposal of organic matter away from soil, e.g. to landfill, incinerators or sewage works, disrupts the carbon cycle. Modern processes could be brought more into line with natural cycles by incentivising farmers to incorporate organic waste into the soil, or the use of biomass for heat and power generation, or biogas to deal with animal waste.

7. PROPERTY RIGHTS AND RESPONSIBILITIES

Some people suggest that the right of private owners to enjoy and exploit their property will result in environmental degradation. The ELO argues the reverse. An important historical lesson from the 20th century is that for most purposes and most land, private property rights proved superior to collectivised property. That is not to say that owners of property are never responsible for environmental harm. Pollution from run-off from fertilisers and crop protection chemicals and inappropriate tillage leading to soil erosion are examples of environmental "bads"; their cost is externalised, that is, borne by society generally rather than their own business. Also, some land managers have failed to supply the environmental "goods" that they could, such as desirable biodiversity and landscape features, because there has been no general market to reward them for the costs involved. However, property rights can be developed to tackle this problem. Tradable emissions rights are an example. They can bring down overall levels of pollution, but also reward efficiency and innovation, unlike monolithic regulation.

The challenge is to harness the behaviour that protects property rights at a time when new challenges such as the food and environmental crisis are arising. But let us be clear that the economic, social and political framework has dramatically changed over the past half century.

THE CASE FOR AN EU FOOD AND ENVIRONMENTAL SECURITY POLICY AMID WORRYING GLOBAL TRENDS

There are mounting concerns about global trends in the world. Corrado Pirzio-Biroli, the President of ELO's Consultative Committee and the CEO of the RISE Foundation, identifies nine major challenges:

1. Population growth: 75 million people more per annum (210,000 a day), 9.4bn people by 2050 with 60% living in urban areas, 3bn with less than $2/day

2. Growing demand for crop products (cereals, plant fat, proteins), and animal feed as meat consumption grows with living standards

3. Growing demand for energy, including bioenergy based on renewable raw materials

4. Globalization and urbanization: production moves to the most competitive regions, trade grows faster than production, trade tends to become more open, but also more and more managed, becoming less predictable in food crises

5. Climate change: agriculture contributes to emissions, but can both suffer and benefit from changing climates

6. Increasing market volatility due to yield fluctuations, food market segmentation, end stock fluctuations, input and output price volatility and €/$ exchange rate volatility as food balances worsen in time, and consumer sensitivity for food safety, quality and price increases

7. Growing public interest in agricultural public services such as food and feed, rural landscapes maintenance, environmental protection, animal welfare, value for money.

8. Social problems such as aging of farmers, farm successions, competition for land

9. Uncertainties with the timing and application of innovations such as biotechnology (GMOs, nanotechnology), precision farming, carbon sequestration, information technology, wood energy.

We might be entering the worst food crisis since World War II, which is accompanied by growing environmental stress. Moreover, climate change is not only happening, but it also intensifies the food and environmental challenges, in particular in the developing countries, the majority of which are net importers of food, catching up with western consumption patterns and loosing agricultural land and top soil. As they seek to avoid food riots which in turn feed internal insecurity and political opposition, these governments act to freeze internal retail food prices on staples, slash import duties, and/or resort to export taxes or embargoes, and/or food subsidies, and cause major budgetary costs and foreign debts. What happens with these countries, their soils and forests, their rural economies and their budgets will have an even greater impact on the world than what happens with ours.

There is a distinct risk that Malthus will eventually be proven right. We must therefore ask whether and how the world's farmers and agricultural industry can double food production by 2030 to meet world demand using less water and less energy and slashing gas emissions. To do this it is essential to protect the long-term food production capacity of the EU without avoidable environmental degradation. Our leaders in Europe will have to recognize the fundamental role that Europe has to play in feeding the world in the context of food scarcity. Our land managers have a crucial role to play and have the right to ask how they can contribute to meeting the world's food demand, to saving energy and water, conserving and caring for the environment and Europe's cultural heritage and providing for economic growth and social sustainability while at the same time surviving the attacks against the CAP which continue to grow. Advocates of scrapping the CAP ignore the risks this would involve. These include production intensification with increased pollution, land abandonment with rural desertification (nature needs to be cared for) and reduced farm output, accelerated urbanization with additional infrastructural and environmental costs, potential difficulties for the internal market, and higher world food prices with serious humanitarian, economic and political consequences. The same holds for the end of agricultural support elsewhere in the world. But, after the Health Check, CAP reform needs to continue step-by-step after 2013.

As mentioned before, European agriculture is becoming even more market driven and turning into a production and services industry. However, due to the fact that the delivery of environmental services by landowners who are in farming or forestry is largely unpaid, these services provide too few "goods" and too many "bads". Appropriate tools need therefore to be put in place to address these widespread market failures.

There is a case for a European Food & Environmental Security Policy; it is based on the Single Market, on evolving EU food and environment policies, on environmental Directives, on the Göteborg declaration and the Lisbon process, and on the cross-border character of nature and climate change. The objectives of such a policy should be to provide incentives for private sector rural resource managers to produce socially optimal quantities of nutritious, high quality food and fibre, renewable energy, biodiversity, landscape, heritage, and soil, water and air management.

Agricultural services such as forestry need to look at new materials for industrial purposes and bio-energy, provided it is competitive and without additional ad hoc subsidies or import protection beyond current levels. Food processing and the food chain require further innovations, modernization, vertical integration, promotion, marketing, and protection of origin. Anti-trust policies, producer cooperatives, farmers' markets, direct sales and other measures should help farmers to recapture a higher share of the final product price.

Such a new policy is a global responsibility of the European Union and other countries that are relatively less affected and better placed to deal with climate change, and have the financial means to lead by example.

The process towards a new approach cannot start from a budgetary framework. Europe must firstly agree upon the challenges that European and world agriculture, farmers and land managers, food industry and the agrifood system, and the rural areas will face over the coming years. Secondly, we must establish the tools to meet those challenges, starting from those that exist, but adding others to them. Only after all that can we assess the budgetary means required. These means no-

tably concern Budget Heading 2 on the Protection and Management of Natural Resources. They need to respond to the fact that the CAP and environmental policy face bigger challenges in the first half of this century for an enlarging EU and a more interdependent world community than they did in the last century

Facing a future so full of uncertainties, agricultural policies will have to be adapted accordingly. In 2008, the French Presidency already tried to box in the status-quo asking all EU members to confirm the treaty-based principles of the CAP: financial solidarity, unified market and Community preference. It failed to get general support. Although the Treaty cannot be changed, the status-quo is not an option. Nor can we expect radical departures from it. Non-distorting farm subsidies will have to stay if food scarcity is not to worsen. Southern hemisphere countries will have to introduce land reforms allowing the poor to accede to the land, and adopt more appropriate food pricing policies. And Europe should put into place a European Food & Environmental Security Policy.

We send out a call for new policy objectives for the next half century, and for special action affecting food supplies and environmental improvements. The demands on what we want from our land managers are increasing. They have a critical role in helping to secure food and environmental security. There are pervasive market failures surrounding these activities, and dealing with these market failures is part of EU policy. This requires the further development of the CAP, as well as the budgetary resources appropriate to meet the food and environmental challenges and produce the required security on both accounts. Wider and more challenging tasks cannot be met with shrinking budgetary means or even by all kinds of burdensome regulations.

The European Union could not achieve its goal without its landowners managing the countryside. They are ready to deliver it but expect the appropriate tools.

ACKNOWLEDGEMENTS

I would like to thank the invaluable help of a group of enthusiastic collaborators without whose work and patience this book would never have seen the light. They have been the co-authors, they have visited the estates that are included in this piece of work, and they have met with the landowners, the managers and the administrators. They have collected information, material and photographs. They have helped in the drafting of texts, the translations, the resulting corrections, and their help has proven to be decisive in the composition and design of the chapters of this book.

To all these people I would like to convey my most profound gratitude.

THE TEAM: AUTHORS OF THIS PUBLICATION

- Baragaño, Professor José. *Drawing up of the texts; Translations; Corrections and Illustrations.*
- Hernández, D.ª Paqui. *Page layout design; Printing and Editing.*
- Janssens de Bisthoven, Guillaume. *Coordination; Visiting estates; Drafting texts; Photography; Translations and Corrections.*
- Joicey, Lord. *Translation; and final corrections.*
- Otero, Professor Carlos. *Editor; Visiting estates; Texts and Direction.*
- Pavía, Ing. Patricia. *General coordination; Translations; Drafting texts and corrections.*
- Ropero, José Mª. *Page layout design and Printing.*

My sincerest thanks for the advice, direction, support and inestimable help of this committee; they helped define the content and the philosophy which formed the foundations of this book.

PUBLICATION COMMITTEE

- Carvalho, João. *Director ANPC Portugal.*
- De l'Escaille de Lier, Thierry. *CEO & Secretary General of ELO and Friends of the Countryside.*
- Grotenfelt, Karl. *Former President of ELO.*
- Otero, Carlos. *Editor, President of IIMA.*
- Pavía, Patricia. *General Coordination, IIMA.*
- Sayer, Michael. *Vice President of Friends of the Countryside.*
- Visconti, Giuseppe. *President of Friends of the Countryside.*

PARTICULAR HELP

Special tribute must go to those who have helped us find the best models and who tried, in selfless manner, to support us in this sometimes difficult project.

- Adelswärd, Johan
- De Dorlodot, Jehanne
- Espirito Santo de Brito e Cunha, João Filipe
- De Radigues, Francois
- Di Marzio, Gabriella
- García de Bobadilla, Francisco
- Mahé, Jean-Francois
- Mikkelsen, Poul
- Radice-Fossati, Federica
- Romero, José Maria
- Von Dallwitz, Wolfgang

We have tried our utmost to correct, check and check again so that the book is as close to perfect as possible. However, with all publications some errors will inevitably remain. As a result, we would greatly appreciate any communication regarding any errors that have crept through, so as to avoid them in the next edition.

Correcting such texts requires a painstaking amount of concentration. Therefore, we would like to thank all the landowners for having taken the time to read and reread the chapter concerning their respective Estates. Again without their contributions, such a project could never have been completed.

CORRECTIONS:

We wish to particularly thank the following for their involvement, interest, time, patience, and their subsequent corrections:

- Baragaño, Professor José
- Cranbrook, The Countess Caroline
- Joicey, Lord
- Sayer, Michael

FRENCH EDITION:

The French edition equally required a tremendous amount of effort, and because of this, we want to thank our collaborators, who worked tirelessly for months on end to complete this edition. They became integral to the completion of this book, and to them we are eternally grateful.

- Goupil de Bouillé, Clotilde
- Janssens de Bisthoven, Guillaume

ILLUSTRATIONS:

Particular thanks must go to all the landowners for their generous contribution with graphic documentation, and their historic, and sometimes very personal photographs. Through them, we can see the Estates in different timelines; as a result these contributions have given life and colour to the book. Our thanks must also go to Thomas de Dorlodot, whom, with his new and innovative techniques, gave us a way to discover unprecedented images "from above" for many of the estates.

Credit must be given to Spanish photographer José Luis Rodríguez, winner of the Veolia Environment Wildlife Photographer of the Year prize 2009, attributed by the Museum of Natural History of London and the BBC Wildlife Magazine, who gave us a few astonishing photographs.

For the original drawings, we could count on Professor José Baragaño, of the Madrid Polytechnic University, who was the author for nearly all the illustrations in this book.

Finally, my biggest thanks go to all the landowners who kindly took the time to open their doors, their archives, their libraries, their personal memories, their secrets, their fears and doubts, and their willingness to share with us the beauty of their properties. This book is for all of you; it shows a segment of society which is seldom understood, a part of society which actively protects Europe's natural heritage and cultural history.

Furthermore, as well as their written contributions many allowed this book to come to life through financial donations. To all of them, as well as to their closest collaborators, all of whose names are mentioned hereafter, our utmost gratitude. If there are any missing names in this acknowledgement, you have my sincerest apologies. However, be safe in the knowledge that you have contributed to a book that has been drafted with love and care. A book that outlines the families and people that love Europe's countryside, and will eternally strive to protect and preserve it for future generations.

Landowners and collaborators

- Abelló, Juan
- Acha, Ignacio
- Adelsward, Gustaf
- Adelsward, Johan
- Afonso, Tino
- Alaniz, Hugo
- Amman, Francesco
- Amman, Saverio
- Amuedo, José Miguel
- Amonn, Thomas
- Anderson, Will
- Arribas, Jesús
- Asenjo, José Luis
- Ateca, Daniel
- Avila, Domenica
- Baragaño, José
- Bauters, Astrid
- Beusekom, Jan
- Blanco, José María
- Boers, Bart
- Bonzi, Emilia
- Brambilla, Lucía
- Brigatti, Nicola
- Budniok, Denise-Marie
- Budniok, Marie-Alice
- Budniok, Michel
- Buttiens, An
- Cabrera, María Luz
- Carvalho, João
- Casalini, Leonardo
- Castro, María Antonia
- Cavendish Grosvenor, Gerald
- Champalimaud, Luis
- Chick, Catherine
- Coimbra, Susana
- Colfox, Philip
- Collalto, Maria-Trinidad
- Colloredo-Mannsfeld, Jerome
- Colthurst, Charles
- Corsini, Jacobo
- Cranbrook, Caroline
- Cuenca, José
- De Brito, Ana
- De Castro, Mónica
- De Corte, Pieter
- De Dorlodot, Jehanne
- De Dorlodot, Thomas
- De la Esperanza, Pilar
- De Lannoy, Stephanie
- De l'Escaille, Gabriel
- De l'Escaille, Inès
- De l'Escaille, Robert
- De l'Escaille, Thierry
- De Limburg Stirum, Francois
- De Looz Corswarem, Raphael
- De Meeus d'Argenteuil, Arnau
- De Radigues, Francois
- De Valroger, Hortense
- Del Amo, Sonia
- Delgado, Nuria
- Di Marzio, Gabriella
- Dib, Youssef
- Dimsdale, Tom
- Draycott, Roger
- Dulac, Philippe
- Dupeux, Delphine
- D'Ursel, Ghislain
- Ebner, Michl
- Efstathiadis, Nicholas
- Egloffstein, Albrecht
- Ehrnrooth, Kari
- Emsens, Jacques
- Emsens, Stanislas
- Espirito Santo, Manuel Fernando
- Espirito Santo de Brito e Cunha, João Filipe
- Fassati, Leonardo
- Fernández de Arévalo, Francisco
- Fernández Prieto, Alfredo
- Flores, Carlos
- Flores, Samuel
- Fournier, Julien
- Frankenhaeuser, Jacob
- Frankenhaeuser, Peggy
- Frankenhaeuser, Thomas
- Frías, Juan Luis
- Frías, Juan Luis Jr.
- Frías, Marcos
- Gabrielsson, Conny
- García de Bobadilla, Francisco
- García Oliver, Pedro
- García Paadin, Fina
- García-Morales, Alfonso
- García-Morales, Carlos
- Goffinet, Francois
- Gómez Torres, Alfredo
- Goulão, Francisco
- Goupil de Bouillé, Clotilde
- Grant, Jo
- Grotenfelt, Albert
- Grotenfelt, Karl
- Guerrero, Martín
- Gullick, Tom
- Gutiérrez, Félix
- Gutiérrez, Julio
- Hardegg, Maximilian
- Harmelink, Ilse
- Hernández, Paqui
- Hromadko, Ladislav
- Hromadko, Peter
- Janssens, Guillaumme
- Joicey, James
- Keane, Charles
- Kinsky, Constantin
- Knops, Louise
- Kostopoulos, Konstantin
- Krejcárek, Pavel
- Landaluce, Francisco
- Landaluce, Francisco Jr.
- Landaluce, Ignacio
- Law, Frank
- Leclerc, Thibault
- Ledesma, María
- Leidekker, Jacob
- Lema, Lino
- Lewis, Sandy
- Ligero, Teresa
- Lobbas, Eija
- Lobo, Mariola
- Luengo, Richard
- Mahé, Jean Francois
- Malbezin, Antoine
- Maldonado, Patricia
- Marugán, Begoña
- Maza, Pancho
- Mejías, Cristian
- Melgarejo, Antonio
- Melviez, David
- Meunier, Velerian
- Mikkelsen, Paul
- Mikosz, Emanuelle
- Miller, Marysia
- Montfort, Sylviane
- Movaghar, Darius
- Natta, Francesco
- Natta, Giuseppe
- Neipperg, Katharina
- Noriega, Ariel
- Norval, Andrew
- Oliveira e Sousa, Eduardo
- Orlov, Mikhail
- Overmars, Anne-Marie
- Padín, Raquel
- Papadopoulos, Stelios
- Pavía, Patricia
- Pazos, Cándido
- Pérez Garvey, José María
- Pirzio-Biroli, Corrado
- Prossen, Barbara
- Quaranta, Francesco
- Quarin, Hugo
- Radice-Fossati, Federica
- Radice-Fossati, Federico
- Rancken, Kristoffer
- Redondo, Víctor
- Reginster, Maxime
- Risom, Jens
- Rivero, Joaquín
- Rocha, Ana
- Rodríguez, José Luis
- Rogers, Gary
- Romero, José Mª
- Ropero, José Mª
- Ruiz de la Torre, Francisco
- Sáinz de Vicuña, Álvaro
- Salgado, Antonio
- Sánchez Lodares, Alejandro
- Sánchez Muliterno, Eduardo
- Sánchez Muliterno, Juan
- Sánchez, Rafael
- Sayer, Michael
- Schiansky, Jethro
- Scholma, Enno
- Sinn, Hermann
- Soares, Antonio
- Solvay, Denis
- Soria, Alberto
- Soria, Alberto Jr.
- Soria, Luz María
- Speeckaert, Eric
- Strulens, Mark
- Süsskind, Gustav
- Süsskind, Sabine
- Svenle, Elna
- Tatin, Laurent
- Tercero, José María
- Terry, Fernando
- Thompson, James
- Tornerhjelm, Rudolf
- Vaisberg, Elodie
- Van der Loo, Fanny
- Van der Stegen, Sophie
- Van Verschuer, Frans
- Van Verschuer, Nathalie
- Van Voorst tot Voorst, Seger E.
- Vara de Rey, Ana
- Vinhas, Mario
- Visconti, Giuseppe
- Von Abendroth, Friedrich
- Von Dallwitz, Wolfgang
- Von Limburg Stirum, Fredrik
- Vranken, Poul
- Wachtmeister, Claes
- Wahlroos, Bjorn
- Weld, James
- Wittouck, Flore
- Zafora, José Manuel
- Zu Stolberg-Stolberg, Christoph

Carlos Otero
Editor

REFERENCES

- **Agger, P.** 2002. *Denmark Geography and the Environment. Preservation and Nature Conservation.* Royal Danish Ministry of Foreign Affairs. Denmark.
- **Anonyme.** 1932. *Bezirksamt Weibenburg i.B.* München und seine Mätressen (Manuskript). Pappenheim o.J.
- **Aronson.** 1968. The tragedy of the common. *Science,* Vol. 162, n.ª 3859, pp. 1243-1248.
- **Bailey, T.** *et al.* 2003. *Agriculture and Environment.* ELO Booklet.
- **Bailie, J.** *et al.* 2005. *The 2004 IUCN Red List of threatened species. A global species assessment: executive summary.* IUCN.
- **Bart, F.G.** 1991. *Insects and Flowers.* Princenton University Press. Princenton, N.J.
- **Birdlife International.** 2004. *Birds in the European Union: a status assessment.* Wageningen. The Netherlands.
- **Bolkovic,** *et al.* 1995. *Food habits of the tree-banded armadillo (Xenartha: dasypodidal) in the Dru Chaco.* Argentina. *J. Mammal,* 76(4): 1199-1204.
- **Boudet, G.** 1995. *Le sel de midi au XIX ème siècle. La reinassance des salines du midi de la France.* Juprimerie A. Robert. Marseille, France.
- **Britt, C., A. Mole, F. Kirkham** and **A. Terry.** 2003. *The herbicide handbook: guidance on the use of herbicides on nature conservation site.* English Natura. Peterborough.
- **Canevari, M.** and **C. Fernández Balboa.** 2003. *Cien mamíferos argentinos.* Ed. Albatros. Buenos Aires.
- **Castel, A.** *et al.* 1993. *Guía de los mamíferos en libertad de España y Portugal.*
- **Chévez, J.C.** 1999. *Los que se van.* Ed. Albatros. Buenos Aires.
- **Costa, H.** *et al.* 2000. *Nomes portugueses das aves do Paleartico Occidental.*
- **Cramp, S.** 1998. *The Complete Birds of the Western Paleartic on CD-ROM.* Oxford University Press. Oxford.
- **Davey, P.** *et al.* 2002. *Holburn Moss SSSI & Ford Moss SSSI/SAC.* English Nature. Northumberland.
- **De la Vega, S.** 2005. *Invasión en Patagonia.* Contacto Silvestre Ediciones. Buenos Aires.
- **Del Moral, J.C.** and **R. Martí.** 2001. *El buitre leonado en la Península Ibérica.* Seo Birdlife. Madrid.
- **Delibes, M., A. Rodríguez,** and **P. Ferreras.** 2000. *Action Plan for the Conservation of the Iberian Lynx in Europe.* Consejo de Europa.
- **Dellafiore, C.** and **N. Maceira.** (Eds.). 2001. *Los ciervos autóctonos de la Argentina y la acción del hombre.* Grupo Abierto de Comunicación. Buenos Aires, Argentina.
- **Di Marzio,** *et al.* 1996-2002. *La Cassinazza, comprensorio agromedioambientale.* Cassinazza di Baselica-Giussago, Pavia, Italy.
- **European Commission.** 2003. *Sustainable Forestry and the European Union.* European Commission. Louxembourg.
- **Fevbre, N.** 1989. Le salin d'Aigues-Mortes. *Courrier du Parc Natural Régional de Camargue.* n.º 15.
- **Fredrickson, L.H.** and **M.K. Laubhan.** 1994. *Managind Wetlands for Wildlife.* In Bookhont T.A. (Ed.). *Research and management techniques for wildlife and habitats.* pp. 623-647. The Wildlife Bethesta.
- **Galeazzo** and **D. Viganó.** 2006. *The best wing shooting in Uruguay.* SouthEnd Publishing. Buenos Aires.
- **González, L.M.** 1991. *Historia natural del águila imperial ibérica (*Aquila adalberti*, Brehm, 1861).* ICONA. Ministerio de Agricultura, Pesca y Alimentación. Madrid.
- **González, L.M.** and **A. Mangalida.** 2008. *Biología de la conservación del Águila Imperial Ibérica (*Águila adalberti*).* O.A. de Parques Nacionales. MMAMMR. Madrid.
- **González, L.M.** and **A. San Miguel** (Coords.). 2004. *Manual de buenas prácticas de gestión en fincas de monte mediterráneo de la Red Natura 2000.* Naturaleza y Parques Nacionales. Ministerio de Medio Ambiente. Madrid.
- **G.T. Águila Imperial Ibérica. Grupo de Trabajo del Águila Imperial Ibérica (CCAA-MMA).** 2004. *Resumen de proyectos y estado actual de la población del Águila Imperial Ibérica.* MMA.
- **Haas, J.N.,** *et al.* 2007. *Holozäne Schneelawinen und Almwirtschaft und ihr Einfluss auf die Subalpine Flora und Vegetation der Schwarzsteinalm im Zemmgrund.* In *Prähistorische Lawinem.* Viena, Verlag der ÖAW. Vol. 16.
- **Heide, R.** 2001. *Samso's green energy island project.* Danish Energy Agency.
- **Heydon, M.J.** and **J.C. Reynolds.** 2000. Fox *(Vulpes vulpes)* management in three contrastiq region of Britain, in relation to agricultural and sporting interests. *Journal of Zoology* 251(2):237-252.
- **IIMA.** 1990. *Plan de conservación de especies amenazadas del sector La Garganta.* Ciudad Real. IIMA. Madrid.
- **Julia, J.,** *et al.* 2000. *Introducción a la Biología. Uso y estatus de los felinos de la Argentina.* REHM. Serie Apuntes, n.º 2. Universidad Nacional de Tucumán. Argentina.
- **Kel, S.** *et al.* 1992. *Handbook of the Birds of Europe the Middle East and North Africa.* Bright Sun Printing Press Co., Ltd.
- **Lasserre, N.** 1989. *Historie populare d'Aigues-Mortes.* Reprint of 1936 edition. C. Lacour. Ed. Nines, France.
- **Leenhart.** 1939. *Les salins du Languedoc.* Imprimerie Sadad. Bellgarde. France.
- **Leseries-Leick, A.** 2002. *Sölkspuren I-III.* Weishaupt, Gnas.
- **Macdonal, S.** 2001. *Monarch of the Glen. "Estate Management".*

- MAFF. 2002. *UK Agriculture: Topic Notes – dairying.* DE-FRA.
- Mayr, S., *et al.* 2009. *Damage in Needle Tissues after Infection with* Grysomyxa rhodendri. *Increases Cuticular Conductance of* Picea abies *in Winter.* Innsbruck. Springer.
- Miller-Aichholz, F. 2007. *Vegetationökologische Analysen interschiedlich intensiv bewirtschafteter Almen im Nationalpark Gesäuse.* MA Thesis. Viena.
- Ministerio de Medio Ambiente. 2002. *Etnobotánica en el entorno del Parque Nacional de Cabañeros.* Secretaría General de Medio Ambiente. Madrid.
- Mogens, J. 2002. *Geography and the Environment – Climate.* Royal Danish Ministry of Foreign Affairs. Denmark.
- Montgomery, G.G. (ed.). 1985. *The evolution and ecology of armadillos, sloths and vermilinguas.* Smithsonian Institution Press. Washintong D.C.
- Moreno-Ono, R. and F. Guil (Coord.). 2007. *Manual de gestión del hábitat y de las poblaciones de buitre negro en España.* Naturaleza y Parques Nacionales. Ministerio de Medio Ambiente. Madrid.
- Narosky, T. and D. Yzurieta. 2003. *Guía para la identificación de las aves de Argentina y Uruguay.* Vázquez Mazzini Editores. Argentina.
- Notario, A. 2009. *Gansos y patos. Guía de especies de interés cinegético del mundo.* Fundación Conde del Valle de Salazar, Editorial Solitario, S.L. Madrid.
- Otero, C. (Ed.). 1999. *Patrimonio natural y propiedad rural en España.* Exlibris Ediciones. Madrid.
- Otero, C. 2003. *Iniciativa privada y medio ambiente: al éxito por la práctica.* FAES. Madrid.
- Otero, C. 2004. *Modelos de gestión integrada para territorios mediterráneos con uso múltiple.* D. Phil. Thesis. Universidad Politécnica de Madrid. IIMA. Madrid.
- Otero, C. and T. Bailey. 2003. Europ's Natural and Cultural Heritage. The European Estate. Exlibris Ediciones. Madrid.
- Otero, C. *et al.* 2007. *Los vallados en la gestión de la caza mayor.* Obra Social Caixa Galicia.
- Pain, D.J. and M.W. Pienkowski (Eds.). 1997. *Farming and Birds in Europe: The Common Agricultural Policy and its Complications for Birds Conservation.* Academic Press. London.
- Parera, A. 2002. *Los mamíferos de la Argentina y la región austral de Sudamérica.* Editorial El Ateneo. Buenos Aires, Argentina.
- Potts, G.R. 1986. *The Partridge. Pesticides, predation and Conservation.* Collins profesional and Technical Books. London.
- Ricci, J.C. 1982. *Quelques aspects de l'ethologie de la perdrix rouge* (Alectoris rufa). Vols. I, II. D. Phil. Thesis. L'Institut National Agronomique.
- Robbins, G.E.S. 1994. *Quail Breeding and Management.* WPA International, Suffork.
- Rodríguez, A. and M. Delibes. 1990. *El lince ibérico en España. Distribución y problemas de conservación.* ICONA.
- Rodríguez Mata, J. *et al.* 2008. *Guía de campo. Aves de Sudamérica.* Letemendia Ed. Buenos Aires.
- Rueda, M.J., J.R. Baragaño and A. Notario. 1987. *The food of wild partridge chicks on farmlands in La Mancha.* E.T.S.I de Montes. Madrid.
- Rueda, M.J., J.R. Baragaño, A. Notario and L. Castresana. 1993. Estudio de la alimentación natural de los pollos de perdiz roja *(Alectoris Rufa). Ecología*, n.º 7. pp. 429-454.
- Sadoul, N. *et al.* 1998. Salinas and nature conservation. *Conservation of Mediterranean Wetland (MedWet).* N.º 9. Tour du Valat. Arles, France.
- San Miguel, A. (Coord.). 2006. *Manual para la gestión del hábitat del lince ibérico* (Lynx pardinus *Ternmick) y de su presa principal, el conejo de monte* (Oryctolafus cunilicus *L.).* Fundación CBD-Hábitat. Madrid.
- Serini, E. *Storia del Paesaggio Italiano.*
- Several Authors. *Los bosques ibéricos. Una interpretación Geobotánica.*
- Sociedad Española de Ornitología y Agencia de Medio Ambiente. 1994. *Atlas de las aves nidificantes en Madrid.*
- Society of Ecological Restoration International (Ed.). 2009. *Cork Oak Woodlands on the Edge.*
- Stadler, B. 1991. *Pappenheim und die Zeit des Dreibigjährigen Krieges.* Winterthur.
- Sundries. 2003. *Vyber vyznamych firem a spolecnosti.* Kompakt s.r.o. Podebrady.
- Thibault, J.C. *et al.* 1993. *Livre rouge des oiseaux des regions Francaises d'outre mer.* ICBP France.
- Thompson, H.V. and C.M. Kuig (Eds.). 1994. *The European Rabbit: The History and Biology of a Succesful Colonizer.* Oxfor Science Publications. Oxford.
- Von Wartenberg, H. and F. Bedeschi. 2004. *Red deer, ciervos colorados en Argentina.* SouthEnd Publishing. Buenos Aires.
- Wieser, G and M. Tausz. (Eds.). 2007. *Trees at their Upper Limit. Treelife at the Alpine Timberline.* Innsbruck. Springer.
- Willians, E.S. and I.K. Barker. 2001. *Infections Diseases of Wild Mammals.* Third Edition. Manson publishing. London.
- Willians, S. 2007. *Wingshooting Argentina and Uruguay.* Patagonia Publishing Company. Buenos Aires.
- Yanes, M., *et al.* 1999. *Efecto de los predadores sobre la caza menor y evaluación de sistemas selectos para refutar los niveles de predación.* CSIC. Spain.